Special Report Series, No. 167

𝔓𝔯𝔦𝔟𝔶 𝔠𝔬𝔲𝔫𝔠𝔦𝔩

MEDICAL RESEARCH COUNCIL

VITAMINS: A SURVEY OF PRESENT KNOWLEDGE

Compiled by a Committee appointed jointly by the
Lister Institute and Medical Research Council

LONDON
PUBLISHED BY HIS MAJESTY'S STATIONERY OFFICE
1932

H.M. Stationery Office Code Number
45-5-67   Universal Decimal Classification
612.392.01 (02)

PREFACE

In 1919 there was published in this series a ' Report on the Present State of Knowledge Concerning Accessory Food Factors (Vitamines)', prepared by a Committee which the Council had appointed jointly with the Lister Institute. The rapid growth of knowledge in this new field of work soon made that monograph obsolete at many points, and a completely new edition, nearly doubled in content, was prepared by the same Committee and issued in 1924. That this summary of methods and results was found useful by workers in this and other countries has been well indicated by the numbers sold—10,000 copies of successive impressions have been distributed already. Fresh advances of knowledge soon made complete revision necessary again, and this was undertaken by the Committee in 1930. On this occasion, however, much more complete revision was seen to be required, and the report now presented is an entirely fresh resumption of current knowledge and of technical methods in this subject.

The Committee in preparing this report had the great advantage of Dr. Arthur Harden's services as general editor. They were assisted in the preparation of material for particular sections by Dr. W. R. Aykroyd, Dr. C. W. Carter, Professor S. J. Cowell, Mrs. M. A. Boas Fixsen, Miss E. M. Hume, Dr. G. F. Marrian, Dr. R. A. Morton, and Miss M. H. Roscoe. All the members of the Committee named on the preceding page are responsible jointly for the final shaping of every chapter and for the whole work as now produced. To all these the Council are greatly indebted, and they believe that their feelings of gratitude will be shared by the innumerable workers now interested in this field of study.

It can hardly be contemplated that the rapid and accelerating growth of the subject can be conveniently followed further by fresh revisions of such a monograph as this. The labour entailed and the sacrifices of time made by research workers in successive revisions of such a monograph are not likely to be justifiable again. The Council have joined with the Reid Library of the Rowett Institute, Aberdeen, and the Imperial Agricultural Bureaux Council, in giving financial support to a new periodical journal, 'Nutrition Abstracts and Reviews', of which the first number appeared in October last. The Council hope that this will provide for the future a regular means of bringing together and making more readily available the results of research work as they accumulate in the now widely distributed and often disconnected fields of work, medical, agricultural, dietetic, and commercial, in which the subject of nutrition is being so rapidly developed.

In an Appendix is given the report of the International Conference on Vitamin Standards, held under the auspices of the Permanent Standards Commission of the League of Nations in London during June, 1931. The recommendations given here for adoption of

international standards for those vitamins of which present knowledge makes this practicable, together with definitions of units of
activity in terms of the standards for use in each case in quantitative estimation of the vitamin, have now been adopted by the League
of Nations.   In their first report of 1919, mentioned already, the
Committee referred to the scepticism, then shown in some quarters,
even of the real existence of the subject of their monograph.   They
admitted that there was then no knowledge of the actual chemical
nature of the vitamins, but they said that 'the study of their
functions is progressing on real and objective lines, and has become
in certain cases even quantitative'.   It is gratifying to notice that
within only a dozen years research work has advanced so far as to
allow not only quantitative study but a formal international
agreement upon precise quantitative standards in the case of no
less than four, the so-called A, B_1, C and D, of the vitamins.

MEDICAL RESEARCH COUNCIL,   10th May, 1932.
    38, Old Queen Street,
        Westminster, S.W. 1.

VITAMINS: A SURVEY OF PRESENT KNOWLEDGE

CONTENTS

CONTENTS

CONTENTS 7

CHAPTER I

HISTORICAL INTRODUCTION.

As food constituents vitamins are characterized by the disproportion between the great importance of their nutritional functions and the very small amounts necessary for the adequate fulfilment of those functions. In a normal dietary they are present in quantities far too small to yield any appreciable contributions to the energy supply of the body, or to bulk appreciably as structural elements for the tissues. They are, nevertheless, definite chemical entities, and in the last eight years much light has been thrown upon the actual chemical nature of some among them. It would seem, indeed, that at least one has now been artificially prepared. During the same period, extended researches have shown that they are more numerous than was earlier suspected. Eight years ago only three were clearly recognized; now we must believe in the existence of at least eight. Each one upon good evidence has been shown to exert its own individual functions in nutrition.

Since a supply of them is essential for the animal body, the vitamins are, of course, generally present in the natural foods which are instinctively consumed by men and animals. They are primarily formed during the synthetic activities of the green plant on the land, or those of algae and other smaller organisms in the sea. From these they are transferred to the tissues of animals, terrestrial or marine. There is some evidence, however, to show that one vitamin at least, and perhaps others, may be synthesized in the organs of certain animal species. Such animals can dispense with, or are less dependent upon, an external supply of the vitamin which their own tissues produce. Such cases are rare, however, and we have no knowledge of such synthetic powers in the human body.

It is not surprising that popular experience should have wholly failed in the past to reveal the existence of nutritional agencies which function in such small amounts, and are unconsciously consumed in every adequate dietary. The distribution of vitamins in vegetable and animal foods alike may be partial and irregular, but broadly speaking it is safe to say that the adult individual finds a good supply of vitamins in his food so long as that food is reasonably varied, has received no artificial or accidental separation into parts, and has had no destructive influence applied to it. This generalization does not, however, cover the nutritional demands of infants and children.

In the observation of phenomena the importance of contributory factors is often overlooked until the effects of their removal come to light. In the case of vitamins and their functions, demonstration, so far as it depended upon observation, first came when commercial adventure or other human enterprise had led to the preparation and consumption of foods in which the natural materials had been fractionated for the sake of taste, appearance, or convenience; treated by destructive methods; or, in other cases, only preserved too long before consumption. Owing on the one hand to the partial and irregular distribution of vitamins in the natural products, or on the other hand to their relative instability, it may happen that they are thus removed or destroyed.

Safety in this connexion is evidently greater when a variety of foods is consumed. In countries where geographical conditions prevent such variety the danger is more imminent. It is a fact, at any rate, that the most striking evidence for the evil effects of the artificial treatment of food first came from rice-eating districts of the East when they had been invaded by milling machinery from the West. The recognition some twenty to thirty years ago of beri-beri and scurvy as deficiency diseases provided good evidence both for the evil effects of fractionating natural foodstuffs such as the cereals, and for the nutritive importance of vitamins.

The evidence from disease would have led sooner to a conception of these food constituents and their functions but for a not unnatural bias in thought. It was difficult to implant the idea of disease as due to deficiency.

Disease is so generally associated with positive agents—the parasite, the toxin, the *materies morbi*—that even expert thought turned naturally to such positive associations and believed with difficulty in causation prefixed by a *minus* sign. Even in the case of deficiencies arising within the body there was a similar tendency. When the importance of internal secretions was first recognized there used to be much hesitation in believing that symptoms might be frankly due to their failure. When each fresh internal secretion was described there was always an effort to show that its function was to 'neutralize' some, always hypothetical, toxic substance. Symptoms on this view were due to the unmasking of a deleterious agent rather than to simple deficiency in a normal and necessary agent. To distinguish between these two possibilities was, of course, a scientific duty ; but, at any rate in the earlier literature of internal secretions, a bias against the simpler view interfered with the fair interpretation of experimental results.

So in connexion with the later conception of disease as due to dietetic deficiencies. Even when a distinguished Dutch investigator, through his admirable studies, which will a little later receive reference, had clearly established more than thirty years ago that beri-beri arose during the consumption of decorticated but not of whole rice (making it clear, therefore, that something in the cortex was necessary to normal nutrition), he was led to suggest, not the simple view that some substance in the cortex was of direct use to the body, but rather that it was necessary to neutralize the otherwise deleterious effect of a diet over-rich in starch.

While it is true that the simpler idea of the nature of deficiency diseases is now generally held, it must be stated that there is good evidence, which is referred to later on, to show that there are times when certain dietetic ingredients necessitate a larger intake of specific vitamins for normal development and function. In such cases some investigators regard the vitamin action as antagonizing those of harmful agents.

Fortunately, in the case of deficiency diseases it proved possible some years ago, by the choice of suitable animals, to supplement clinical and sociological observation by controlled experiments. As usual, experimental work on animals made knowledge more quantitative, and in some cases revealed some well-known pathological conditions as deficiency diseases. Illustrations of this will shortly be given.

If, however, the evidence for the existence and importance of vitamins had arisen entirely from the study of deficiency diseases our views might have remained too limited, too much confined to the standpoint of pathology and therapeutics. But in the very years during which the aetiology of beri-beri was being cleared up, and the suggestion established that a qualitative food deficiency may be responsible for striking pathological symptoms, experiments were in progress on quite independent lines to show that something more than a supply of energy and protein is required to maintain so fundamental a physiological phenomenon as growth, and to demonstrate that normal metabolism as a whole is not possible without the influence of food constituents which, because of their minute amount, could justifiably be spoken of as ' accessory ' food factors in nutrition.

From such experiments, then, the conception of the vitamin rose, and at the present time the evidence from all kinds of feeding experiments, whether carried out from the physiological or pathological standpoint, is being consolidated. The earlier stages in the history of such researches will be now reviewed.

As often happens in the development of science, a fundamental idea is foreshadowed in many quarters, but has long to wait before it emerges as a basis of accepted knowledge. As in other cases, so with recognition of vitamins as physiological necessities. Their existence was suggested long ago, but a certain right moment in the history of the science of nutrition had to arrive before it could attain to universal recognition. Some workers had discovered suggestive facts, but failed to realize their full significance ; while the work and words of true pioneers lay forgotten because published when average minds were not ready to appraise them at their right value.

No one can deny that the recorded experience of voyagers and explorers in the eighteenth century, and particularly, perhaps, the records of the British Navy which deal with the incidence and cure of scurvy, would have directed thought towards our modern conception of vitamins had the times been ripe. The knowledge concerning nutrition was then, however, entirely vague, and the days of animal experiment in such matters had not yet come. The earliest experiments, indeed, supplied evidence which was of an independent kind, reached from a different angle.

It is now generally agreed that the first clear evidence, based upon experiment, for the existence of dietary factors of the nature of vitamins, came from the school of Bunge at Basel. In 1881 Lunin, one of the workers in that school, fed mice upon an artificial mixture of the individual constituents of milk, of all the constituents, that is, which were then known, namely, the proteins, fats, carbohydrates, and salts. He found that upon such a mixture the animals failed to survive, and was led to conclude that '*a natural food such as milk must therefore contain besides these known principal ingredients small quantities of unknown substances essential to life'* [1881]. Such a statement, already half a century old, when allowed to stand out clear and apart from a context which tended to bury it, seems to contain the essentials of what is believed to-day.

It will not be uninstructive to seek for an explanation as to how such a significant remark could remain for years almost without notice, instead of being an immediate challenge to further investigation. It may be noted first of all that the title of Lunin's paper [1881] 'Ueber die Bedeutung der anorganischen Salze für die Ernährung des Thieres', was one prone to conceal the important but incidental suggestion it contained. The thought of the Bunge school was, as a matter of fact, both then and long afterwards, concerned largely with the inorganic factors of nutrition. After an interval of ten years, during which, so far as one can discover, no effort had been made to follow up the pregnant suggestion of Lunin's work, another member of the school came again to Lunin's point of view. He, however, was once more concerned primarily with the study of an inorganic element in nutrition. Socin, the worker in question, though, as the title of his paper [1891] 'In welcher Form ist das Eisen resorbiert?' indicates, he had not set out to seek further for those wholly unknown substances essential to life the existence of which Lunin had predicted, was nevertheless, owing to the nature of his experiments, inevitably driven to a belief in them. Socin, it is true, was led to think that the ineffectiveness of the synthetic diets employed by him might be due to an inadequacy in the quality of the protein contained in them, a view not wholly unjustified and foreshadowing knowledge which only long afterwards became definite and proven. He became convinced, however, that other and unknown substances must be sought, substances which, he states, are certainly present in whole milk and egg yolk. He remarks, moreover, with conviction that to discover them was the first task to be faced before new feeding experiments were undertaken. Here was a strong enough challenge to investigate, yet we have again no knowledge of any attempt in Bunge's laboratory to follow up the challenge. Perhaps an explanation of this is to be found in the circumstance that Bunge, though in his well-known book he observes that it would be worth while to continue the experiments which had suggested the existence of unknown nutritional factors, was himself inclined to disbelieve in them. He thought that the real error in the synthetic diets used by his pupils (which was, so to speak, 'dissected' milk) was that the method of its preparation had involved the separation of inorganic constituents from certain organic combinations, in which latter form alone could they adequately subserve the purposes of metabolism. Other causes may have contributed to the long neglect, first of Lunin's and then of Socin's suggestions. It must be admitted, indeed, that no *experimentum crucis* was carried out in Bunge's laboratory. In Lunin's experiments the fate of six mice only (those placed by him upon a normal salt mixture—all others had been given deficient mineral supplies) really brought suggestions for the existence of unknown factors; and no data are given as to their consumption of food. Neither Lunin nor Socin made any attempt to complete the evidence by making discriminate additions to the diets which had proved inadequate. Lastly, as already suggested, since the main intention of their work and the titles of their publications were remote from the special issue, their significant remarks might well have appeared as little more than *obiter dicta* when read without the light of modern developments.

Fourteen years after these observations were described an investigator distinguished in many fields was led to repeat and extend them. This was the late Professor Pekelharing, whose conclusions [published in 1905] unhappily remained wholly unknown to the majority till recently. It is, indeed, remarkable that the results of such significant statements as his, though published in the Dutch language alone, should not have become rapidly broadcast. After speaking of experiments carried out on lines similar to some of those done in Bunge's laboratory, and indicating that they pointed to the existence of some unknown essential, Pekelharing goes on to say : ' Till now my efforts, constantly repeated during the last few years, to separate this substance and get to know more about it have not led to a satisfactory result, so I shall not say any more about it. My intention is only to point out that there is a still unknown substance in milk which even in very small quantities is of paramount importance to nutrition. If this substance is absent, the organism loses the power properly to assimilate the well-known principal parts of food, the appetite is lost and with apparent abundance the animals die of want. Undoubtedly this substance occurs not only in milk but in all sorts of foodstuffs both of vegetable and animal origin. ' Here we have a clear statement of the vitamin doctrine already a quarter of a century old. It is to be regretted that Pekelharing refrained from publishing any of his experimental data. There is little doubt that he was led to undertake his physiological experiments because of his intimate knowledge, not then shared by the majority of workers outside Holland, of the important researches now to be mentioned. For there was at this time other evidence available to indicate that orthodox teaching concerning nutrition was incomplete—evidence different in kind from that just discussed. It demonstrates for the first time the existence of what we have now learnt to call Deficiency Disease.

Following researches carried out from 1890 onwards Christiaan Eijkman, who was at the time a military doctor in the Dutch Indies and later became Professor of Hygiene at Utrecht, had, in 1897, come to the conclusion that the disease beri-beri resulted from the continuous consumption of decorticated (polished) rice. His view was more particularly supported by a study made with his collaborator Vorderman of diet and health in no less than 101 of the prisons in Java [Eijkman, 1897, 2]. The evidence so obtained was striking enough, but Eijkman's view was strengthened by his discovery that birds (fowls, pigeons, and ducks) when fed upon polished rice developed a disease, which he named *polyneuritis gallinarum*, the symptoms of which closely resembled those of human beri-beri. He found further that the avian disease failed to develop when the birds were fed upon whole rice, or rice grains still associated with the pericarp or 'silver skin'. This observation made it possible to add the results of controlled animal experiments to those of statistical studies and greatly contributed to advance in the subject.

Eijkman himself, as was mentioned above, at first viewed the facts he had discovered from a standpoint more in accordance with the thought of contemporary pathologists than with our present conceptions. He concluded that foods such as rice, over-rich in starch, produced a substance in the intestine which acted as a poison to nerve cells, for which the outer layers of the rice grain contained an antidote. Somewhat later, however, another Dutch scientist, Grijns [1901], gave a different interpretation to the facts in putting forward the view that beri-beri, whether in birds or man, was due to a 'deficiency'—to the absence from the food of an essential nutrient. This, in rice, happens to be confined to the cortical parts of the grain which are removed by polishing. To Grijns belongs the credit of first picturing clearly what is to be justly called a deficiency disease, as well as that of first investigating the properties and distribution of a vitamin.

In 1907 Braddon further established the correctness of Eijkman's observations upon the influence of rice diets by widely extended studies upon rice-eating native races [1907]. They were fully supported, moreover, by the discriminating investigations of Fraser and Stanton [1909].

It is now difficult to understand how, even long before Eijkman's work, scurvy failed in practical medicine to obtain recognition as a disease due to a deficiency in food. The possibility of such causation was doubtless, just as in the case of beri-beri, against the trend of thought in current pathology. A better reason, perhaps, was the absence of definite evidence based upon controlled animal experiments to replace the vaguer impressions of clinical experience. The means for such experimental studies was first provided in 1907 by the researches of two Norwegian scientists, Holst and Frölich, who showed that typical scurvy could be produced in guinea-pigs by deficient diets and as easily cured by suitable additions. That this opportunity for experiment, like that given by Eijkman's discovery of polyneuritis in birds, has since greatly advanced the subject will be made clear in later sections of this monograph.

A survey of the literature of the first decade of the present century will show that the facts brought to light by the researches so far described had by then exerted little or no effect upon orthodox views and teaching concerning human nutrition. Calorie-supply, protein-minima and such factors still dominated the general conception of nutritional adequacy. We are now to see that researches described in the course of the next three years led to a change in the outlook.

Reference may first be made to the work of Stepp [1909; 1911; 1912]. This author's original concern was to decide whether fats and lipoids must be supplied in the food in order that life may be maintained. He found that whereas mice lived satisfactorily for several months upon certain foods, such as wheat bread made with milk, they were unable to live longer than a month when fed upon the same diet after it had been subjected to prolonged extraction with alcohol and ether. That the extraction itself had only lowered the nutritive value of the foodstuffs by removing some essential component was demonstrated by restoring the extract to the extracted food, when it once again became adequate for the nutrition of the mice.

Stepp made a number of experiments in order to ascertain the nature of the essential factor removed by the extraction process. The addition of the ash of the extract, or of certain neutral fats in a pure condition, did not remedy the deficiency, but he found that milk and egg-yolk did. This led him to suggest the existence of an unidentified indispensable dietary unit, which he appears to have regarded as a member of the lipoid class. He was unable to identify this substance with cholesterol, lecithin, kephalin, or cerebrone, since all members of that class of substance failed to restore the nutritive value of the extracted foodstuffs. He remarks in one of his later papers: *It is not impossible that unknown substances indispensable for life go into solution with the lipoids, and that the latter thereby become what may be termed carriers for these substances.*

Attention should now be turned to the classic experiments carried out by Hopkins in this country. As early as 1906 he wrote as follows: 'But further, no animal can live upon a mixture of pure protein, fat, and carbohydrate, and even when the necessary inorganic material is carefully supplied, the animal still cannot flourish. The animal body is adjusted to live either upon plant tissues or other animals, and these contain countless substances other than the proteins, carbohydrates, and fats. Physiological evolution, I believe, has made some of these well-nigh as essential as are the basal constituents of diet; lecithin, for instance, has been repeatedly shown to have a marked influence upon nutrition, and this just happens to be something already familiar, and a substance that happens to have been tried. The field is almost unexplored, only it is certain that there are many minor factors in all diets, of which the body takes account. In diseases such as rickets, and particularly in scurvy, we have had for long years knowledge of a dietetic factor, but though we know how to benefit these conditions empirically, the real errors in the diet are to this day quite obscure. They are, however, certainly of the kind which comprises these minimal qualitative factors that I am considering. Scurvy and rickets are conditions so severe that they force themselves upon our attention, but many other nutritive errors affect the health of individuals to a degree most important to themselves, and some of them depend upon unsuspected dietetic factors' [1906].

Some results of his experiments, which had extended intermittently over several years, were published in 1912 [Hopkins, 1912]. Young rats were fed upon an artificial food mixture containing caseinogen, starch, cane sugar, lard, and inorganic salts. When the animals were fed upon the diet composed of these constituents in the crude condition, they were able to live and to show a certain amount of growth. When, however, the components had been carefully purified, growth invariably ceased after a comparatively short period, and the rats declined and died. In experiments of the kind it is of the utmost importance that the material of which the control synthetic diet is composed should be fully purified. Inadequate purification led earlier workers. and, as we are to see, later workers also, to claim that successful nutrition may be obtained on artificial dietaries. Hopkins employed diets in which very complete purification of the protein, carbohydrate, and (as the author then thought) of the fats administered was a special feature. A novel feature of these experiments was that Hopkins showed by estimations of the energy consumptions of the animals that this failure was not due to an insufficient food intake. It was found that growth ceased at a time when the animals were consuming food in more than sufficient quantity to maintain normal growth.

Another series of animals which received, in addition to the basal ration of purified foodstuffs, a very small daily allowance of milk afforded a great contrast to those just described. In all cases the milk addendum, although its total solids amounted to only 4 per cent. or less of the whole food eaten, induced normal growth, and greatly improved the general condition of the animals.

The extraordinary effect of this apparently insignificant addition to the diet upon the growth of the experimental rats is well illustrated by Figures 1 and 2, which have been reproduced from the original paper. A similar growth-stimulating action was exerted by the addition of protein-free and salt-free extracts of milk solids, or of yeast, to the basal diet. As the milk ration was administered separately and in advance of the administration of the main dietary, it could not have affected the palatability of the food or diminished its monotony. Some authors have stated their inability to obtain normal growth with amounts of milk so small as those used by Hopkins. It is true that when an animal depends entirely on milk for its vitamin supply growth cannot be maintained for long periods on so small an amount.

In discussing his results Hopkins remarked: 'It is possible that what is absent from artificial diets and supplied by such addenda as milk and tissue extracts is of the nature of an organic complex (or of complexes) which the animal body cannot synthesize. But the amount which seems sufficient to secure growth is so small that a catalytic or stimulative function seems more likely.'

After reference to possibilities which had more weight when his paper was written than now, he wrote in conclusion: '*If the attachment of such indispensable functions to specific accessory constituents of diets is foreign to current views upon nutrition, so also is the experimental fact that young animals fail to grow when they are absorbing daily a sufficiency of formative material and energy for the purpose of growth.*'

Attention should now be turned to the work and writings of Casimir Funk, to whom we owe the term Vitamine, which, slightly modified by omission of the final e, has now become indissolubly attached as a class name to the substances with which this monograph is concerned. This investigator has greatly helped to advance our knowledge of the subject, and at a time when

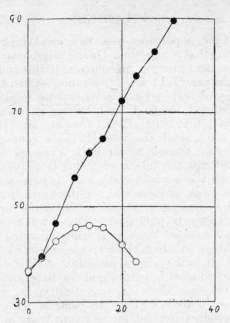

Fig. 1. Lower curve, six rats on artificial diet alone. Upper curve, six similar animals receiving in addition 2 c.c. of milk each per diem. Abscissae, time in days; ordinates, average weight in g. (Reproduced by permission from the *Journal of Physiology*, 1912, 44, 432.)

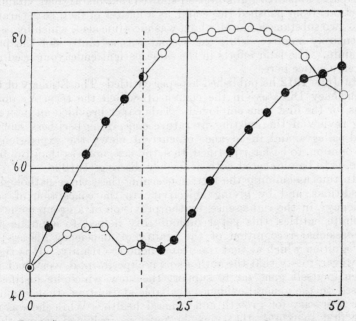

Fig. 2. Lower curve (up to eighteenth day), eight male rats upon pure dietary; upper curve, eight similar rats taking 3 c.c. of milk each a day. On the eighteenth day, marked by vertical dotted line, the milk was transferred from one set to the other. Average weight in g., vertical; time, horizontal. (Reproduced by permission from the *Journal of Physiology*, 1912, 44, 433.)

B

recognition of its importance was only awakening he did much towards securing that recognition. Owing to publications by William Fletcher, Fraser and Stanton, Schaumann, Grijns and others during 1907–10, by the year 1911 much fresh interest had been awakened in the aetiology of beri-beri and in its experimental cure. In that year Funk entered the field, and having experimented at the Lister Institute, first with E. A. Cooper, and then alone, he described, at the end of the year [1911], a courageous attempt, which was largely, though not entirely, a pioneer effort, to isolate from rice polishings the substance which is active in the cure of the disease. In the actual isolation of a pure active substance the endeavour was unsuccessful. Others we may note were engaged at the time upon a similar endeavour and the results were soon afterwards published. These we now know were equally without success. Funk, it is true, separated fractions from the rice polishings in which the active agent was very much more concentrated than in the original material. A crystalline fraction to which he attached most importance at the time, and for which he provided an empirical formula, was curative for polyneuritis in pigeons in doses of about 20 mg. In contrast with this, however, a crystalline product, isolated during recent years in the laboratory where Eijkman did his fundamental work, which is possibly, though not certainly, the pure vitamin, has proved to be many thousand times as active as Funk's preparation. A year and a half after his first paper appeared Funk himself showed that his original 'vitamine fraction' from polished rice could, as a matter of fact, be separated into two substances, one of which was nicotinic acid, which by itself is entirely inactive, while the second was certainly not the pure vitamin. His later efforts in the same patient endeavour need not receive notice here.

In June 1912 he published a paper entitled 'The Etiology of the Deficiency Diseases' in the course of which the term Vitamine was for the first time employed. This paper provided an interesting review of the existing literature concerning beri-beri, scurvy, and pellagra, and, in advance of current views, the expression of an opinion, to be later justified, that the last, not less than the first two, is to be numbered with deficiency diseases [1912].

In thus assembling the facts concerning these three pathological conditions, and by giving objectivity to the conception of ' deficiency ', in the right sense, by the provision of a group name for definite entities, this paper undoubtedly helped to a public and professional recognition of the reality of deficiency disease ; a recognition which at that time came none too readily. It is right, however, to say that the author's own experimental work had not then in itself gone far to support the view which he justifiably based on the general evidence available at the time, that vitamins are necessary for growth and general health. While he was not the first to express that view he must be reckoned among those who first impressed it upon scientific opinion.

It is certain that publications which appeared in the years 1911–13 led ultimately, though with some delay, to the full beliefs of to-day. It is not easy or necessary to attempt an estimate of the exact share of each in producing that desirable result.

A few words may be said here concerning Funk's choice of the term Vitamine. The prefix *vita* connotes of course the importance of the substances to life ; the ending *amine*, owing to the special significance of the word in organic chemistry, implies that they are of the nature of organic bases, or compounds derived from ammonia by substitution. Funk separated bases of this kind in his attempted isolation mentioned above, and he believed that the nature of vitamines in general could be thus defined. Complete proof, however, that any one of them has this constitution is yet lacking, and we now know that two of them at least do not even contain nitrogen. Funk has nevertheless argued with some reason that the readiness with which the term was accepted proved its convenience and adequacy. The suggestion due to J. C. Drummond, that by dropping the final *e* the unjustifiable connotation just mentioned might be to a degree avoided, was nevertheless a wise one, and the name *Vitamin* is now established.

The work of Osborne and Mendel at Newhaven, Conn. [1911 ; 1912 ; 1913, 1, 2, &c.], and of McCollum and his colleagues in Wisconsin (later in Baltimore), published from 1912 onwards, yielded results of much importance. Alike at Newhaven and Wisconsin the conviction that vitamins are essential to life came, however, rather slowly. It will not indeed be out of place here to say a few words concerning the progressive experience of the American workers which ultimately led to that conviction. That experience when duly surveyed becomes very instructive.

Osborne and Mendel had, for some years previous to 1912, been carrying out experiments, of which the results have become classical [1911], on the relative nutritional value of various pure proteins. These experiments, carried out on rats, called for the use of synthetic dietaries in which the proteins to be tested were combined with carbohydrates, fats, and mineral salts. Of necessity it became of prime concern with these investigators to decide whether such diets when made of pure materials had defects other than those which might appertain to any particular protein under study. It is noteworthy that at one stage in their studies Osborne and Mendel decided that a synthetic diet of the above nature, if containing an adequate protein, could, as a matter of fact, support life and growth. They published curves demonstrating excellent growth in young rats, and remark : ' These are so far as we know the first successful feeding experiments in which lasting growth has been obtained with carefully purified foodstuffs and artificial salt mixtures.'

In view of the later experience of the authors themselves, and of that of a multitude of more recent investigators, it may seem difficult to explain the apparent success of these particular experiments. It was doubtless due in the main to the circumstance that the diet contained about one-fourth of the carbohydrate supply as milk sugar which had not been specially purified. It was pointed out a little later that when milk sugar was used in such experiments it was necessary that it should be carefully purified.

The sugar when first separated from its source adsorbs a consider-able proportion of the milk vitamins. Using purified milk sugar Hopkins and Neville [1913] could obtain no growth with a diet otherwise exactly similar to that employed in the above experiments.

It should be understood, however, that the greater number of Osborne and Mendel's experiments, made both before and after the dates of those just discussed, were not carried out on purified foodstuffs alone. During the earlier stages of their studies they had met with experimental difficulties, especially (as they then believed) in the endeavour to secure an efficient salt mixture for their synthetic diets. Their chief interest, as we have seen, was in the nutritive value of proteins. Now whole milk had been shown to form by itself an adequate diet for rats ; it can support growth for long periods, if not indefinitely. Osborne and Mendel saw that if the proteins were removed from milk, and the proteins alone, all other substances necessary for proper nutrition should remain in the fluid. The milk protein could then be replaced by any individual protein under study. By a happy inspiration therefore such 'protein-free-milk' was made a constituent of their experimental diets, and, except during the period when the above-mentioned experiments for a while deceived them, they looked upon it as probably essential for nutritional success. It was employed primarily as a means of obtaining a physiologically correct salt mixture, but the authors came to recognize that it might supply other constituents of impor-tance. As a matter of fact their protein-free preparation contained, as we now know, some of the vitamins of the original milk.

During the following year, however, Osborne and Mendel en-deavoured to repeat their experiments, but now taking care that all materials used should be of 'the highest degree of purity'. 'To our surprise,' they write when discussing the results, 'the artificial protein-free milk made with these purer chemicals failed in every case but one to promote more than slight growth.' They still sup-posed at first that some mineral deficiency was in question ; but, as appears later in the paper just mentioned, a critical examination of their data led them at last to conclude that some specific essential was present in the fats of natural milk. 'It would seem', they wrote, 'as if a substance exerting a marked influence upon growth was present in butter . . .' [1913, 1, p. 319].

The experience of the investigators at the Wisconsin centre will next be described. McCollum and various colleagues had been engaged, from 1907 onwards, in scientific studies of nutrition, with special reference to the rationing of farm stock. Special attention had been given to the determination of nitrogenous and mineral deficiencies in individual cereals and in other food materials used in practical dietaries. McCollum apparently came to feel, as others have felt, that many nutritional problems would be simplified if the adequacy of dietaries could be defined in terms of their indi-vidual pure constituents, and during the year 1912 he was engaged with Davis in testing the ability of synthetic diets to maintain health and growth in rats—a line of inquiry which of necessity has already received frequent reference in this historical survey. Like

Osborne and Mendel, McCollum and Davis came at first to the conclusion that they could obtain adequate nutrition with such diets. They found later, however, that the growth, apparently promoted by these, ceased abnormally soon, and in a paper published in 1913 they describe an experience which first brought their investigations into the field of vitamin studies [1913]. They had found that when, on a synthetic diet of which the fat constituent was lard, growth had prematurely ceased, the administration of butter fat or ether extracts of egg yolk secured its immediate resumption. They were then led, like Osborne and Mendel, to recognize that a factor essential to nutrition was associated with certain (but not all) fats. It may be noted as of interest that their paper just mentioned was submitted for publication in the same month (June 1913) as Osborne and Mendel's paper also dealing with the specific influence of butter fat, to which reference has been made.

A year later McCollum and Davis [1914] demonstrated at once the objective nature of the factor associated with animal fats and its relative stability by showing that it could be transferred from saponified butter fat to olive oil which otherwise contains none of it.

In 1915 these authors published an important paper [1915, 2] in which it was made clear that at least two 'accessory' diet factors were essential for normal growth. Owing to the special interest which Eijkman's studies had conferred upon polished rice, McCollum, who had previously employed wheat-grain in his studies, decided at this time to make the former the basis of a synthetic dietary. McCollum and Davis had been convinced by previous experience that growth and well-being could be maintained in animals fed on a mixture of purified proteins (casein), starch, *milk sugar*, butter fat, and a suitable mixture of mineral salts. They held, therefore, that polished rice, if its low content of protein and certain mineral deficiencies were first corrected by suitable additions, ought when mixed with butter fat to form a completely adequate dietary. When submitted to trials, however, this diet entirely failed to induce any growth in young rats. The explanation soon came to hand. It will have been noticed that the above-mentioned synthetic diet, the apparent success of which led to the expectation that the rice diet would be adequate, contained milk sugar. Once more the circumstance that this sugar adsorbs the vitamins of milk had led to unreal success with an artificial dietary. Hopkins and Neville's earlier experience on this point had not till then impressed these later investigators. McCollum and Davis found, as did Osborne and Mendel, that purification of the commercially 'pure' lactose it contained could make all the difference between adequacy and inadequacy in a synthetic diet. Such experiences should not be looked upon as trivial in their bearings. They illustrate how exceedingly small may be the amounts in which accessory components of food can exert a potent action, a significant circumstance wholly unrealized by earlier students of nutrition and involving a lesson which had to be learned by all experimentalists. McCollum and Davis quickly saw the significance of the facts before them. They realized that what was associated with the unpurified sugar could not consist in the main at least of the substance associated with butter fat. They sought for this second substance elsewhere and found it widely spread in natural food materials, wheat germ being specially rich in it. They now suggested the names 'fat-soluble A' and 'water-soluble B' as labels for these two entities, so introducing the current alphabetical nomenclature of vitamins, which, though displaying some inconveniences owing to the increasing complexity of the field, has yet justified itself on the whole.

Evidence derived from the observed distribution of 'water-soluble B' and the antiberi-beri vitamin discovered by Eijkman pointed to an identity between these two dietary factors, which has since been disproved. For a considerable time from 1915 onwards the relatively simple conception held the field that only three vitamins, fat-soluble A, water-soluble B, and antiscorbutic vitamin C, were capable of demonstration by biological methods. Following E. Mellanby's discovery in 1918 of the existence of an antirachitic vitamin associated with certain fats, evidence for the subdivision of the fat-soluble vitamin into vitamin A and an antirachitic vitamin D gradually accumulated. More recently the existence of the fertility vitamin E has been discovered and laborious researches on water-soluble B have brought to light the complex nature of this factor and necessitated the recognition in it of at least five different principles. The historical sequence of the researches leading up to our present knowledge of the subject will be dealt with in detail in later sections of this monograph.

CHAPTER II

THE FAT-SOLUBLE VITAMINS. VITAMIN A.

Historical.

AFTER the recognition by McCollum and Davis [1913] of the existence of a fat-soluble vitamin necessary for growth, observations gradually accumulated which indicated that more than one accessory food factor was present in some of the natural fats and oils.

A convenient starting-point for the history of the further development of the subject is found in the recognition by E. Mellanby [1918–19, 1, 2; 1919; 1920; 1921] of rickets as a deficiency disease. He was able to demonstrate that experimental rickets could be induced in puppies by withholding from the diet a substance (the antirachitic vitamin) which appeared to be similar as regards distribution and properties to the fat-soluble vitamin A. Although calcium and phosphorus deficiencies were naturally of importance, the potency of the antirachitic vitamin in effecting the calcification of bone was so pronounced as to imply that the substance held a key position in the aetiology of rickets. Cod-liver oil was much superior to all the other fats tested (e.g. beef suet, butter, lard, and various vegetable oils) in promoting the calcification of bone and in preventing rickets. Mellanby was inclined to identify this antirachitic vitamin with the fat-soluble A recognized by McCollum and Davis some five years earlier [1913]. The evidence was not complete, but further support to the idea was given by the observation that butter through which oxygen was bubbled at 120° C. lost both its growth-promoting [Hopkins, 1920] and antirachitic power [Mellanby, 1921].

The advance due to Mellanby was consolidated and extended to experiments on rats by Sherman and Pappenheimer [1920–21; 1921]; Korenchevsky [1922]; McCollum, Simmonds, Parsons, Shipley and Park [1921]; and other workers. The experimental procedure necessary for the production of rickets in rats emphasized the importance of the calcium/phosphorus ratio in the diet, as well as the deficiency of antirachitic vitamin. The following results gained widespread acceptance:

(1) A fat-soluble vitamin similar in many respects to vitamin A is necessary for the production of perfectly formed bones, even when the calcium and phosphorus content of the diet is adequate and well-balanced.

(2) Deficiency of either calcium or phosphorus or an unbalanced proportion of these two elements increases the importance of an adequate supply of antirachitic vitamin.

(3) The power of controlling calcification of bone and of promoting growth is most potently exerted by fish-liver oils [Goldblatt and Zilva, 1923]. Body fats exhibit some little potency with the exception of lard, which, like most vegetable oils, is usually devoid of both antirachitic

and growth-promoting activities. Egg yolk and milk usually contain both vitamins.

(4) Rickets is a disease associated with growth and affects suscep- tible animals at their most active period of development; with increasing age an animal becomes less dependent on the antirachitic vitamin.

The similarity in distribution of vitamin A and the antirachitic vitamin extends to lean meat, milled cereals, and yeast, all of which contain very little or none of either principle. The antirachitic vitamin, like vitamin A, is associated with the unsaponifiable portion of fat, and no connexion can be traced with fatty glycerides as such [Steenbock and Boutwell, 1920, 1; Steenbock, Nelson and Hart, 1921; Drummond and Coward, 1921; Zucker, Pappenheimer and Barnett, 1921–22; Zucker, 1922]. Both substances are resistant to heat alone, but in the presence of oxygen destruction of both occurs at elevated temperatures.

Separation of the two Fat-soluble Vitamins.

McCollum, Simmonds, Becker and Shipley [1922] showed that the antixerophthalmic action of cod-liver oil was destroyed by 12–20 hours' oxidation at 100°C., whereas its antirachitic action could be demon- strated after this treatment [see also Steenbock and Nelson, 1923]. Similarly it was found by Goldblatt and Zilva [1923] that the rates of destruction by heat and oxidation of these two properties in cod-liver oil differed markedly, the antirachitic principle being much the more resistant to oxygenation and to heat. Vitamin D was not unattacked but was only decomposed by a more prolonged or more drastic treat- ment than was necessary to effect the destruction of vitamin A.

In addition to this evidence differences were recorded, both qualita- tive and quantitative, in the distribution of these two principles in foodstuffs. McCollum and his co-workers made the very significant observation that butter, while much weaker than cod-liver oil in both its antixerophthalmic and antirachitic actions, was relatively much stronger in the former than the latter, thus indicating that these two different properties of butter depended on two different substances. These workers also found that coco-nut oil, which, like many other vegetable fats was lacking in fat-soluble vitamin A, unlike these con- tained 'a substance which stimulates the deposition of calcium salts in rickets in a manner similar to cod-liver oil' [McCollum, Simmonds, Becker and Shipley, 1922].

This conclusion was strengthened by the gradual accumulation of evidence from 1923 to 1925 that antirachitic (vitamin D) but not antixerophthalmic (vitamin A) properties could be produced by the action of certain radiations upon the animal organism or upon natural foodstuffs composing the diet (see pp. 69, 70). Since then it has been accepted that vitamin A (the antixerophthalmic vitamin) and vitamin D (the antirachitic vitamin) are distinct fat-soluble dietary factors, both of which are required by mammals for satisfactory growth and nutri- tion [Steenbock and Nelson, 1923; 1924–25; Steenbock and Black, 1924; Hess and Weinstock, 1924, 1, 2; 1924–25; 1925, 1, 2, 3].

Vitamin A.

THE EFFECTS OF VITAMIN A DEFICIENCY.

Growth.

THE first indication that a fat-soluble accessory food factor, not identical with any of the common triglycerides or any of the known "lipoid" substances, was necessary to ensure satisfactory health and growth in small laboratory animals fed on artificial diets, was provided by the work of Stepp [1909; 1911; 1912]. Stepp showed that mice fed on foodstuffs which had been previously extracted with alcohol and ether died after a few weeks. If the alcohol-ether extract was restored to the diet, the animals were enabled to live in good health. The unknown factor involved was shown not to be inorganic, since the addition of the ash of the extract to the diet did not remedy the deficiency. The addition of various triglycerides, or of cholesterol, lecithin, or kephalin to the extracted diet was equally ineffective. There is little doubt, however, that the dietary deficiency studied by Stepp was complicated by the removal by the alcohol of factors other than those which we now regard as fat-soluble, possibly of the water-soluble B vitamins, since butter was found to be deficient and skimmed milk relatively rich in the missing constituents.

More clear-cut results were obtained when McCollum and Davis [1913] discovered the ' fat-soluble A ' vitamin and showed that rats failed to grow normally when fed on artificial rations in which lard or olive oil was the only source of fat. Good growth, however, followed the addition of an ether extract of egg yolk or of butter to the diet. Similar results were shortly after published by Osborne and Mendel [1913, 1, 2].

At this period and during the following few years no distinction was recognized between vitamin A and the antirachitic fat-soluble factor discovered later by Mellanby. It is certain, therefore, that the dietary deficiency studied by many early workers in this field was a deficiency of both vitamins A and D and not simply of vitamin A.

Young rats fed on a diet deficient only in vitamin A usually grow for a few weeks. This period is followed by one in which the body weight remains at an approximately constant level. The animals then show a sharp decline in weight and death rapidly follows. The timely administration of adequate supplies of vitamin A is soon followed by a resumption of growth.

The initial growth of animals fed on diets free from vitamin A is believed to correspond with the period during which they are utilizing their own reserves of vitamin A. The duration of this initial period of growth depends therefore largely on their previous dietary history [Smith and Chick, 1926].

Xerophthalmia.

Many years before the discovery of the vitamins the belief was widely held that certain types of conjunctivitis occurring in children were of dietary origin. M. Mori [1904] made the important observation that the disease known as 'hikan', prevalent among children in Japan and characterized by xerosis of the conjunctiva, could be prevented by giving various fish-liver oils. He concluded that the cause of the condition was a deficiency of fat in the diet. Bloch [1917, 1, 2, 3] and Monrad [1917] as a result of studying cases of conjunctivitis occurring in Danish children also concluded that the disease was a dietary one. The former, while agreeing with Mori in believing that a fat deficiency was the main aetiological factor, suggested that a vitamin deficiency might be a contributory cause. Monrad, on the other hand, definitely inclined to the belief that a deficiency of accessory food factors was the cause.

Knapp [1908] described an infective condition of the conjunctiva of rats fed on inadequate dietaries. Osborne and Mendel [1913, 2; 1914; 1915] called attention to the frequency with which infected eyes in rats were associated with a deficiency of what was then known as the fat-soluble accessory factor, and they pointed out that the administration of fats rich in the factor resulted in a prompt alleviation of the symptoms. Similar observations were recorded by McCollum and Davis [1915, 1].

The analogy between the human disease and that occurring in rats as a result of a deficiency of 'fat-soluble A', was clearly pointed out by McCollum and Simmonds [1917], who held that 'xerophthalmia' should be regarded as a deficiency disease.

In rats, the first symptom observed is a swelling of the eyelids which is followed by an inflamed condition of the conjunctiva. Haemorrhagic and purulent discharges follow ; the cornea becomes affected and ultimately blindness results. The first symptoms are usually observed shortly before or simultaneously with the slowing in the rate of growth [Osborne and Mendel, 1921].

The histological changes which occur have been studied in detail by Stephenson and Clark [1920]; Wason [1921]; S. Mori [1922, 1, 2]; Yudkin and Lambert [1921-22, 1, 2]; and G. M. Findlay [1925] among others. There have been some differences of opinion as to whether the bacterial invasion, which invariably accompanies the disease, is the primary cause of, or a secondary effect following, the changes that occur in the conjunctiva and cornea. Stephenson and Clark were unable to detect any histological change in the eyes preceding the bacterial invasion, and they therefore considered that the primary change was a lowering of resistance to infection. S. Mori stated that the primary change occurred in the lachrymal glands and that the resulting diminution of the secretion was the cause of the xerosis of the cornea and conjunctiva. Similar views have been advanced by Findlay, who has also made the important observation that the tears of rabbits fed on vitamin A-deficient diets are definitely deficient in lysozyme, thus providing an explanation for the extreme susceptibility to local bacterial infection in the eyes of these animals.

Hume [1922] and Goldblatt and Soames [1922] simultaneously showed that exposure of rats, fed on diets deficient in fat-soluble vitamins, to ultra-violet radiation was ineffective in preventing the appearance of the symptoms of xerophthalmia, although at first promoting growth. Since ultra-violet radiation was known to be specific in the cure of rickets, this fact suggested that the aetiological factors responsible for xerophthalmia and rickets were different. Further work by Bloch [1924, 1, 2], drawing attention to the infrequency with which dietary conjunctivitis accompanied rickets in children, pointed to the same conclusion. It was realized, therefore, when a distinction was made between the two fat-soluble factors, vitamins A and D, that a deficiency of the former was the cause of xerophthalmia.

Xerophthalmia is not an invariable symptom of vitamin A deficiency. Emmett [1920] observed that 120 out of 122 rats developed the typical symptoms when fed on vitamin A-deficient diets. On the other hand, Osborne and Mendel [1921] recorded an incidence of only 50 per cent. and Green and Mellanby [1928, 2] of 38 per cent. With more highly purified diets Osborne and Mendel [1924] reported an 80 per cent. incidence. Stammers [1924, 1], and Sherman and Storms [1925] have shown that adult rats are less susceptible to the disease than the young. It seems probable, therefore, that variation in age and in the degree of purity of the diets employed may to some extent account for the irregularity in the occurrence of xerophthalmia.

The specificity of xerophthalmia to vitamin A deficiency was at one time questioned by McCollum, Simmonds and Becker [1922], who observed a similar condition in rats receiving adequate supplies of vitamin A, but whose diet was unbalanced with regard to its inorganic constituents. S. Mori [1923] concluded from histological studies that the anatomical changes occurring in the eyes of rats in this condition were identical with those observed in xerophthalmia caused by vitamin A deficiency. Subsequently [Simmonds, Becker and McCollum, 1927, 1, 2; J. H. Jones, 1927; McCollum, Simmonds and Becker, 1926–27] it was shown that the cause of this new type of xerophthalmia was the substitution of ferrous sulphate for ferric citrate in the diet and the destruction of the vitamin A in the diet by the ferrous sulphate. Jones regarded the destruction of the vitamin to be the result of an oxidation catalysed by the ferrous salt.

Night-blindness (Hemeralopia).

For many years ophthalmologists have recognized a connexion between the occurrence of conjunctivitis in human beings and certain types of hemeralopia or night-blindness (see p. 234). Fridericia and Holm [1925] have shown that vitamin A-deficient rats placed in the dark after exposure to light show a subnormal rate of regeneration of the visual purple. Holm [1925] tested the ability of rats to jump off a table in a dim light, after previous exposure to bright sunlight. In this way it was shown that vitamin A-deficient rats had developed a well-defined hemeralopia, 'at a stage where it was impossible to perceive any other signs of avitaminosis'. This condition did not develop unless the animals were previously exposed to bright light for considerable periods. The administration of vitamin A to hemeralopic rats resulted in a disappearance of the symptoms within two to three days.

These results have been confirmed by Tansley [1931], who followed the course of the regeneration of the visual purple in normal and vitamin A-deficient rats. The visual purple was extracted from the retinas by a dilute solution of digitonin and quantitatively estimated by a photographic method. She was able to show that the retinas of the deficient rats contained in every case subnormal amounts of the visual purple.

Susceptibility to Infection.

The history of the development of knowledge relating vitamin A to infection has been complicated by the slow differentiation of the fat-soluble vitamin complex. It is true that at a relatively early stage in the history of this work the absence of vitamin A from the diet had been associated with xerophthalmia, and the fact that irradiation of the animal did not cure xerophthalmia [Hume 1922] was interpreted by Steenbock and Nelson [1923] as evidence that vitamin A and the antirachitic vitamin were different entities. Since all the earlier work concerned with vitamin A deficiency also involved a vitamin D deficiency, the expression 'fat-soluble vitamin' deficiency will be used in describing this earlier work.

Early attempts to correlate immunity reactions with vitamin deficiencies failed to bring out any connexion between the two. Thus Zilva [1919, 2] found that animals fed on 'vitamin A'-deficient diets showed no diminution in agglutinin or amboceptor titres. Findlay and Mackenzie [1922] were unable to show any decrease in the opsonic activity of the blood-serum of 'vitamin A' deficient rats. Cramer, Drew and Mottram [1922] detected a marked thrombopenia in rats deprived of vitamin A, to lack of which they ascribed this increased susceptibility. Bedson and Zilva [1923], on the other hand, were only able to detect a slight decrease in the platelet count and did not regard the observed change as a specific lesion produced by the deficiency. Cramer, Drew and Mottram [1923], however, maintained their original findings, but in a later paper [Cramer and Kingsbury, 1924] the thrombopenia was regarded as a result of, rather than the cause of, the bacterial invasion. The observations of Falconer [1926] were in close agreement with those of Bedson and Zilva.

McCollum [1917] was the first to draw attention to the susceptibility of rats when fed on diets deficient in fat-soluble vitamin to respiratory infection [see also Drummond, 1919, 2]. Under similar dietetic conditions puppies also often developed broncho-pneumonia [E. Mellanby, 1919]. This question of the relation of diet to infection later attracted more interest [Steenbock, Sell and Buell, 1921] and was extended to the intestine by Cramer [1923]. Following up S. Mori's [1922, 2] observations on the hyperplasia of epithelium produced by diets deficient in fat-soluble vitamin, Wolbach and Howe [1925] discovered the metaplasia of epithelium and the keratinization changes produced by this dietetic defect. Although primarily concerned with the epithelial changes they also noted the local infective conditions often found at the seats of epithelial change. It is interesting to note that Wolbach and Howe remarked on the 'cysts' found under the tongue in these animals, a condition later alluded to as abscesses by Sherman and Munsell [1925], one of the commonest forms of infection to be found in rats fed on diets deficient in fat-soluble vitamins. Cramer and Kingsbury [1924] no doubt meant the same lesion, or a similar one of the submaxillary glands, when they referred to a 'subcutaneous abscess in the neck' in animals eating diets defective in this respect.

As regards the differentiation of the parts played by vitamins A and D respectively in susceptibility to infection, E. Mellanby [1926, 2] analysed the dietary of a large number of puppies which had died from, or escaped, an epidemic of broncho-pneumonia and found that the susceptibility to this disease was correlated with a deficiency of fat-soluble vitamin in the diet, but that this susceptibility was not related to the calcification of the bones. Dogs, for instance, whose diet included butter, although often developing defective bone and even local ate-lectasis (collapse) of the lungs, escaped broncho-pneumonia : when the butter was heated and oxygenated, broncho-pneumonia often developed as well as badly calcified bones. Cod-liver oil produced perfect bones and also protected against broncho-pneumonia.

Goldblatt and Benischek [1927] repeated the work of Wolbach and Howe on the dietary factor responsible for hyperplasia and metaplasia of epithelium, but they took the added precaution of giving vitamin D in the basal diet in the form of irradiated cotton-seed oil, so that the diet was deficient only in vitamin A. The epithelial changes were thus proved to be due to deficient vitamin A intake, and the infective lesions also found, such as keratomalacia, broncho-pneumonia, and enteritis, could now be definitely ascribed to lack of this particular vitamin.

Green and Mellanby [1928, 2] reinvestigated this problem on a large scale with the object of finding out why animals ceased to grow and died on diets deficient in vitamin A. They found that rats on such diets almost invariably died with multiple infective foci of the type described by previous workers, and that these lesions could be readily observed macroscopically. The addition of vitamin D in the form of irradiated ergosterol did not increase the resistance to bacterial infec-tion—in fact, this addition often appeared to hasten the onset, possibly because of the increased rate of growth. The incidence of the infective foci in 92 rats fed on diets deficient in vitamin A was as follows :

Xerophthalmia, 38 per cent.
Abscess at base of tongue, 72 per cent.
Infections of lungs, 9 per cent.
Infections of genito-urinary tract (including renal and bladder calculi), 44 per cent.
Middle-ear abscess and septic nasal sinuses, 20 per cent.

Other seats of infection were prostate glands, seminal vesicles, spleen, intestine, and ovaries. Fifty control rats on the same diet with the addition of some source of vitamin A, as for example dried cabbage, butter or cod-liver oil, developed no sign of any of these infections. Green and Mellanby therefore gave the name 'anti-infective vitamin' to vitamin A to signify that animals deprived of this substance died of bacterial infective lesions.

A further development of this work was the demonstration by Green and Mellanby [1930] that carotene (see p. 39) also has the specific effect of preventing the local infections above described as well as the hyperplastic changes of the epithelium. A point of interest about this work is the quantitative relationship between the amount of carotene ingested and the degree of infection. Thus a daily dose of 0·08 mg. of the specimen of carotene used prevented the development of all infective foci in the young rat ; 0·01 mg. allowed a moderate degree of infection ; while 0·005 mg. had no significant protective effect.

Two important problems in this connexion remain for future investigation :

(1) The specificity of vitamin A in its relation to bacterial resistance.

(2) The significance of this relationship in the case of man and other animals.

There is a general consensus of opinion that in the case of other vitamins deficiency of intake also lowers the resistance of animals to infection, but there is no evidence that the relationship is as direct as in vitamin A deficiency. For instance, the work of Grant, Suyenaga and Stegeman (1927, 1, 2), and of Eichholz and Kreitmair [1928] has shown that a lowered resistance to certain types of bacterial infection results from vitamin D deficiency.

To what extent these results are applicable to some human infections remains to be established. The fact that some of the infective conditions observed in rats are commonly found among human beings, especially children, suggests that a deficiency of vitamin A intake is a factor of importance in the aetiology of these human diseases. This might well apply, for instance, to broncho-pneumonia, middle-ear disease, and septic nasal sinuses. Several attempts have been made to see whether vitamin A therapy, either curative or prophylactic, can influence certain cases of infection. For instance, Mellanby and Green have treated puerperal septicaemia with diets specially rich in vitamin A, and their results indicate an increased resistance in cases of this disease, except in those of the fulminating type and in those complicated with peritonitis and septic thrombo-phlebitis [1929 ; Green and Mellanby, 1930]. The same workers have also recorded the results of treating women late in pregnancy with vitamin A preparations and have compared the amount of puerperal sepsis which developed after parturition in these cases with that in an equal number of women who received no such addition to the diet. Here again the results showed a definite increase in resistance to infection in the former group [1930] (see p. 270). Donaldson and Tasker [1930] at the Crown Gold Mines, Johannesburg, tested this form of treatment in cases of pneumonia among the native workers. To 100 cases of pneumonia they gave daily $\frac{1}{2}$ lb. of liver, to a second 100 radiostoleum (a preparation containing vitamins A and D), and a third 100 received no additional treatment. The untreated cases had a mortality of 13 per cent., that of the first and second groups was 8 per cent. On the whole, therefore, although the evidence is at present no more than suggestive, it seems possible that the animal results may prove to have some bearing on certain types of human infection. It is of interest to note that Bloch [1921] in an analysis of 64 cases of vitamin A deficiency in human beings, diagnosed on the basis of xerophthalmia, found a high rate of other infective conditions. There were 15 cases of pneumonia, 12 of bronchitis, 15 of otitis media, 27 of pyuria, and 14 of pyodermia.

The animal experimental method has also been used to see whether vitamin A deficiency influences the resistance to infections transmitted to the animals and not developed autogenously. Thus Lassen [1930] has found that rats inoculated by mouth and by subcutaneous injection with Breslau bacilli (paratyphoid) succumb more readily when the diet is deficient in vitamin A than when rich in this substance. An obvious difficulty in this type of work is that animals deprived of vitamin A have much less vitality than animals on complete diets and therefore die more readily when exposed to the strain of a septicaemia. Topley, Greenwood and Wilson [1931] determined the mortality of mice consuming diets respectively rich and adequate in vitamin A when associated with other mice infected with *B. aertrycke*. They found no increase in resistance in the mice fed on the richer diet.

The subject is one of great practical importance and is attracting much attention among laboratory and clinical investigators. For the time being it is impossible to assess the significance or the limitations of the animal results so far as human disease is concerned. It may be, as claimed by Cramer and Kingsbury [1924], that a deficiency of this substance in the body simply brings about a breakdown of the local defences of such organs as the intestine, eyes, and lungs against bacterial invasion and has no effect on the general humoral defences. Even if this is its mode of action, the prophylactic and therapeutic uses of vitamin A in human disease ought to be of great value.

Susceptibility of the Central Nervous System to Toxic Influences.

The experimental production of a syndrome resembling subacute combined degeneration of the spinal cord has recently become a problem of some interest and promises to open up to scientific study from a nutritional aspect a number of human nervous diseases which have hitherto been almost entirely subject to clinical study alone.

Hart, Miller and McCollum [1916] described changes in the anterior horn cells of pigs' spinal cords caused by diet. No changes in the conducting fibres were described and the authors decided that they were dealing with a form of beri-beri, not, however, due to a deficiency of vitamin B, which was present in abundance in the wheat germ contained in the diet. Indeed the pathological condition was ascribed rather to a toxic action of the wheat germ. The changes in the cord could be prevented by adding alfalfa meal and meat scraps to the diet and the protective action of these foodstuffs was attributed to a combined action of additional proteins, fat-soluble vitamins, and a better salt mixture, but not to any one of these substances alone. Hughes, Lienhardt and Aubel [1929] observed degeneration of fibres in the spinal cord, and in some peripheral nerves, of pigs after feeding them from the time of weaning on white corn, tankage and bone-ash. They also found that these changes could be prevented by cod-liver oil, butter fat, yellow corn, and alfalfa leaf meal, and suggested that the preventive dietary factor was probably vitamin A

Some years previously E. Mellanby [1926, 1] described the production in dogs of a condition resembling combined system disease with degenerated nerve fibres in tracts of the cord by the use of diets rich in cereals, especially in wheat germ, and deficient in fat-soluble vitamins. He ascribed this effect to a nerve toxamin in the cereals, which like the de-calcifying toxamin also contained in cereals could only operate in the absence of a fat-soluble vitamin.

In 1929, in a lecture in Kenya, E. Mellanby [1930, 1, see also 1931, 1, 2] gave further results of the experimental production by dietary measures of subacute combined degeneration of the cord, which he found could be hastened and intensified by adding a small quantity of ergot (2–5 g. daily) to the diet. Vitamin D which was found to be a constituent of ergot [Mellanby, Surie and Harrison, 1929] played little or no part in the processes. The addition of vitamin A-containing substances such as mammalian-liver oil or butter prevented the neuro-toxin contained in ergot from being effective. Carotene (about 5 mg.) or carotene-containing substances (c. g. carrots or cabbage) also prevented degeneration of the spinal cord, and this condition, if permitted to develop, was rapidly improved by the addition of carotene or vitamin A to the diet, and the degeneration of the central nervous system was arrested.

It is not yet possible to make any definite statements as to the significance of these facts with regard to nervous disease in man. E. Mellanby suggests, however, that they probably explain the appearance in epidemic form of convulsive ergotism, a condition which was common at one time in rye-eating countries. These epidemics appear in times of famine and drought and are no doubt due partly to the consumption of ergotized rye and partly to the fact that butter, vegetables, and other sources of vitamin A and carotene are unprocurable. If the diet is rich in vitamin A dogs can eat large quantities of ergot continuously without causing any affection of their nervous system [E. Mellanby, 1931, 2].

Lathyrism is another disease associated with degenerative changes in the spinal cord similar to those occurring in dogs fed on vitamin A-deficient diets with addition of ergot. This disease which is often widespread in some Indian provinces is also a disease of poverty and develops in persons eating largely of peas (*Lathyrus sativus*). In this case also it is possible that the absence of vitamin A and carotene from the diet allows a neuro-toxin in the peas to exert its harmful effect on the nervous system [E Mellanby, 1931, 2].

In pellagra somewhat similar degenerative changes are found in the nervous system. In view of the fact that pellagra occurs commonly, but not exclusively, among maize-eating populations, it is of interest to note that yellow maize not only does not produce the characteristic demyelination of the cord in dogs when it forms the cereal element of diets deficient in vitamin A, but actually prevents ergot from producing this effect [E. Mellanby, 1931, 2]. Yellow maize apparently contains sufficient carotene to give the necessary protection against the neuro-toxin of ergot. White maize has been found to possess little or none of such a protective property.

Whether administration of vitamin A or of carotene results in any great improvement of the nervous manifestations of pellagra has not been tested. Clinical evidence suggests that vitamin A may play a significant part in preventing the development of certain other conditions characterized by nerve demyelination which are more commonly found in this country. Pernicious anaemia, for instance, and disseminated sclerosis have been treated with mammalian liver, and good results have been claimed. Whereas it is now recognized that the abnormal condition of the blood in pernicious anaemia can be successfully treated with watery extracts of mammalian liver [Minot and Murphy, 1926], this substance has no curative or preventive action on the lesions in the central nervous system, often present in the later stages of that disease. It is reported, however, that whole liver has been found to be curative both of the blood condition and of the nervous lesions [Ungley and Suzman, 1929]. In this case, the beneficial effect on the cord may be due to the vitamin A contained in the liver, as suggested by E. Mellanby's experiments. Similar curative effects of whole liver in disseminated sclerosis have been described by Goodall and Slater [1931]. Owing to the well-known fact that remissions often occur normally in cases of disseminated sclerosis, it is too early yet to accept liver therapy as a specific treatment in this disease, but the evidence so far is promising. The argument based on the frequent occurrence of remissions in this disease is, however, double-edged and may imply unrecognized dietetic influences, as was proved to be the case in pernicious anaemia.

Keratinization of Epithelial Cells.

Closely linked with the question of susceptibility to bacterial infections are the pathological changes in epithelial surfaces that have been repeatedly observed as a symptom of vitamin A deficiency. S. Mori [1922, 1, 2] was the first to draw attention to these changes which he observed in the larynx, trachea, and in the ducts of various glands. Wolbach and Howe [1925, 1928] showed that the substitution of stratified keratinizing epithelium for normal epithelium in the alimentary tract, the respiratory tract, the genito-urinary tract, the eyes, the parocular glands, and the pancreatic duct was a character-istic effect of vitamin A deficiency in rats and guinea-pigs. They claim [1925] 'that the substitution of keratinizing epithelium in all locations is not secondary to infections, and presumably is a primary effect of the withdrawal of factors essential for the chemical activities or maintenance of differentiation of the epitheliums concerned'. As Green and Mellanby [1928, 2] have stated, the susceptibility to infec-tion may be 'due to the favourable medium which obstruction by desquamated keratinized cells provides for bacterial growth'.

The continued appearance of keratinized epithelial cells in the vaginal tract of the rat has been observed by several workers and used as a criterion of vitamin A deficiency [Evans and Bishop, 1922, 1, 2; Macy, Outhouse, Long and Graham, 1927 ; Coward, 1929, 1]. Since in the normal rat the presence of keratinized epithelial cells indicates the period of oestrus, Evans and Bishop at first wrongly assumed that the prolonged keratinization observed was due to a prolongation of oestrus, but later experiments [Evans, 1928, 3] clearly showed that this could not be so since the same phenomenon was observed even after double ovariectomy. Coward [1929, 1], and Coward, Morgan and Dyer [1930], on the other hand, found this symptom of little use for the diagnosis of vitamin A deficiency, since not only did they fail to find constantly a 'cornified' vaginal smear after cessation of growth, but in certain cases the vaginae of the young rats did not open until after the other symptoms of vitamin A deficiency had appeared.

Reproduction.

Failure in reproduction by rats deprived of vitamin A has been observed for many years [Drummond, 1919, 3 ; Sherman and MacLeod, 1925]. Parkes and Drummond [1926] tried to determine the nature of this sterility by histological examination of the gonads of animals in different stages of vitamin A deficiency. No degeneration or other abnormalities of structure were found even in rats which had ceased to grow when far below adult weight. When similar rats were changed to a vitamin A-rich diet, they grew to maturity and reproduced freely. Since, however, it is now realized that these rats were probably also suffering from a shortage of vitamins D and E, the effects cannot be ascribed simply to a deficiency of vitamin A.

Sure [1928, 1] demonstrated that a deficiency of vitamin A leads to resorption of the foetus, as does a deficiency of vitamin E.

Properties and Attempted Isolation of Vitamin A.

Properties.

In the early literature on the general chemical properties and stability of fat-soluble A, many apparent contradictions are to be found. These can partly be ascribed to the difficulties encountered in even roughly quantitative estimations of the vitamin by animal growth tests. On the other hand insufficient care to exclude more than one factor influencing the stability of the vitamin has led in many cases to confusion. A striking example of the latter is seen in the question of the stability of vitamin A to heat. McCollum and Davis [1914] originally pointed out that since the fat extracted from boiled eggs was highly active, the vitamin must be resistant to heat. Osborne and Mendel [1915; 1920, 1] found that the vitamin in butter fat was highly thermostable, while Steenbock and Boutwell [1920, 2] were able to show that the vitamin from vegetable sources was also stable to heat. On the other hand Steenbock, Boutwell and Kent [1918], and Drummond [1919, 2] reported experiments which indicated that the vitamin in butter fat was destroyed to a large extent by heat.

The explanation of these discrepancies became clear when it was shown by Hopkins [1920] that although the vitamin in butter was resistant to temperatures up to 120° C. it was readily destroyed by aeration at all temperatures. Hopkins's results on butter fat were independently confirmed by Drummond and Coward [1920], while Zilva [1920, 1; 1922] showed that the vitamin in fish-liver oils was also destroyed by aeration at ordinary temperatures and more rapidly if ozone were employed.

Attempts to isolate Vitamin A.

The important observation that vitamin A was resistant to alkaline saponification was made by McCollum and Davis [1914]. This fact, confirmed by Steenbock and Boutwell [1920, 3], Steenbock, Nelson and Hart [1921], and Drummond and Coward [1921], formed the basis of many of the subsequent attempts to concentrate and isolate the vitamin from various sources. Provided that adequate precautions against oxidation are observed, the vitamin in cod-liver oil is stable to treatment with a hot solution of alcoholic potash or sodium ethoxide, and may be quantitatively recovered in the unsaponifiable fraction by extraction of the soaps with ether or some other suitable solvent. Since the unsaponifiable matter present in many natural fats and oils containing the vitamin forms only a small fraction of the total bulk, a considerable degree of concentration may be accomplished by this process.

The technique of the process [Steenbock, Sell and Buell, 1921; Drummond, Channon and Coward, 1925] was modified by Takahashi et al. [1925], who converted the soaps into calcium salts and obtained the unsaponifiable matter from the alcoholic extract of these, and by Marcus [1928] who extracted the semi-solid mass of soaps with ethylene dichloride and claimed to have obtained quantitative extraction of both vitamins A and D. Dubin and Funk [1923] extracted cod-liver oil with acetic acid and saponified the extract in the usual way.

The cholesterol in the unsaponifiable fraction of cod-liver oil can be precipitated by digitonin without removing any of the vitamin A activity [Drummond and Coward, 1922]. Since approximately 50 per cent. of the unsaponifiable matter of many natural oils containing the vitamin consists of cholesterol, a still further degree of concentration can be obtained by such a process, and the cholesterol-free unsaponifiable matter has been the starting-point for several attempts to isolate this vitamin. This fraction has been shown to contain carbon, hydrogen, and oxygen, but no nitrogen, phosphorus, iodine or other halogens [Takahashi, 1922; Drummond, Channon and Coward, 1925]. The absence of iodine is of particular interest since at one time the suggestion was put forward that the therapeutic action of cod-liver oil was due to traces of this element [Kopp, 1836, 1, 2].

Takahashi and his colleagues [1922; 1923; 1925] made extensive studies of these active concentrates and by fractional distillation under reduced pressure isolated material which they regarded as the pure vitamin [1925]. This material, termed by them 'biosterin', was described as a reddish-yellow transparent viscous oily substance, and was assigned the formula $C_{27}H_{46}O_2$. The suggestion that this substance was an unsaturated alcohol related to the sterols was advanced by them.

Drummond, Channon and Coward [1925], following up earlier work [Drummond and Coward, 1924] on the chemical nature of the cholesterol-free unsaponifiable fraction of cod-liver oil, were able to show that the claim of Takahashi to have isolated the vitamin was unfounded. They succeeded in effecting some degree of concentration by distillation in a high vacuum, but the most active fraction, of the same order of activity as 'biosterin', proved to be a complex mixture containing, amongst other substances, the unsaturated hydrocarbon squalene, and a solid saturated alcohol. These two substances were found to be devoid of growth-promoting activity. Since the remainder of the most active fractions appeared to consist largely of a complex mixture of unsaturated alcohols, physiological tests on oleyl alcohol, selachyl alcohol, and phytol were carried out. All these substances were inactive. The inactivity of phytol was also demonstrated by Javillier, Baude and Lévy-Lajeunesse [1925].

A further unsuccessful effort to isolate vitamin A from liver oil was made by Drummond and Baker [1929], using the colour test (p. 37) as criterion almost exclusively. Attempts to concentrate the cholesterol-free unsaponifiable fractions of both cod-liver oil and sheep-liver fat by distillation at low pressures met with no success, since the extensive decomposition which occurred led to considerable losses in the total vitamin activity. On the other hand, distillation of the unsaponifiable matter of shark-liver oils yielded certain fractions possessing a higher activity than the original material. The most active fractions were found to consist very largely (90–95 per cent. or more) of selachyl, batyl, chimyl, and oleyl alcohols, each of which was physiologically inactive. The vitamin was probably present only to the extent of less than 1 per cent. in such unsaponifiable fractions, and the difficulties in the way of the isolation of vitamin A from these sources would appear to be great.

The physiological activity of vitamin A preparations does not appear to be impaired by chemical treatments which involve reactions with hydroxyl groups, e.g. acetylation, benzoylation, etc. On the other hand, processes which affect double bonds, e.g. oxidation, hydrogenation, bromination, lead to complete destruction of the activity [Drummond, Channon and Coward, 1925].

Karrer and his co-workers [Karrer, Morf and Schöpp, 1931, 1, 2; Karrer *et al.*, 1931] have confirmed the observation first made by Rosenheim and Webster [1927, 6], that the liver oils of certain fishes, such as the halibut, are much richer sources of vitamin A than cod-liver oil. They used livers of halibut (*Hippoglossus*) and of mackerel as starting materials, and the colour reaction with $SbCl_3$ was relied on for controlling the progress of purification. This consisted mainly in saponification of the liver oil and removal of the sterols by cooling to $-60°$ C. a methyl alcoholic solution of the unsaponifiable portion. The final purification was effected by fractional adsorption on fibrous alumina and furnished a faintly yellow viscous oil, which, it is claimed, contains at least 50 per cent. of vitamin A. The oil (obtained from halibut) had a colour value of 10,000 (cod-liver oil = 1) and a biological activity of 0.5γ (i.e. the smallest amount producing distinct increase in growth). It still contained about 5 per cent. of vitamin D. A molecular weight estimation in camphor (Rast) gave mol. wt. 320, a figure in agreement with the mol. wt. 333 calculated by Bruins, Overhoff and Wolff [1931] on the basis of diffusion experiments and colour tests.

The oil obtained from the unsaponifiable fraction of the liver oil of mackerel had similar properties to that from halibut, but was free from vitamin D (vitamin A activity not stated). Its elementary analysis gave figures agreeing with the formula $C_{20}H_{30}O$ (or $C_{22}H_{32}O$) and it yielded uncrystallizable esters with acetic and *p*-nitrobenzoic acids, the elementary composition of which again agreed with the above formula. On ozonization both preparations furnished geronic acid.

On the basis of this work Karrer, Morf and Schöpp [1931, 1, 3] make the interesting suggestion that both vitamin A and carotene contain the ring-system of β-ionone, since geronic acid is obtained by similar treatment from both β-ionone and carotene. A constitutional formula containing the β-ionone ring-system with an aliphatic side-chain, similar to that present in carotene, is tentatively advanced.

Heilbron, Heslop, Morton, Drummond and Rea [1932] have obtained results which in many respects confirm those of Karrer and his co-workers. Specially selected halibut oils were used and the extraction was followed spectroscopically. The final stages of the concentration were effected by fractional vacuum distillation at pressures below 0·00001 mm. The product resembled that described by Karrer, namely a poly-ene alcohol, of molecular weight *circa* 300. The degree of unsaturation appears to correspond with 4 or 5 double bonds, whilst the carbon content (*circa* 82 per cent.) is lower than would be expected for $C_{20}H_{30}O$. The distilled preparations promote growth in rats in daily doses of 0·1γ.

The Colour Reactions and Absorption Spectrum attributed to Vitamin A.

Attention was drawn to the possible significance of the colour reactions of cod-liver oil when it was recognized by Rosenheim and Drummond [1920] that the purple colour developed with sulphuric acid is due to a chromogen which is also a normal constituent of all liver fats, whether derived from fish, bird, or mammal. The distribution and general properties of this chromogen, such as resistance to saponification, solubilities, lability towards oxygen, suggested to them a relationship with vitamin A [cf. Drummond and Watson, 1922]. The extremely unstable nature of the reaction, however, prevented its use for quantitative comparison of different oils.

The discovery that arsenic trichloride and similar reagents give with cod-liver oil, and other liver fats, a brilliant blue colour reaction, which is sufficiently stable for colorimetric purposes, paved the way for the quantitative application of this reaction [Rosenheim and Drummond, 1925]. It was found that the distribution of this chromogen is similar to that of vitamin A, whilst the positive reaction given by carotene strengthened the previous suggestions of a relationship between this pigment and vitamin A. There is an essential difference between the absorption spectra (see later) of the colour produced in the reaction with carotene and of that produced from the cod-liver oil chromogen, but the fact that the cod-liver oil chromogen appears in the livers of vitamin A-deficient rats after administration of carotene [Moore, 1930, 1931] provides additional evidence of the specificity of this reaction for vitamin A.

By substituting antimony trichloride for arsenic trichloride and using Lovibond's graded colour glasses, Carr and Price [1926] made it possible to measure accurately and to compare the colour value of different oils. The reaction is carried out by mixing chloroform solutions of the oil and the reagent. The rapid matching of the transient blue colour is greatly facilitated by the use of the colorimeter described by Rosenheim and Schuster [1927]. In order that different observers should obtain concordant results it is essential that standardized conditions should be adhered to. These have been defined by the Pharmacopoeia Commission [1931], as it was considered that this colour test might prove of value for indicating the degree of deterioration of pharmaceutical cod-liver oils. The Pharmacopoeia Commission deprecates the use of the term 'blue unit' in expressing the colour value of cod-liver oil and points out that 'the figures given to a glass on the Lovibond scale represent merely a grading in a series of glasses, and do not represent an amount of biological activity'.

The application of the test is limited, as pointed out originally by Rosenheim and Drummond [1925], to medicinal cod-liver oils and similar liver fats, which are usually only slightly pigmented. Since other carotenoids as well as carotene, such as xanthophyll, lycopin, and crocetin, give colours with $AsCl_3$ and $SbCl_3$ which are superficially similar to those given by cod-liver oil, the blue colour alone cannot be regarded as a specific test for vitamin A. The colour given by the yellow pigment carotene can, however, be differentiated from that of the colourless vitamin A contained in cod-liver oil by its specific absorption at 590 $m\mu$ [Dulière, Morton and Drummond, 1929].

Whilst the maximum intensity of the absorption band of the product of the $SbCl_3$ reaction of liver oils was stated to be at 614 $m\mu$ by Wokes [1928] and at 608 $m\mu$ by Drummond and Morton [1929], it has been found by Gillam and Morton [1931] that the blue colour is complex, and possesses two absorption bands with maxima at 572 $m\mu$ and 606 $m\mu$. The relationship of these bands to each other and to vitamin A remains undefined, although certain evidence (see later) suggests that the chromogen giving rise to the band at 572 $m\mu$ is probably related to vitamin A, and that the band at 606 $m\mu$ is due to the product of slow oxidation of another substance present in liver oils [Heilbron, Gillam and Morton, 1931].

Fish-liver oils show selective absorption in the ultra-violet region of the spectrum at about 320–328 $m\mu$ [Takahashi et al., 1925 ; Schlutz and Morse, 1925 ; Heilbron, Kamm and Morton, 1927 ; Woodrow, 1928], which has been brought into relationship with vitamin A by Morton and Heilbron [1928]. Their results showed a striking parallel between the depth of the blue colour given by the $SbCl_3$ reagent and the intensity of the selective absorption at 328 $m\mu$ in various fish-liver oils, etc. Later work led these authors [Gillam and Morton, 1931 ; Heilbron and Morton, 1931] to the view that the substance responsible for the ultra-violet absorption band at 328 $m\mu$ is probably identical with the chromogen giving rise to the 572 $m\mu$ band in the $SbCl_3$ reaction.

Coward, Dyer, Morton and Gaddum [1931] found that the intensity of the colour produced by the action of antimony trichloride on the unsaponifiable fraction of an oil [see also Norris and Church, 1930, 1, 2, 3, 4 ; Smith and Hazley, 1930] was in better agreement with the result of their biological test for vitamin A than the intensity of the colour produced with the oil itself. It seems therefore advisable in all cases to make the colour test on the unsaponifiable fraction rather than on the fat itself. Tests based on measurement of the intensity of absorption of the oil at 328 $m\mu$ gave slightly better agreement with the results of the biological tests, but certain of the oils examined showed serious discrepancies between the results of the biological tests and both of these physical tests, so that the latter cannot yet be regarded as trustworthy measures of vitamin A. Until the specificity for vitamin A of the chemical and physical tests has been fully established by the isolation of vitamin A itself, biological evidence must obviously remain indispensable as final proof for the presence of vitamin A.

Other colour reactions. A red colour reaction with pyrogallol and trichloroacetic acid was considered characteristic for vitamin A by Fearon [1925 ; cf. Willimott and Moore, 1926 ; Euler, Myrbäck and

Karlson, 1926], but was found to be non-specific by Rosenheim and Webster [1926, 3, 4].

A blue colour reaction with $AsCl_3$, $SbCl_3$ etc., superficially resembling that shown by cod-liver oil with the same reagents, is given by 'oxycholesterol' [Rosenheim, 1927], a mixture of chemically undefined substances obtained by treatment of cholesterol with oxidizing agents [Lifschütz, 1913]. The reaction differs from that given by cod-liver oil in its absorption spectrum and other characters. When tested biologically, the product was found to be devoid of vitamin A activity [Rosenheim, 1927]. As Seel and Dannmeyer [1930; 1931] and Seel [1931] ascribed antixerophthalmic and growth-promoting properties to 'oxycholesterol', the subject was reinvestigated and the results showed that three different preparations of 'oxycholesterol', when tested in doses up to 1 mg. daily, failed to prevent the death of rats deprived of vitamin A or to cure xerophthalmia [Rosenheim, Hume and Crawford, unpublished results, 1931.]

THE RELATION OF VITAMIN A TO CAROTENE.

The close parallel that exists between the vitamin A potency of many foods of vegetable origin and their content of yellow fat-soluble pigments has frequently been commented upon (see p. 45). Steenbock and his colleagues [1919; 1920, 1, 3; 1921] emphasized this relationship and suggested that the vitamin was identical with, or closely related to, one of these pigments. Similar views were expressed by Rosenheim and Drummond [1920] and by Coward [1923], who, working with the white and yellow petals of flowers, stated that 'some lipochrome—generally carotene—is always associated with the vitamin in plant tissues'.

Steenbock and Boutwell [1920, 3] showed that on fractionating the unsaponifiable matter of pigmented vegetable oils with light petroleum and aqueous alcohol, the vitamin A activity was associated with the carotene fraction, soluble in light petroleum, rather than with the xanthophyll fraction. Furthermore, Steenbock, Sell, Nelson and Buell [1921] claimed that carotene which had been recrystallized several times, when fed to animals on vitamin A-deficient diets, caused a resumption of growth. Steenbock suggested that vitamin A might be the leuco-compound of a lipochrome [1919]. Palmer and Eckles [1914, 1, 2, 3, 4, 5] and Palmer [1915] had previously shown that the plant carotenoids are the source of the so-called animal lipochromes. Since the animal organism was known to depend upon vegetable foods for its supplies of vitamin A, this fact seemed to supply additional support for the view that vitamin A was closely related to the carotenoids.

On the other hand, it was soon found that the parallel between vitamin A potency and yellow pigmentation did not extend to fats of animal origin. Steenbock, Sell and Buell [1921] found that although highly pigmented butters tended to possess a high vitamin activity, the relationship was not constant, and in the case of cod-liver oil the activity was vastly greater than would have been expected from the colour.

Palmer and his colleagues [1919, 1, 2, 3 ; 1921] were unable to agree with the views expressed by Steenbock and his co-workers, and by experiments in which chickens and rats were successfully reared on diets free from carotenoids, but containing pig's liver, claimed to have demonstrated the non-identity of the vitamin with any of these pigments. No vitamin A potency was demonstrated in pure crystalline carotene by Drummond [1919, 2], Rosenheim and Drummond [1920], Stephenson [1920], or Drummond, Channon and Coward [1925], while Stephenson [1920] found that the yellow pigment could be removed from butter fat without causing loss of vitamin activity.

The weight of evidence against the theory that vitamin A was identical with one of the carotenoid pigments thus appeared overwhelming and for some years the theory was abandoned.

The feeding tests with pure carotene were carried out by the above-mentioned authors at a time before it was clearly understood that vitamins A and D were separate principles and that vitamin D itself was also necessary to maintain growth in young rats. Attention was drawn to this point by Euler, Euler and Hellström [1928]. These workers were struck by the fact that the colour reactions supposed to be due to vitamin A were also positive for carotene, as had already been pointed out by Rosenheim and Drummond [1925]. Euler and his colleagues therefore subjected crystalline carotene to a further feeding test, with the result that this pigment was found to supplement satisfactorily a vitamin A-deficient diet in doses of about 0·005 mg. per rat per day. These findings were confirmed in a later communication [Euler, Euler and Karrer, 1928]. Xanthophyll [cf. Willimott and Moore, 1927]; lycopin, α-crocetin, capsanthin, bixin, and norbixin were found to be inactive.[1] The suggestion was tentatively advanced by Euler and his colleagues that vitamin A activity was associated with a certain system of double bonds present in the molecules both of carotene and of the vitamin A contained in liver oil.

The vitamin A-like activity of crystalline carotene was shortly afterwards confirmed by Collison et al. [1929], and by Moore [1929, 1, 2], although the fact that pure carotene became decolorized by oxidation in ethyl oleate solution [Hume and Smedley-MacLean, 1930; Drummond, Ahmad and Morton, 1930], whilst impure specimens were more stable, led at first to some confusion [Dulière, Morton and Drummond, 1929].

Although it was apparent that the classical vitamin A of cod- and other fish-liver oils (nearly colourless) was not identical with carotene (orange-red), the possibility still remained that the activity of carotene might be due to the presence of traces of the former. Carotene is less potent than some liver-oil concentrates; if therefore the activity of the pigment were due to traces of the liver-oil vitamin, the absorption band at 328 $m\mu$ attributed to vitamin A might be visible in carotene solutions. Capper [1930, 1] was unable to detect this band in such solutions, although the absorption due to the pigment itself was insufficient to obscure it if present.

The blue colours given by carotene and the liver-oil vitamin A with antimony trichloride have been shown to differ appreciably. The colour given by carotene is characterized by an initial band at 590 $m\mu$ [Euler, Euler and Hellström, 1928; Dulière, Morton and Drummond, 1929; Moore, 1929, 2]. The blue colour due to the liver-oil vitamin on the

[1] The claim that dihydro-α-crocetin was active has not been sustained.

other hand shows a band at about 610 $m\mu$. Moore [1929, 3; 1930] has put forward evidence that carotene is converted into the 'liver-oil vitamin' *in vivo*. The rat proved to be an exceptionally suitable animal for this experiment, since as Palmer and Kennedy [1921] showed, this animal normally contains little carotene in its body. The liver fat of rats suffering from vitamin A deficiency was found [Rosenheim and Webster, 1926, 3] to give no blue colour with antimony trichloride but, after feeding with large amounts of purified carotene, the liver fat was found by Moore to show the characteristic absorption band at 328 $m\mu$, and to give an intense blue colour with antimony trichloride with a band at 610–630 $m\mu$. These findings were shortly afterwards confirmed by Capper [1930, 2] and by Drummond, Ahmad and Morton [1930].

These results suggest either that carotene is converted into vitamin A *in vivo*, or else that the growth-promoting potency both of the pigment and of liver-oil concentrates is due to the presence of traces of the same intensely active substance. In this connexion the possibility should not be lost sight of that photo-synthetical production of both vitamin A and carotene might be the cause of their association in the plant. The statement, based on spectroscopic observations only, has been made that carotene is converted in the liver into vitamin A by the agency of an enzyme, provisionally called carotenase [Olcott and McCann, 1931].

The relation of vitamin A to carotene is conveniently summarized in the following table :

Carotene	Vitamin A of liver oils
Synthesized in the plant.	Stored in animal.
Orange-red	Almost colourless.
328 $m\mu$ absorption band absent.	328 $m\mu$ absorption band present.
Greenish-blue SbCl$_3$ reaction showing absorption at 590 $m\mu$.	Vivid blue SbCl$_3$ reaction showing absorption at 572 and 606 $m\mu$.

It has been shown that 'carotene' from carrots and other sources is a mixture of isomerides of widely differing optical activity [Kuhn and Lederer, 1931, 1, 2; Karrer, Euler *et al.*, 1931; Rosenheim and Starling, 1931]. Specimens of carotene prepared by the usual method [Willstätter and Stoll, 1913; for details see Escher, 1909] from carrots or leaves of spinach, chestnut, nettle, etc., possess the same elementary composition, agreeing with the formula $C_{40}H_{56}$, but vary in their optical activity from $[\alpha]_{cd} < 5°$ to $+60°$. The dextrorotatory component of the mixture has been called α-carotene and is slightly more soluble than the optically inactive β-carotene. The existence of a laevorotatory form is indicated by the earlier work of Kohl [1902] and the recent observations of J. H. C. Smith [1931], and of Karrer *et al.* [1931].

The highest recorded rotations of α-carotene are $_{cd}[\alpha] + 380°$ [Kuhn and Lederer, 1931, 2] and $[\alpha]_{6075} + 458°$, the latter having been observed by Karrer and Morf [1913, 2] in a specimen prepared by Kuhn, presumably from carrots. Red palm oil appears to be a good source of α-carotene [Kuhn and Brockmann, 1931, 2], whilst carotene prepared from paprica [Zechmeister and Cholnoky, 1927] seems to consist mainly of β-carotene. The most easily accessible product from carrots is a mixture of α-carotene and β-carotene, containing from 75 to 90 per cent. of the latter.

The methods for the separation of 'carotene' into its constituents are as yet far from satisfactory, and depend primarily on the relatively slight differences in solubility of the isomerides in such solvents as light petroleum, pyridine, etc. Fractional recrystallization is followed by fractional precipitation with iodine and removal of the latter with sodium thiosulphate. For the final purification of α-carotene fractional adsorption on suitable adsorbents (fibrous alumina) is essential.

On account of the difficulties of the separation process, it has not yet (December 1931) been ascertained whether α- and β-carotene have equal growth-promoting activity [See Karrer et al., 1931 ; Kuhn and Brockmann, 1931, 1].

The Biological Estimation of Vitamin A.

The biological estimation of vitamin A is generally based on its growth-promoting property, though some American workers claim to have obtained good results by estimating its antixerophthalmic potency.

Any test which depends on the growth-promoting property of the vitamin under examination demands that (a) the basal diet should be uniformly free from that vitamin, and (b) all growth-promoting factors other than the one under test should be abundantly supplied. Much of the early work on the distribution of ‘vitamin A’ was done before there was proof of the separate existence in the fat-soluble complex of the antirachitic vitamin D. Steenbock and Nelson [1923] in the course of work on the differentiation of vitamins A and D recognized the growth-promoting action of the latter, and demonstrated the necessity of supplying it in the basal diet of all experiments dependent on the growth response of test animals. They suggested providing vitamin D in tests for vitamin A either by the irradiation of the test animals or by supplying aerated cod-liver oil which exhibited no antixerophthalmic potency ; the exact technique of the method was described later [Steenbock, Nelson and Black, 1924–25]. Drummond, Coward and Handy [1925] proposed to administer irradiated choles-terol and Steenbock and Coward [1927] suggested the irradiation of the whole basal ration as a means of supplying this factor. Much of the earlier work on vitamin A has therefore been repeated with the tests modified so as to include adequate supplies of vitamin D in the basal diet and many of the early results have been found still to hold good. This is probably due either to the fact that vitamin D was being administered along with the vitamin A, as was the case with butter and cod-liver oil, or to the fact that the vitamin D reserves of the animals were large. On the other hand, some later work has given different results from the early work, which must presumably have been done on animals whose reserves of vitamin D were exhausted. A notable example of this is shown in the work on carotene, which was repeatedly found to be inactive when a basal diet was used which was devoid of vitamin D, but its activity is readily demonstrated when the basal diet contains vitamin D.

The necessity for an adequate ration of the vitamin B complex and for increasing this as the test animals get older is also stressed for all basal diets used in the estimation of vitamin A.

Technique of the Biological Test.

Standard of reference. Much work has been carried out with the aim of discovering for vitamin A (as for other vitamins) some stable substance which could be used as a standard of reference in estimations of this vitamin and in terms of which a unit could be defined. The International Conference on Vitamin Standards held by the Health Section of the League of Nations (London, June 1931) adopted as provisional standard of reference a sample of crystallized carotene, the unit being defined as the vitamin A activity of 1γ (0·001 mg.) (see Appendix II).

Experimental animals. Young rats immediately after weaning, of about 40 g. weight, are suitable. The breeding stock should be so fed that the young rats are not endowed with excessive reserves of vitamin A and, though healthy, cease to grow at about 100 g. weight when fed upon a vitamin A-free diet.

Experimental diets. Seeing that the estimations of vitamin A potency are based on a growth response, the basal diet should contain optimal amounts of all other essential constituents. The different basal diets employed usually consist of :

Caseinogen	15–20 per cent.
Starch (sometimes partially dextrinized) about . .	75 per cent.
Dried yeast or yeast extract, about	8 per cent.
Salt mixture—Osborne and Mendel's or	
McCollum's or Steenbock's, about . . .	4 per cent.
A 'hardened' vegetable oil (vitamin A-free) about . . .	15 per cent.

Coward, Key, Dyer and Morgan [1930 ; 1931] found that 'light white' caseinogen was more satisfactory than other preparations. Some workers consider the provision of fat in the basal diet unnecessary.

An adequate amount of vitamin D must also be given. About 4 units (International Standard, see p. 83) twice a week are required for each rat. The vitamin D may be given as irradiated ergosterol or by irradiation of the rat or of the oil or yeast contained in the diet.

Arrangement of the test. The test may be either prophylactic or curative. In the former, doses of the material to be tested are given either from the beginning of the feeding with the experimental diet or from about three weeks after, when the rat's reserves of vitamin A have been partially exhausted. The doses are given daily until consistent differences between negative controls and test animals are obtained. Comparisons are made between doses of different test materials (or of test material and standard) which cause equal increments in weight when the averages are compared for groups of about ten animals on each dose. The rats from each litter used must be so distributed among the groups that equal numbers occur in each group, and the sexes should be represented as equally as possible in each group. A test with the standard material should be included in each estimation.

In a curative test, the animals are allowed to exhaust their reserves of vitamin A, as indicated by cessation of growth, after which doses of the test substance are administered for about five weeks. In this test comparisons are also drawn between doses which give equal average increments in weight. Owing to the large margin of error in estimations of this type it is often difficult to decide how closely these average increments in weight should coincide in order that the doses causing them may be considered equal in vitamin A potency. Some workers find it more satisfactory to determine the doses which just maintain weight in the test animals [Collison *et al.*, 1929].

An economy in animals and labour is said to be effected by the method described by Coward, Key, Dyer and Morgan [1930; 1931]. They have drawn up a 'curve of response' in which the mean increase in weight during five weeks of groups of rats, which had previously become steady in weight by deprivation of vitamin A, is related to the daily dose of a standard sample of cod-liver oil. The curve covers a range of daily doses from 0·25 mg. to 7·5 mg. and the most useful part of it is that dealing with a mean weight increase of about 20 g. in five weeks. The curve is used in the following way. About 10–12 animals similarly prepared receive the same daily dose of the test substance (e.g. 1 or 2 mg. of cod-liver oil, 0·1 g. butter) for five weeks. The mean increase in weight of members of the group is determined. The dose of the standard cod-liver oil which brought about the same increase is read from the curve, and the ratio of this to the dose of test substance measures the vitamin-A potency of the unknown substance relative to that of the standard oil. In this way substances may be compared either at the same time, or at different seasons of the year, by determining their potency in terms of that of the original oil.

If further research should confirm the general applicability of such reference curves to vitamin testing, it would obviously be necessary to construct such curves for the standard materials suggested for international adoption.

Until such are available and proved to be trustworthy it is preferable to retain the usual principle employed in the biological estimation of vitamins—that of equating the vitamin potency of doses of test material and standard which produce an equal biological effect.

The Distribution of Vitamin A in Naturally Occurring Foodstuffs.

The important question of the distribution of vitamin A among the commonly used foodstuffs of both vegetable and animal origin has for many years received much attention. Of necessity much of the work has been largely qualitative in nature, making anything but a rough comparison between such foodstuffs difficult. Many of the results obtained will be found in Table XXI, Appendix I.

In assessing the relative values of different foodstuffs as sources of vitamin A in human dietaries, it must be borne in mind that the real dietetic value of any particular foodstuff depends not only upon its vitamin-A content calculated on a weight basis, but also upon the amount which may with convenience be included in a normal diet. Thus milk and butter, while being relatively poor in vitamin A when compared on a weight basis with cod-liver oil, are nevertheless extremely valuable sources of this factor, owing to the prominent position which they occupy in a normal human diet.

Foodstuffs of Vegetable Origin.

Although it seems possible that the vitamin-A potency of vegetable tissues may be due *solely* to the presence of the yellow lipochrome pigment carotene (see p. 39), the fact has not been proved. The total amount of carotene present in a vegetable foodstuff may nevertheless be a valuable indication of its value as a source of vitamin A [Euler et al., 1930]. The relationship between yellow pigmentation and vitamin-A content as determined by biological tests has been shown to hold for a variety of vegetable foodstuffs. Thus Steenbock and his collaborators [Steenbock, Boutwell and Kent, 1919; Steenbock and Boutwell, 1920, 1, 3] pointed out the marked superiority of yellow maize over white maize as a source of vitamin A. This observation has since been confirmed by several workers, notably Hauge and Trost [1928; 1930], Hauge [1930] and W. C. Russell [1930]. Hauge has pointed out that the vitamin-A value of maize is related to the degree of yellow pigmentation in the endosperm and bears no relationship to the colour of the pericarp. The superior vitamin-A content of the outer green leaves of lettuce to that of the inner white ones [Dye, Medlock and Crist, 1927], can, in a similar manner, be correlated with the larger amounts of carotene which are contained in leaves in which photosynthesis is active. Crist and Dye [1929] have shown the same relationship to hold between green and bleached asparagus.

Green vegetables are rich sources of vitamin A owing to their high carotene content. Spinach, cabbage (green outer leaves), lettuce, Brussels sprouts, green peas, the French artichoke [Morgan and Stephenson, 1923], and watercress [Coward and Eggleton, 1928], all contain large quantities of this factor. Among root vegetables, carrots, and yellow sweet potatoes are rich in vitamin A, while white potatoes, turnips, onions, parsnips, mangolds, radishes, and beetroot contain little or none.

Some fruits, such as the tomato, banana, and date, contain amounts of this factor comparable with those present in many green vegetables. Morgan and Smith [1928–29] have shown that much greater amounts are present in the ripe tomato than in the green fruit. The tropical fruit papaya is reported to be exceptionally rich in vitamin A [H. G. Miller, 1926–27] and the mango contains about as much as an average sample of butter [Perry and Zilva, 1932]. Apples, figs, oranges, lemons, grapefruit, pineapple, and peaches contain small but appreciable amounts. Morgan [1923] has shown that the oil of orange peel contains vitamin A, whereas the oils from lemon and grapefruit peel are inactive.

Cereals are in general rather poor in this factor, but, as has already been mentioned, yellow maize contains appreciable amounts. Nuts, while containing large amounts of fat, are usually poor sources of the vitamin [Coward and Drummond, 1920]; Rose and MacLeod [1921–22], however, reported fairly large amounts in almonds. Many vegetable oils such as arachis oil, linseed oil, cotton-seed oil, olive oil, and coco-nut oil contain little or no vitamin A; red palm oil and some samples of maize oil [Stammers, 1924, 1] are rich sources.

Foodstuffs of Animal Origin.

Animal organisms possess the power of storing reserves of vitamin A which have been obtained directly or indirectly from vegetable sources. The amounts of vitamin present in the different tissues of an animal will therefore depend not only upon the power of that tissue to store reserves, but upon the previous dietary history of the animal. Thus the amounts of reserve vitamin A stored in the tissues of a grass-fed animal are usually much higher than those stored in the tissues of a stall-fed animal. The importance of this fact in the consideration of the vitamin A content of milk and butter is obvious (see p. 219).

By far the greater proportion of the reserve vitamin A in the animal body is contained in the liver. Sherman and Boynton [1925] studied the distribution of vitamin A among the tissues of the rat. It was shown that the lung and kidney contained more than forty times, and the liver two hundred to four hundred times, that present in the muscle. Significant quantities were also shown to be present in the blood. As might be expected therefore, the liver fats of grass-fed animals, such as the sheep and ox, are among the richest sources of vitamin A known, being often much richer than cod-liver oil [Rosenheim and Webster, 1927, 6].

Cod-liver oil. Osborne and Mendel [1914] were the first to show that cod-liver oil, the therapeutic value of which had long been known, contained what may now be termed the 'fat-soluble complex'. A few years later Zilva and Miura [1921, 2] in the course of the elaboration of their quantitative method demonstrated the extremely high vitamin content of cod-liver oil, 2·2 mg. being sufficient to induce growth in rats previously deprived of 'vitamin A', while over 200 times the quantity of butter was required to produce the same effect. They therefore concluded that the high therapeutic value of cod-liver oil was due to its high vitamin content. Other fish-liver oils were found to be as potent as cod-liver oil [Zilva and Drummond, 1921]; examples are the liver oils of the herring, salmon, hake, pollock, shark, halibut, and haddock.

It is important to realize that different samples of cod-liver oil may differ by as much as 30-fold in their vitamin-A potency [Coward, Dyer, Morton and Gaddum, 1931]. This may be due partly to a difference in the potency of the original oil [Zilva and Drummond, 1922] and partly to the effect of storage. Zilva, Drummond and Graham [1924] found that neither the sexual condition nor the age of the fish was responsible for the variable potency of cod-liver oil, and they suggested that possibly variation in the food might be the cause of this.

It had already been shown by E. Mellanby [1918–19, 1 ; 1921] that cod-liver oil was rich in the antirachitic vitamin.

That the ultimate origin of the fat-soluble complex present in the liver of the cod was probably to be found in the marine algae which are capable of effecting a synthesis of this factor was suggested by the researches of Drummond, Zilva and Coward [1922]. In this connexion it has been shown by Ahmad [1930] following up earlier work by Jameson, Drummond and Coward [1922] that a marine diatom (*Nitzschia closterium*) can synthesize vitamin A when grown under artificial conditions. The whole of the activity present in the diatom could be accounted for in the supposition that 3 per cent. of the yellow pigment present in the ether-soluble material obtained was carotene. Ahmad suggests that such marine diatoms are the ultimate sources of the vitamin A in fish-liver oils, the carotene which they synthesize being converted into vitamin A in the body of the fish which feed upon them. No vitamin D however was detected in *N. closterium* (see p. 87).

In view of the widespread use of cod-liver oil medicinally, the question of the effect of the different methods of preparation and refining on the vitamin content is of considerable importance. Work bearing on this problem has been carried out notably by Holmes and by Drummond and Zilva. The monograph by Drummond and Hilditch [1930] summarizes much of the more important work done in this direction and presents a large amount of new and valuable data.

It has been known for some years that exposure of cod-liver oil to light results in a loss of its vitamin-A activity [Peacock, 1926]. The ease with which vitamin A is destroyed by oxidation has already been pointed out in preceding paragraphs. Since, therefore, oils such as cod-liver oil contain a large number of autoxidizable substances (e.g. the unsaturated fatty acids), it might be expected that loss of vitamin would occur in such oils on exposure to the air. The problem of the storage of cod-liver oil for medicinal use, under conditions which will ensure a minimum destruction of vitamin A by light and oxidation, is a question of great practical importance. The matter has been investigated by Drummond and Hilditch [1930]. Experiments in which various bottled samples of cod-liver oil were stored in the dark or exposed to the light, clearly showed the necessity of storing such oils in dark coloured containers or in the dark.

Huston, Lightbody and Ball [1928] have extended the work of Moureu and Dufraisse [1928] on antioxidants to the question of retarding the destruction of vitamin A in milk fat and cod-liver oil. Loss of vitamin activity was decreased by the addition of relatively high concentrations (0·05–0·1 per cent.) of quinol (hydroquinone). Drummond and Hilditch have studied the effects of different amounts of quinol on the oxygen uptake of cod-liver oil, with the result that although the oxygen uptake is lessened, 'amounts of hydroquinone that might be regarded as practicable on the industrial scale are of little or no value in protecting the oil from oxidation'.

CHAPTER III

VITAMIN D (THE ANTIRACHITIC, CALCIFYING VITAMIN).

In the previous chapter vitamin D has been described as a fat-soluble substance having the specific function of controlling the deposition of calcium and phosphorus in tissues. Since bones and teeth are largely composed of calcium phosphate it is evident that the structure of these tissues is largely determined by the adequacy of the vitamin D supplied to the body during their period of development. Although these are the tissues most prominently influenced by this factor it is certain that calcium-phosphorus metabolism is a process affecting other organs of the body, and to this extent, therefore, these organs are influenced by vitamin D. Knowledge on this point is still, however, meagre. Like vitamin A, vitamin D can also be regarded as necessary for growth (Steenbock), since young animals deprived of it ultimately cease to increase in weight but resume growth on its addition to the food. This property of growth-promotion is also probably related to the regulation of calcium-phosphorus metabolism by vitamin D.

Before considering the properties and function of vitamin D in greater detail two points of general interest may be stated.

(1) The relation of vitamin D to calcium and phosphorus metabolism is the only instance in the present knowledge of vitamins where it is possible to state the function of a vitamin in terms of chemistry. This, of course, does not mean that we know how the vitamin acts, but the biological problem can be presented in terms of known chemical entities.

(2) The extent of defective bone formation, as seen in the high incidence of rickets in countries in the temperate zone, the widespread defect in the structure of teeth and the high incidence of dental caries suggest that a deficient intake of vitamin D may be the most important dietetic defect at present known.

Although our knowledge of the chemistry of vitamin D has in recent years been greatly increased, all fundamental studies of this substance are still dependent on its biological properties and the only methods of estimation at present available are biological. In the present chapter, therefore, the part played by this vitamin in the animal body is first described and its chemical and physical properties are dealt with later.

Biology of Vitamin D.

Vitamin D in relation to Rickets and Allied Disorders.

While some bone defects develop independently of the vitamin D intake, those most commonly found in man, namely rickets, osteoporosis, and osteomalacia, are directly related to this vitamin. These bone conditions are alike evidence of an abnormal calcium-phosphorus metabolism and this fact explains many of the difficulties which faced the earlier workers interested in the antirachitic vitamin. It is true

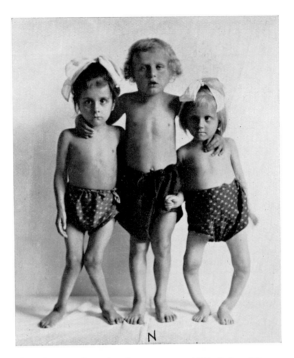

Fig. 3. Children 6 years of age showing severe rachitic deformities compared with normally grown child (centre) of the same age.

Vienna, 1920. Amerikanische Kinderheilstätte.

To face p. 49]

that there is still much to be learnt as to the factors which determine the development of one or other of these bone defects apart from the deficient supply of vitamin D. It is known, however, that the type of animal under investigation, the rate of growth, the age and the composition of the defective diet all influence the form taken by the defects in calcification of the bones. Some of these subsidiary influences will be described more fully in later sections.

THE DIAGNOSIS OF RICKETS.

Simple clinical examination will often enable a diagnosis of human rickets to be made when a combination of such signs as beading of the ribs, deformity of the limbs, head, and chest wall, and enlargement of the epiphyses is present (see Fig. 3). But even in such cases it may not be possible to decide at once whether the changes found in the bones are due to defective calcification still proceeding (active rickets) or are the result of such a process which was formerly active but has now ceased (healed rickets). The deformities in the bones may long outlast the period of active rickets as shown radiographically. In such cases radiography is of great service and usually enables a satisfactory diagnosis of the state of activity of the disease to be made. Eliot [1925] and M. G. Wilson [1926] consider that the very earliest stages of rickets can be recognized in radiograms of the infant's forearms long before any clinical symptoms are apparent. In their experience radiographical evidence of very slight rickety changes in the bones may be recognized even in the majority of apparently healthy infants, though these changes do not progress if measures are taken to provide some source of the antirachitic factor for the infants.

Estimations of the concentration of inorganic phosphorus in the blood have been employed, particularly in the United States, both as a means of diagnosing active rickets and as an indication of the progress of the disease following treatment. Although in general the blood-phosphorus is low in clinical as in experimental rickets and is raised towards the normal figure shortly after the institution of therapeutic measures, several workers have expressed doubt as to the reliability of blood-phosphorus estimations as an indication of the healing of rickets. Koch and Cahan [1927] obtained perfect calcification of bones in rats which showed persistently low blood-phosphorus values. Hess, Weinstock, Rivkin and Gross [1930] found that giving very small doses of irradiated ergosterol to rats raised their inorganic phosphorus to a normal level without healing the rickets. On the other hand, small doses of cod-liver oil might cause rickets to heal in rats without raising the inorganic phosphorus of their blood. These observers occasionally saw cases of active rickets in infants in which there was a high level of inorganic phosphorus in the blood, and consider this test not infallible, although at times useful, in helping to establish a diagnosis.

An attempt was made by Redman [1928] to apply to children suffering from rickets the test originally described by Zucker and Matzner [1923–24], namely, the determination of the reaction (pH) of the faeces, which in dogs and rats is changed from alkaline to acid when active rickets is controlled by any therapeutic measure [Jephcott and Bacharach, 1926; Grayzel and Miller, 1928]. The results in children, however, were too variable to give the test any practical value.

For all ordinary purposes clinical examination supplemented by radiography suffices to establish the diagnosis, and a series of radiographs taken of any individual at regular intervals should enable a sufficiently accurate estimate to be made of the efficacy of any particular treatment adopted. (See Fig. 6.)

EXPERIMENTAL RICKETS AND OSTEOPOROSIS IN ANIMALS.

Most of our knowledge of the aetiology of rickets and allied disorders has developed as the result of the application of the experimental method to animals. In some, e.g. the dog, rickets is a naturally occurring and commonly found disease just as it is in children, and the deformities produced are of the same kind (see Figs. 4 and 5). In others, for instance the rat and the rabbit, the disease is probably unknown in nature but can be easily produced under laboratory conditions.

The detection of these diseases in animals and the determination of their degree of intensity depend upon a technique similar to that used in the case of human beings. Whereas, however, accurate clinical examination in children is usually restricted for obvious reasons to radiography, histological and chemical examinations of the bones are also greatly used in experimental work on animals. In animal experiments each of these methods has its own particular value. For instance, the radiographic method will at once reveal the presence of rickets by the characteristic changes at the epiphyseal ends of the growing bones. This mode of examination has the merit of being possible during the life of the animal and may be repeated at will. Slight degrees of osteoporosis may, however, be undetected by this method.

Histological diagnosis involves the preparation of the bones for microscopic examination, but allows the determination of both rickets and osteoporosis and their differentiation. In rickets the abundant uncalcified osteoid tissues, present at the epiphyses in varying amount according to the intensity and duration of the disease, can be distinguished from the normally calcified bone. In osteoporosis, a condition in which there is absorption of old bone and defective formation of new bone, the bony trabeculae and periosteal bone are small in amount and osteoid tissue may be deficient or absent. Often rickets and osteoporosis are present in the same bone.

The chemical examination of bone in these diseases in animals has the advantage of giving a numerical answer as regards the degree of calcification, but does not allow any differentiation between rickets and osteoporosis.

Further consideration of these methods will be given in a later section (p. 84) where methods of determining vitamin D are discussed.

THE AETIOLOGY OF RICKETS.

Prior to the experimental work on puppies [E. Mellanby, 1918–19, 1, 2; 1919, 1920, 1921, etc.] in which it was shown that the antirachitic vitamin was the corner stone of the aetiology of rickets, many

Fig. 4. Photograph of two puppies after being fed for 18 weeks after weaning on the same diet deficient in vitamins A and D. Puppy 1 (left) was the offspring of a mother fed during pregnancy and lactation on a diet rich in A and D and containing bread as the cereal, whereas the mother of puppy 2 (right) was fed on a diet deficient in these vitamins and having oatmeal as the cereal. It will be noted that puppy 1 shows little sign of rickets, while puppy 2 has developed severe rickets.

Fig. 5. Rickets following a diet of 175 c.c. whole milk, white bread ad lib., and 10 c.c. linseed oil per diem. Time of experiment, $5\frac{1}{2}$ months. Increase in weight during period of experiment 2,670 g.

To face p. 50]

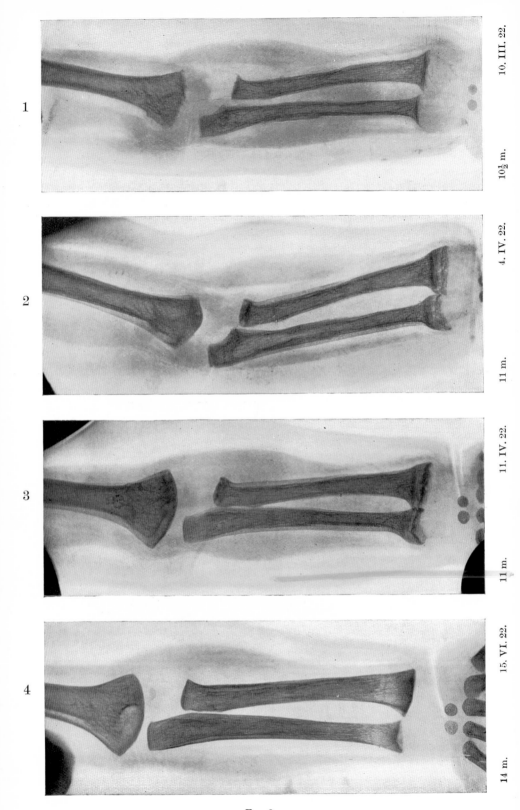

10, III. 22.

$10\frac{1}{2}$ m.

4. IV. 22.

11 m.

11. IV. 22.

11 m.

15. VI. 22.

14 m.

FIG. 6.

(Reproduced by permission from Special Report Series, No. 77, of the Medical Research Council.)

To face p. 51]

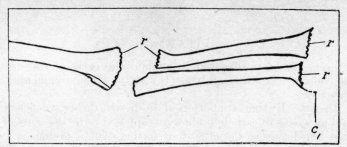

1. (10.3.22.) Florid rickets, no evidence of healing. Osteoporosis present. The structure of the bones is coarse, and the compact bone of the shafts ill-defined and irregular. The metaphyseal margins are frayed (r). The distal end of the ulna is slightly cupped, and there is a faint shadow indicating the margin of the expanded, uncalcified zone of osteoid tissue (c_1) which can be detected clinically as an enlargement.

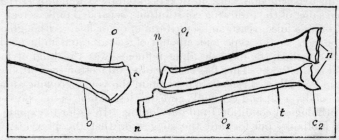

2. (4.4.22.) Healing in progress after 27 days' treatment, showing (1) the deposition of calcium along the shafts of radius (o_1), ulna (o_2), and humerus (o); (2) calcium deposition at the metaphyseal margins and in the osteoid zones previously uncalcified and, therefore, scarcely visible (c_2). These areas are bounded on the side towards the epiphysis by irregular lines of shadow which represent the newly formed zone of preparatory calcification (n).

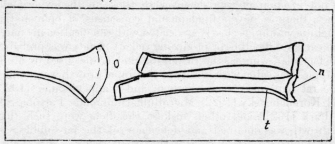

3. (11.4.22.) Rapid progress in healing. Note (1) the line of dense calcification at the metaphyseal margins (n) corresponding to the new preparatory calcification zone, and (2) the increase in periosteal calcification (osteophyte layer) showing calcified trabeculae (t) running at right angles to the long axis of the layer, (3) calcification of the centre of ossification at the distal end of the humerus.

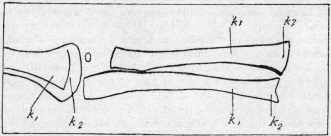

4. (15.6.22.) Healing well advanced after 3 months' treatment. The contour of the shafts is nearly normal, and the coarse structure has become more finely meshed. A band about 0.5 cm. wide of newly formed bone (k_2) is clearly visible at the distal end of the humerus. At the distal end of the radius and ulna the corresponding band is also to be seen. It can be distinguished by its fine homogeneous structure from the portion of the shaft (k_1) formed before the onset of rickets.

Explanatory drawings for Fig. 6, showing X-ray photographs illustrating severe rickets in a child of ten months and recovery after treatment with cod-liver oil.

hypotheses had been advanced to explain the cause of this disease. These could be classed roughly as (1) dietetic, (2) environmental, and (3) infective.

1. *Dietetic.* By some supporters of the dietetic theory, a deficiency of fat and an excess of carbohydrate were supposed to be the cause of the disease, but deficiencies of other food factors such as protein and calcium were also regarded by some authorities as of importance. These views were mainly based on clinical observation; the small amount of experimental evidence available seemed to point against the dietetic explanation [L. Findlay, 1908].

In his experimental work on rickets in puppies, Mellanby [1918–19, 2] used a diet of the following constitution : separated milk, cereal, lean meat, orange juice, yeast, and some form of oil or fat. Although other factors such as the type and amount of cereal eaten influenced the results obtained, the main deciding influence was the kind of fat included in the food. Thus fats such as olive oil, cotton-seed oil, linseed oil, and lard allowed rickets to develop in the young growing animals, while cod-liver oil and egg yolk, and to a less extent butter, prevented the pathological condition from developing. In order to explain this result Mellanby put forward the suggestion that the preventive fats contained an antirachitic vitamin, the properties and distribution of which appeared at the time to correspond fairly closely with those then recognized for vitamin A.

Some years later [1921] experimental work on rickets was extended by other workers to rats, and although the results obtained at first were not in complete agreement with those of the experiments on puppies, there is now a fundamental consensus of opinion that an antirachitic vitamin is closely associated with calcification in bone. One of the earlier difficulties of producing rickets in rats was probably due to the fact that, whereas the rickets-producing diet used by Mellanby for puppies was eaten with avidity so that rapid growth was maintained, in the rat experiments of Sherman and Pappenheimer [1920–21; 1921], Korenchevsky [1922], McCollum, Simmonds, Parsons, Shipley and Park [1921], and other workers, the diets were such that but poor growth was obtained and deficiency of the fat-soluble vitamin frequently led to osteoporosis rather than rickets. Korenchevsky, however, obtained the definite result [1922] that deprivation of fat-soluble vitamins alone, the diet containing adequate amounts of all other elements, produced rickets in rats provided the age was not greater than 3–6 weeks at the beginning of special feeding. The question of age had been shown previously to be of great importance in puppies [Mellanby, 1920]. Goldblatt [1923] found that the percentage of calcium deposited in the bones of rats decreased as the supply of antirachitic vitamin was diminished, and that rachitic lesions were produced along with osteoporosis even when the diet still contained a small but insufficient amount of the vitamin. Korenchevsky and Goldblatt, therefore, confirmed Mellanby's conclusions, namely that experimental rickets can be produced by deprivation of fat-soluble vitamins alone, the diet being adequate in all other respects. It is clear, however, that in order to produce rickets in rats with certainty it is usually necessary to alter the calcium-phosphorus ratio as well as to exclude the antirachitic vitamin (see p. 59). In puppies

Mellanby [1921] found that although the calcium-phosphorus ratio influenced the development of rickets, this effect was not of significance when abundant antirachitic vitamin was present in the diet.

2. *Environmental.* The effect on the production of rickets of bad hygienic conditions and of lack of exercise was emphasized by Lataste [1884] and by Hanseman [1906] who developed the Domestication Theory of Rickets. This view arose mainly from observations on the common occurrence of rickets in wild animals confined in cages. It is a matter of interest, however, to note that Bland-Sutton [1889] had succeeded in raising lion cubs in the Zoological Gardens free from rickets by feeding them on diets which included cod-liver oil and bones. L. Findlay [1908] from experiments on puppies also came to the conclusion that lack of exercise was the main cause of rickets. In the light of E. Mellanby's work this conception was re-examined by Findlay in conjunction with Paton, from both the experimental and statistical points of view. These workers found puppies brought up in the country and properly exercised to be free from rickets, whereas others reared in the laboratory, although receiving a diet containing much more butter fat, developed the disease [see L. Findlay, 1922].

Fergusson and L. Findlay [1918] made an inquiry into the dietaries and home conditions of rachitic and non-rachitic families in Glasgow and drew the conclusion that there was little difference in the diets of the two classes, but that the onset of rickets was favoured by imperfect maternal care, by improper housing, and by the absence of facilities for open-air life, the child being thus deprived of the desire to exercise its muscular system. A more careful scrutiny of the diets on the basis of Mellanby's work with puppies showed, however, that the diets of the rachitic families were such as might be expected to result in more rickets than those of the non-rachitic families [E. Mellanby, 1918–19, 2; 1919].

Observations made in India by Hutchison and Shah [1922] supported the 'confinement' hypothesis and dealt with the incidence of the disease in India among the Mahomedans and Hindus of the labouring classes, as compared with those of higher caste who adopt the practice of 'purdah'. The higher caste women marry when twelve years old and thereafter are confined to houses which admit but a minimum of light and fresh air. Their diet was found better than that of the labouring inhabitants in that it contained more milk, eggs, and butter, but, in spite of this, rickets was much more commonly found in the children, and late rickets in the women, of the higher caste.

The Glasgow School thus held the view that rickets was due primarily to confinement and lack of exercise and that diet was of little or no significance. Mellanby [1920] however, in experiments devised to test the point, found that confined puppies did not develop rickets on an adequate diet, whereas those allowed complete freedom on a defective diet acquired the disease: nor did confinement prevent the cure of the disease when suitable diets were administered containing, among other things, substances rich in the antirachitic vitamin such as cod-liver oil, milk, and egg yolk. Mellanby concluded that exercise played a subsidiary part in the aetiology of rickets and that diet was of prime importance.

During this controversy as to the relative importance in the aetiology of rickets of the antirachitic vitamin and of lack of exercise, important evidence from other quarters was accumulating which finally settled the issue.

As long ago as 1890 Palm [1890] drew attention to the relation between the geographical distribution of rickets and the incidence of sunlight. The significance of these observations remained for long unrealized, and interest was centred on the alternative views that rickets arose from either faulty diet or unsuitable environment. It gradually became clear, however, from the results of more recent work that a lack of sunlight was the dominating factor in the environmental conditions conducive to rickets. Huldschinsky [1919 ; 1920] and other workers found that infantile rickets could be cured by exposure of the patient to the ultra-violet rays of the mercury-vapour quartz lamp, whilst Hess and Unger [1921, 1, 2,] showed that a similar result was obtained by exposure to sunlight. The latter workers have pointed out that the seasonal incidence of this disease is in all probability closely related to the prevalence and active power of sunlight, the great majority of cases developing between November and May. The extended investigations of Chick and her colleagues in Vienna [1922 ; 1923] afforded conclusive evidence of the therapeutic value of sunlight and ultra-violet rays in infantile rickets.

By 1922, therefore, it was established that both the dietetic and environmental hypotheses were required to elucidate the aetiology of rickets and that the specific factors influencing this disease were (1) the antirachitic vitamin supplied in the food and (2) the action of sunlight and ultra-violet radiation on the skin. The extraordinary story describing the correlation of these two effects is related elsewhere (p. 74).

3. *Infective.* The hypothesis that rickets is due to an infection was advanced by many workers including Morpurgo [1902 ; 1907], J. Koch [1912], Marfan [1911], Paton [1920], and Bull [1918] and received wide support from clinicians. In recent years the idea has been discarded, although it is probably true that after suffering from an infection children are more prone to rickets, and also that rachitic children are often more susceptible to infection.

DEFICIENCY OF VITAMIN D IN THE DIET.

Since the methods that have been shown to prevent or cure rickets in experimental animals are equally efficacious in human rickets, it is highly probable that vitamin D plays the same part in the calcification of bone in the human subject as in experimental animals. It has long been observed that infants fed at the breast are much less liable to contract rickets than those fed on cow's milk, and it would therefore be expected that human milk would contain a greater amount of vitamin D than cow's milk. Hess, Weinstock and Sherman [1927], and later Outhouse, Macy and Brekke [1928], were not able to demonstrate by rat-feeding tests that this was true. No satisfactory explanation of this discrepancy has been forthcoming. It is well known that breast-feeding itself is by no means a certain safeguard against the development of rickets, whereas giving vitamin D to infants affords a much more reliable degree of protection.

The vitamin D content of cow's milk is a variable quantity, the antirachitic potency depending on the environment and diet of the cow. In summer the potency of the milk is influenced by the seasonal effect of sunlight and in winter the vitamin D content can be raised considerably by including cod-liver oil or irradiated yeast in the diet of the animal (see p. 220).

The known poverty of some samples of cow's milk in respect of vitamin D may well be a factor in determining the incidence of human rickets. Milk is at no time a rich source of this vitamin and skim milk contains mere traces of it. The fact that rickets is common in some districts among infants whose diet consists largely of cow's milk is therefore compatible with the view that the absence of a sufficient supply of vitamin D is responsible for the occurrence of human rickets.

The only natural products which are known to be rich in vitamin D are egg yolk and cod-liver oil and other similar fish oils. Cream and butter contain small amounts and certain animal fats, such as beef suet, have a definite antirachitic effect on laboratory animals. Fresh vegetables, fruit, and meat have no appreciable antirachitic activity, and cereals, as will be seen later, may actually favour the development of rickets. Children who, on account of poverty or for any other reason, cannot be supplied with adequate amounts of dairy produce, including eggs, and consume vegetable fats (in the form of margarine) containing no vitamin D, in place of animal fats, are obviously liable to suffer from a deficiency of this vitamin unless its supply is ensured in some special way as by administration of cod-liver oil or by exposure to natural or artificial ultra-violet radiation.

Relation of Rickets to Sunlight and other sources of Ultra-violet Rays.

It is an interesting fact that the stimulating effect of ultra-violet rays on calcification was first discovered in the case of children (p. 54), and that only at a later stage were the observations confirmed by investigations made on animals.

Using a diet upon which young rats in the laboratory invariably contract rickets, Hess, Unger and Pappenheimer [1921-22, 1] kept six rats in complete darkness and found that they all contracted rickets in 22-34 days. Seven other rats, on the same diet, exposed daily to sunlight in the open air for 15-20 minutes, but otherwise kept under the same conditions, failed to develop rickets in the same period. These investigators also observed [1921-22, 2, 3, 4] that the curative power of the sunlight was lost when it passed through a flint glass window, and that the rays from the mercury quartz lamp and the carbon arc lamp were also effective. When the time of exposure was reduced to the minimum sufficient to protect white rats, black rats were not protected, probably owing to the greater absorption of the rays by the pigment. This suggests that a similar function of the pigment in negro infants may be a factor in the abnormal susceptibility of these children to rickets in northern climates.

Similar results were simultaneously obtained by Powers and his colleagues [Shipley, Park, Powers et al., 1921-22; Powers, Park, Shipley, McCollum and Simmonds, 1922, where a detailed historical

account of the discovery of the action of light waves in rickets is given]
with a diet containing twice the optimal amount of calcium but low
in phosphorus and fat-soluble vitamins.

The exact position of the active rays of the spectrum was investigated by Hess and Unger [1922] and it was found that the curative
rays were confined to that part of the spectrum having wave-lengths
about 300 $m\mu$ or shorter. Huldschinsky [1926; see also Luce, 1926]
stated that the active rays were of wave-length 289–320 $m\mu$, and
finally Hess and Weinstock [1926–27] fixed the wave-length as 303 $m\mu$,
or possibly 313 $m\mu$ on the basis of experiments with filters. Rays of
wave-length less than 290 $m\mu$ are more effective than those between
290 and 313 $m\mu$. These observations accounted for the negative results
with sunlight filtered through glass, since window glass is opaque to
the radiations noted.

The penetrating power of ultra-violet rays of this order of wave-
length is very small and necessitates the assumption that the primary
process in the antirachitic action of sunlight is restricted to a very
thin layer of skin. The transmission of epidermis for a 0·08 mm.
layer falls from 55 per cent. at 313 $m\mu$ to 44 per cent. at 300 $m\mu$, 26 per
cent. at 294 $m\mu$ and then very sharply to 2·9 per cent. at 289 $m\mu$
[Lucas, 1931; cf. Glitscher and Hasselbach, 1926]. The spectrum of
sunlight includes a considerable range of ultra-violet rays, the intensity
falling off rather rapidly in the region of 330 to 296 $m\mu$. The
shortest wave-lengths detectable vary somewhat with the seasons, and
the intensity of ultra-violet rays is subject to wide variations [see
Luckiesh, 1930]. From December to February the shortest rays
have been given as 312 $m\mu$; from September to November, 308 $m\mu$;
from March to May, 301 $m\mu$; and from June to August, 296 $m\mu$. The
summer intensity of ultra-violet rays may often be ten times that
recorded in winter.

The effects of ultra-violet rays striking the skin are not confined
to a favourable effect on the calcification of bone. For instance, latent
and actual tetany have been cured by these rays [Huldschinsky, 1920].
This is of special interest in view of the fact that tetany, at least in
children, is nearly always related to rickets, and many facts point to a
common factor in the aetiology of the two diseases (p. 64). Powers,
Park, Shipley, McCollum and Simmonds [1922] observed that sunlight brought about a greater consumption of food in rats, stimulated
activity, improved the appearance, and increased their reproductive
capacity.

There is no doubt that a deficiency of sunlight can play a very
important part in determining the incidence of human rickets. The
geographical distribution of the disease indicates that this is the case.
Certainly the disease occurs in all parts of the world and affects all
races of mankind, but it is particularly frequent among the urban
populations of temperate climates, where it has a seasonal incidence
corresponding to the months of the year when there is least available
sunshine [Hess and Unger, 1921, 2; Chick et al., 1922; 1923]. A high
incidence of rickets in children has been observed in manufacturing
centres, no doubt partly on account of the screening effect of a smoky
atmosphere on the ultra-violet radiation from the sun. Climates noted
for their long hours of bright sunshine are not, however, incompatible

with a high incidence of rickets. The disease has been reported as prevalent in certain districts in Southern Europe, North Africa, China, Australia, and Central America. It is possible for children brought up in tropical countries to be largely protected from the direct rays of the sun during their early years. The fact that such children may develop rickets does not therefore indicate that sunshine is a negligible factor in the aetiology of the disease. When the skin is deeply pigmented the protective effect of ultra-violet radiation is lessened, as was noted by Hess, Unger and Pappenheimer [1921–22, 4] in rats. It is probably for this reason that negro children are peculiarly susceptible to the disease when they live in temperate climates and are habitually clothed in the European style.

The relation between vitamin D and sunlight was studied in connexion with human rickets by Chick *et al.* [1922, 1923] at the University Kinderklinik, Vienna. Observations on prophylaxis were made upon young infants receiving two types of diet in the same wards. Diet I consisted of undiluted fresh milk with added sugar ; diet II of standardized full-cream dried milk with the addition of cod-liver oil. Between the months of May and October no case of rickets was detected among a total of 42 infants. Between November and April, 13 out of 51 infants developed rickets, and all these cases occurred among the 25 infants receiving diet I. During the summer months the infants spent a great part of their time out of doors and the authors ascribe their protection from rickets to the action of sunlight. During the winter the infants receiving diet II were protected by the vitamin D contained in their cod-liver oil. Further observations demonstrated that cases of active rickets could be cured in the summer by exposure to sunlight, no matter whether the subjects received diet I or diet II. In the winter rickets could be cured by diet II but progressed on diet I.

Systematic radiographic studies were made during the cure of cases of well-developed rickets by administration of cod-liver oil and by exposure to sunshine or the radiations of a mercury-vapour lamp respectively. The types of healing in these three cases, as shown in X-ray photographs, were found to be indistinguishable from one another [Wimberger, 1922].

The mechanism by which ultra-violet radiations from the sun or artificial sources exert their antirachitic action has not been fully explained, but it seems probable that vitamin D is produced in the skin itself or in the blood circulating immediately below the surface by activation of a precursor already present (see p. 75).

Such an assumption is strengthened by the fact that the presence of ergosterol has been demonstrated in animal and human skin [Rosenheim and Webster, 1927, 5 ; Hentschel and Schindel, 1930]. Hess and Weinstock [1925, 2] showed that excised human skin fed to rats conferred an absolute protection against rickets after it had been irradiated by a mercury-vapour lamp, but no protection without such irradiation. More recently Falkenheim [1928] found that parts of the skin which had not been directly irradiated, but which had been contiguous to areas exposed to ultra-violet rays, developed an appreciable antirachitic activity. It is therefore probable that irradiation of the skin compensates for a deficiency of preformed vitamin D in

the diet by activation *in situ* of the precursor of vitamin D (i.e. ergosterol) the activated product then being available for carrying out its
specific activities in the tissues generally in the same way as if it had
been absorbed from the alimentary tract. The fundamental cause of
rickets is therefore a deficiency of vitamin D, but this deficiency can
be supplied either by the ingestion of the pre-formed vitamin or by the
exposure of the surface of the body to radiations which have the
power of producing it in the tissues.

RELATION OF RICKETS TO THE MINERAL AND OTHER CONSTITUENTS OF THE DIET.

Mellanby's conclusion that a deficiency of a fat-soluble vitamin in
the diet resulted in the appearance of rickets in puppies could not at
first be confirmed in the case of young rats [Sherman and Pappenheimer, 1920-21 ; 1921 ; McCollum, Simmonds, Parsons, Shipley and
Park, 1921 ; Korenchevsky, 1922]. It was found that rickets could
only be produced in these animals by giving diets deficient in
calcium and phosphorus, or containing them in unbalanced proportions. The disease could then be cured by correcting the balance of
these elements without any addition of fat-soluble vitamin, in which
the diets were deficient. Deprivation of fat-soluble vitamin alone
with a normal supply of calcium and phosphorus resulted in osteoporosis rather than rickets. Korenchevsky [1922], however, was able
to produce rickets in rats by depriving them of fat-soluble vitamin
alone, the diet containing adequate amounts of all other known requirements, provided their age was not greater than 3–6 weeks at the
beginning of the period of special feeding. Other workers have also
succeeded in producing rickets in rats simply by depriving them
of fat-soluble vitamin [Goldblatt, 1923]. There is no doubt, however,
that a deficiency of either calcium or phosphorus, or a faulty balance
of these elements, in a diet containing inadequate supplies of the calcifying vitamin will intensify the rickets-producing effect of the diet.

Deprivation of Calcium Alone.

Korenchevsky [1922] found that young rats kept on a diet containing
very small amounts of calcium, but otherwise complete, developed
osteoporosis and in some instances mild rickets. If the mothers of
the young rats had been kept on a calcium-deficient diet during lactation, the changes produced in the bones of the young rats were more
pronounced, resembling those of rickets of moderate severity. This
latter pathological condition was not prevented by moderately large
doses of cod-liver oil given both to mothers and offspring.

Deprivation of Calcium and Vitamin D.

A combined deficiency of calcium and fat-soluble vitamin has
been shown to produce rickets in rats more effectively than the
deficiency of either factor alone. As with calcium deficiency alone,
the intensity of the effect was greatest when the defective diet was
begun at an early age [Korenchevsky, 1922]. Mellanby [1921]
found that moderately severe rickets could be produced in dogs
that were receiving butter, which contains only small amounts of

vitamin D; when calcium salts were added to the diet containing butter, rickets was either prevented or appeared in a much less severe degree.

Deprivation of Phosphorus and Vitamin D.

Reference has already been made to the work of Sherman and Pappenheimer [1920-21 ; 1921] in which rickets was first produced in rats by a diet deficient, among other things, in phosphorus and fat-soluble vitamin, and then cured by the addition of basic potassium phosphate. For a time this and similar work of other American investigators resulted in a widespread belief that phosphorus deficiency rather than any vitamin deficiency was the most important aetiological factor in the production of rickets. Mellanby's experiments on the rickets-producing effect of certain cereals [1922 ; 1925 ; Green and Mellanby, 1928, 1], which will be referred to again in a later section, demonstrated, however, that both in dogs and in rats a severe type of rickets could be produced with an adequate supply of phosphorus in the diet.

Balance between Calcium and Phosphorus.

McCollum, Simmonds, Parsons, Shipley and Park [1921] suggested that the relative proportions of calcium and phosphorus in the diet were of greater importance than their absolute amounts in determining the occurrence of rickets in rats. In the absence of an adequate supply of vitamin D rickets may be produced in the rat by diets containing either an abnormally high or an abnormally low ratio of calcium to phosphorus. It is known that excess of calcium in the diet diminishes the amount of phosphate absorbed [see Forbes and Keith, 1914]. Mellanby [1921] has suggested that excess of phosphorus as compared with calcium, leading to a loss of calcium from the body, may be the determining cause of the greater rickets-producing effect of acid-caseinogen, which contains phosphorus but no calcium, than of casein, which contains calcium as well as phosphorus. Mellanby's work referred to above (p. 52), in which the diets were composed of natural foodstuffs including cereals and small but inadequate supplies of vitamin D, made it clear that for dogs the ratio of calcium to phosphorus does not necessarily determine the rickets-producing action of a diet. Moreover, this ratio can be varied within very considerable limits without the appearance of rickets provided an adequate amount of vitamin D is supplied. The usual modern technique of testing foods and other substances for vitamin D depends upon the fact that this vitamin can compensate for the imperfect calcium-phosphorus ratios generally provided in experimental rickets-producing diets (McCollum No. 3143 ; Steenbock No. 2965).

Relation of Mineral Supply to the Occurrence of Human Rickets.

The fact that rickets occurs in infants who are receiving the bulk of their food in the form of milk suggests that neither calcium nor phosphorus deficiency plays any determining rôle in the causation of the human disease. Human milk contains much less phosphorus than cow's milk, so that if phosphorus deficiency were as important a factor in determining the occurrence of rickets in infants as it appears to be in young rats, rickets should be much commoner in infants fed at the breast than in those receiving cow's milk. Actually the reverse is found to be true, so that the conclusion seems inevitable that phosphorus deficiency is not the determining factor. It is, however, possible that a deficiency of calcium or phosphorus, or of both elements, plays a part in causing rickets in older children who may receive little or no milk and an insufficient supply of vitamin D. Direct evidence on this question is, however, difficult to obtain.

Relation of the Acid-Base Balance in the Diet to the Occurrence of Rickets.

The suggestion has frequently been made that a disturbance in the acid-base balance of the diet plays a part in determining the occurrence of rickets [Aub, 1928–29; Elliot, Crichton and Orr, 1922; Jones, James and Smith, 1923–24; Zucker, Johnson and Barnett, 1922–23]. The marked discrepancies in the results obtained by these workers, however, suggest that the acid-base ratio of a diet can be of relatively little importance in determining the development of rickets.

Relation of Vitamin D to Cereals.

Excess of carbohydrate in the food has long been regarded as a factor predisposing to rickets in infants [Cheadle, 1906]. This hypothesis has now been placed upon a definite scientific basis by Mellanby's experimental work with puppies [Mellanby, 1922; 1925]. He showed that when the diets of puppies were deficient in the antirachitic vitamin, the intensity of the rickets which they developed was related to their intake of cereal. When all other factors in the diet and environment were kept constant, rickets was most strongly developed in those animals which ate the most bread. The explanation seemed to be that the consumption of extra quantities of bread induced a greater rate of growth, which necessitated an increased supply of calcifying vitamin to promote normal calcification of the bone. Since this supply was not forthcoming the bones were less efficiently calcified than in those animals which grew at a less rapid rate. It appeared most likely that it was the carbohydrate in the bread which was responsible for the more intense rickets, and in the few instances in which it was possible to induce puppies to eat large amounts of pure starch or sugar for a period of several months, it was found that the calcification of the bones was less perfect than in puppies that had not received such additions. The whole effect produced by increasing the bread in a diet did not, however, appear to be explained by these experiments. Further investigations on the rickets-producing effect of different cereals showed that the carbohydrate moiety of a cereal was not the only factor concerned with intensifying the severity of rickets in the absence of a sufficient supply of vitamin D. Of the cereals studied oatmeal produced the most severe rickets, then maize and barley, and finally rice and wheat flour, which interfered least with bone calcification. The germ of wheat added to a diet also intensified its rickets-producing effect. Oatmeal contains 67·5 per cent. of carbohydrate, while flour contains 76·4 per cent. [Sherman, 1920, 1], so that it cannot be an excess of carbohydrate which endows oatmeal with its greater rickets-producing effect.

The nature of the offending substance or substances has been sought in a long series of feeding experiments [Mellanby, 1925]. It could not be definitely identified with the protein fraction of the cereal, nor with the absolute or relative amounts of calcium and phosphorus. Oatmeal contains about three and a half times as much calcium, and four times as much phosphorus, as white flour, so that giving oatmeal in place of white flour certainly does not lead to any quantitative deficiency of either of these elements. Moreover, a consideration of the ratios of calcium to phosphorus in the various cereals fails to support the view that imperfect balancing of these elements is responsible for their rickets-producing effect. The ratio of calcium to phosphorus in oatmeal is $1:5\cdot7$, and in white flour $1:4\cdot6$. These figures are not very different, but the two cereals differ widely in their power of interfering with normal calcification. Wheat germ has a calcium-phosphorus ratio of $1:14\cdot8$, and rice of $1:10\cdot7$; these figures are of the same order, though differing widely from those of oatmeal and white flour and yet wheat germ interferes greatly with calcification, while rice interferes much less. Mellanby [1926, 1] has suggested that the name *toxamin* might be employed for the agent in question to indicate its unfavourable action and the fact that it can be neutralized by a sufficiency of vitamin D. Efforts to trace the chemical identity of this factor associated with cereals have so far not been successful.

If oatmeal is boiled with 1 per cent. hydrochloric acid until all the starch is converted to sugar and the solution is achromic to iodine, the 'toxamin' action of the cereal is destroyed [E. Mellanby, 1925]. On the other hand Holst [1927] found that the rickets-producing effect of oatmeal could be demonstrated in the filtrate from the cereal after it had been boiled with $0\cdot5$ per cent. hydrochloric acid. Thus, whereas a short period of boiling with dilute acid appears to bring the rickets-producing substance into solution, more prolonged boiling of the cereal destroys its action.

The antagonistic effect of cereals, and especially oatmeal, to bone-calcification, has been demonstrated with rats as well as with dogs [Green and Mellanby, 1928, 1; Holst, 1927]. How far this effect of cereals is of practical significance in relation to the production of human rickets remains to be proved. The animal-feeding experiments showed that the cereal effect could be obtained only when the diets were deficient in vitamin D. Even when large quantities of oatmeal were given, normal calcification could be brought about by giving cod-liver oil at the same time, and a considerable degree of protection against rickets could be secured by exposing the animals to ultra-violet radiation. It is probable that when the diets of young children contain a bare minimum of vitamin D, and when at the same time the amount of exposure to sunshine is strictly limited, the consumption of large quantities of cereals may determine the onset of frank rickets.

Vitamin D and Maternal Feeding in Relation to Rickets.

It has been the experience of those studying rickets, both in rats and dogs, that when mothers receive in their diets during pregnancy and lactation some potent source of vitamin D, their young are distinctly less susceptible to rickets when themselves subjected to vitamin D deficiency than other young animals whose mothers have not been well supplied with this vitamin. Thus both Korenchevsky [1922] and Goldblatt [1923] found that when rats were given cod-liver oil during pregnancy and lactation their young did not develop rickets when later receiving diets totally devoid of antirachitic vitamin. Grant and Goettsch [1926] kept rats during pregnancy and lactation on diets deficient in vitamin D but adequate in other respects, and found that their first two or three litters did not develop rickets when diets deficient only in vitamin D were subsequently given to them, but the fourth and fifth litters developed severe rickets under these conditions. In this instance it appeared that the mother's original stores of vitamin D took a considerable time to become depleted and that until the birth of the fourth litter she was able to pass on sufficient vitamin D to her young to protect them subsequently from rickets. When the mothers' diets were deficient in calcium as well as vitamin D, severe rickets developed in the first litter.

Mellanby observed early in the course of his experiments with dogs that if the mother had received cod-liver oil during pregnancy and lactation it was much more difficult to induce rickets in her puppies when they subsequently received diets deficient in vitamin D (see Fig. 4). He demonstrated, moreover, that the influence of the maternal feeding lasted for a considerable period in the life of the offspring [1926, 2]. Two bitches were allowed to become pregnant at the same time and to one was given cod-liver oil during pregnancy and lactation, while to the other was given olive oil. After weaning the puppies were divided into six pairs, each containing one from each mother, and received diets some of which were designed to have a rickets-producing action. In each case the puppy from the mother which had not received cod-liver oil developed severe, or moderately severe, rickets, while the corresponding puppy from the other mother developed no rickets or only slight rickets, depending on the rickets-producing potency of the particular diet which it received. Cod-liver oil was given to both members of one pair and their bones developed quite normally. After the lapse of four months when the animals were well grown, the diet of this pair was changed to one containing minimal quantities of vitamin D and a rickets-producing cereal. After six further months of such feeding the animal whose mother had received cod-liver oil during pregnancy remained free from any suggestion of bone abnormality, while the other whose mother had not received cod-liver oil developed definite bony changes which resembled those found in late rickets in man.

It is not yet certain what degree of protection against human rickets can be obtained by the consumption of adequate quantities of vitamin D by pregnant and nursing women (see p. 269). Hess and Weinstock [1924, 1] tried the effect of giving cod-liver oil to mothers during the last two months of pregnancy, but concluded that it had no appreciable prophylactic effect, for almost all the babies developed rickets during the subsequent winter. Weech [1927] found that administering large doses of cod-liver oil to women during lactation definitely diminished the severity of rachitic manifestions in their infants, although it could not be relied on to afford absolute protection (see also p. 273).

In the light of animal results it would certainly be expected that at least some degree of protection would be afforded to infants by ensuring liberal supplies of vitamin D to the mothers during pregnancy and lactation. In any case, as will be seen in the later section dealing with osteomalacia, for the mother's own sake it is advisable that she should receive ample supplies of vitamin D during this period.

If any considerable degree of protection is afforded to a young animal by antirachitic measures applied to the lactating mother, it might be expected that such measures would produce a demonstrable increase in the vitamin D content of the mother's milk.

Much work on this point has yielded conflicting results, but the balance of evidence supports the view that the young receive at least some measure of protection from rickets if the mothers are supplied liberally with vitamin D during pregnancy and lactation.

SPECIAL CONDITIONS FAVOURING THE OCCURRENCE OF RICKETS IN CHILDREN.

According to our present knowledge of the aetiology of rickets the supply of vitamin D is the most important factor, and this can either be ingested ready-made in the diet or can be produced in the skin under the influence of ultra-violet radiation. As far as the production of vitamin D in the skin is concerned the usual limiting factors are the intensity of the solar ultra-violet radiation, the duration and extent of exposure of the body surface to light, the degree of pigmentation of the skin, and the nature and amount of the clothing worn. Under ordinary circumstances efficient protection against rickets can be secured by supplying vitamin D in the diet; nevertheless, cases are sometimes met with in which rickets develop in spite of what appears to be an adequate supply of vitamin D.

Prematurity. Premature infants are notoriously liable to develop rickets. It has been suggested that the normal infant receives from its mother during the last few weeks of pregnancy important stores of vitamin D which help to protect it from rickets during its post-natal career. Whether failure to receive this supply explains the increased incidence of rickets in premature children or not, there are reasons for supposing that administration of vitamin D has the same effect in these as in normal children. Gerstenberger and Nourse [1926] state that cod-liver oil can protect premature infants against rickets, but it must be given almost immediately after birth and in rather large doses. Hess [1930] records cases in which rickets appeared in premature infants receiving cod-liver oil, but irradiated ergosterol caused healing of the rickets.

Coeliac disease. In this disease which is associated with infantilism one prominent and constant feature is the passing of bulky stools containing abnormally large amounts of undigested fat. There is a general failure of growth and an osteoporotic condition of the bones, which may or may not show typical rickety changes in addition. The main disturbance appears to consist in an inability to absorb fat from the intestinal canal, and seeing that vitamin D in food is associated with fats, there is likely to be simultaneous deficient absorption of this vitamin, even though the supply in the food may be adequate for protection against rickets in a normal child. It is stated by Parsons [1927] that 'coeliac rickets' can be cured by exposing the patient to ultra-violet radiation and giving vitamin D by mouth in the form of irradiated ergosterol.

Renal rickets. There is a form of chronic nephritis in children which leads to infantilism and often to rickets. In this condition the concentration of inorganic phosphorus in the blood may be raised far above the normal level. The appearance of rickets in these cases is not associated with any deficient supply of vitamin D, for there is no healing response to foods rich in vitamin D, even when well digested by these patients, and no response to irradiated ergosterol or to irradiation with ultra-violet light.

Infantile Tetany.

The association of laryngismus stridulus, carpopedal spasms, or generalized convulsions with rickets in infancy has been commented upon for many generations. These symptoms occasionally appear in infants who do not exhibit the classical signs of rickets, and those suffering from obvious rickets sometimes exhibit an increased excitability of their nerves (latent tetany) without showing any of the more severe manifestations of tetany. The incidence of infantile tetany is similar to that of rickets. Both show a pronounced seasonal variation [Japha, 1905; Moro, 1926] with exacerbations in the winter and early spring, and both are particularly liable to affect premature infants; in the United States negro infants are more frequently affected than white infants. There is one point of difference. Florid rickets is seldom met with in poorly nourished infants, for this condition is essentially one associated with good growth, but tetany, especially the latent form, is by no means uncommon in cases of malnutrition.

A pronounced lowering of the concentration of calcium in the serum is one of the more constant findings in tetany, but not in rickets, unless tetany is also present. A lowering of the serum calcium, associated with rickets, can be produced in rats by feeding them on diets deficient in vitamin D and in calcium, but relatively rich in phosphorus [Shipley, Park, McCollum and Simmonds, 1922]. Shohl, Bennett and Weed [1928] produced tetany in rats by giving them alkaline phosphates after they had been on a rickets-producing diet; the tetany appeared in spite of the fact that the rickets showed histological evidence of being cured. This type of tetany is probably similar to that found in the alkalosis produced by forced breathing.

The fact that infantile tetany and rickets are so closely associated suggests that the lowering of the blood-calcium in the former is connected with a deficiency of vitamin D. This view is strongly supported by observations on vitamin-D therapy in infancy. Adequate doses of cod-liver oil are found to prevent tetany just as they prevent rickets. Cod-liver oil is also effective as a curative agent, although its effect is sometimes delayed. Irradiated ergosterol has a more rapid action and may raise the serum calcium to a normal level in 10 or 14 days.

The acute symptoms may be rapidly alleviated by giving large doses of calcium chloride or of ammonium chloride, which latter salt is stated by Gamble, Ross and Tisdall [1923] to increase the proportion of ionized calcium in the blood ; but a real cure can only be assured by supplying in some form sufficient vitamin D to restore to normal the disturbed calcium metabolism.

THE RELATION OF VITAMIN D TO THE PARATHYROID GLANDS.

MacCallum and Voegtlin [1909] discovered that when the parathyroids of dogs were removed the calcium in the blood was lowered, an observation which indicated that these glands played a part in calcium metabolism.

Erdheim [1914] on the basis of pathological anatomical studies of human osteomalacia and of experimental work with rats traced a connexion between osteomalacia or rickets and abnormalities in the parathyroid glands.

In recent years, largely through the work of Mandl [1926 ; 1929], Collip [1925], and Aub and his collaborators [1928–29], the subject has again become one of great interest, and it is now recognized that the parathyroid secretion is an important factor in calcium-phosphorus metabolism. Anybody who has seen the dramatic effects produced by removal of a parathyroid cyst on the bone and blood condition in osteitis fibrosa cystica, or the effect of Collip's extract (parathormone) in tetany, must have been impressed by this relationship. The administration of vitamin D is also effective in the treatment of tetany, so that it is a matter of interest to know how parathormone and vitamin D are related.

The relation of the parathyroids to calcium-phosphorus metabolism has been elucidated by three types of observation :

(1) By determining the effect of removal of the glands.

(2) By observing the effect of injecting extracts of the glands [Collip, 1925 ; 1926 ; Greenwald and Gross, 1925 ; 1926].

(3) By observing the effect of the removal of parathyroid tumours in cases of osteitis fibrosa cystica [Mandl, 1926].

Removal of the glands from normal animals brings about a reduction of the calcium in the blood. The tetany which also results may be relieved temporarily by giving milk and other foods rich in calcium and abolished by repeated subcutaneous or intramuscular injection of extracts of the parathyroid glands. Parathormone raises the serum calcium in these animals to normal. Large doses produce hypercalcaemia, a condition which in normal animals especially is associated with illness and sometimes death.

After parathyroidectomy dogs excrete smaller quantities of calcium than the normal. On the other hand, the injection of parathormone increases the excretion of both calcium and phosphorus (Greenwald and Gross). In hyperparathyroidism the excretion of calcium and phosphorus is abnormally high, whether this condition is produced artificially in normal animals by the injection of parathyroid extract or is due to a tumour of the parathyroid glands in clinical cases. In hyperparathyroidism associated with osteitis fibrosa cystica, the blood has a high calcium and a low phosphorus content [Harrison, Shorr,

E

McClellan and Du Bois, 1930]. Removal of the tumour lowers the calcium of the blood greatly and increases the phosphorus but to a less extent. The excretion of both elements is greatly reduced by this form of treatment.

The effect of the secretion of the parathyroid is to maintain or raise the calcium and phosphorus excretion at the expense of the bones. Administration of vitamin D, however, in ordinary amounts brings about the incorporation of calcium and phosphorus in bones. Their actions are therefore in opposite directions. The fact that both vitamin D and parathyroid extract relieve tetany might suggest that they had a similar type of action. Vitamin D seems to raise to normal the calcium of the blood in cases of tetany by increasing the retention in the body of calcium which may be available in the food supplies. Parathyroid extract, on the other hand, raises the calcium in the blood by withdrawing it from the great tissue reserve of this substance, namely the bones.

Experiments have been made to ascertain whether vitamin D and the parathyroids are related by administering the vitamin to parathy-roidectomized animals. Some observers have found that vitamin D acts just as well under these conditions as in the intact animal, large doses of irradiated ergosterol (400 to 800 times the therapeutic dose) producing hypercalcaemia even in the absence of the parathyroids. There is also evidence that these large doses of vitamin D (in the form of irradiated ergosterol) raise the blood calcium at the expense of the bones [Kreitmair and Hintzelmann, 1928 ; Baumgartner et al., 1929 ; Hess, Weinstock and Rivkin, 1928–29 ; 1929–30], an action which is similar to that of the parathyroid extracts.

Taylor, Weld, Branion and Kay [1931, 1, 2] have presented evidence to show that the action of large doses of irradiated ergosterol in producing a rise in serum calcium takes place through the intermediary of the parathyroid glands, and have shown for example that large doses had no effect in relieving the tetany produced in dogs after an intensive operation in which thyroid and parathyroid glands and all accessory parathyroid tissue had been removed.[1]

VITAMIN D IN THE PROPHYLAXIS AND TREATMENT OF RICKETS AND ALLIED DISORDERS.

Rickets, osteomalacia, and infantile tetany have been shown to be due primarily to a deficiency of vitamin D, although other factors such as the supply of cereals and mineral salts may play an important part in their causation when there is a coincident partial deficiency of vitamin D. The prevention and treatment of these diseases should therefore not present any great difficulty, for there is a considerable choice of methods available for supplying vitamin D. Many of these methods have already been tested on a large scale, and though they may all have been found efficacious in achieving their immediate purpose, there may be advantages and disadvantages associated with some of them which require a somewhat detailed examination.

[1] For a review of work on the parathyroid glands, see Hunter [1931].

General Adjustment of Diet.

Much may be done to prevent rickets and osteomalacia by including in the diet a regular supply of natural foods containing vitamin D and by cutting down the amount of cereal.   There are few natural foods rich in vitamin D, unless cod-liver and similar fish oils are considered natural foods.   Egg yolk is powerfully antirachitic and may be given even to young infants.   Milk, cream, and butter may contain appreciable quantities of the vitamin and the amount can be increased by feeding cows in the open air on good pasture.   Milk is of considerable value also on account of its relative richness in calcium.   Animal fats such as suet and dripping contain small amounts of vitamin D which give them a better nutritive value than vegetable fats which usually contain none.

The problem of cutting down the cereal content of a diet without increasing its cost is by no means easy to solve.   It is quite true that the anti-calcifying effect of cereals can be neutralized by adequate supplies of vitamin D, but some evidence has been obtained in connexion with the work of M. Mellanby [1924 ; Mellanby and Pattison, 1926], on carious teeth in childhood, that even small supplies of vitamin D may be more efficacious in promoting normal calcification if the diet contains minimal quantities of cereals [see also Boyd *et al.*, 1928 ; 1929].   As regards cereals, it seems advisable to choose those which have the least anticalcifying action, such as white bread and rice. It is possible, as will be mentioned below (p. 70), to render cereals such as oatmeal antirachitic by irradiation.   Greater use may be made of fresh vegetables and potatoes with little increase in the cost.

Insistence upon the breast-feeding of infants is strongly advised whenever possible.

Cod-liver Oil Therapy.

The specific properties of cod-liver oil as an antirachitic agent were first proved experimentally by E. Mellanby [1918–19, 1]. Since then it has been abundantly shown that cod-liver oil can almost always be relied upon to cure rickets if it is given in adequate doses.   It contains large amounts of vitamin A as well as vitamin D and it appears likely that some of the beneficial effects observed after giving it to children are due to this fact.   As a prophylactic agent it should be given early in the infant's career, especially to premature infants and during the winter months.   Many experiments have been carried out on a large scale to test its prophylactic effect.   Hess and Unger [1917] demonstrated that giving cod-liver oil to negro infants was more effective than breast-feeding in protecting them from rickets. Gerstenberger and Nourse [1926] found that 3·5 c.c. a day protected premature infants. Eliot [1925] could not altogether check what she interpreted as radiographic evidence of early rickets in infants by giving cod-liver oil, although those receiving it were protected from obvious clinical manifestations of the disease. Similarly M. G Wilson [1926] considered that cod-liver oil had no great influence in preventing the radiographic changes in the bones which she considered to indicate very early rickets.   According to these observers a very slight degree of rickets may be regarded as physiological and almost universal in apparently healthy young infants even when they receive cod-liver oil.

In climates where there is little available sunshine the prevention of
rickets depends on supplying liberal quantities of vitamin D by
cod-liver oil administration. There are no serious objections to its
routine use in infancy and childhood. Most young children not merely
tolerate it but grow to like it. It may be given as a prophylactic
measure after the second or third week of life in doses of one quarter
of a teaspoonful, and be increased so that the dose at the age of three
months is one-half teaspoonful twice a day, and at eight or nine
months two teaspoonsful a day. There appears to be no danger whatever of these doses causing untoward symptoms in infants corresponding to those described by Agduhr [1926, 1, 2] in experimental animals.

The healing effect of cod-liver oil can often be detected radiographically within two or three weeks, but the treatment should be continued
for at least a year, during which time most of the growth deformities,
even in severe cases, will become rectified. Cases are sometimes met
with in which vitamin D concentrates, such as irradiated ergosterol,
promote healing when ordinary doses of cod-liver oil given for many
weeks have had no appreciable effect.

The toxicity of cod-liver oil. It is a matter of common experience
that cod-liver oil, especially in the adult, may produce anorexia and
gastric discomfort. Much of this effect is psychological and results
from its disagreeable taste and oily nature. A part is undoubtedly
due to its physiological effect in inhibiting gastric secretion and motility,
for, as has been shown by Roberts in the treatment of hyperchlor-
hydria [1930], cod-liver oil is much more effective in this respect than
more highly saturated fats such as olive oil and butter fat. In these tests
the various oils and fats were placed directly in the stomach so as to
eliminate any psychological effect due to flavour.

Apart from these detrimental effects there is some evidence that
cod-liver oil can do harm under certain conditions after absorption
from the alimentary canal.

Normal adults taking large quantities of cod-liver oil (say 2 ounces
daily) occasionally develop some degree of tachycardia and praecordial
discomfort, even when there is no question of gastric disturbance
[E. Mellanby, 1924]. The subject has been brought into a position
of prominence by the investigations of Agduhr [1926–29], who found
that cod-liver oil, when given continuously to animals, may produce
toxic effects on the heart and the development of the following
abnormalities—pigment degeneration and fatty degeneration of the
heart-muscle, transformation of the muscle-cells into connective tissue,
and calcareous incrustations. Parallel experiments with other oils,
e.g. olive oil, rape oil, and cocoa fat, did not show alterations in the
heart comparable with those produced by cod-liver oil.

It is undoubted that under certain experimental conditions cod-liver
oil produces degenerative changes in the heart and the problem is
to decide to what extent such results may be extended to man.
Agduhr's results were undoubtedly magnified by the type of diet chosen
for his work. Just as vitamin D in excessive doses produces much
greater toxic effects when added to synthetic diets than when added to
diets of natural foodstuffs [see Harris and Innes, 1931], so also the toxic
effects of cod-liver oil are much greater under these same experimental
conditions. The inhibition of the toxic effect of excessive cod-liver

oil by increasing the supply of the vitamin B complex, as shown by Harris and Moore [1929, 2], indicates the importance of testing the action of cod-liver oil in a well-balanced diet.

Another criticism of Agduhr's results applies especially to those experiments in which he obtained the greatest effects, namely in calves and herbivorous animals. These animals take cod-liver oil or any form of fat very badly, and indeed rabbits die soon after the addition of small quantities of fats to the food unless green vegetables are also given liberally [M. Mellanby and Killick, 1926]. It seems desirable that some of Agduhr's work should be repeated with animals eating well-balanced diets and receiving quantities of cod-liver oil more comparable to the relatively small amounts taken by an average human being. At the same time the results should probably be used as a warning that constant administration of large quantities of cod-liver oil to children and adults on ill-balanced diets may have an insidious and untoward toxic effect especially on the muscle-cells of the heart.

There is no reason to believe that any of the toxic actions ascribed to cod-liver oil are due to its vitamin content. Norris and Church [1930, 3] have shown that small doses of *iso*amylamine, as found in cod-liver oil, and also choline, given continuously, may produce paralysis, convulsions, and lack of growth, and that these symptoms can be prevented by giving more yeast. They suggest that these bases may be the toxic agents in cod-liver oil.

Exposure to Sunshine or Artificial Sources of Ultra-violet Radiation.

When the composition of the diet is such that it is neither powerfully rickets-producing nor powerfully protective, exposure of the skin to ultra-violet radiation from the sun, even in an unfavourable climate, may suffice to protect the individual from rickets or allied disorders. Chick and co-workers [1922; 1923] demonstrated the protective value of natural sunshine in Vienna; rickets could be both prevented and cured in the summer by allowing infants to remain in the open, although this effect could not be obtained in the winter.   Huldschinsky's [1919] observations on the curative effect of artificial ultra-violet irradiation mark an epoch in the study of rickets and have been repeatedly confirmed. In many parts of the world Light Clinics have been established for the purpose of providing protection against rickets in districts where natural sunshine is not available during a considerable part of the year.   This method of prophylaxis is undoubtedly effective, but is costly in operation and not free from danger, and must entail considerable time and expense on the part of the mothers who have to attend regularly with their children. It has, moreover, the disadvantage, as compared with the administration of cod-liver oil, of not supplying vitamin A, which is frequently also deficient in the diets of children suffering from a lack of vitamin D.

Concentrated Preparations of Vitamin D.

Since the discovery of the extremely powerful antirachitic activity of irradiated ergosterol, it has been possible to give much larger doses of vitamin D than could previously be given in the form of cod-liver oil. The efficacy of this substance, both in the prevention and cure of rickets, has been proved by numerous observers in all parts of the world. It has also been shown to be effective in the treatment of tetany and osteomalacia [Hottinger, 1927, 1 ; Starlinger, 1927]. Several interesting comparisons have been published between the effects of cod-liver oil and irradiated ergosterol in preventing or curing rickets. Barnes, Brady and James [1930] found that one drachm of cod-liver oil given three times a day to children prevented or cured rickets in 95 per cent. of cases. Daily doses of irradiated ergosterol of equivalent potency as tested on rats prevented or cured rickets in 44 per cent. of cases only. De Sanctis and Craig [1930] gave three drachms of cod-liver oil daily to 103 infants and found that 97 were protected from rickets ; ten minims daily of the American preparation of irradiated ergosterol known as 'viosterol', which, according to rat dosage, should afford good protection, prevented rickets in only 77 out of 123 infants.

These results show the desirability for enforcing standardization of commercial preparations of vitamin D sold for therapeutic use and the need which existed for the efforts which have been successfully made to secure international agreement as to a standard substance to be adopted for purposes of comparison in vitamin D tests and as to the unit in which the results are to be expressed (see Appendix II).

Irradiation of Foods.

The observation of Steenbock and Black [1924] that foods previously without antirachitic value were capable of preventing or curing rickets after they had been exposed to ultra-violet radiation (p. 74), led to clinical trials of the antirachitic effect of irradiated foods [Steenbock and Daniels, 1925]. The fact that vegetable oils develop high antirachitic potency after irradiation suggests that they might be irradiated with advantage before being incorporated into margarines.

Mellanby [1925 ; see also Green and Mellanby, 1928, 1] has shown that the anticalcifying effect of oatmeal is neutralized by exposure to the radiation from a mercury-vapour lamp for thirty minutes. If the oatmeal is freed from fat, irradiation does not increase its calcifying action. On the other hand, irradiated oatmeal loses its calcifying action when its fat is extracted and the fatty moiety can be shown to stimulate calcification. These facts indicate that the ergosterol present in the oatmeal is changed to vitamin D by the ultra-violet rays. When this substance is removed the anticalcifying effect of the cereal remains [M. Mellanby, 1929].

Toxicity of Irradiated Ergosterol.
Hypervitaminosis D.

This subject has become a question of practical interest, especially to those concerned with the care of children. While, on the whole, it would appear that the danger to children of this form of therapy is very small, especially if their diet is otherwise balanced, it is not possible at the present time to lay down any clear cut rules as to the limits of safety.

Pfannenstiel [1927 ; 1928] observed in rabbits and Kreitmair and

Moll [1928] in rats, cats, rabbits, dogs, and guinea-pigs, that large doses (from 1-40 mg. daily) of irradiated ergosterol brought about death of the animals in periods ranging from 15-40 days. The symptoms were rapid loss of weight, anorexia, diarrhoea, and roughening of the coat, while examination of the tissues revealed large deposits of calcium in the arteries, myocardium, lungs, kidneys, stomach, and intercostal muscles.

These results have been confirmed by numerous workers and the pathological lesions have been described by Huckel and Wenzel [1929, 1, 2], Varela et al. [1929], Spies and Glover [1930], Duguid [1930], Hoyle [1930, 1, 2] and others. The predominating lesion is in the arteries and appears to be primarily a degenerative change in the muscular layer followed by calcification. The calcifying process extends from the larger to the smaller arteries, especially the renal vessels, until almost all are involved. A premature calcification of growing cartilage was observed by Collazo et al. [1929] and Schmidt-mann [1928]. Klein [1929] and Harris and Stewart [1929] recorded a large increase in the calcium and inorganic phosphorus content of the blood after massive doses of irradiated ergosterol. There is an increased urinary excretion of both calcium and phosphorus, and this loss has been shown by Kreitmair and Hintzelmann [1928] and Baumgartner et al. [1929] to be associated with a decalcification of the bones particularly affecting the ribs.

There is, however, an extremely wide margin between the therapeutic and toxic doses. Kreitmair and Moll [1928] obtained toxic effects with 5,000-10,000 times the curative dose ; Harris and Moore [1928] used 100,000 times the prophylactic dose ; Bills and Wirick [1930] state that 100 times the prophylactic dose is harmless in rats, 1,000 times is just perceptibly harmful over a long period, whilst 4,000 times is definitely toxic.

Some workers have been unable to obtain these toxic effects even when very large doses of irradiated ergosterol were given. There is a great lack of uniformity in experimental conditions, including the species of animal used, the nature of the diet and the mode of irradiation of the ergosterol, all of which appear to be important factors. These divergent results have raised the question as to whether the toxic effect was actually due to the antirachitic principle or to some toxic by-product produced during the irradiation of ergosterol. The opinion that the antirachitic and toxic actions are the effects of different substances [Holtz and Schreiber, 1930] has been rendered very improbable by the observation that calciferol (p. 77), the purest form of vitamin D yet known, is also toxic in large doses [Askew et al., 1932]. Most workers find ergosterol itself to be non-toxic though Kreitmair and Moll [1928] produced calcification in the vessel walls by its administration, but only after large doses for a very long period.

Many of the negative results mentioned above have been obtained by workers using natural diets rather than laboratory synthetic diets. Schmidtmann [1928] and Rabl [1929] have shown that a high calcium diet favours the early production of lesions, while according to Herzenberg [1929] a low calcium diet delays the appearance of lesions ; Harris [1930] notes that a high Ca, low P diet definitely increases the toxic effect. Duguid et al. [1930] found that irradiated ergosterol was much more toxic to rats living on a synthetic high Ca, low P diet than to rats fed on a mixed diet of bread and potatoes. The work of Hoyle [1930, 1,2] also showed that the nature of the diet was a very important factor : 80,000 times the usual therapeutic daily dose of ergosterol irradiated in alcohol caused death of rats on a synthetic diet in 2–3 weeks, while rats on bread and milk, apart from retarded growth after 30 to 40 days, showed no lesions except occasional urinary calculi. Neither bread alone nor milk alone, nor a synthetic diet constituted to resemble the bread and milk diet prevented the toxic action. When the dose was increased to 200,000 times the normal dose the bread and milk diet lost its protective effect.

There are other conflicting observations. Harris and Moore [1929, 1] noted a loss of toxicity when irradiation of the ergosterol in alcohol was prolonged sufficiently to destroy the antirachitic factor, whilst Hoyle [1930, 1, 2] finds no such loss under similar conditions. The nature of the solvent in which ergosterol is irradiated possibly influences the toxicity, though Harris and Moore [1929, 1] found that a pure specimen of ergosterol irradiated in air could still, in adequate doses, produce typical lesions. Dixon and Hoyle [1928] using ergosterol irradiated in oil found that a dose as high as 17 mg. daily caused poor growth, but apart from the presence of calcium phosphate calculi in the urinary tract there were no morbid lesions. Hoyle and Buckland [1929] with a larger dose confirmed this result in the main, while Hoyle [1930, 1] found that ergosterol, after irradiation in alcohol, caused intense tissue calcification although urinary calculi were rare.

Very few instances of toxic effects due to irradiated ergosterol have been described in human beings, which is not surprising in view of the enormous doses required to produce these effects in animals. Large doses of irradiated ergosterol have, indeed, been given to infants without the appearance of toxic symptoms. Hess, Poncher et al. [1930] in a prophylactic investigation, observed no toxic symptoms after daily administration of 20–52 times the prophylactic dose of irradiated ergosterol ('viosterol') for long periods and of 250 times for short periods. The children were lively, the appetite was increased ; constipation was the rule. Bamberger [1929] records loss in weight, vomiting, anorexia, with blood, albumin, and hyaline casts in the urine and a raised blood calcium and phosphorus content in 10 of 11 tuberculous children receiving large doses of 'vigantol' (0·2–0·25 mg. irradiated ergosterol per kg. body-wt.). No such effects were observed with a cod-liver oil concentrate given in amounts equivalent in antirachitic potency; it would therefore appear that the toxic effect of 'vigantol' was not due to its vitamin D content. György [1929] observed anorexia, vomiting, renal disturbances, and hypercalcaemia in tuberculous children on daily doses of 5–10 mg. irradiated ergosterol, but normal children did not show such symptoms or hypercalcaemia on a dose of 6 mg. Hess and Lewis [1928] report toxic effects in 9 out of 22 normal and rachitic children receiving doses of 0·5–6·6 mg. per kg. body-wt. Klausner-Cronheim [1930] records the appearance of albumin, red cells and casts in the urine of 3 rachitic children receiving from 1 to 5 mg. of irradiated ergosterol daily. Putscher [1929] found abnormal calcification similar to that seen in animals in a child that had received 6 drops of 'vigantol' daily.

Bamberger and Spranger [1928] describe parenchymatous nephritis in a child dead from 'vigantol' poisoning.

Although there appears to be a wide margin of safety in the use of irradiated ergosterol in human therapeutics, it is clearly desirable that it should be prescribed on a standardized basis and that the possibility of toxic effects, particularly as revealed by urine examination, should be borne in mind. Animal experiments suggest that there is more danger when the diet is deficient or faulty in some respect.

General Conclusions.

A deficiency of vitamin D is the principal factor which determines the occurrence of rickets, defectively formed teeth and infantile tetany. The same deficiency is the cause of osteomalacia, a disease which may be regarded as the pathological analogue of rickets, occurring in adult life under special conditions of deprivation and often associated with pregnancy (see p. 239).

Deficiency of vitamin D arises either from a lack of vitamin D in the diet or from a deficient exposure of the skin to those radiations of short wave-length which are capable of producing vitamin D at the surface of the body. When the total amount of vitamin D supplied from either or both of these sources is large, rickets and the allied conditions will be prevented, although normal bones cannot be formed in the absence of the necessary minimum quantities of mineral elements. When the amount of vitamin D supplied is small, the occurrence of rickets may depend on other factors in addition to vitamin D deficiency. Thus rapid growth, a large intake of cereals, deficiency of calcium or phosphorus, an unsuitable proportion of the one to the other, or a defective supply of vitamin D to the mother during pregnancy and lactation may then determine the onset in individual cases. It is unlikely that all the factors which may influence the occurrence of rickets in the presence of limited amounts of vitamin D are at present recognized; nevertheless, except in rare pathological cases, liberal supplies of vitamin D can apparently counteract them all.

Chemistry of Vitamin D.

A remarkable result of the work on rickets was the discovery that light rays—either in the form of direct sunlight or of the radiation from the mercury-vapour quartz lamp—exert a profound influence on the disease. The first observations were clinical (see p. 55) and not only failed to clarify the problem, but tended to complicate the issue by raising the apparent paradox that rickets could be cured by two such dissimilar agents as ultra-violet rays and dietary factors. The attack on the problem by the biochemist, which finally led to its solution, only became possible when means were found to study the question experimentally in the laboratory on animals, rats in particular, kept on a rachitogenic diet. Since the sunlight effects could not be satisfactorily explained in terms of calcium and phosphorus metabolism alone and were similar to those produced by including cod-liver oil in the diet, the idea arose that sunlight striking the skin might cause a photosynthetic production in the skin of the antirachitic vitamin, which was then liberated into the blood-stream. Its production would thus be analogous to that of vitamin-A potency in green leaves, which probably occurs as a result of photosynthesis.

Activation of Synthetic Diets by Irradiation.

A valuable clue, directing the experimental attack into the right channel, was unexpectedly supplied by the discovery that the effect of irradiation on the animal could be equally well evoked by irradiation of its rachitogenic diet. The experimental work which led up to this discovery was carried out by Hume [1922], Hume and Smith [1923], and by Goldblatt and Soames [1923, 1, 2].

Hume [1922] had observed that ultra-violet irradiation could replace cod-liver oil up to a point as far as the promotion of growth was concerned, but that it could not permanently supply the growth-promoting function of the oil, nor could it prevent xerophthalmia. Hume and Smith [1923] reported that rats eating a diet deficient in fat-soluble vitamins, when kept in glass jars which had been exposed to radiation from a mercury-vapour lamp for ten minutes on alternate days, maintained growth longer than control rats not so treated. The implication that the air in the jars could be activated by the rays was negatived by Webster and Hill [1924], who only obtained growth effect by exposing the animals themselves to the radiation [cf. Chick and Tazelaar, 1924; Nelson and Steenbock, 1924–25; 1925, 2; Hughes, Nitcher and Titus, 1925]. Hume and Smith [1924] then observed that rats housed in previously irradiated glass jars containing sawdust and fed on a diet deficient in fat-soluble vitamins grew as well as those undergoing direct irradiation, and that the degree of bone calcification was directly proportional to the growth. The growth-promoting and calcifying properties resided in the irradiated sawdust consumed by the rats, and were later shown to be due to the sterols of the sawdust which had become antirachitic by irradiation (see p. 75).

About the same time Goldblatt and Soames [1923, 2] found that the livers of irradiated rats on a diet deprived of fat-soluble vitamins had acquired growth-promoting properties, whilst the livers from non-irradiated rats were entirely inactive.

Steenbock and Black [1924] confirmed this observation and extended it by irradiating liver and the deficient diet directly, and they offered what is now known to be the correct explanation. The observed effects are due to the production, not of vitamin A, but of vitamin D, and both growth-promoting and bone-calcifying properties are imparted by irradiation to animal tissues and to synthetic diets deficient in the antirachitic vitamin. In confirmation of this view they discovered that various foodstuffs, incapable in themselves of preventing or curing rickets, became endowed with antirachitic power on exposure to ultra-violet rays. Hess and Weinstock [1924, 2; 1924–25; 1925, 1] arrived at similar conclusions. On further analysis it was found that the capacity to become activated resided only in those constituents of the diet which contained fats. The fats themselves, i.e. edible vegetable oils such as olive oil, cottonseed oil, arachis oil, &c., although inactive by themselves, became antirachitic after irradiation. It was also noticed that this activity was completely lost again on prolonged irradiation. This remarkable property of fats is not due to their main constituents, the fatty acids and glycerol, but is restricted entirely to that small moiety of substances composing the 'unsaponifiable' fraction.

Subsequently three distinct groups of investigators [Steenbock and Black, 1925; Hess, Weinstock and Helman, 1925; and Rosenheim and Webster, 1925] discovered independently and simultaneously that the animal sterol, cholesterol, and the plant sterol, phytosterol, could be converted under the action of ultra-violet rays into very rich sources of vitamin D, although neither substance possessed any antirachitic action prior to irradiation. Even when cholesterol (obtained from brain) was subjected to purification by recrystallization more than twenty times, it retained the power of acquiring antirachitic potency under the action of ultra-violet rays.

THE RECOGNITION OF ERGOSTEROL AS THE PARENT SUBSTANCE OF VITAMIN D.

It was found by Rosenheim and Webster [1926, 1] that after irradiation of cholesterol more than 99 per cent. remained unchanged. By taking advantage of the insolubility of the digitonin-cholesterol compound, the antirachitic factor could be accumulated in a small amount of an amorphous substance not precipitable by digitonin. Such a behaviour is analogous to that of the vitamin D of cod-liver oil, which is also not precipitable by digitonin [Nelson and Steenbock, 1925, 1]. The preparation obtained from irradiated cholesterol sufficed to meet the antirachitic requirements of rats when administered at what was then considered the extraordinarily small dosage of 0·01 mg. per rat per day. Rosenheim and Webster also observed that the sterol of fungi, ergosterol (obtained from ergot of rye or from yeast fat) when irradiated became 'highly protective even in doses of 1 mg.'

A very large number of substances allied to cholesterol (isomerides, hydrocarbons, oxidation products, &c.) were then investigated [Rosenheim and Webster, 1926, 5; 1927, 2; Hess and Windaus, 1926-27]. The negative results obtained in this work, together with other considerations, led Rosenheim and Webster [1926, 5] to recognize that cholesterol contained a significant impurity which could not be eliminated by recrystallization. Cholesterol, in view of its single ethenoid linkage, readily forms a dibromide, from which the sterol can be regenerated by reduction with sodium amalgam and acetic acid. It was found that the cholesterol, purified by way of the dibromide, no longer possessed the power of becoming antirachitic after irradiation with ultra-violet rays. Such cholesterol is very transparent in the ultra-violet, no trace of selective absorption being shown. From this work of Rosenheim and Webster, it seemed probable that the precursor substance (provitamin D) was more readily attacked by bromine than cholesterol, or, at any rate, that it was destroyed in the purification process. It seemed legitimate therefore to assume that, since it resisted separation from cholesterol and was precipitated by digitonin, the provitamin was either an unsaturated sterol or a cholesterol derivative. From this point progress proved to be rapid, and spectroscopic investigations afforded valuable contributory evidence.

The first preliminary spectroscopic investigations were carried out by Hess and Weinstock [1925, 2, 3] who recorded a qualitative change in absorption on irradiation. The activated material absorbed ultra-violet rays somewhat less strongly than the non-irradiated cholesterol, a difference in the integrated absorption over a range of wave-lengths being detected by means of a thermopile and galvanometer. Schlutz and Morse [1925] and Schlutz and Ziegler [1926] carried the matter farther when they recorded that highly purified cholesterol (M.P. 148·5°) showed 'two characteristic absorption bands at about 294 and 279 $m\mu$ wave-length'. They further suggested that the absorption might be due to a small amount of a highly absorptive impurity.

A quantitative study of the absorption spectrum of cholesterol was carried out by Heilbron, Kamm and Morton [1926 ; 1927]. Large quantities (2 kg.) of cholesterol were subjected to fractional crystallization from ethyl acetate, and the various fractions examined spectrographically. It was established that ordinary cholesterol contained a small quantity of another compound, capable of being accumulated in the least soluble fraction. The intensity of absorption in the original cholesterol was only one-fourth of that obtained with this fraction. A sample of the concentrated product was subsequently irradiated and tested biologically by Rosenheim and Webster [1927, 3] and found to possess an antirachitic potency 3–4 times as great as that obtained by irradiating the original sample of cholesterol. The 'impurity' in cholesterol was characterized by three well-defined absorption maxima in the ultra-violet at 293·5, 281·5, and 270 $m\mu$ respectively. Since these maxima disappeared on irradiation and at the same time the material acquired antirachitic activity, it became evident that the bands provided criteria for a photosensitive precursor substance. Pohl [1926] published similar data, arrived at independently and by a different technique. The spectroscopic observations thus effectively strengthened the evidence of the biological and chemical work and led to a search for the 'impurity' (provitamin D), which proved successful in a short time.

Attention was directed again to the fact that Rosenheim and Webster [1926, 1] had obtained positive results with ergosterol. This trebly unsaturated sterol is destroyed by bromine, it is precipitated by digitonin, and can be activated. When Rosenheim and Webster first examined irradiated ergosterol they obtained complete protection with 1 mg., but did not test smaller amounts. By progressively reducing the dosage, it was found that the antirachitic potency was of a much higher order than that obtained with any other substance. The daily dose of irradiated ergosterol needed to protect a rat against rickets is exceedingly small, 0·0001 mg. or less sufficing. It was also found that ergosterol possessed a highly characteristic absorption spectrum, showing the same maxima as those recorded by Pohl and by Heilbron, Kamm and Morton, but with enormously increased intensity as compared with cholesterol. The identification of ergosterol with provitamin D was jointly announced by Rosenheim and Webster [1927, 3, 4] and by Windaus and Hess [1927].

The laboratory results obtained by animal experiments were rapidly confirmed by extensive clinical experience and enabled the dietetic and environmental theories of the aetiology of rickets to be at last reconciled (p. 52). It is obvious that among the factors of hygiene advocated at different times as influencing rickets, sunlight and ultraviolet rays are of pre-eminent importance. *Diet and sunlight both influence the calcification of bone, the former by virtue of its content of vitamin D, sunlight by generating vitamin D in the skin from ergosterol.* Thus, many observations which formerly could not be brought into intelligible relationship are now seen to be consistent.

The Isolation of Crystalline Vitamin D (Calciferol).

When ergosterol is irradiated a complex resinous mixture of at least six substances is formed, either simultaneously or consecutively, one of which is the antirachitic vitamin. In spite of the persevering attempts of chemists in many countries, this intractable resinous mixture could not be brought to crystallization. Success was more than once announced [Jendrassik and Kemenyffi, 1929 ; Reerink and van Wijk, 1929 ; 1931], but the claim that the crystalline products represented vitamin D itself was not substantiated. It seems, however, as if the final stages in the isolation of the vitamin had now been reached, concurrently in England and in Germany, and fittingly in the same laboratories in which the original discovery of the parent substance of vitamin D was simultaneously made in 1927.

The first step towards success was taken when Bourdillon and his co-workers [Askew *et al.*, 1930, 1] produced from the irradiation mixture small amounts of a crystalline substance of high antirachitic activity by the use of an ingenious new method, distillation *in vacuo* combined with fractional condensation. Later they were able to obtain several grams of this substance, termed by them calciferol, which retained its biological and physical properties unchanged on repeated recrystallizations [Angus *et al.*, 1931]. This fact did not, in their opinion, exclude the possibility that the substance was a mixture or a molecular compound of a highly active substance with an inactive isomeric one. It was then found that calciferol, as obtained by distillation, yielded a well-characterized crystalline ester, the 3 : 5-dinitrobenzoate [Callow, 1931], by means of which it could be freed from an inactive isomeric admixture of very high dextro-rotation. The latter substance, pyrocalciferol, is formed by thermal effects during the process of distillation of the irradiation product. Pure calciferol has an antirachitic activity of 40,000 international units (see p. 83) per mg., M.P. 115-117°, $[\alpha]_{5461} + 122°$, and has been isolated as the dinitrobenzoate directly from the undistilled crude mixture of irradiation products of ergosterol [Askew *et al.*, 1931; 1932].

Meanwhile Windaus [1931] also obtained a crystalline substance, differing from calciferol in its optical activity, by applying the reaction of Diels [1929] with maleic or citraconic anhydride to the products of long-wave irradiation of ergosterol. This substance had an antirachitic activity of 20,000 international units per mg. and the subsequent isolation by Linsert [1931] of a second crystallized product of apparently equal activity led Windaus and Lüttringhaus [1931] to assume the existence of two vitamins, 'vitamin D_1' and 'vitamin D_2'. They subsequently recognized the identity of their vitamin D_2 with calciferol, since it furnished a dinitrobenzoate identical with that of calciferol previously described by Askew *et al.* In addition they stated that 'vitamin D_1' is a molecular compound of calciferol (their vitamin D_2) with another inactive, but isomeric alcohol. Reerink and van Wijk's [1931] crystalline product, 'substance L', appears to be an unstable mixture of various substances, of which calciferol is probably a constituent.

It would therefore seem probable that calciferol (vitamin D_2 of the German workers), a stable crystalline substance of the highest antirachitic activity yet obtained, is vitamin D in a state of purity.

The Chemical Changes occurring on Irradiation of Ergosterol.

One of the most striking chemical changes induced by the action of ultra-violet rays on ergosterol is the loss of precipitability by digitonin [Rosenheim and Webster, 1927, 5], which indicates a steric inversion connected with the secondary alcohol group. The hydroxyl group, however, seems to be only indirectly involved in the activation process, since the irradiated esters of ergosterol are inactive as such, but acquire high activity after hydrolysis [Windaus and Rygh, 1928]. The acetate, benzoate, and palmitate form the only exceptions, their activity after irradiation probably being due to the nature of the acid radical which may easily be split off by the esterases of the animal organism. The fact that ergosterol methyl ether cannot be activated, although spectroscopically almost identical with ergosterol [Heilbron *et al.*, private communication], is further evidence for such a view.

Reduction of the irradiation products with metallic sodium destroys the antirachitic activity, and a crystallized isomeride of dihydro-ergosterol can be obtained from the reaction mixture [Windaus, 1930, 1]. The inactive products resulting on prolonged irradiation yield on treatment with cyanic acid a mixture of allophanic acid esters, from which two crystallized isomerides of ergosterol, suprasterol I and suprasterol II, have been separated by Windaus *et al.* [1930].

The strong laevo-rotation of ergosterol decreases slowly under the influence of irradiation and gives place to a slight dextro-rotation [Windaus and Linsert, 1928]. According to the same authors the hydroxyl group itself and three double bonds are still present in the reaction mixture freed from ergosterol, and the molecular weight and composition remain the same as those of ergosterol.

Irradiation apparently induces a stereoisomeric change or a rearrangement of ethenoid linkages, or a combination of changes of these types, the nature of which will remain unknown until the elucidation of the constitution of calciferol has been achieved. Calciferol is an alcohol, isomeric with ergosterol, and, like the latter, yields well-crystallized esters. Two of these have been described, the *p*-nitrobenzoate and the 3 : 5-dinitrobenzoate, the latter of which led to its isolation [Askew *et al.*, 1931]. Like ergosterol it possesses a system of conjugated double linkages, as demonstrated by the Diels reaction (condensation with maleic or citraconic anhydride), a fact made use of by Linsert in the alternative method of isolation [1931].

A specific relative position, as yet unknown, of the three double bonds in the ring system of ergosterol is probably essential for its photo-chemical conversion into calciferol, giving rise to the specific groupings to which antirachitic activity is due.

Colour Tests for Vitamin D.

Shear [1925–26] found that cod-liver oil and irradiated cholesterol gave a characteristic red colour with a solution of aniline hydrochloride in excess of aniline. The suggestion that this reaction might serve for the detection of vitamin D was disproved by Rosenheim and Webster [1926, 1] and by Sexton [1928]. Bezssonoff's [1924, 1] phospho-molybdotungstic acid reagent was also found to be unspecific by the same observers. A number of other colour reactions have been proposed from time to time [Jendrassik and Kemenyffi, 1928; Steigmann, 1928; Stoeltzner, 1928; Meesemaecker, 1930; Cruz-Coke, 1930], but so far none of them has proved to be specific for vitamin D. The colour reactions of calciferol, so far described, are not sufficiently specific for its detection in the presence of other irradiation products of ergosterol.

Specificity of Ergosterol as Provitamin D.

Ergosterol is the only substance known to acquire intense anti-rachitic activity on irradiation. It would seem that this is an inherent property of the substance and not due to an impurity, for Windaus and Brunken [1928] found that ergosterol recovered from its inactivable peroxide still becomes highly active on irradiation.

This unique property of ergosterol appears to be due to its molecular structure, and in particular to the specific position of the three unsaturated bonds in their relation to the hydroxyl group. None of the artificially prepared isomerides, of which twelve are already known, can be activated (iso-ergosterol [Reindel et al., 1927], u-ergosterol, ergosterol D [Windaus and Auhagen, 1929], ergosterol F, suprasterol I and suprasterol II [Windaus et al., 1930] etc.). Other substances which gave negative results, although possessing sterol structure, are digitaligenin, choledienic and choletrienic acids, dehydro-ergosterol, dihydro-ergosterol, dihydro-cholesterol, coprosterol, sitosterol, stigmasterol, cholesterilene, and oxycholesterilene; further, all the open chain unsaturated compounds examined: squalene, nerolidol, ψ-ionone and sphingosine.

The relatively slight activity acquired by naturally occurring sterols (cholesterol, zymosterol, fungisterol, α-sitosterol, &c.) is assumed to be due to admixture of ergosterol, the evidence for its presence being based so far mainly on spectroscopic observations. The difficulty of removing the last traces of admixed ergosterol probably accounts for the results reported by various observers [Jendrassik and Kemenyffi, 1927; Bills et al., 1928; Koch, Koch and Lemon, 1929; Koch and Ragins, 1929] who found irradiated purified cholesterol slightly anti-rachitic when administered in large doses. It has also been claimed by the last-named authors that products possessing after irradiation a low but definite antirachitic activity are obtained by heating purified cholesterol above its melting-point under conditions which avoid appreciable oxidation. These undefined substances seem to be of the same type as those described by Bills and McDonald [1926], which are formed from cholesterol by the action of fuller's earth (floridin). These authors considered that the mode of action of their products differed from that of vitamin D, a conclusion confirmed by Kon, Daniels and Steenbock [1928].

PHOTOCHEMISTRY OF ERGOSTEROL.

The Technique of Irradiation.

Many sources of radiation have been tried, but it seems probable that the quartz mercury lamp is the most convenient. It suffers, however, from the defect that the output of ultra-violet rays falls off with use, and for accurate work the output needs to be controlled [cf. Gillam and Morton, 1927]. Windaus and his collaborators made extensive use of the magnesium spark. The preparations obtained from ergosterol by means of either source of ultra-violet rays show no essential differences in antirachitic activity or stability.

It is difficult to define optimal conditions. Provided that measures are taken for an efficient circulation or stirring of the solution, and for exclusion of oxygen during the irradiation, preparations of high activity may easily be obtained if not less than 35 per cent., and not more than 80 per cent. of ergosterol are changed in the process. The rate of change may be ascertained by estimating, by precipitation with digitonin, the amount of unchanged ergosterol in the irradiated product.

Effect of Radiations of Different Wave-length on Ergosterol.

It would appear that only ultra-violet rays and, to a less extent, cathode rays [Knudson and Moore, 1928, 1929] are able to supply the form of energy which is suitable for the conversion of the ergosterol molecule into vitamin D. The ultra-violet radiations of relatively long wave-lengths contained in sunlight are adequate for this purpose [Rosenheim and Webster, 1927, 5], and are presumably the source of energy by means of which the synthesis of vitamin D from ergosterol is effected in nature.

It seems to be established that irradiation with wave-lengths shorter than 270 $m\mu$ ('short-wave irradiation') leads to a rapid inactivation of the vitamin which is formed, and that in 'long-wave irradiation' (with wave-lengths longer than 280 $m\mu$) both the production and the inactivation of the antirachitic substance take place at a slower rate.

X-rays do not produce any antirachitic activity, and according to Morrison, Peacock and Wright [1928] even exert an inactivating effect on ergosterol irradiated by ultra-violet rays [cf. Sumi, 1929].

Exposure to white light in the presence of sensitizers (eosin, chlorophyll, haematoporphyrin, &c.) changes ergosterol into well-defined crystalline products, which are devoid of antirachitic activity [Windaus, Borgeaud and Brunken, 1927]. Attempts to activate ergosterol by the action of heat with catalysts, or by purely chemical methods, have also been unsuccessful.

Role of Temperature.

Antirachitic activity is produced by irradiating alcoholic solutions of ergosterol over the wide temperature range of $-195°$ to $+78°$ C. [Webster and Bourdillon, 1928, 1, 2]. The products obtained at −183° and −195° are definitely less active. Cholesterol containing ergosterol as an impurity can also be activated when irradiated at −183° [Bills and Brickwedde, 1928]. The results provide no grounds for departing from the assumption that the formation of vitamin D from ergosterol and its subsequent inactivation are purely photochemical processes.

Stability.

Although irradiated ergosterol has been found to be unstable, the crystalline vitamin D preparation, calciferol, is remarkably stable under ordinary laboratory conditions. On heating *in vacuo* to 180° it loses its antirachitic potency and undergoes a change (isomerization ?) which has not yet been fully investigated. A similar effect is produced by further irradiation with long- or short-wave ultraviolet rays.

From evidence collected by the Accessory Food Factors Committee it appears that solutions of irradiated ergosterol in olive oil, prepared under certain defined conditions, retain their activity unchanged for 2 years at 0°, but are liable to lose their activity slowly at room temperature. (See Appendix II.)

Whilst the stability of the irradiation mixture in oily solutions seems therefore well established [cf. Holtz and Schreiber, 1930], the experience of different observers as to its stability when kept in a dry condition is somewhat conflicting. This may partly be due to differences in preparation and to the difficulty of completely excluding traces of oxygen during the irradiation. But even when all the operations were carried out in an evacuated system constructed of quartz and glass, Windaus and Auhagen [1931] found a decrease in the optical activity and an increase in absorption of their preparations when kept in a high vacuum at ordinary temperature. The changes due to 'age', however, seem to be unconnected with the vitamin itself, for the decrease of antirachitic activity is only slight in comparison with the rapid change of the other properties. At temperatures between 100° and 200° the antirachitic activity is lost, and a stable substance with an intense absorption at 290 $m\mu$ is formed.

These facts seem to confirm the suggestion advanced by Askew *et al.* [1930, 1] that one of the first products of irradiation of ergosterol is an unstable substance of low absorption and no antirachitic activity, which is converted by heat into a substance absorbing at 290 $m\mu$. The remarkable stability of calciferol, whether prepared from the crude irradiation product by means of the dinitrobenzoate or maleic anhydride or by distillation, is probably due to the removal of this unstable substance by the processes employed.

The Absorption Spectrum of Vitamin D.

The discovery of the fact that a highly antirachitic substance is produced from ergosterol by a photochemical reaction raised the hope that a study of the changes taking place in its ultra-violet absorption spectrum during irradiation would lead rapidly to the elucidation of the mechanism of the vitamin formation. In spite of many years' intensive and laborious research, the information supplied by photo-

F

chemistry has proved disappointing in its results and the isolation of the crystalline substance, considered to be vitamin D, was finally effected by the methods of organic chemistry.

A detailed discussion of the extensive literature dealing with the spectrographic data, often contradictory, is outside the scope of this Report. The early investigators were misled by the disappearance of the characteristic absorption bands of ergosterol on irradiation, and the appearance of a new band at 247 $m\mu$ [Pohl, 1927; Morton, Heilbron and Kamm, 1927]. They assumed that this new band was characteristic for vitamin D, but such a view, although offering a simple explanation of what proved to be a complex reaction, became untenable. It was soon shown that the exposure of ergosterol to ultra-violet irradiation produced a mixture of substances, and that the amount of vitamin present in the mixture was independent of the period of irradiation, apparently owing to simultaneous formation and inactivation of the vitamin [Rosenheim and Webster, 1927, 5]. Moreover, animal experiments proved that the substance (or substances) showing absorption between 230–250 $m\mu$ was devoid of antirachitic activity [Webster and Bourdillon, 1923, 2; Bills, Honeywell and Cox, 1928; Bourdillon et al., 1929]. For a time it was assumed that three groups of substances were formed in succession, the first of which had an absorption similar to that of ergosterol (maximum at 280 $m\mu$), but twice as intense, and was tentatively held to be vitamin D [Bourdillon et al., 1929]. This view also was later abandoned [Bourdillon et al., 1930], mainly on account of the results obtained with filters, which allowed a differentiation between the action of irradiation with rays of short and long wave-length respectively [Reerink and van Wijk, 1929; Windaus, 1930, 2; Askew et al., 1930, 2].

The uncertainty concerning the absorption spectrum was finally settled by the isolation of the crystalline vitamin D. The absorption of calciferol was found to be between 260 270 $m\mu$ with a maximum of $\epsilon = 48.5$ at 265 $m\mu$ which disappears rapidly on further irradiation with short or long waves. The fact, however, that the absorption between 260–270 $m\mu$ is liable to be increased by the simultaneous formation of small quantities of substances with high absorption at 280 $m\mu$ and 290 $m\mu$ makes the study of absorption of doubtful utility for the estimation of vitamin D in mixtures.

The Estimation of Vitamin D.

At the present time purely chemical or physical methods for estimating vitamin D are not available. The only methods are biological, and depend on the power of vitamin D to promote or restore normal bone formation in rats which would otherwise become rachitic when maintained on diets lacking vitamin D and containing calcium and phosphorus in an unfavourable ratio.

Standard of reference. A standard preparation of irradiated ergosterol (vitamin D) has been made available for workers in all laboratories by the National Institute of Medical Research of Great Britain [Med. Res. Council, 1930], and has been provisionally adopted by the (League of Nations) International Conference 1931 on Vitamin

Standards and Units (see Appendix II). By reference to this standard it is possible to state the antirachitic potency of any substance in terms of the unit of the standard, and the results obtained in different laboratories are directly comparable, whether the criteria employed in the tests are macroscopic or X-ray examination of the bones or estimation of the ash content. Further, the use of a stable standard enables trustworthy comparison to be made of results obtained at different times in the same laboratory, and makes it possible to obtain relative values of the antirachitic potencies of substances such as summer and winter milk which obviously cannot be compared directly.

The unit of Vitamin D adopted by the International Conference is defined as the amount of vitamin that possesses the antirachitic activity of 0·001 g. of the standard solution. This corresponds approximately to 1/10,000 mg. of the ergosterol originally used in the preparation of the standard.

Animals suitable for vitamin D tests. The young rats used in tests for vitamin D should be obtained from a healthy and vigorous colony. The stock breeding diet should be kept as nearly uniform as possible throughout the year and be so low in vitamin D content that the reserves of that factor in the young animals are not too great to permit of the development of a suitable degree of rickets on standard rachitogenic diets.

Experimental diets. A severe degree of rickets can in general be produced in young rats by feeding them for about three weeks on a diet devoid of vitamin D and having a high-calcium, low-phosphorus content. The two such diets in common use, in each of which the ratio Ca : P is about 4 : 1, are :

(*a*) McCollum's diet No. 3143 [McCollum, Simmonds and Becker, 1922] consisting of :

Ground yellow maize	33 per cent.
Whole wheat	33 ,, ,,
Wheat gluten	15 ,, ,,
Gelatin	15 ,, ,,
Sodium chloride	1 ,, ,,
Calcium carbonate	3 ,, ,,

and (*b*) Steenbock's diet No. 2965 [Steenbock and Black, 1925] consisting of :

Ground yellow maize	76 per cent.
Wheat gluten	20 ,, ,,
Sodium chloride	1 ,, ,,
Calcium carbonate	3 ,, ,,

These diets may be given dry or mixed with water to form a stiff paste. It should be noted, however, that the constituents may vary in rachitogenic properties.

At the end of three or four weeks' feeding on this diet, young rats will have noticeably swollen wrists and show other signs of rickets, provided that their initial reserves of vitamin D were not too great. Control with X-ray examinations is desirable before beginning the period of test feeding when the curative method is employed, p. 85.

COMPARISON OF TEST SUBSTANCE WITH THE STANDARD.

Three methods of estimation have been recommended by the Accessory Food Factors Committee, viz. (*a*) estimation of the ash content of the bones (humeri or femora) [Steenbock and Black, 1924; Chick, Korenchevsky and Roscoe, 1926; Soames and Leigh-Clare, 1928], (b) McCollum's 'line' test using the tibia or ulna and radius [McCollum, Simmonds, Shipley and Park, 1922; Steenbock and Black, 1925; Dyer, 1931; Key and Morgan, 1932], (c) X-ray examination of these bones [Poulsson and Lövenskiold, 1928; Schulz, 1929; Bourdillon et al., 1931]. Whichever method is used, the rats of each litter must be divided equally between test and standard.

(a) Ash Content of Bones (Prophylactic Test).

Young rats of about 40 grams weight are used. The aim is to find a dose of test substance which, given daily for 3-4 weeks to young rats on one of the above diets, will cause the production of bones having the same percentage of ash as those produced when some selected daily dose of the standard is administered. A preliminary experiment may be necessary to find an approximation to these doses. This is followed by a further comparison using a large number of animals (about 10 on each dose); if the average ash contents in bones of the two groups of rats are not in reasonable agreement, a further experiment is performed with doses more nearly equal in antirachitic value.

To determine the ash content of the bones the animals are killed by coal gas, the bones of both hind legs dissected free from all flesh (the patella being also removed), weighed, dried at 105° to constant weight, extracted with alcohol and ether to remove fatty substances, weighed, ashed, and the ash is weighed. The extraction of fat in this process is important, since the fat content of the bones varies widely with differing nutritional conditions of the animals [Chick, Korenchevsky and Roscoe, 1926].

The calcium in the bones has been shown to be a constant proportion (37 per cent.) of the total ash. The degree of calcification (or degree of rickets) can, therefore, be expressed either as A, the percentage of ash contained in the dried, fat-extracted bone, or as the A / R ratio, the ratio of the amount of ash in the bone to the amount of organic material, other than fat.

A convenient dose of the standard preparation for this test is 0.1 unit daily, but 0.05 to 0.2 may also be used. These doses cover the useful range. The standard and, if necessary, the test substance, should be so diluted with an inert oil that the daily dose is contained in some amount easily and accurately administered.

(b) The 'Line Test' (Curative).

Rats of about 50-60 grams weight are fed on one of the rachitogenic diets for 3-4 weeks, after which period the selected doses of test material and of standard are given daily for 10-14 days. At the end of that time the rats are killed, the distal ends of the ulnae and radii are removed and immersed in 4 per cent. formaldehyde for 24 hours to clear. They are then split longitudinally, immersed in 1.5 per cent. silver nitrate for a few minutes and exposed to light. This converts the phosphates of the bones into silver phosphate, which is reduced on exposure to light, black colloidal silver being deposited in the calcified parts of the bones. The degree of healing produced by the doses is estimated by macroscopic examination of the blackened areas of the cut surfaces.

The degree of rickets produced in control (untreated) rats is shown by the wide uncalcified cartilaginous metaphysis between the shaft and the head of the bone. In a completely healed rat, this region is completely calcified, i.e. blackened. Different degrees of healing are indicated by narrower or wider 'lines' of calcification across the metaphysis. By comparing the widths of these 'lines' the efficacy of the various doses in curing rickets may be compared. It is useful to draw up a scale of reference showing degrees of healing to which are given values 1 to n, where n is the number of different degrees which the worker finds distinguishable with his own technique. This scale can then be used to assess the result for each rat and from the values thus obtained an average can be calculated for those of a group receiving the same dose. A preliminary experiment is often necessary to determine the dose approximately equal to the selected dose of the standard. When this has been found, a larger experiment should be made with about ten animals on the dose of standard and ten on the dose of test substance that appears to be equal in activity.

A convenient dose of standard for this test is 0.5 or 1 unit.

The bones of rats used in a prophylactic test may be examined by this method also and judged according to the width of metaphysis produced.

(c) X-ray Examination (Prophylactic or Curative).

The bones of rats treated as described in either of the two previous methods are examined by X-ray photography and the degrees of rickets or degrees of healing respectively judged with the use of a scale of reference drawn up as described in the 'line' test.

If the curative method is used the degree of rickets can be estimated at the end of the preparatory period by an X-ray photograph of one knee-joint after lightly anaesthetizing the rat with ethyl chloride. Daily doses of the standard and of the material to be tested are then administered to rats of the same litter, which, after 14 days, are killed with coal gas, and X-ray photographs taken of the same joint as before.

(d) Ash Content of the Bones and Degree of Growth of Rats on Basal Diets deprived of Vitamin D but complete in other respects (Prophylactic Tests).

Methods (a), (b), and (c) are those commonly in use and, though of undoubted practical value, are open to criticism on theoretical grounds because the basal diets are defective not only by absence of the vitamin to be estimated, but also by the unfavourable salt mixture they contain. In method (d) the basal diet contains a normal salt mixture and is deprived only of fat-soluble vitamins, vitamin A being conveniently added in the form of 20 per cent. wheat embryo [Soames and Leigh-Clare, 1928].

The period of experimental feeding lasts 50 to 60 days, after which the rats are killed and the leg bones removed and analysed as in method (a). The increase in body-weight during the test period may also be used as a measure of the efficacy of the vitamin D dose which has been received [Steenbock, Nelson and Black, 1924-25].

In this method the period of experimental feeding is much longer than in the other methods, but on the other hand, the experimental diet contains optimal proportions of all constituents other than vitamin D; the general health of the rats is more satisfactory and intercurrent illness is avoided. At the present time, however, there is but limited experience of this method and it has not been employed in routine tests.

(e) *Estimation of Vitamin D by the change produced in Faecal pH.*

Curative tests. This method elaborated by Jephcott and Bacharach [1926; 1928] is based on the change in reaction of the faeces from slight alkalinity to slight acidity observed when healing takes place in rachitic rats [Zucker and Matzner, 1923–24]. The authors obtained quantitative results when certain precautions were observed, and adopted, as unit for measurement of vitamin D, 1 / 10 of the amount required to change the faecal pH from 7·3 to 6·7. At present there is, however, little evidence of the applicability of this method in practice [see Redman, 1928; 1929].

Comparison of Methods.

In comparing the above methods, it is evident that X-ray examination has the advantage that the condition of the joints prior to the curative test can be controlled. The procedure is rapid and a permanent photographic record for future reference is provided. In the 'line' test photographs can also be taken of the macroscopic appearance of the bones. Both these methods are extensively used, although involving an error depending on the judgment of the observer in matching the scale values. Estimation of the ash content of the bones has the advantage that the criteria adopted are entirely objective; the tests, on the other hand, are more laborious and time-consuming than in the other methods.

Distribution of Vitamin D in Foodstuffs.[1]

So far as it is possible to compare the distribution of the different vitamins, it would appear that vitamin D occurs more sparsely distributed in natural foodstuffs than the other vitamins. This is at least partially compensated for by the direct influence of sunlight on the skins of animals, for it has been shown experimentally that vitamin D from irradiated impure cholesterol can be absorbed through the skin of rats and rabbits when it has been rubbed on the surface of the skin after shaving off the hair [Hume, Lucas and Smith, 1927]. There is also experimental evidence that some birds derive vitamin D from the oil of their sebaceous 'preen' gland, which is expressed from the gland by pressure of the beak, and the ergosterol of which becomes activated by exposure to sunshine on the surface of the feathers when the birds preen themselves [Hou, 1928, 1929].

The chief sources of vitamin D in the ordinary food supplies of human beings are milk, butter, eggs, and, to a very small extent, fresh green salads and vegetables. For therapeutic purposes cod-liver oil and certain other oils are valuable, and in some cases proprietary preparations of irradiated ergosterol of stated potency are useful.

[1] See Table XXI, Appendix I.

Milk, Butter, and Eggs.

Crawford, Golding, Perry and Zilva [1930] have shown that vitamins D and A are associated wholly with the fat of milk. Thus the potency of the butter may be taken as a measure of the antirachitic activity of the milk from which it was made.

The antirachitic potencies of milk, butter, and eggs vary according to the diet on which the cows and hens respectively have been fed. With ordinary methods of feeding, summer milk is more potent than winter milk, and eggs laid in summer are richer than those laid in winter. Winter milk may, however, be made as rich in vitamin D as summer milk [Golding and Zilva, 1928] and winter eggs as rich as summer eggs [Bethke, Kennard and Sassaman, 1927] by giving the cows and hens cod-liver oil daily in amounts which need not be great enough to flavour the milk, butter, or eggs. The vitamin D content of the milk of cows has also been raised by the daily addition of 200 g. of irradiated yeast to the cows' diet [Wachtel, 1929; Hart, Steenbock, Kline and Humphrey, 1930 ; Steenbock, Hart, Hanning and Humphrey, 1930]. Direct sunlight incident on the animal also influences the potency of the milk of the cow according to Chick and Roscoe [1926, 2] and of the goat according to Steenbock, Hart *et al.* [1925], but the latter workers were unable to increase the vitamin D content of milk by irradiation of the cow from a quartz mercury lamp [Hart, Steenbock, Scott and Humphrey, 1927 ; Steenbock, Hart, Riising, Hoppert *et al.*, 1930]. The milk from the same cow was, however, increased about fifteen times in potency by direct irradiation from the same lamp.

Green Vegetables.

The cow, when on pasture, probably obtains some vitamin D from grass, which appears to contain a small amount of this factor when directly under the influence of sunlight, though the vitamin so formed seems to be destroyed when the green leaf is cut and stored for a day or two either in the light or in darkness [Coward, unpublished results on artificial irradiation of growing plants]. Thus it is probable that green salads and vegetables contain appreciable amounts of vitamin D immediately after cutting, if previously exposed to direct sunlight, but that by the time they are purchased from retail shops, they probably contain almost none. Slight amounts of vitamin D have been detected in summer spinach, but none in winter spinach [Chick and Roscoe, 1926, 1 ; Roscoe, 1927, 1 ; Boas, 1926]. None was found in the green marine diatom (*Nitzschia closterium*) grown under laboratory conditions, when exposed to sunshine through filters permeable to the ultra-violet portion of the sun's spectrum [Leigh-Clare, 1927, 1].

The vitamin D content of eggs has been increased appreciably by the irradiation of hens kept in pens on a winter feed [Hart, Steenbock, Lepkovsky, Kletzien and Johnson, 1925], but when the hens are kept out of doors in the sunlight and given an adequate diet, irradiation cannot bring about any further improvement.

Mellanby, Surie and Harrison [1929] found that mushrooms bought in the open market in winter were inactive. Vitamin D has, however, been found in ergot of rye (from which ergosterol was first isolated by Tanret in 1889), and also in the embryo of rye by

Mellanby, Surie and Harrison [1929]. Scheunert and Rescke [1931] have shown that the fungi 'Pfifferlinge' and 'Steinpilze', freshly collected or preserved, also contain vitamin D. Preserved 'Morchel' also contained this factor; but 'Champignons' grown in the dark and tested when fresh or preserved were inactive. The daily rat dose necessary to indicate the presence of vitamin D in these plants was about 2 g. per day.

Liver Oils.

Fish-liver oils constitute the richest known source of vitamin D in nature. A valuable quantitative survey of liver oils from different species of fish is given by Bills [1927] who found the antirachitic value of the liver oil from the puffer fish to be fifteen times that of the cod and shark, which were roughly equal to one another in potency [see also Hess and Weinstock, 1925–26]. In comparison with these, negligible amounts only would seem to be present in the liver and body fats of mammals, such as whale, seal, sheep and ox [Rosenheim and Webster, 1927, 6]. According to Poulsson [1929] and S. and S. Schmidt-Nielsen [1930] the liver oils of cartilaginous fishes (dogfish, etc.) contain less vitamin D than cod-liver oil, and this is also true of the liver oils of Cyclostomata (lampern and sea lamprey) [Callow and Fischmann, 1931].

The stomach oil of the fulmar petrel (*Fulmarus glacialis*) [Rosenheim and Webster, 1927, 1] and of the Australasian petrel (*A estralata lessoni*) [Leigh-Clare, 1927, 2] have been found rich in vitamin D, though inferior to a good sample of cod-liver oil.

Potency of liver oils compared with that of other sources of vitamin D. By the use of the standard of reference described in the section on the estimation of vitamin D (p. 83) the relative antirachitic potencies of samples of milk, butter, cod-liver oil, and other oils can be expressed in terms of the unit there defined.

Of thirteen samples of milk thus tested at different times of the year at the Pharmaceutical Society's Laboratory in London, using the 'line' test, the two most potent contained only 0.2 vitamin D unit per c.c., or 112 units per pint. These samples were produced in the months of August and October respectively. Using a similar method of estimation, the vitamin D value of twelve samples of butter bought in the open market varied from 0.1 to 1.5 units per g., the average being about 1.0 unit per g. The two most potent samples were obtained in May and June and contained 1.4 and 1.5 units per g. respectively.

Thirty-one samples of cod-liver oil similarly examined had potencies ranging from 25 to 200 units per g. Even higher potencies are given for some cod-liver oils by Drummond and Hilditch [1930]. Thus cod-liver oil may possess from 20-400 times the potency of an equal weight of fresh butter in summer and 1 g. of cod-liver oil may possess the vitamin D value of a pint of fresh milk.

It must be remembered, however, that in milk the rich supply of calcium salts and phosphates enhances the efficiency of the relatively small amount of vitamin D which it contains. The value of milk as an antirachitic agent in diet would be therefore much underestimated if gauged only by its content of vitamin D (see also p. 217).

Origin of vitamin D in cod-liver oil.   There is, as yet, no satisfactory explanation of the rich deposits of this vitamin which are present in the liver oils of many fishes.   It is difficult to suppose that a deep-sea fish, such as the cod, is exposed to a sufficient intensity of sunshine to activate a precursor in its superficial tissues and it has been assumed that the antirachitic vitamin in its liver is derived from the food it consumes.   The ultimate source of the fat-soluble vitamins has been traced by Drummond, Zilva and Coward [1922] and others, through a series of intermediaries which include the smaller fish on which the cod feeds, and the copepods and mollusca in the plankton which forms the diet of the former, to unicellular marine organisms.   The liver oil of the caplin, *Mallotus villosus*, which forms the chief food of the Newfoundland cod in midsummer when its liver is richest in oil and in vitamin D, is, however, relatively poor in this vitamin [Bills, 1927] and although a marine diatom *Nitzschia closterium* was found able to synthesize large amounts of fat-soluble vitamin A [Jameson, Drummond and Coward, 1922], no traces of vitamin D have been detected in it [Leigh-Clare, 1927, 1].   It must be remembered, however, that although the amount of vitamin in the daily food of the fish may be small, it may be retained in the liver so effectively that in the mature fish the accumulation will be considerable.

The suggestion that the rich depots of vitamin D in fish-liver oils may be formed by some unknown method of direct synthesis has been made by Bills [1927] on the basis of some interesting experiments with young catfish (*Ictalurus punctatus*) under laboratory conditions.

CHAPTER IV

VITAMINS AND DENTAL TISSUES.

THE importance of vitamins in relation to teeth and associated perio-dontal tissues has been revealed by experimental investigation on animals. In some cases the results have been afterwards subjected to clinical trial on human beings and the facts obtained by animal investigation have been shown to be of significance in human dental problems. Clinical trials on man are obviously necessary before any appraisement can be made of the relative importance of the experi-mental results obtained with animals, because of the variation among different species in their reaction to deficiencies of the various vitamins.

Two types of dental defect are commonly found in civilized man : (1) dental caries, and (2) periodontal disease, including pyorrhoea alveolaris. The first of these concerns the tooth itself, the second involves both the soft structures adjacent to the tooth and the hard alveolar bone. The aetiology of these diseases seems to be closely bound up with the dietetic factors which control the structure of the hard and soft dental tissues respectively. Various vitamins seem to control the structure of these tissues, although other factors of the diet appear also to be of importance. Thus vitamin D is concerned with the structure of the teeth and alveolar bone, while vitamin A plays a similar part with regard to the structure of the marginal epithelium of the gums. Experimental work on guinea-pigs has demonstrated that a deficiency of vitamin C in the diet also produces pathological changes in the teeth and periodontal tissues.

VITAMIN D IN RELATION TO THE TEETH.

The investigations carried out by M. Mellanby (1918–30) have included animal experiments and clinical investigations on man. The former have demonstrated the importance of specific dietetic factors in controlling the development of the teeth, and in determining their reaction to harmful stimuli. The earlier experiments proved that the production of normal or perfectly calcified teeth in young dogs could be ensured by an adequate supply during the period of growth of a fat-soluble vitamin, later identified as vitamin D, thus showing a complete analogy with the production of well-calcified bones and protection from rickets [M. Mellanby, 1918; 1920; 1923, 2; 1929].

Young puppies fed on diets deficient in vitamin D exhibit obvious defects in the development of their teeth and jaws, the most important of which are the following :

1. Delay in the eruption of the permanent teeth, affecting particu-larly those teeth which normally erupt at a late period.

2. Thickening of the jaw bones and irregularity in the arrangement of the teeth, most noticeable in the lower incisors.

3. Irregularly formed and poorly calcified enamel, the surface of which is pitted and grooved and frequently pigmented.

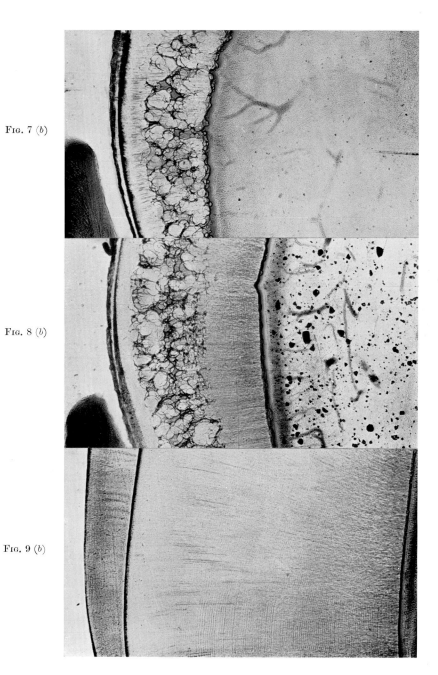

FIG. 7 (b)

FIG. 8 (b)

FIG. 9 (b)

4. Defective development and irregular calcification of the dentine, which can be satisfactorily studied only by microscopic examination of ground sections of the teeth.

5. Abnormal development of the calcified tissues at the gingival margin and hence irregularity of the periodontal membrane.

Macroscopical and microscopical appearances of the structure of well and badly formed teeth are represented in Figs. 7–17. It will be seen that when olive oil, which contains no vitamin D, was given as a supplement to a rachitogenic diet, the tooth surface in puppies was rough and pigmented, only a thin layer of enamel was formed and the subjacent dentine was not only defective in amount, but was also irregularly laid down, and contained numerous dark areas of defective calcification (the so-called interglobular spaces) interspersed between the spheroidal masses of calcium deposit. When an adequate supply of cod-liver oil, which contains abundance of vitamin D, was given in place of olive oil, the surface was smooth, white, and shiny, and much thicker layers both of enamel and of dentine were produced; the dentine exhibited a perfectly uniform structure with a complete absence of interglobular spaces. It was easily possible to devise diets intermediate in their calcifying activity between these two examples.

M. Mellanby urges that the term hypoplasia should not be limited to gross naked-eye defects, but should be used for any defect of tooth structure. This point is of considerable importance in connexion with the relation of dental structure to dental disease.

Reference to Figs. 7b, 8b, 9b makes it clear that during the period of growth the quantity and character of the dentine laid down at any given time may depend on the vitamin D content of the diet at that time. The puppy whose tooth is figured in Fig. 8b received no vitamin D for 5 months, during which time only a small amount of badly calcified dentine was laid down. For the next month it received cod-liver oil, and during this period the dentine formed was quite regular in structure and was almost equal in amount to that formed during the previous five months. The change from a diet with poor to one with good calcifying qualities was found to be reflected very quickly in an improvement in the structure of the developing teeth, whereas the reverse change from a good diet to a poor one was followed by defective calcification of the teeth only after a long and variable period. This delay is interpreted as indicating a utilization of vitamin that has previously been stored.

Effect of Maternal Feeding.

The amount of vitamin D consumed by a bitch during pregnancy and lactation was found to influence the calcification of the deciduous teeth of her offspring [M. Mellanby, 1921; 1928; 1929]. These teeth erupted at an earlier age and were better calcified when the mother received liberal supplies of vitamin D. Of great practical importance was the observation that the feeding of the mother during pregnancy and lactation might have an even greater effect on the development and structure of the permanent, than of the deciduous, teeth of the offspring. When the puppies themselves received a liberal supply of vitamin D after weaning, the character of the previous maternal feeding had only a comparatively slight influence on the development of the permanent teeth. But when the puppies were fed after weaning on diets deficient in vitamin D the previous maternal feeding had great influence on the state of calcification of these teeth. When the mother's diet had possessed poor calcifying properties the teeth of her offspring erupted at a later date, and their structure was much more defective than when her diet had contained liberal supplies of vitamin D. Even after a puppy had been fed for a period on a good diet the character of the dental tissues laid down subsequently during a spell of bad feeding was influenced by the previous maternal feeding. The results demonstrated that the principles of maternal feeding which have been found to operate in the case of experimental rickets operate also in determining the structure of the teeth.

FACTORS OTHER THAN VITAMIN D WHICH MAY INFLUENCE THE STRUCTURE OF THE TEETH OF PUPPIES.

Variations in the amount of protein or pure carbohydrate in the diet of puppies were found to have no definite effect on the structure of the developing teeth, whether the basal diet contained much or little vitamin D. Similarly the quantity of fat in the diet had little influence, although the quality, that is to say its content of vitamin D, was of paramount importance. The water-soluble vitamins, including the B complex and C, had little or no effect. The principal food factors, other than vitamin D, which were found capable of influencing the calcification of the teeth, were the type and quantity of cereal and the amount of calcium [M. Mellanby, 1929].

Effect of Cereals on the Structure of the Teeth.

When the diet of a puppy contained an abundant supply of vitamin D, the developing teeth exhibited a perfect structure whatever the quantity or type of cereal. But when there was little or no vitamin D in the diet, both the quantity and quality of the cereal might exert an influence on the type of calcification of the teeth. The observation that the greater the amount of carbohydrate eaten, either in the form of cereal or of starch or sugar, the more defective is the development of the teeth, may possibly be explained in part by the suggestion that the more rapid increase in weight which occurs with an increase in the energy-producing portion of the diet demands an increased supply of vitamin D, and if this is not forthcoming the relatively greater deficiency of the vitamin will be reflected in more defective calcification of the teeth. But that this is not the whole explanation is clear from the results obtained with different cereals. Of those tested, white flour and rice were associated with the production of the least badly calcified teeth and oatmeal of the worst. Rye, barley, and maize were intermediate in their effects. The anticalcifying action of the cereal in the puppy's diet was observed only in the absence of an adequate supply of vitamin D, and could be completely controlled by liberal quantities of this factor, no matter what type of cereal was included in the diet [M. Mellanby, 1923, 2 ; 1929].

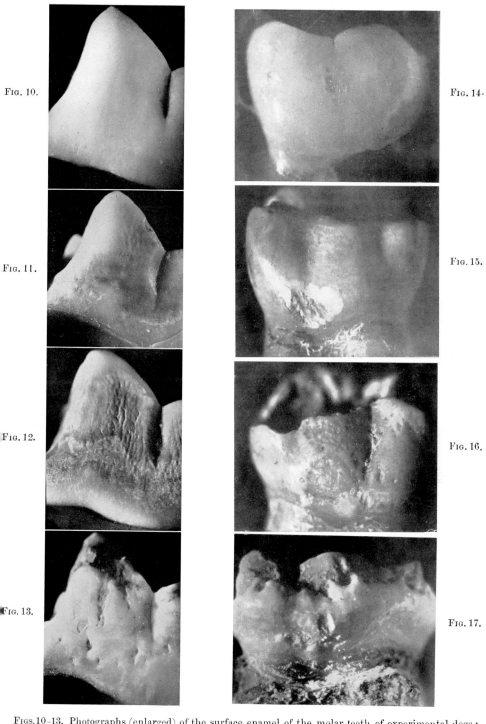

FIG. 10.

FIG. 11.

FIG. 12.

FIG. 13.

FIG. 14.

FIG. 15.

FIG. 16.

FIG. 17.

FIGS. 10-13. Photographs (enlarged) of the surface enamel of the molar teeth of experimental dogs ; 10, abundance of fat-soluble vitamins ; 11, some fat-soluble vitamins ; 12, little supply of fat-soluble vitamins ; 13, very little supply of fat-soluble vitamins. FIGS. 14-17. Photographs (enlarged) of the surface enamel of human molars.

FIGS. 10 and 14. Normal—smooth and shiny.

FIGS. 11 and 15. Hypoplasia—some roughness.

FIGS. 12 and 16. Severe hypoplasia—rough.

FIGS. 13 and 17. 'Gross' hypoplasia—comparatively large areas of deficient enamel.

Effect of the Mineral Supply on the Structure of the Teeth.

The absolute or relative amounts of calcium and phosphorus in an experimental diet were found to influence the degree and character of the calcification of the teeth.   When there was little or no vitamin D in the diet extra supplies of calcium in the form of carbonate resulted in a slight but distinct improvement in the structure of the teeth. The effect of adding phosphates under these conditions was variable, but the beneficial effect sometimes observed was only slight.   The addition of calcium salts, the carbonate, phosphate, or hydrogen phosphate, to diets containing butter resulted usually in great improvement in the calcification of the teeth.   When liberal quantities of vitamin D were given, the addition of calcium salts to a diet otherwise containing very little of this element sometimes resulted in the production of an increased amount of dentine, though the structure was always perfect or nearly perfect even when the diet contained only small amounts of calcium.   In the presence of sufficient quantities of vitamin D the ratio of calcium to phosphorus could also be varied within considerable limits without producing any effect on the development of the teeth. It therefore appears safe to conclude that an adequate supply of vitamin D is of greater importance in determining the perfect development of the teeth than an abundant or carefully balanced supply of calcium and phosphorus [M. Mellanby, 1923, 2 ; 1929].

Effect of Ultra-violet Irradiation on the Structure of the Teeth.

Exposure of puppies fed on diets deficient in vitamin D to the rays of a mercury vapour lamp for half an hour three times a week resulted in a distinct improvement in the calcification of their teeth [M. Mellanby, 1924 ; 1929].   When the diets had a potent ant-calcifying action, as for example when they contained large amounts of oatmeal, the effect of irradiation was comparatively slight ; in no instance did the irradiation of puppies under these conditions bring about the same improvement in the structure of the teeth as was observed when a potent source of vitamin D was included in the diet.

The irradiation of food destined for the feeding of animals that received no other source of vitamin D was followed by a great improvement in the calcification of their teeth.   Fats such as olive oil which previously had no stimulating effect were found after irradiation to be capable of promoting the formation of teeth with an almost perfect structure.   Oatmeal, after exposure to the mercury vapour lamp, not only ceased to have a deleterious effect on calcification, but actually acquired definite calcifying properties, which were due in all probability to the activation of the parent substance of vitamin D (ergosterol) originally present in the cereal. Precisely similar results were obtained by irradiating the germ of wheat and maize. The administration of small quantities of irradiated ergosterol to puppies resulted in the production of teeth of good structure.

The series of experimental results just outlined makes it quite clear that a plentiful supply of vitamin D during the period of growth is essential for the production of normal or perfect teeth in the dog. M. Mellanby has carried out similar experiments on rabbits and rats

[1930, 2], which indicate that this principle holds good for these species also. Toverud [1926, 1931] studied the calcium content of the teeth of rats fed on complete and deficient diets. His analysis showed the calcium and phosphorus of the ash of the teeth to be reduced and the magnesium increased, especially with diets poor in calcium and fat-soluble vitamins, while with diets poor in calcium and rich in vitamin almost normal values were obtained. Toverud also concluded from his experiments that the chemical composition of the molars is influenced if the mothers have been fed during pregnancy on diets deficient in calcium and fat-soluble vitamins. Orban [1927], also working with rats on defective diets, found big differences in the rate of growth of the incisors as well as in the structure of the developing dental tissues. He concluded that milk, cod-liver oil, and calcium salts greatly improve calcification.

APPLICABILITY OF ANIMAL RESULTS TO MAN.

The same factor, therefore, which influences the calcification of the long bones in the dog, the rabbit and the rat, determines the calcification of the teeth in these species. Since it has been abundantly proved that this factor is just as effective in promoting good calcification of the bones in the child as in experimental animals, it may reasonably be expected that the calcification of the teeth of the child will also be influenced by the available supply of this factor during the period of growth. Although it has not yet been possible to test this assumption on any large scale, limited trials have shown [M. Mellanby, 1928] that the addition of a daily dose of cod-liver oil to children's diets results in the production of good teeth which appear sound to naked-eye examination and show a normal structure microscopically.

Vitamin D however is usually deficient in the ordinary diet, especially of the poorer classes, and on the assumption that this factor is of primary importance in the development of normal deciduous teeth in man, as well as in dogs and other animals, it might be expected that the teeth of the average child would be defective in structure. This, indeed, has been shown to be the case [M. Mellanby, 1923, 1 ; 1927, 1]. Microscopic examination of a large and representative collection of human teeth showed that the majority were defective in structure, contrary to the view generally expressed that only a negligible proportion of children's deciduous teeth in England are defective, or hypoplastic. The sections examined varied considerably in structure, from perfect teeth, as seen in dogs fed on diets containing liberal amounts of vitamin D, to very defective teeth resembling those seen in dogs on diets very deficient in this vitamin. It soon became evident that the macroscopical structure of the majority of these teeth was also defective or hypoplastic, as revealed by a careful examination of the enamel surface for discoloration and obvious pits and grooves, and more especially for the general 'feel' as gauged by rubbing with a blunt probe. The macroscopic appearance is, in fact, related to the histological structure of the enamel and dentine, teeth with varying grades of roughness usually showing corresponding histological defects (see Figs. 10-17). With practice it is generally possible to predict the internal structure of a tooth from a superficial examination.

In Tables I and II are classified according to their microscopical

structure over 1,000 shed and extracted deciduous teeth of British
children. These teeth were obtained partly from private sources
and partly from children attending public elementary schools.

TABLE I.

Teeth obtained from private sources.

	Number examined.	Normal Per cent.	Slight hypoplasia Per cent.	Hypoplasia Per cent.
Incisors . . .	113	53	43	4
Canines . . .	54	11	57	32
1st molars . .	55	14	31	55
2nd molars . .	40	0	15	85
Total	262	28.3	39.3	32.4

TABLE II.

Teeth obtained from children attending public elementary schools.

	Number examined	Normal Per cent.	Slight hypoplasia Per cent.	Hypoplasia Per cent.
Incisors . . .	123	45	31	24
Canines . . .	102	6	27	67
1st molars . .	194	5	16	79
2nd molars . .	355	1	6	93
Total	774	9.7	15.4	74.9

These results show that varying degrees of abnormality were found
in 72 per cent. of the former and in over 90 per cent. of the latter,
indicating that the majority of children's deciduous teeth are defective
in structure, that the old criteria of dental structure are not justified,
and that the teeth of poorer children are more defective than those
of the child in better circumstances.

RELATION OF STRUCTURE OF TEETH TO DENTAL DISEASE.

To demonstrate the possibility of promoting the development of
good teeth in man would be in itself a noteworthy achievement.
From the point of view of preventive medicine, however, it is still
more desirable to be able to lessen the incidence of dental caries. It
has not been easy to study in detail the influence of food factors on
the production of dental caries, for the reason that it is difficult
to produce this condition in experimental animals. McCollum,
Simmonds, Kinney and Grieves [1922] and Marshall [1922], Bunting
[1925] and others have described caries-like lesions in rats fed on diets
deficient in fat-soluble vitamins and calcium. M. Mellanby [1930, 2]
found it almost impossible to produce dental caries in dogs, even when
their diets were thoroughly bad in the sense both of producing defective
calcification and of encouraging fermentation in the mouth. Nevertheless, she had previously found it possible to study the effect of variations in the diet on the response of dog's teeth to harmful stimuli other
than microbic invasion [M. Mellanby, 1923, 3; 1930, 2]. When the
teeth of puppies or grown dogs are filed at regular intervals it is found
that the dentine in such teeth exhibits a reaction to the injury. Changes
can be seen in the already existing primary dentine, and over a localized

area, corresponding with the site of injury, a new formation of secondary dentine occurs adjacent to the pulp. The amount and the quality of this secondary dentine were found to vary in the dog according to the calcifying properties of the diet on which the animal was fed during the experiment. With a liberal supply of vitamin D in the diet, abundant well-formed secondary dentine was usually produced, while, with an insufficient supply of the vitamin, secondary dentine was either not produced at all or was obviously defective in character. The animal experiments therefore demonstrated that the calcifying properties of a diet influenced the character of the reaction of teeth to injury as well as their original structure.

DENTAL CARIES.

Relation between Structure and Presence of Caries in Human Teeth.

M. Mellanby [1923, 1; 1927, 2] concluded from a study of a large number of human deciduous teeth that there was a close relation between structure, or calcification, and liability to caries, as indicated in Table III. Out of a total of 1,036 teeth examined superficially and microscopically, 925 were found to support the general principle that caries is liable to occur in teeth that are imperfectly calcified, while well-calcified or properly formed teeth are not subject to caries.

TABLE III.

	Normal 149.		Slight hypoplasia 223.		Hypoplasia 256.		Severe hypoplasia 408.	
	No.	Per cent.	No.	Per cent.	No.	Per cent.	No.	Per cent.
No caries . .	89	60.0	104	46.6	*11*	*4.3*	26	6.3
Slight caries.	31	20.6	46	20.6	39	15.1	22	5.4
Caries . . .	*6*	*4.0*	50	22.4	86	33.9	59	14.5
Severe caries	*23*	*15.4*	*23*	*10.4*	120	46.7	301	73.8

It is obvious that in a rough estimate of caries and structure in teeth, some of which were shed, some extracted and some obtained postmortem, it was impossible to regard as exceptions teeth showing no caries although slightly hypoplastic. It was therefore decided to regard as exceptions to the main rule only those teeth in Table III, the figures for which are printed in italic type, and which number 111.

An explanation of most of these discrepancies was forthcoming when the character of the secondary dentine was examined. Of 59 teeth in which the primary structure of the tooth was defective and there was no caries, 33 had well calcified secondary dentine. Similarly, of 52 teeth with carious cavities and yet well calcified primary dentine, 47 either had no secondary dentine, or it was badly calcified. It would therefore appear likely that in 80 of the 111 exceptions to the general principle, the resistance to caries had been raised or lowered after eruption by the same factor which had been shown in experimental animals to determine the character of the response of their teeth to harmful stimuli, namely the calcifying potency of the diet at the time of application of the stimulus.

These facts suggest strongly that one very important factor determining the incidence of dental caries is the initial structure of the teeth, which in turn depends on the specific calcifying properties of the diet taken during the period of their development, and especially on the presence of sufficient vitamin D. They also suggest the possibility that even when the initial structure of the teeth is defective the resistance to dental caries may be raised by increasing the calcifying potency of the diet, which ensures the formation of well calcified secondary dentine at any spot where bacterial invasion may be threatened or may actually have begun. This second suggestion has been put to the test of direct experiment.

The Influence of Dietetic Factors on the Initiation, Spread and Healing of Dental Caries in Children.

A series of four investigations to test the effects of dietetic variation on the spread of dental caries in children was made by M. Mellanby and Pattison in a Sheffield Hospital for surgical tuberculosis. In the first of these [M. Mellanby, Pattison and Proud, 1924] the diets of different groups were varied so as to differ as far as possible in calcifying properties. Thirty-two children aged about 7 years were divided into three groups; group 1 were given a diet which was designed to promote perfect calcification of the teeth; group 3 received a diet which had poor calcifying properties, including little vitamin D and no extra sources of calcium, but much cereal; group 2 were kept on the ordinary hospital diet. The teeth were carefully examined at the beginning of the investigation, records being made of the position, extent, and degree of hardness of each carious point. After a lapse of seven and a half to eight months the teeth were again examined. The results are given in Table IV.

TABLE IV.
Sheffield Investigation I.

Diet.	Average no. of teeth per child showing initiation or increase of caries.	Average amount of 'arresting' of caries per child.
1. Abundant fat-soluble vitamins (no oatmeal).	1.4	1.5
2. Intermediate amount of fat-soluble vitamins.	2.9	1.0
3. Comparatively little fat-soluble vitamins (some oatmeal).	5.1	0.7

In the second investigation [M. Mellanby and Pattison, 1926] 71 children of ages varying from 6 to 12 were also arranged in three groups. The diets given to the members of the three groups were similar to those used in the first experiment, but were so adjusted that the total quantities of protein, carbohydrate, and fat were approximately the same. The energy values of the diets, the calcium and phosphorus intake and ratios, and the acid-base ratios were also fairly uniform. Every child used a toothbrush twice a day. At the beginning of the investigation the teeth of the children about to receive the best calcifying diet were, according to careful naked-eye examination, rather worse calcified and were more carious than those of the other children. At the end of the period of special feeding ($6\frac{1}{2}$ months) examination of the teeth gave the results shown in Table V.

TABLE V.

Sheffield Investigations II, III, and IV.

Diet.	Average no. of teeth per child showing initiation or increase of caries.	Average 'degree' of increase of caries per child.	Average amount of 'arresting' (hardening) of caries per child.
II. 4. Abundant fat-soluble vitamins (no oatmeal)	1·8	2·0	2·0
5. Intermediate amt. of fat-soluble vitamins (no oatmeal).	3·0	4·0	1·2
6. Comparatively little fat-soluble vitamins (some oatmeal).	5·8	6·7	0·04
III. 7. Much vitamin D added (Irradiated ergosterol).	1·0	1·1	3·9
IV. 8. Cereal-free; much vitamin D.	0·37	0.32	4.7

The striking correspondence between the results of these two investigations leaves little room for doubt that the initiation, spread, and arrest of dental caries in children can be controlled to a very considerable extent by including in their diets an abundance of those food factors which had previously been shown in animal experiments to exert a favourable influence on the calcification of the teeth.

In the third investigation undertaken by M. Mellanby and Pattison [1928] the effect on the spread of caries of giving a liberal supply of vitamin D in the form of irradiated ergosterol only without other alteration in the hospital diet was tested on 21 children. After these children had received the vitamin D preparation for $6\frac{1}{2}$ months it was found that the average number of teeth per child in which caries had spread was 1·0, the average 'degree' of increase 1·1 and of hardening 3·9 (see Table V, Investigation III, diet 7). In many instances the soft and active caries observed at the beginning of the test was found to be undergoing arrest or actually to have become arrested when the final examination of the teeth was made. This experiment makes it clear that it is the fat-soluble vitamin D that is responsible for raising the resistance of the teeth to caries and not the fat-soluble vitamin A, which in the previous investigations had been supplied to the children together with vitamin D.

Since 1928 an extension of the Sheffield investigations has been in progress in three 'Cottage Homes' in Birmingham, under the auspices of the Dental Disease Committee of the Medical Research Council. Although in this case the basal diets were not standardized as in the Sheffield work and the vitamin additions were less, this scheme had the advantage of extending over a longer period and of involving larger numbers of children (332). The results corroborate those obtained in Sheffield, as will be seen from Table VI, p. 99. In this Table the Sheffield results are given in a form comparable with the Birmingham figures. The progress of caries was significantly reduced in the group receiving additional fat-soluble vitamins as cod-liver oil and in the group having additional vitamin D in the form of irradiated ergosterol.

By analogy with the animal experiments, showing that cereals, and especially oatmeal, interfere with calcification, it seemed probable

that extra cereals in the form of oatmeal might increase the spread of
caries when the supply of vitamin D was limited. Extra oatmeal was
given to a group of children in the Sheffield investigations, and the
spread of caries in this group was found to be greater than in any other.
The effect of the omission of cereals was not tested in the investigations described above. Independently, Boyd and Drain [1928;
Boyd, Drain and Nelson, 1929] observed during the routine examination of the teeth of children attending a hospital department that in
twenty-eight instances arrest of previously extensive and active caries
was taking place. It was then found that without exception these
children were receiving treatment for diabetes and were being strictly
dieted, their food consisting chiefly of milk, cream, butter, eggs, cod-
liver oil, meat, bulky vegetables, and fruit. Two most noticeable features
of such diets are their richness in fat-soluble vitamins and mineral
salts and their poverty in cereals, features which had characterized
the diets used by M. Mellanby and her co-workers to raise the
resistance of children's teeth to caries.

TABLE VI.

	Percentage of teeth carious.			Percentage increase in ' degree' or extent of caries.
	First examination.	Final examination.	Increase.	
Sheffield :				
Olive oil group. (Diet 6)	25.96	35.96	**10.00**	62.13
Cod-liver oil group. (Diet 4)	42.86	44.41	**1.55**	10.28
Vitamin D group. (Diet 8)	45.13	46.14	**1.01**	6.57
Birmingham :				
Olive oil group.	15.59	23.22	**7.63**	45.85
Cod-liver oil group.	19.26	22.23	**2.97**	9.81
Vitamin D group.	22.18	24.27	**2.09**	10.12

Further observations on the effect of giving similar diets to thirteen
children not suffering from diabetes were carried out by Boyd and
Drain, who report that in each instance pre-existing caries was completely arrested in ten weeks or less. It was found that considerable
quantities of carbohydrate could be taken by the children without
hindering the progress of the arrest of their caries, providing that
dairy produce, cod-liver oil, vegetables, and fruit were consumed in
sufficient quantities at the same time. Incidentally it was remarked
that oral hygiene did not seem to play any part in the arrest of caries,
for this was noted in several instances in which the children did not
use a toothbrush.

Believing that the results obtained by Boyd and Drain were due to
the fact that vitamin D was given in abundance while cereals were
absent from the diet (although these authors did not themselves make
any statement to this effect) M. Mellanby and Pattison [1932] have
carried out a similar investigation to test this supposition. The results
(see p. 98, Table V, Investigation IV, diet 8) indicate that the total
omission of cereals from the diet, together with the addition of vitamin D, hastens the arrest of existing caries and prevents the initiation
of new carious points to greater extent than the addition of vitamin
D to a diet containing cereals.

Bunting and his collaborators [1930] have compared the active caries in children in different institutions in which the dietary was controlled to some extent. In one of these each child had one pint of milk, some fruit and green vegetables daily ; the amount of sugar was reduced and a mouth wash was used. At the end of one year, the teeth of 80 per cent. of the children were found to be free from active decay as compared with 24 per cent. in a second institution in which the mouth wash alone was used, and 18 per cent. in the control institution where no additions to the diet were made and no mouth wash used. They therefore conclude that caries is a specific infective process the activity of which is dependent on certain metabolic changes, and state that, of the methods they employed for combating dental caries, dietary measures appeared to be the most important.

There is, therefore, a considerable body of evidence pointing to the fact that dietetic factors, and especially vitamin D, determine to a large extent the resistance of children's teeth to dental caries. For practical purposes the ideal to aim at is by correct feeding during prenatal life, infancy, and childhood, to encourage the production of normal or perfect teeth in the adult. This, with the continuance of a sound dietetic régime throughout life, should result in a very greatly diminished incidence of dental caries in the community.

Periodontal Disease.

Dogs, especially pet dogs, are, like man, very susceptible to periodontal disease. These animals were therefore chosen by M. Mellanby for an extensive study of the aetiology of this disease of the tissues surrounding the teeth [1920; 1929; 1930, 1, 2]. It was found that dogs could be kept under laboratory conditions for periods up to 8 years and, so long as the diet was complete from birth onwards, they remained free from periodontal disease. If, however, the diet was deficient in vitamins A and D and rich in cereals, especially during the period of growth in the early months of life, this disease ultimately developed. These dietetic defects acted in two ways, (1) by allowing the abnormal development of periodontal tissues, and (2) by allowing these abnormally formed tissues to change their anatomical relations to the teeth and become subject to invasion by micro-organisms.

Vitamins A and D in relation to the Structure of Periodontal Tissues.

Experiments on puppies brought up on diets rich and poor respectively in both vitamins A and D, or deficient in either vitamin A or D only, showed that vitamin A primarily controls the normal development of the soft periodontal tissues, including the sub-gingival epithelium and the underlying connective tissues, while, as might be expected, vitamin D is largely responsible for the normal calcification of the alveolar bone and the other hard tissues.

Thus, if the diet is deficient in both fat-soluble vitamins A and D, as for instance when olive oil replaces cod-liver oil, the following abnormalities develop :

(1) Thickening of the gingival region (see Figs. 18, 20; cp. Fig. 19).

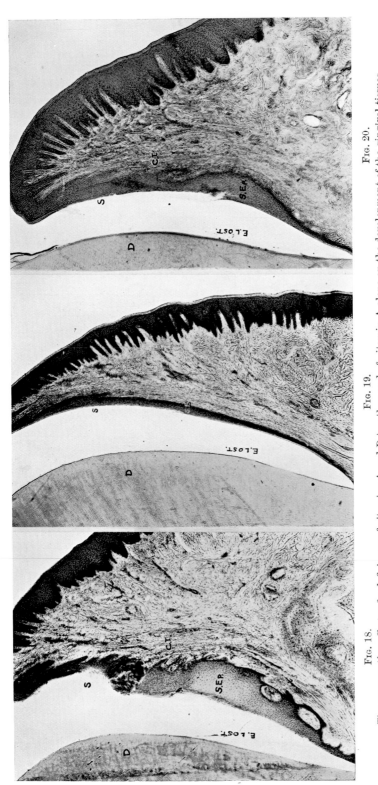

FIG. 18.

FIG. 19.

FIG. 20.

The comparative effects of a deficiency of vitamins A and D together and of vitamin A alone on the development of the gingival tissues.

Photomicrographs (X 40) of the gingival regions of the carnassials of three dogs. *Note*: The alveolar bone and periodontal membrane are not seen here. (Sections decalcified and cut in celloidin; enamel therefore lost.)

Fig. 18. Diet poor in vitamins A and D. *Note*: Gingival regions hypertrophied; sub-gingival epithelium (S. Ep.) much hypertrophied and irregular with small processes; some connective tissue reaction or cell infiltration (C.I.) in corium.

Fig. 19. Liberal supply of vitamins A and D in diet. *Note*: Gingival region thin; sub-gingival epithelium (S. Ep.) thin and regular; no connective tissue reaction or cell infiltration in corium.

Fig. 20. Much vitamin D but very little vitamin A in diet. *Note*: Gingival region hypertrophied; sub-gingival epithelium (S. Ep.) hypertrophied and irregular with some processes; some connective tissue reaction or cell infiltration (C.I.) in corium.

To face p. 101]

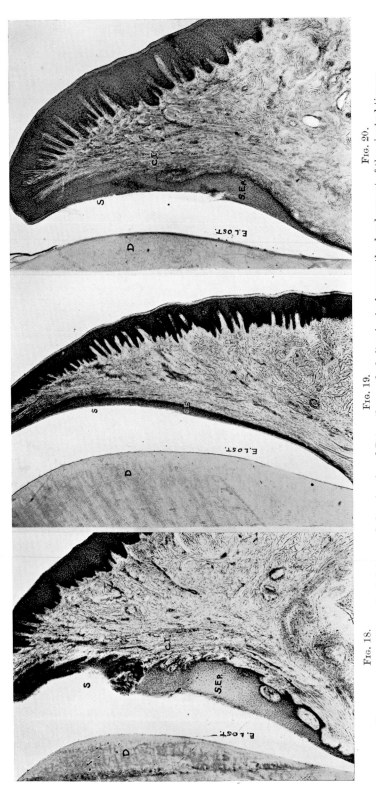

FIG. 18.

FIG. 19.

FIG. 20.

The comparative effects of a deficiency of vitamins A and D together and of vitamin A alone on the development of the gingival tissues.

Photomicrographs (X 40) of the gingival regions of the carnassials of three dogs. *Note* : The alveolar bone and periodontal membrane are not seen here. (Sections decalcified and cut in celloidin ; enamel therefore lost.)

FIG. 18. Diet poor in vitamins A and D. *Note* : Gingival regions hypertrophied ; sub-gingival epithelium (S. Ep.) much hypertrophied and irregular with small processes ; some connective tissue reaction or cell infiltration (C.I.) in corium.

FIG. 19. Liberal supply of vitamins A and D in diet. *Note* : Gingival region thin ; sub-gingival epithelium (S. Ep.) thin and regular ; no connective tissue reaction or cell infiltration in corium.

FIG. 20. Much vitamin D but very little vitamin A in diet. *Note* : Gingival region hypertrophied ; sub-gingival epithelium (S. Ep.) hypertrophied and irregular with some processes ; some connective tissue reaction or cell infiltration (C.I.) in corium.

To face p. 101]

(2) Imperfect development of the alveolar bone, particularly of the alveolar crest, and of the laminae durae, with the inclusion of osteoid tissue and poorly calcified bone.

(3) Imperfection of the epithelial attachment to the hypoplastic enamel.

(4) Poor calcification of the laminae durae.

(5) Hypertrophy of the sub-gingival epithelium, with the development of finger-like processes (see Figs. 18, 20, cp. Fig. 19).

(6) Abnormal arrangement of the connective tissue of the corium, with connective tissue reaction and cell infiltration (see Figs. 18, 20, cp. Fig. 19).

(7) Irregular thickness of the periodontal membrane.

Irregular alignment of some of the teeth and tilting of the teeth in relation to the jaw are also sometimes found when the diets are deficient in vitamins A and D.

Vitamins A and D in relation to Periodontal Disease.

The term 'periodontal disease', which is susceptible of various meanings, is here used in its widest sense, that is to say, to denote any morbid condition affecting the tissues surrounding the teeth, ranging from simple gingivitis to 'pyorrhoea alveolaris' with extensive absorption of bone.

McCollum, Simmonds, Kinney and Grieves [1922] found what they term 'attaching-tissue' lesions after death in some rats fed on experimental diets, especially when these were low in calcium, phosphorus and fat-soluble vitamins.

In M. Mellanby's experiments [1930, 1, 2] the majority of the dogs used were about 2 months old when the experiments were begun, and in some cases were born in the laboratory from mothers whose diets were controlled throughout pregnancy and lactation. In a few experiments in which curative rather than prophylactic measures were tested, the animals were several years old when brought to the laboratory suffering from periodontal disease.

The periodontal tissues of dogs kept in kennels in a laboratory and fed from the time of weaning for 8 years on a diet containing among other ingredients white bread and a liberal supply of vitamins A and D are rendered very resistant to periodontal disease. On the other hand, the periodontal tissues of animals kept under similar conditions of diet and environment, but receiving comparatively little vitamins A and D for the first $6\frac{1}{2}$ years, are very susceptible to the disease.

These experiments stress the fundamental importance of including vitamins A and D in the diet during the early developmental period if the periodontal tissues are to resist disease. A large supply of these vitamins given later, even from the fifth month onwards, does not entirely compensate for a deficiency during the early period of life, although vitamin A given in large doses may then prevent the spread of the pathological condition. Conversely, the addition of a liberal supply of vitamins A and D to a diet composed largely of white bread, for nearly a year after weaning (i.e. for the full developmental period), renders the periodontal tissues resistant to disease in later life, even when the diet of the adult animal is deficient in these vitamins for long periods.

It will be noted that hyperplasia of the squamous epithelium adjoining the teeth produced by vitamin A deficiency in the developing period of growth is a special instance of the general effect of this deficiency (see p. 33). The susceptibility to bacterial infection of this hyperplastic epithelium of the gums or gingival margin is a condition which would also be expected from other known instances, in which infective foci and epithelial overgrowth are commonly associated with a deficient intake of this vitamin. Just as the administration of vitamin A in such conditions tends to correct the pathological changes of the epithelium and to heal the septic foci, so also in pyorrhoea alveolaris in dogs massive vitamin A therapy seems to increase the resistance of the gum tissues to micro-organisms to the extent that the exudate of pus is greatly diminished and may even be suppressed [M. Mellanby, 1930, 2].

Vitamin C and Dental Tissues.

One of the earliest investigations on the influence of the diet on the teeth was that of Zilva and Wells [1919], who fed guinea-pigs on a scorbutic diet of oats, bran, and autoclaved milk. Ground and decalcified sections of the teeth showed defects in the pulp, odonto-blasts and dentine. In the pulp various degrees of degeneration of a type designated as 'fibroid' were found, and in the dentine an irregular 'osteoid' condition. Changes in the teeth were observed even in the mildest degree of scurvy, but never when a sufficiency of vitamin C was added to the basal diet (see Figs. 21–24).

Howe [1919; 1921; 1923] has also carried out much experimental work on guinea-pigs and monkeys, primarily, however, with a view to establishing the relation of diet, and in particular of vitamin C, to caries. He concludes that a deficiency of this vitamin leads to decal-cification of the teeth. Toverud [1923; 1926] made a histological and chemical examination of some of the teeth of Howe's guinea-pigs and found the defects described by Zilva and Wells. Robb and collaborators [1921] found similar changes in the teeth of guinea-pigs on a scorbutic diet.

Extensive investigations by Höjer [1924; 1926; Höjer and Westin 1925] and others have also emphasized the importance of vitamin C in determining the structure of the teeth in guinea-pigs. They summarize the defects that follow vitamin C deficiency as follows:

(1) The gradual change and disappearance of the odontoblastic layer.

(2) The amorphous calcification of the 'predentine' and the absence of canals in this layer.

(3) The previously calcified dentine becomes porous.

(4) The dilatation of the vessels in the pulp.

(5) The production of nerve lesions and oedema of the pulp tissues.

As a result of these investigations a method was devised for the estimation of the antiscorbutic value of foods (p. 204).

The results experimentally obtained on guinea-pigs have not been tested on man and it is difficult to appraise their value in terms of human beings. In the case of the dog, M. Mellanby [1929] was unable to show that vitamin C played any significant part in the

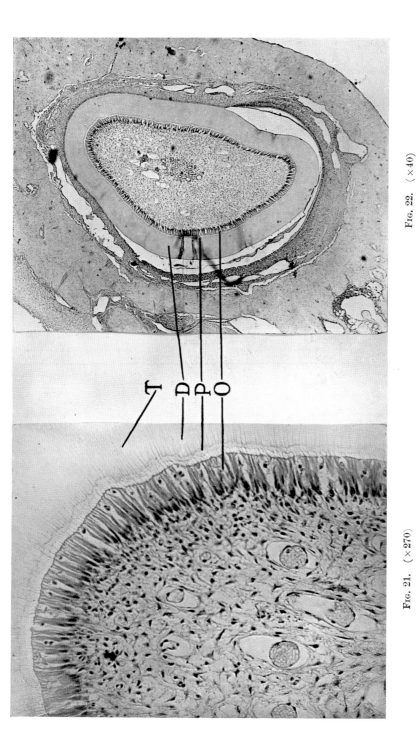

Fig. 21. (×270)

Fig. 22. (×40)

Effect of vitamin C deficiency on the teeth of guinea-pigs. Photomicrographs of transverse section of the decalcified incisor root, stained with haematoxylin-eosin.

Figs. 21 and 22. Guinea-pig protected from scurvy (10 c.c. of decitrated lemon juice per diem).

Tomes canals (T) well marked in the uniformly stained broad layer of dentine (D), 'predentine' (P) lightly stained, odontoblasts (O) long and parallel.

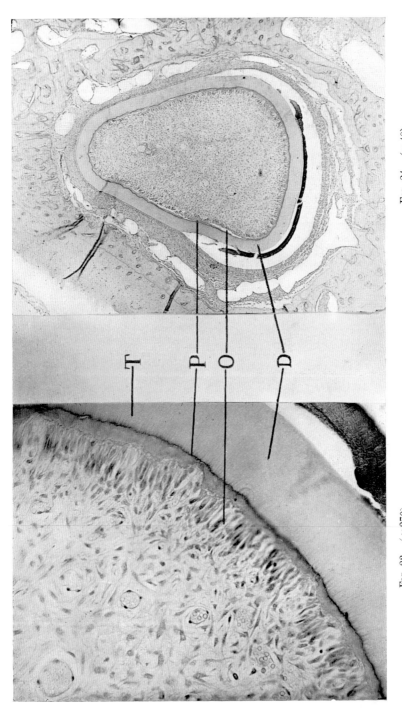

Fig. 23. (×270)   Fig. 24. (×40)

Effect of vitamin C deficiency on the teeth of guinea-pigs. Photomicrographs of transverse section of the decalcified incisor root, stained with haematoxylin-eosin.

Figs. 23 and 24. Guinea-pig partially protected from scurvy after 14 days on experimental diet.

Tomes canals (T) in dentine (D) poorly marked, and absent in the 'predentine' (P) which is darkly stained, odontoblasts (O) short, disorganized and separated from the dentine (D).

calcification and structure of dental tissues, but this may be explained by the relative insusceptibility of the dog to the absence of this vitamin from the food.   Rats also appear to exist in health on diets lacking this vitamin.

Florid scurvy in man is now relatively rare except in persons living under special conditions.   When it occurs, periodontal changes similar to those described by Zilva and Wells in scorbutic guinea-pigs may develop.   Since periodontal disease in man is pathologically similar to that observed in guinea-pig scurvy, it has been unduly assumed that it is related to a vitamin C deficiency.   In dogs it has been shown experimentally that this is not the case [M. Mellanby, 1930, 2], but that periodontal disease is related to vitamin A deficiency. As regards man, Hanke [1929 ; 1930] claims to have produced evidence that dental caries and pyorrhoea are sometimes associated with a deficiency of vitamin C alone.   If vitamin C deficiency plays a part in the aetiology of human periodontal disease, it seems clear that the deficiency is only partial and is not accompanied by other well-recognized scorbutic changes.   The work of Zilva and Wells has clearly shown that dental tissues in guinea-pigs are peculiarly susceptible to vitamin C deficiency and are among the earliest to suffer from this dietetic defect.   It may be, therefore, as they suggest [1919], that this also applies to man and that the so-called 'latent scurvy' may play a part in human dental disease.   Whether this is the case or not remains to be tested by further work.

CHAPTER V

VITAMIN E.

HISTORICAL.

IT is only within the last ten years that the existence of a specific vitamin essential for reproduction (at any rate of the rat and mouse) has been established. The view held previously was that a diet which would satisfy the animal's needs for growth and well-being would also be adequate for reproduction. The first indication that this was not necessarily the case was given by Mattill and Conklin [1920], who found that rats reared on whole milk, though growing well and appearing to be in good health, were usually sterile. They therefore suggested that milk was deficient in some dietary factor essential for reproduction. Evans and Scott [1922], during a study of the effect of nutrition on the oestrous cycle, found that rats reared on a diet containing adequate amounts of protein, of salts and of all the known vitamins were partially sterile in the first generation and wholly so in the second. This sterility was corrected by an unknown substance X, present in certain natural foodstuffs, e.g. fresh lettuce leaves, wheat embryo, and dried alfalfa. In subsequent investigations Evans and Bishop [1923, 1, 2, 3] showed that X was fat-soluble, but was not identical with any of the known vitamins. In the female, sterility was a disturbance of uterine function leading to foetal death and resorption. Evans's standard sterility diet contained caseinogen 18, starch 54, lard 15, butter fat 9 and salts 4 per cent., the rats receiving in addition a daily ration of dried whole yeast. If the butter fat was replaced by 2 per cent. of cod-liver oil the results were unchanged.

Sure [1923, 1, 2], during an investigation of the influence of diet on reproduction, had independently come to the same conclusion as Evans and Mattill and their co-workers. He found that sterility resulted when rats were maintained on diets containing whole or skim milk as the source of protein, with cod-liver oil and an alcoholic extract of wheat embryo to supply vitamins A, D, and B respectively. This sterility was neither corrected by increasing or improving the supply of protein, nor by increasing the dose of water-soluble vitamins. It disappeared, however, when an unknown substance, apparently identical with Evans's factor X, present in Georgia velvet bean pod meal, polished rice, yellow corn, rolled oats, and lettuce leaves, was added to the diet. Sure suggested that the new factor should be called vitamin E and this suggestion was universally adopted in 1925.

Mattill and his co-workers [Mattill and Carman, 1922-23; Mattill and Stone, 1923; Mattill and Congdon, 1924; Mattill, Carman and Clayton, 1924], in the course of further work on milk diets, became satisfied that vitamin E corresponded with the essential factor which they had considered to be lacking in whole milk. They described degeneration of the testes resulting from deprivation of this dietary factor.

The chief opposition to the acceptance of the existence of vitamin E as an essential anti-sterility dietary factor came from the work of Nelson. Mattill, Evans, Sure and Daniels and Hutton [1925–26] had all reported failure of reproduction when rats were fed on diets containing milk as the only possible source of vitamin E, but Nelson and his co-workers [Nelson, Heller and Fulmer, 1923; Anderegg, 1924] and also Mazé [1925], Woods [1925], and Palmer and Kennedy [1922–23] obtained good reproductive records when rats were reared on diets of whole milk powder alone. When, however, a certain amount of lard was added to such a diet, sterility occurred. Nelson suggested that the sterility-producing power of Evans's diet was due to its high lard content. The resulting high calorie value of the diet would occasion a low intake and hence a possible deficiency of some of the known dietary essentials. Though at one time more inclined to accept the existence of vitamin E [Anderegg and Nelson, 1925], Nelson and his co-workers were still unconvinced in 1926 [Nelson et al., 1926; Guest, Nelson, Parks and Fulmer, 1926], and reported that whereas sterility resulted from the ingestion of a skim-milk diet, supplemented by cod-liver oil and dried yeast, in the form of a dry powder, good reproduction occurred when the same diet was fed as a liquid paste [Anderegg and Nelson, 1926]. Sure was, however, unable to confirm this [1926, 3; 1927, 1].

The arguments of Nelson and his co-workers against the existence of vitamin E have been satisfactorily met [Mattill, Carman and Clayton, 1924; Mattill and Clayton, 1925, 1926; Evans, 1924, 1; Evans and Burr, 1927, 1]. These workers agree that lard has the power of increasing the sterility-inducing properties of a diet, but claim that this does not invalidate the proof of the need of the rat for vitamin E. That a high content of fat is not in itself sterility-producing was shown by the fertility associated with diets containing a high content of butter fat.

It was afterwards shown that lard neutralizes the effect of vitamin E when the latter is mixed with the diet and not given as a separate ration [Evans and Burr, 1927, 2, 3]. This fact accounts for many discrepancies in the literature of the subject. Butter fat constituting 5 per cent. of the diet appeared to be an inadequate source of vitamin E when the diet also contained 15 per cent. of lard, but proved an effective source when mixed in a diet, low in fat, such as was used by Nelson and his co-workers.

Sure's later investigations of vitamin E [Sure, 1924–25; 1925; 1926, 1, 2, 3; 1927, 1, 2, 3, 4; 1928, 1; 1929–30] have been collected in a single pamphlet [1930]. The researches of Evans and his co-workers [Evans, 1924, 1, 2; 1925; Evans and Bishop, 1924; Evans and Burr, 1924; 1925, 1, 2] were summarized in a monograph in 1927 which contains most of the established facts concerning vitamin E [Evans and Burr, 1927, 1]. When not otherwise stated the information given below is derived from this monograph.

The Results of Deprivation of Vitamin E.

Female Sterility.

In female rats rendered sterile by deprivation of vitamin E, the ovaries are undamaged, ovulation and oestrus occur as usual, and the proportion of successful matings is within normal limits. Implantation of the fertilized ovum is proved by the appearance of red blood-cells in the vaginal smear—the 'placental sign' of Evans and Burr—at the normal time, about the fifteenth day of pregnancy. Instead, however, of the birth of a litter at the end of term, the foetuses die in the uterus and are resorbed. The weight curve of the pregnant rat follows at first the curve of normal pregnancy, but soon falls more and more below it: after the twentieth day there is a gradual loss of weight. The foetus shows the first signs of retarded development at the eighth day of gestation. By the twelfth day defects in the blood system are shown by the solid appearance of the liver and by the deficiency of blood islands in the yolk sac and of erythroblasts in the heart and blood-vessels. Death of the foetus occurs about the thirteenth day, the allantois at this stage showing complete atrophy. Resorption of the foetus is accomplished by the twentieth day. The placenta, which is unaffected, persists and grows after the death of the foetus until, the twentieth day; after this it also is rapidly resorbed. Foetal death appears to be due to starvation and asphyxia resulting from defects in the allantois and yolk sac.

The sterility in the female is not incurable as is the case in the male. The ingestion of vitamin E in adequate amounts will always permit a successful gestation, however long has been the previous period of deprivation. The minimum daily dose need not be given until the fifth day after mating, but administration must be continued until the nineteenth day. Parenteral injection has been found to be as effective as oral administration.

Male Sterility.

In male rats and mice [Beard, 1925-26, 1, 2] lack of vitamin E causes a gradual loss of reproductive power leading to complete and incurable sterility within 85 to 150 days [Evans and Burr, 1927, 1; Mason, 1925; 1926]. These observers agree that the susceptibility of different rats to deprivation of vitamin E shows a wide range of variation. Mason found that young rats placed at weaning on a diet devoid of vitamin E showed the first signs of sterility within 50 to 65 days, while if the rats were sexually mature before they were deprived of this factor, no ill effects were seen for 75 to 100 days. Evans and Burr showed that rats born of mothers deprived of vitamin E, except for minimal amounts during gestation, if reared without addition of vitamin E had no period at all of fertility.

Evans and Burr divide the onset of sterility in the male into six stages. In the first stage, in spite of a sufficiency of apparently normal spermatozoa, there is a loss of reproductive potency; in the second the spermatozoa lose their motility. In the third stage groups of spermatozoa fused together are found in the vaginal plug, which is, in the succeeding stage, devoid of spermatozoa. The penultimate stage is characterized by loss of power to form the plug, although some degree of sex interest is retained. This disappears in the final stage.

Mason [1926] in a careful study of the histology of the testis found a gradual degeneration and removal of the germinal epithelium completed in 35 to 50 days. The germ cells degenerate in an order which is the reverse of that of their formation, the mature spermatozoa being the first to disappear.

The histological studies of Evans and Burr [1927, 1], Juhasz-Schäffer [1931], and Mattill, Carman and Clayton [1924] are in accord with those of Mason, except for the fact that Mattill and his co-workers found a great proliferation of the interstitial tissue in the degenerated testis. Evans and Burr showed in addition that a considerable degree of sterility, as shown by mating tests, precedes any abnormality of the testis which can be detected by histological examination. Both sets of observers found great variations in the susceptibility to lack of vitamin E of the different tubules of the same testis. This variation explains the fact that a partial success sometimes appears to attend curative efforts. Once degeneration has set in, in any given tubule, the process in that tubule cannot be arrested by the administration of vitamin E. If, however, when the attempted cure is begun the testis still contains a few normal tubules, these can be preserved and thus a certain measure of reproductive power retained.

Mason [1929] found a normal erythrocyte and haemoglobin content in the blood of sterile male rats suffering from deprivation of vitamin E. No histopathological changes were shown by the adrenals, spleen, liver, pancreas, thymus, thyroids, or lymph glands.

Verzár et a . [1931] noted a lowered basal metabolism in male rats reared on a diet devoid of vitamin E.

Vitamin E and Lactation.

Sure [1925; 1926, 3; 1927, 1, 3] brought forward evidence tending to indicate that vitamin E consisted of two parts, one thermostable and promoting reproduction, and the other thermolabile and promoting lactation. He [1928; 1930] stated later, however, that he could not find sufficient satisfactory evidence in favour of this theory, and has since concluded that vitamin E is not needed in lactation.

Evans and Burr [1928, 2] reported the development of paralysis about the time of weaning in suckling young of mothers deprived of vitamin E. Approximately 35 per cent. of the animals thus affected died, about 17 per cent. recovered, and the remaining 48 per cent. remained paralysed but appeared otherwise healthy. Prophylaxis with vitamin E administered either to the mother or directly to the young was successful, but curative measures failed. Sure [1930] has not observed this paralysis.

Decreased Growth and Vigour.

The earlier work on vitamin E was generally taken to show that rats receiving a diet deficient in vitamin E, but complete in all other respects, exhibit normal growth. Evans and Burr [1927, 1] noticed, however, when attempting the cure of male sterility, that although the cures were not successful, yet the administration of vitamin E was marked by an increase in the rate of growth. Evans [1928, 2] subsequently investigated this point more fully, and found that rats of both sexes reared on a diet deficient in vitamin E showed, after the eighth month of life, but not before, a consistently poorer rate of growth than did rats when receiving the same diet supplemented daily by a few drops of wheat germ oil. The same effect was obtained by using the unsaponifiable fraction in place of the crude oil, showing that it must be attributed to the vitamin E content of the oil rather than to any other constituent. As castrated rats behaved in the same way, it appeared that the growth and well-being of the rat did not depend on the condition of the testis. Mason [1929] recorded that in groups of male rats receiving a sterility-inducing diet, the ingestion of fresh or dried lettuce leaves or dried alfalfa markedly improved the rate of growth. Since this effect was apparent in young rats from the beginning of the experiment, it does not appear that Mason was dealing with the same condition as Evans. The possibility that the differences in the stock diets used by different observers may cause variations in the amount of vitamin E present in the bodies of rats bred on these diets must not be disregarded. A careful consideration of Mason's work, however, suggests that the increased growth in his experiments might have been due to the vitamin B_2 content of the leaves rather than to their content of vitamin E.

Juhasz-Schäffer [1931] observed a 150 per cent. increase in the rate of growth of embryonic chicken tissues, cultured in adult chicken's plasma, as the result of the addition of wheat germ oil. If the oil was autoclaved, no such effect was observed (see p. 110).

Uterine Deciduomata.

Evans [1928, 1] stated that when pseudopregnancy was induced in rats by mating with vasectomized males, a large proportion (50 per cent.) developed uterine deciduomata. When, however, such females received vitamin E in abundance, the proportion developing the tumours was only 3–7 per cent. No explanation of this phenomenon is yet available.

FUNCTION OF VITAMIN E IN THE BODY.

The part played by vitamin E in the reproductive processes is far from clear. In the pregnant female, lack of this vitamin appears to cause intra-uterine death by preventing the normal development of the yolk sac and allantois. The maternal parts of the placenta remain unaffected and the germ cells suffer no damage. In the male, on the other hand, permanent degeneration of the germinal epithelium occurs. The fact that vitamin E plays such different parts in male and female reproductive organs led Mason [1929] to suggest that vitamin E might be composed of two factors, one influencing the testis and the other concerned with uterine function. He found evidence for this in the observation that dried lettuce was less effective than fresh in preventing male sterility, whereas Evans had reported that desiccation of lettuce caused no decrease in its power to cure female sterility. Mason, however, himself concluded that there was insufficient evidence for this theory of a dual nature of vitamin E.

Vitamin E disappears from the body of the female rat during normal metabolism at a rate which is unaffected by the occurrence of gestation. It would appear, therefore, that it either fulfils some definite function even when pregnancy does not occur, or is excreted unused.

Verzár [1931] found that the intraperitoneal injection of vitamin E concentrates from wheat germ caused a genital hypertrophy in young female rats similar to that following the injection of anterior pituitary hormone. He also noted [Verzár and Kokas, 1931, Verzár et al., 1931] that male rats, reared on a diet devoid of vitamin E, had a silky infantile coat like that of castrated rats, and that if, during the period of deprivation, anterior pituitary hormone was injected daily, the rats developed, instead, the bristly coat characteristic of the normal male. He suggested, therefore, that vitamin E is necessary for the synthesis of the hormone of the anterior lobe of the pituitary.

STORAGE OF VITAMIN E.

Rats reared from weaning on a standard sterility-inducing diet show an extent of initial fertility which indicates that the animal has a considerable power to store vitamin E. Once the body's reserve has been exhausted there is no return of fertility, and the second generation is consistently sterile. Vitamin E has been found present in normal rat muscle and absent from the tissues of rats deprived of this factor. Further proof that storage takes place is given by the fact that a single large dose of a curative substance given either orally or parenterally about the day of mating, produces an effect equal to that of the same total amount administered in small daily doses during gestation. It has been observed that a sterile female, enabled by the ingestion of a diet rich in vitamin E during pregnancy to give birth to a litter, will sometimes store sufficient of this factor to carry through one or more successful gestations after a return to the sterility-inducing diet. The extent of this after-fertility will depend upon the amount of the vitamin administered.

Vitamin E content of faeces. The amount of vitamin E present in the faeces depends on the amount ingested by the rat [Juhasz-Schäffer, 1931]. There is no evidence that the factor is synthesized in the alimentary canal.

CHEMICAL INVESTIGATION OF VITAMIN E.

Solubility. Vitamin E is fat-soluble and can be extracted by fat solvents; light petroleum, ether, acetone, benzene, absolute alcohol, and 76 per cent. alcohol have all provided successful extracts. Extraction with alcohol is not so complete as with ether; in the latter case the extracted residue was found to have lost all power to prevent or cure sterility. Vitamin E is very slightly soluble in water and highly soluble in methyl alcohol, but the solubility falls away rapidly on dilution with water. It is more soluble in pentane than is sitosterol, a fact which is of use in preparing a concentrate of the active fraction.

Stability. Saturation with bromine in glacial acetic acid, treatment with acetic anhydride, and exposure to ashing temperatures are all destructive of vitamin E. It is also partially destroyed by exposure to ultra-violet radiation for 45 minutes. It is undamaged by hydrogenation, by distillation *in vacuo* at 250° C., by exposure in air for two hours to a temperature of 170° C., or by autoclaving at 20 pounds pressure for two hours [Sure, 1926, 3]. If any destruction occurs when a current of air is passed through it at a temperature of 97° C. it only does so at a very slow rate. Neither strong acids (e.g. 20 per cent. HCl) nor the enzymes naturally occurring in wheat germ destroy it. Vitamin E is not destroyed by saponification, and is found present in the unsaponifiable fraction.

Vitamin E, therefore, appears to be remarkably stable to heat, resembling in this respect vitamin A. The evidence was, however, all obtained by Evans and Burr in experiments with wheat germ oil, and it does not necessarily follow that the vitamin will prove to be equally stable when present in other foodstuffs. Evans and Burr found that the vitamin E content of many animal and vegetable tissues was unaffected by cooking or by rapid drying, as judged by the power to cure female sterility. Mason [1929] recorded, however, that when lettuce was dried most of the power to prevent male sterility was lost, but he used a lower temperature than did Evans and Burr and in consequence the period of desiccation was more prolonged. Evans and Burr were unable to obtain a potent unsaponifiable fraction from ox muscle, but Sure [1927, 1] was successful in doing so from cotton-seed oil.

Under certain conditions vitamin E is susceptible to oxidation. Supplee and Dow [1925] observed that whole-milk powder packed in air lost its content of this vitamin after two years, whereas the same sample of powder kept in the presence of de-oxygenated air for the same length of time had retained all its original potency. Mattill [1927] stated that vitamin E was destroyed by the oxidative changes which accompany the development of rancidity in fats and oils. This process was accelerated by the presence of ferrous sulphate and by some other conditions, but was delayed by the presence of substances containing hydroxy-groups, and the stability of vitamin E in wheat germ oil was probably due to the abundance of these groups in the oil. Butter fat when protected from oxidative changes was found to contain a considerable amount of vitamin E.

This connexion between rancidity and the destruction of vitamin E was further elucidated by Evans and Burr [1927, 2, 3]. This work was undertaken to investigate the fact, repeatedly observed, that a high lard content increased the sterility-inducing power of a diet. On a diet containing 9 to 15 per cent. of lard there was a certain amount of initial fertility, which, when the lard was increased to 22 per cent., disappeared. At the same time a daily dose of wheat germ oil was still effective in inducing fertility, showing that the lard was not in itself responsible for the sterility. Evans and Burr found further that, if the wheat germ oil given as a daily dose was replaced by wheat germ mixed with the other constituents of the diet, there was a definite ratio between the amount of lard in the diet and the amount of wheat germ which must be included to ensure fertility. (This observation was not confirmed by Mattill and Clayton [1926]). The same relation held true with wheat germ and hardened cotton-seed oil or oleic acid, but not with butter or stearic acid. It appeared that lard, hardened cotton-seed oil, and oleic acid in some way neutralized or antagonized the vitamin E in the wheat germ. This antagonism was found to increase with the degree of rancidity of the fats, but it was not proportional to the acid number. The unsaponifiable fraction of commercial oleic acid was found to contain most of the antagonistic or destructive body [Evans and Burr, 1927, 3].

Waddell and Steenbock [1928; 1931] demonstrated an apparent destruction of vitamin E in their stock diet and in wheat germ when an ethereal solution of ferric chloride was poured over the diet, the ether afterwards being allowed to evaporate. Both male and female sterility occurred. If the ferric chloride was dissolved in water, no such effect was observed. Although female rats might have large reserves of vitamin E they were apparently unable to use them while consuming the iron-treated ration. These reserves became effective when the diet was replaced by one devoid of the vitamin.

Cummings and Mattill [1931] suggested that the destructive action of certain fats on vitamin E was due, as suggested by Fridericia [1924] in the case of vitamin A, to the action of peroxides produced during autoxidation. They showed that the fats, such as cod-liver oil and lard, which most readily destroy vitamin E, are those which have the highest autoxidizable value. These fats contain powerful pro-oxidants while anti-oxygenic capacity is shown by wheat germ oil, cotton-seed oil, and other substances.

Olcovich and Mattill [1931; see also Olcott and Mattill, 1931, 1, 2] obtained from the unsaponifiable material of green lettuce leaves a non-crystallizable fraction containing both vitamin E and the anti-oxidant. Separation of the two was effected by solution in light petroleum and subsequent treatment with 92 per cent. methyl alcohol. Vitamin E remained in the petroleum and the anti-oxidant passed into the alcohol. Fractional distillation of the latter *in vacuo* yielded a fraction distilling at 160–180° C. which, on cooling, gave monoclinic crystals with marked anti-oxidant capacity. The formula of this substance appeared to be $C_{13}H_{14}O_5$ and one hydroxyl group of a phenolic character was present.

CONCENTRATION OF VITAMIN E.

Evans and Burr obtained from wheat germ oil a concentrate of the active principle which represented 0·25 per cent. by weight of the original oil, and of which 5 mg. given as a single dose to the female rat on the day of mating supplied sufficient vitamin E to permit of the birth of a litter. The concentrate was prepared as follows. The unsaponifiable fraction was treated with cold pentane and the precipitate removed, after which hot methyl alcohol was added to the solution and another precipitate discarded; after standing, the additional precipitate formed on cooling was removed and the portion soluble in light petroleum was treated with digitonin to remove sterols. The remaining solution was again saponified and the sterols in the unsaponifiable fraction removed by precipitation with digitonin. After extraction with methyl alcohol, the active fraction was distilled *in vacuo* at 200–233° C.

The refractive index of the concentrate was about 1·5018, the iodine number 220, and the molecular weight 400. Analysis gave a composition of 81·7 per cent. C, 12·2 per cent. H, 6·1 per cent. O. This work emphasizes further the strong similarity between vitamin E and vitamin A (see p. 37).

METHODS EMPLOYED IN TESTING FOR THE PRESENCE OF VITAMIN E.

Rats reared on a diet deficient in vitamin E show wide variations in the length of the period of initial fertility. Some are able to give birth to two or even three litters in succession before sterility occurs. This is partly due to the reserves of vitamin E stored in the body at birth and partly to the presence in the basal diet of small amounts of the vitamin. For this reason the most satisfactory method of testing a foodstuff for the presence of vitamin E is to investigate its power to restore fertility to a female rat which has exhibited one or more typical resorptions as the result of receiving a sterility-inducing diet. A typical resorption cannot be presumed in the absence of any one of the following conditions :

(1) a normal oestral cycle and ovulation, proved by taking vaginal smears ;

(2) insemination at the time of oestrus, proved by the presence in the vagina of the vaginal plug containing spermatozoa ;

(3) implantation of the fertilized ovum, proved by the placental sign ;

(4) foetal death and resorption, proved by the characteristic weight curve.

The normality of the reproductive power of the rat must be subsequently established by the successful birth of a litter after vitamin E has been administered.

It has been generally accepted that resorptions of the foetus as described above are characteristic only of the deprivation of vitamin E, but Sure [1930] has claimed to have observed resorptions of apparently identical character in rats deprived of vitamin A but receiving abundance of vitamin E. In view of the cessation of ovulation in rats deprived of vitamin A, these observations are hard to interpret.

The other method of testing for vitamin E is to add the substance under investigation to a diet deficient in vitamin E but complete in all other respects, and to observe the reproductive behaviour of young rats reared from weaning on this diet. This method is inconclusive unless observation is continued for a very long period. A report of sterility in female rats mated with males bred on the same diet is obviously inconclusive of deprivation of vitamin E : resorptions must be observed after mating with normal males.

Distribution of Vitamin E in Nature.

The suggestion of Cummings and Mattill [1931], that vitamin E is destroyed during the autoxidation of fats, offers an explanation for the conflicting nature of some of the evidence regarding its distribution in nature. If the test substance is incorporated in a diet containing lard or some other highly autoxidizable fat, the estimated vitamin E content will be much lower than would have been the case had the lard been replaced by butter or cotton-seed oil, or the test substance been offered as a separate ration. The efficiency of any natural substance as a source of vitamin E will depend not only on the actual amount of the factor contained in it, but also on the balance of anti- and pro-oxidants associated with it. The reserves possessed by the experimental animals will also markedly influence the results obtained.

Evans is the only observer who has consistently employed the curative test, which is far more satisfactory than any other method, owing to the wide variations existing in initial fertility (see p. 112).

The richest natural sources of vitamin E appear to be green leaves and the embryos of seeds. From wheat germ an oil can be extracted that is effective in the cure of female sterility in the rat in daily doses of 15 to 20 mg. Vitamin E is absent from the endosperm of cereals. Vegetable oils, as a rule, contain definite but small amounts of this vitamin.

Vitamin E is present in small amounts in animal tissues, the richest sources being the muscle and subcutaneous fat. Ox and cow tissues appear to be uniformly richer than the corresponding tissues of the pig or rat. Although vitamin E is present in fresh pig fat, lard owing to high autoxidizability is almost entirely devoid of it. Simmonds, Becker and McCollum [1928], however, reported the presence of vitamin E in samples of lard.

Vitamin E is present in milk and butter, the varying results obtained by different observers being partly due to differences in technique and partly to variations in the samples used. Mattill [1927] showed that much of the vitamin E in the original milk-fat was lost in the usual processes of butter-making.

Owing, presumably, to its high autoxidizable index, cod-liver oil is as a rule a poor source of vitamin E [Evans and Bishop, 1923, 1; Sure, 1927, 2; 1930; Mattill, 1922; Hogan and Harshaw, 1926], but evidence has been produced that some samples of the oil may contain it [Simmonds, Becker and McCollum, 1928; Nelson et al., 1927].

Evans and Hoagland [1927] carried out some experiments which indicated a synthesis of vitamin E by green and etiolated Canadian field pea seedlings grown in nutrient solution. The possibility of contamination of the solution by bacteria was not, however, ruled out.

The accompanying Table VII gives an approximate estimate of the distribution of vitamin E in those substances which have been investigated. When the dose is expressed in g. it indicates that this amount was given as a separate daily dose; when expressed as per cent., that the substance was included in this proportion in the dry diet.

H

TABLE VII.
Distribution of Vitamin E.

o indicates that the vitamin was not detected; + that the material contains the vitamin; + + that it is a good source of it; + + + that it is a rich source of it.

Foodstuff.	Anti-Sterility Value.	Curative Dose.	Prophylactic Dose.	Observer.
Fats and Oils.				
Almond oil	o	...	...	Sure [1926, 1]
Butter fat pasture	+	24 %	5–10 %	,, [1927, 4]; Nelson et al. [1926]
,, ,, dry feed	o	...	24 %	Evans and Burr [1927, 1] (high lard diet)
Coco-nut oil	o	...	15 %	,, ,, (high lard diet)
Cod-liver oil	o to +	< 12 %	4–5 %	,, (high lard diet); Sure [1927, 2]
Cotton-seed oil	+ + +	...	3–15 %	Simmonds et al. [1928]; Nelson et al [1927]
,, ,, hydrogenated	+	...	15 %	Evans and Burr [1927, 1]; Sure [1927]
Hemp-seed oil	+	...	5 %	Kennedy and Palmer [1926]
Lard	o	...	...	Sure [1924–25]
Linseed oil	+	...	15 %	Evans and Burr [1927, 1]
Maize oil	+ +	...	...	Simmonds et al. [1928]
Mustard-seed oil	+	5.0 g.	3 %	Sure [1926, 1]
Mutton fat	o	...	...	,,
Oat oil	+	...	5 %	Evans and Burr [1927, 1]
Olive oil	+	...	5–15 %	Kennedy [1926]
Palm oil	+	...	5 %	Evans and Burr [1927, 1]; Sure [1926, 1]
Palm-kernel oil	o	...	...	Sure [1926, 1]
Peach-kernel oil	+	...	...	,,
Peanut oil	+	...	5 %	,,
Pig fat	o	5.0 g.	< 5	Evans and Burr [1927, 1]
Sesame oil	+	22 %	...	Sure [1926, 1]
Walnut oil	+	0.025 g.	...	Evans and Burr [1927, 1]
Wheat germ oil	+ + +	...	...	,,
Yeast fat	o	...	...	,,

		Amount	Percentage / fertility	Reference
Cereals.				
Flour, white wheaten	o	...	60–62 %	Evans and Burr [1927, 1]
Maize, whole grain, yellow	++	...	5 %	Sure [1923, 2]; Miller and Yates [1924]
,, embryo	+++	0.5 g.	...	Evans and Burr [1927, 1] (lard diet) Miller and Yates [1924]
Rice, polished	o to +	<76 %	62 %	,, (lard diet) Sure [1923, 2]
,, polishings, ether extract	+++	<0.1 g	...	,, ,, ,,
Wheat, whole grain	+++	5.0 g.	50 %	,, ,, ,,
,, embryo	+++	0.12 g.	33 %	,, ,, ,,
Oats, whole grain	+	33 %	62 %	Sure [1923, 2]
,, rolled	...	...	...	,, [1923, 2]
Legumes.				
Georgia velvet bean pod meal	++	...	20 %	,, [1926, 1]
Soya bean	++	...	50 %	Evans and Burr [1927, 1]
Other Seeds				
Alfalfa seed	+++	0.5 g.	...	,, ,,
Lettuce ,,	+++	0.5 g.	...	,, ,,
,, ,, ether extract	+++	0.046 g.	...	,, (lard diet)
Nuts.				
Coco-nut press cake	+++	<1.0	16 %	,, (lard diet)
Peanuts	+++	22 %	...	Miller and Yates [1924]
Walnuts	+++	...	...	Evans and Burr [1927, 1]; Mason [1929]
Vegetables.				
Alfalfa, fresh	+++++	0.6 g.	...	Mason [1929]
,, dried	+++++	2.5 g.	...	Evans and Burr [1927, 1]
Begonia leaf, fresh	+++	...	...	,, ,,
Kale, green fresh	+++	2.5 g.	...	,, ,,
Lettuce, fresh	+++++	(0.25 gm dry wt.)	20 g. (male fertility)	,, ,,
,, dried	++	0.25 g.	5.0 g. (male fertility)	
,, ether extract	+++	...	...	
Pea seedlings, green, fresh	+++++	4.0	1.6 g. (male fertility)	
,, etiolated, fresh	+++	4.0	...	
Tea leaf, dried	+++++	<1.0 g.	...	

TABLE VII (continued).

Foodstuff.	Anti-Sterility Value.	Curative Dose.	Prophylactic Dose.	Observer.
Fruits.				
Banana, fresh	++	27 g.	...	Evans and Burr [1927, 1]
Orange juice	++	4-16 c.c.	...	,,
Meat.				
Ox, hypophysis	+++	4.0	5.0, <20 %	,, ; Clayton [1929]
,, liver	+++	5.0	1.0, 20 %	,, ; ,,
,, muscle	+++	<5.0	...	,, ; ,,
Pig, heart	+++	<5.0	...	,,
,, liver	+++	<5.0	...	,,
,, muscle	+++	5.0	...	,,
,, pancreas	+++	5.0	...	,,
,, spleen	+++	5.0	...	,,
Placenta, human	+++	<5.0	...	,,
Rat, heart	+++	<1.25	...	,,
,, kidney	+++	<2 kidneys	...	,,
,, liver	+++	9.0	...	,,
,, muscle	+++	8.0	...	,,
,, testes	++	<2 testes	...	,,
Milk and Milk Products.				
Caseinogen	++	...	18 %	,, (lard diet)
Milk, cow's, fresh		...	100 %	,,
,, ,, dried	+	...	No fertility with 25 %	Anderegg and Nelson [1925] ,, (lard diet).
,, ,, skimmed, dried	o	...	50 % (no lard)	Evans and Burr [1927, 1]
Miscellaneous.				
Cholesterol	++	...	...	Knudson and Randles [1925]
Egg-yolk, raw	++ to +	⅓ of one yolk	...	Evans and Burr [1927, 1]
Yeast	o to +	...	5 %	,, ; Mattill and Stone [1923]

Practical Applications of the Work on Vitamin E.

The discovery of vitamin E is of practical importance to those engaged in the breeding of rats for experimental purposes. In many cases it is desirable to plan stock diets, which, while securing adequate growth and health, do not produce young rats with large stores of the other fat-soluble vitamins. A knowledge of the distribution of vitamin E will prevent the occurrence of sterility as the result of the use of such diets.

Some work of Vogt-Møller and Bay [1931] indicates that vitamin E may be of importance to the farmer and stock-breeder. They investigated the effect of intramuscular injection of single doses of wheat germ oil on 11 healthy but sterile cows; in 9 cases pregnancy ensued.

Card *et al.* [1929; 1930] found that if hens were deprived of vitamin E for a sufficient length of time, their eggs failed to hatch, though development started normally.

A number of workers are at present investigating the part played by vitamin E in the problems of human fertility. The only results as yet published are those of Vogt-Møller [1931]. Two women who had experienced 4 and 5 previous miscarriages were treated with wheat germ oil. In both cases a successful pregnancy occurred.

CHAPTER VI

THE VITAMIN B COMPLEX.

Multiple Nature of the Vitamin B Complex.[1]

In 1915 McCollum and Davis [1915, 1, 2] reported that young rats, fed on a purified synthetic diet containing butter fat to supply the fat-soluble vitamin already discovered by them [1913], required for normal growth an additional food factor, which was named 'water-soluble vitamin B' in the following year [McCollum and Kennedy, 1916]. 'Water-soluble vitamin B' was considered by McCollum and his co-workers to be identical with the antineuritic vitamin discovered by Eijkman [1897, 1], and found by him and many others to be preventive and curative of polyneuritis developing in birds on a diet of polished rice. It had already been shown by Eijkman and numerous clinical investigators, that the antineuritic vitamin was protective against human beri-beri, and avian polyneuritis and beri-beri were and are generally taken to be analogous.

The fact that the distribution and properties of the water-soluble B factor, as ascertained by the use of rats, closely agreed with those of the antineuritic factor established by experiments on pigeons, coupled with the similarity of the symptoms exhibited by rats and pigeons suffering from deficiencies of these factors, led to the supposition that these two factors were identical [see Drummond, 1917, where the evidence is summarized]. This supposition was provisionally accepted by most workers, the evidence to the contrary [see Mitchell, 1919, where this evidence is critically reviewed] being regarded as insufficient to decide the question [see, for example, Emmett and Luros, 1920].

More recent work, however, on the rat, has shown that this animal requires for normal growth at least two water-soluble vitamins, here called vitamin B_1 and vitamin B_2 (see note below), both of which are

---

[1] *Note on the Nomenclature of the Vitamins of the B Complex.*

In England the Biochemical Society has adopted the plan of indicating the various vitamins of this complex by subscribed numbers, e.g., B_1, B_2, B_3, &c., a descriptive adjective or phrase being added when necessary.

The following terms are at present in use :

Vitamin B_1 for the more heat-labile, antineuritic (antiberi-beri) vitamin, discovered by Eijkman [1897, 1].

Vitamin B_2 for the more heat-stable, 'P-P' (pellagra-preventive) factor discovered by Goldberger and others in 1926, found necessary for prevention of dermatitis in rats.

Vitamin B_3 for a heat-labile factor of this group, described by Williams and Waterman [1927–28], present in yeast and whole wheat and necessary for full normal nutrition in the pigeon.

Vitamin B_4 for the heat- and alkali-labile factor described by Reader [1929, 2], present in yeast and necessary for the rat ; this factor has been known previously as 'vitamin B_3'.

Vitamin B_5 for the factor described by Carter, Kinnersley and Peters [1930, 1, 2], which is necessary for weight maintenance of pigeons.

Factor Y for the heat- and alkali-stable factor described by Chick and Copping [1930, 2], present in yeast and many other foodstuffs, deficient in egg-white.

All the above are found in fresh yeast.

In America some workers use the term vitamin B for vitamin B_1, as defined above

contained in water-soluble vitamin B. It can now be seen that the assumption that 'water-soluble vitamin B' as originally defined by McCollum and his colleagues was a single entity and identical with the antineuritic vitamin was due to several reasons. Since the antineuritic vitamin—vitamin B_1— necessary for life, is also necessary for growth, it forms an important part of the vitamin B complex; to find some similarity between its distribution and properties and those of 'water-soluble vitamin B' was natural, since in experiments with rat growth no substance could be found rich in 'water-soluble vitamin B' unless it contained a due proportion of the antineuritic factor. The abundant presence of both factors in yeast, a substance much used in nutritional researches, assisted in the confusion. Again, an observation of Chick and Roscoe [1928], that caseinogen, the usual source of protein in vitamin experiments with rats, is only with great difficulty completely freed from vitamin B_2, suggests that the study of 'water-soluble vitamin B' may sometimes have approximated to that of vitamin B_1 alone, owing to the presence of some vitamin B_2 in the basal diet.

EVIDENCE FOR THE MULTIPLE NATURE OF VITAMIN B.

Vitamins B_1 and B_2. For some years before vitamin B was shown clearly to be separable into two or more components, suggestions of its multiplicity are to be found in the literature. Schaumann [1911]. Cooper [1912] and Chick and Hume [1917–19, 1] demonstrated that some materials, potent in the prevention or cure of polyneuritis, were incapable of maintaining the weight of birds on a diet of polished rice. Cooper [1912; 1914, 1], working with pigeons, observed that the weight-maintaining and antineuritic factors are differently distributed in natural foodstuffs. The factors which avert loss of weight in rice-fed birds are, however, not identical with vitamin B_2, and are apparently not all essential for the growth of young mammals. R. R. Williams and Waterman [1927-28, 1928] and Eddy, Gurin and Keresztesy [1930] have found that one 'pigeon' factor, now termed vitamin B_3, is thermolabile and present in substances which are relatively lacking in the more heat-stable vitamin B_2.

Smith and Hendrick [1926] recorded an observation of importance in the history of vitamin B research. In attempting the chemical identification of vitamin B, Seidell and his co-workers [Seidell, 1921, 1, 2; 1922, 1, 2; 1924, 1; 1925; R. R. Williams and Seidell, 1916; Bertrand and Seidell, 1923] had learned that the vitamin, after adsorption on fuller's earth, could be extracted therefrom by sodium hydroxide or baryta solution and converted into a crude picrate, which given in small doses was found to protect rice-fed pigeons from polyneuritis. Smith and Hendrick discovered that a daily dose of 1 or 2 mg. of Seidell's vitamin picrate could not induce growth in rats when given as the sole source of vitamin B in an otherwise complete diet. When autoclaved yeast was added to the ration good growth occurred, though loss of weight and death were the result when autoclaved yeast was

and vitamin G for vitamin B_2, whilst others term the antineuritic factor vitamin F (Sherman). Funk gave the name of vitamin D (now reserved for the antirachitic vitamin) to 'Bios'.

given without the picrate.   Since the antineuritic vitamin is known
to be rapidly destroyed by temperatures much over 100°C., it followed
that the growth-stimulating factor in autoclaved yeast could not be
that vitamin.

   Shortly afterwards Goldberger, Wheeler, Lillie and Rogers [1926]
put forward some parallel results.   During the previous ten years
Goldberger and his colleagues in the U. S. Public Health Service
had been engaged in a clinical investigation of pellagra, the
various steps of which will be recounted later (p. 177), and it was
with direct reference to their clinical researches that the laboratory study of vitamin B in rats was undertaken.   Goldberger and his
co-workers observed that autoclaved yeast could not sustain growth
in young rats when given as the sole source of vitamin B in amounts
equal to 30 or 40 per cent. of the basal diet.   40 per cent. of an
85 per cent. alcoholic extract of whole maize, capable of curing polyneuritis in the rat (and, therefore, potent in vitamin B_1), was likewise ineffective for growth.   But when small amounts of both were
given together (10 per cent. autoclaved yeast : 5 per cent. maize
extract), the rats grew normally.   It was thus clearly shown, in this
and the preceding experiment, that the antineuritic vitamin will not
of itself promote growth in rats fed on diets totally lacking in vitamin
B, unless supplemented by a second factor present in autoclaved
yeast.

   In the same year Goldberger and Lillie [1926] produced by means
of diet a 'pellagra-like' condition in the albino rat.   It was found
that when 6 per cent. of the alcoholic maize extract, rich in the
antineuritic vitamin B_1, was fed to rats on a vitamin B-free diet,
the animals failed to grow and a certain number developed 'a dermatitis at one or other of the following sites : ears, front of neck and
upper part of chest, forearms, backs of forepaws, shins, and the backs
of the hind paws.   This dermatitis, particularly as it affected the paws,
was sharply defined and bilaterally symmetrical.'   The dermatitis
rapidly disappeared and growth was resumed when 9 per cent. of
autoclaved yeast or 6 per cent. of Seidell's [1922, 1] 'activated solid',
a preparation containing both factors in the vitamin B complex, was
included in the diet.   Goldberger and Lillie tentatively suggested
that the experimental rat disease, which developed on diets deficient
in the B-vitamin contained in autoclaved yeast, was the analogue of
pellagra in man.   They termed this vitamin the P-P, or pellagra-
preventive factor.   It is now known in this country as vitamin B_2
(antidermatitis) and is termed vitamin G by some American authorities.

   Confirmation of Goldberger's results, and those of Smith and
Hendrick, came from Chick and Roscoe [1927].   These workers fed
to young rats as the sole source of vitamin B an alcoholic extract
made from material adsorbed on charcoal in Peters's [1924] process
for purification of the antineuritic vitamin contained in brewer's yeast.
This extract, known to be highly effective in curing polyneuritis in
pigeons, was found incapable of sustaining growth in rats unless
supplemented by autoclaved yeast.   Animals fed on the extract alone
remained stationary in weight, and in some cases, after six to eight
weeks, developed symptoms roughly similar to those described by Goldberger—loss of hair, blood-stained urine, conjunctivitis, and red,

inflamed patches of skin on the nose and the backs of the forepaws, which later became oedematous.

Almost simultaneously with the publication of the experiments of Goldberger and his colleagues, and those of Chick and Roscoe, a number of investigators put forward further evidence indicating that vitamin B is separable into two components. Randoin and Lecoq [1926, 1, 2; see also Scotti-Foglieni, 1926, 2] showed that certain yeasts of different origin, possessing equal power of maintaining growth, varied in their antineuritic potencies. Hauge and Carrick [1926, 1] discovered that a certain brand of yeast would produce growth in chicks and yet not prevent the development of polyneuritis, while whole maize possessed converse properties. It was observed by Salmon [1927] that the seeds of the velvet bean were more effective than the leaves in preventing polyneuritis in pigeons, while the leaves were superior for the maintenance of growth in young rats.

R. R. Williams and Waterman [1927–28] found that when an aqueous yeast extract was passed through fuller's earth, a substance was adsorbed (vitamin B_1), which prevented polyneuritis in pigeons on a vitamin B-free diet, yet did not promote growth in rats unless supplemented by autoclaved yeast. Sherman and Axtmayer [1927] recorded a supplementary relationship between whole wheat and autoclaved yeast and between whole wheat and dried skim milk, when these were used to supply vitamin B in an otherwise complete diet.

Among others who contributed data bearing indirectly on the question of the complex nature of vitamin B may be mentioned Hassan and Drummond [1927], who observed that a yeast extract autoclaved in alkaline solution at 120° C. for one hour could accelerate growth in rats fed on diets excessively high in protein and low in vitamin B; Palmer and Kennedy [1927, 1, 2], who found that when wheat embryo, an excellent source of vitamin B_1, was given as the sole source of vitamin B, better growth could be obtained by the addition of autoclaved yeast; and Evans and Burr [1928, 3], who recorded that 'tikitiki', a dilute alcoholic extract of rice polishings used with good effect in infantile beri-beri, is deficient in the second component of the vitamin B complex. Other results obtained by these last two groups of investigators, and by Chick and Roscoe [1928], suggested that commercial caseinogen is liable to contain some vitamin B_2. Careful purification is thus necessary if caseinogen is to be used for experimental work on this vitamin.

To sum up, it may be said that differences in heat-stability, distribution in nature, and solubility in alcohol made possible the identification and separation of the components of the vitamin B complex now known as vitamins B_1 and B_2.

FURTHER COMPONENTS OF THE VITAMIN B COMPLEX.

Vitamins B_3 and B_5. It has been found that pigeons require for their nutrition not only vitamin B_1 but a second factor, vitamin B_3 [R. R. Williams and Waterman, 1927–28], which occurs in wheat but is only present in traces in marmite, and without which the birds fail to increase in weight. These two factors, however, do not suffice for the full normal nutrition of the pigeon, a third, vitamin B_5, being also required [Kinnersley and Peters, 1925; Carter, Kinnersley and Peters, 1930, 1, 2] (see p. 165).

Vitamin B₄. Reader [1929, 2 ; 1930, 1, 2] has demonstrated that rats require for their growth, in addition to vitamins B_1 and B_2, a third factor (vitamin B_4) which is thermolabile and differs from the vitamin B_3 required by the pigeon. Its presence is necessary for the growth of the rat and its deficiency leads to characteristic symptoms (p. 167).

Factor Y. In addition to the foregoing it has been shown [Chick and Copping, 1930, 2] that yeast and watery yeast extracts contain a factor (factor Y) differing from all the preceding by not being inactivated by prolonged heating in alkaline solution. It is necessary for the continual normal growth of the rat and although plentiful in yeast is entirely absent from egg-white, which is rich in vitamin B_2 (p. 167).

The rat thus requires for satisfactory nutrition four vitamins of this group, B_1, B_2, B_4, and factor Y ; the pigeon at least three vitamins, B_1, B_3, and B_5.

Our present knowledge of the various components of the vitamin B complex is rendered imperfect and unsatisfactory by the conflicting statements of different workers on such properties as solubility and stability to the action of heat and alkali. These discrepancies are especially marked in case of the antidermatitis vitamin B_2, and the facts suggest that these characteristics are greatly affected by the source from which the vitamin is derived and the medium in which the test is carried out.

Properties such as the above are largely used as criteria in the experimental work directed to separation of the different members of the group from one another and in the evidence produced for their separate identity. The study of the more recently described members of the group, vitamins B_3, B_4, B_5, and 'factor Y' is thereby greatly complicated.

Vitamin B₁ (Antineuritic Vitamin).
BERI-BERI.

There is now a general consensus of opinion that beri-beri is a disease of dietetic origin. It occurs principally among the rice-eating populations of Japan, India, the Malay Peninsula, Dutch Indies, and Philippine Islands, but is also endemic among the inhabitants of Newfoundland, Labrador, etc., who subsist largely on a diet of white wheaten flour. In Europe under normal peace conditions beri-beri is rare owing to the great variety of foods consumed, but in war time when the diet becomes considerably restricted there is a liability to outbreaks of the disease.

Beri-beri may appear in two well-marked forms. In one ('dry' type) there is great muscular wasting, anaesthesia of the skin, and finally paralysis of the legs, and in some cases of the arms, diaphragm and intercostal muscles. There is an associated degeneration of the peripheral nerves involving both motor and sensory fibres. In the 'wet' type of the disease the most marked symptom is oedema involving the limbs and trunk and effusion of fluid into serous cavities. There is marked dilatation of the heart, particularly of the right side, together with congestion of the liver and abdominal viscera. There is usually little or no congestion of the pulmonary circulation. Heart failure, frequently sudden in onset, is common and the mortality is high.

As regards the aetiology of beri-beri the earlier workers [Eijkman, 1897, 1, 2, 3; Grijns, 1901; Braddon, 1907; Fraser and Stanton, 1909; Strong and Crowell, 1912; and many others] have laid stress on the association of the disease with the eating of highly milled rice from which the germ and pericarp have been removed, and its cure or prevention when these milling products are restored to the diet (see Fig. 25).

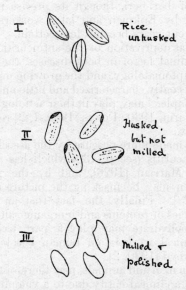

FIG. 25. Showing the various stages in milling of the rice grain. I. Rice grain in the natural condition. retaining the husk or enclosing glumes. II. After removal of the husk, but retaining the pericarp or 'silver-skin', and the embryo, which is shaded. III. After milling and polishing; both 'silver-skin' and embryo are removed and the grains are then 'polished' by rubbing with talc between sheepskins.

As early as the year 1885 Tahaki [1885; see also 1887; 1906] had found that beri-beri in the Japanese navy was abolished by changes in the dietary, the chief of which consisted in the partial replacement by barley of the polished rice which had been the staple article of diet.

In 1886 a commission was appointed by the Dutch Government to investigate the cause and nature of beri-beri. After the departure of the Commission from Java, Eijkman, who was one of the assistants to the Commissioners, Pekelharing and Winkler, continued the investigation in a laboratory attached to the military hospital of Batavia (Java) and observed a sudden outbreak among the laboratory experimental fowls of a disease strongly reminiscent of human beri-beri, the birds developing marked polyneuritic symptoms. The epizootic lasted only about five months and was traced to the use by the laboratory assistant, on economical grounds, of boiled rice from the hospital kitchen for feeding his fowls. The disease disappeared when a new chef in the hospital kitchen refused to supply 'military' rice for fowls which were under the 'civil' administration of the laboratory [Eijkman, 1890, 1896, 1929].

Following this pioneer observation the development of polyneuritis in animals, and in particular in fowls and pigeons, has been the subject of intensive study on the part of Grijns, Schaumann, Vedder, Chamberlain, Funk, and McCarrison among others. [For bibliographies upon the subject the following should be consulted: Braddon, 1907; Schaumann, 1910; McCarrison, 1921; Funk, 1922; Kruse and McCollum, 1929; Peters, 1930, 1, 2; Sherman and Smith, 1931.]

The discovery of avian polyneuritis was an important step towards the elucidation of beri-beri, though its precise relation to human beri-beri, accepted by Eijkman and later workers as an analogous disease, has of recent years become less certain. While there is no room for doubt that deprivation of the antineuritic vitamin must be regarded as a cardinal factor in both diseases, the diversity of their pathology and symptomatology, and the growing uncertainty as to the rôle which other recently characterized and little-understood factors of the 'vitamin B complex' may play in their aetiology [R. R. Williams, Waterman and Gurin, 1930; Peters, 1930, 1, 2] render the problem extremely complex.

The question is made more obscure by the association of inanition with avian polyneuritis (see p. 130) which has been stressed by Drummond and Marrian [1926], and by the possibility that a coexistent inanition may be masking the picture of pure deficiency [McCarrison, 1928]. Finally the fact that an ill-balanced diet involving deficiencies of proteins and inorganic salts and an excessive allowance of carbohydrate may play a part has been repeatedly mentioned by clinical workers on human beri-beri, and has been discussed by Aykroyd [1930, 2].

Beri-beri, both in man and animals, may therefore prove to be a syndrome rather than a clinical entity due to a vitamin deficiency.

In an extensive study of avian polyneuritis McCarrison [1928] has distinguished two types of the disease, which he terms polyneuritis columbarum, analogous to the condition described by Eijkman and others, and beri-beri columbarum.

Polyneuritis columbarum is characterized by loss of appetite, asthenia, intestinal fluxes, and symptoms attributable to derangements of the nervous system (opisthotonos, emprosthotonos, peripheral neuritis) (see Figs. 26, 27, 28). Pathologically the condition shows:
(1) Degeneration of a variable number of cells of the central nervous system.
(2) Diminution in the size of the heart.
(3) Adrenal enlargement.
(4) Atrophy of all other organs (the pituitary in males excepted).
(5) Degenerative changes of the alimentary canal.
(6) Diminution of blood volume, anaemia, acidosis, and in some cases, oedema.

Beri-beri columbarum is indistinguishable clinically from polyneuritis columbarum. The pathological features of avian beri-beri which serve to distinguish it from polyneuritis proper are the hypertrophy and dilatation of the heart, particularly of the right side, associated with fatty degeneration of the cardiac muscle and sub-

Figs. 26 and 27.

Fig. 28.

Fig. 26. Pigeon suffering from polyneuritis and showing head retraction (opistho-tonos) as the result of a diet of polished rice.

Fig. 27. The same pigeon the day after having received a curative dose of yeast preparation.

Fig. 28. Pigeon suffering from polyneuritis, showing emprosthotonos.

(Reproduced from Schaumann (1910). *Arch. Schiffs. u. Tropenhyg.* 14, Beiheft. 3.)

To face p. 124]

serous ecchymoses; the chronic passive congestion of the abdominal
viscera; the more marked degenerative changes of the central nervous
system and skeletal muscles; and the high proportion of cases
manifesting oedema, hydropericardium, hydrothorax, and ascites.

The cardiac enlargement found in human beri-beri has been ascribed
by Aalsmeer and Wenckebach [1929] to oedema of the cardiac muscle
which results in an interference with its contractile power without
disturbance of its excitability. Newcomb [1930], on the other hand,
was unable to detect any significant difference in the water content of the
heart-muscle from cases of beri-beri and polyneuritis in pigeons, and
concluded that the cardiac enlargement in the former case was a true
hypertrophy of the ventricular muscle-fibres.

McCarrison regards polyneuritis columbarum as a true form of
deficiency disease, whereas beri-beri columbarum, in its fully developed form, is believed to be something more than the manifestation
of a specific dietary deficiency. He considers that in the latter type of
the disease there is superimposed on a pure vitamin deficiency a toxic
factor which is related rather to a relative deficiency of the antineuritic
factor than to an absolute lack of it in the diet. This can be seen
by reference to Table VIII. Where the intake of the antineuritic
vitamin was withheld completely, uncomplicated polyneuritis resulted.

Table VIII.

Vitamin intake expressed as percentage of normal requirement.	Percentage of cases developing beri-beri columbarum.
20	3
50	23
64	40

[After McCarrison, 1928.]

McCarrison found no evidence to suggest that the toxic factor was
produced from rice as a result of bacterial action, and he regarded it
as being a product of disordered metabolism, as are the ketone
bodies in diabetes mellitus. Thus he says: 'the diversity of symptoms and pathological changes resulting from vitamin deficiency
will be determined by the varying biochemical response of different
individuals to this influence, and by the extent to which the specific
excitant of true beri-beri is produced within their bodies.' The conception that beri-beri is in part at least a toxaemia is no new one. Eijkman
[1897, 3] first suggested that a substance present in the cortical
layers of rice was required to neutralize the deleterious effects
of a diet over-rich in starch. A toxic factor was stressed as a causative agent in the writings of Mott and Halliburton [1899], of Stanley
[1903], of Hamilton Wright [1905], of Braddon [1905; 1907] and
notably of Walshe [1917–18; 1920] among others.

McCollum, Simmonds and Pitz [1916] believed that wheat embryo
contained a toxic factor which could be extracted by ether. R. R.
Williams [1927] has described a toxic condition in pigeons, characterized by loss of weight and appetite, mild diarrhoea, nerve
degeneration sometimes associated with paralysis, and head retraction, when the birds were fed on exclusive diets of rice-bran or rice
polishings, both potent sources of the antineuritic vitamin. No such
symptoms were observed on a diet equivalent to whole rice. Williams

suggests that toxaemias may play a role in determining the symptoms of deficiency diseases. The foodstuffs productive of these diseases are not necessarily toxic in the ordinary sense, though they may become so when other dietary defects remain uncorrected.

A beri-beri-like condition has been described in swine restricted to diets of corn and wheat grain or the outer coats of rice [Moore, 1914; Hart and McCollum, 1914; and Hart, Miller and McCollum, 1916]. These diets were rich in the antineuritic vitamin though deficient in proteins and inorganic salts.

It is important to remember that the diets in countries where beri-beri is prevalent are invariably ill balanced, and that there are other deficiencies in the diet which may modify the character of beri-beri.

With regard to deficiencies of proteins or salts there is comparatively little evidence, although Kohman [1920] produced oedema in rats on a diet deficient in protein.

Finally, the possibility that vitamin deficiencies other than that of the antineuritic vitamin B_1 may be involved in the aetiology of beri-beri must be considered. A number of little understood but suggestive facts indicate that the clinical and pathological picture characteristic of a particular deficiency disease may be profoundly modified when there is a coexistent deficiency of other dietary factors. Thus a rat fed on a diet involving a total deficiency of the vitamin B complex rarely develops either paralysis or dermatitis, but rapid death usually ensues without symptoms of either.

Rosedale [1927] has claimed that both rats and pigeons need a factor other than vitamin B_1, in the absence of which beri-beri-like symptoms develop, characterized by oedema and intestinal stasis. A similar view was expressed by Vedder and Williams [1913]. R. R. Williams, Waterman and Gurin [1930], and Peters and his colleagues [Peters, 1930, 2] have confirmed the finding of Jansen and Donath [1927], that highly purified preparations of the antineuritic vitamin do not protect pigeons from loss of weight in the absence of other factors, and these authors have concluded that avian beri-beri is a disease involving multiple deficiencies, which may account for its varied symptomatology.

Peters [1930, 1, 2] obtained evidence that protection against avian polyneuritis after the 30th day of polished-rice feeding is not afforded by doses of vitamin B_1 that are entirely effective in this respect before this period. The inference drawn from this observation is that in such cases the traces of vitamin B_1 contained in the diet and in the animals' own reserves are sufficient to prolong life until the development of secondary deficiencies of other vitamin factors, the store of which in the body is depleted more slowly than the antineuritic factor.

The study of polyneuritis in the rat has yielded results substantially similar to those observed in pigeons. Schaumann [1910] observed paralysis in the hind limbs of rats fed on a diet of horse flesh previously autoclaved at 120° C. Drummond [1918, 1] reported that only a small proportion of animals deprived of 'water soluble B' developed signs of paralysis. A detailed study of this condition was made by Hofmeister [1922], who found that it could best be studied in a more chronic form where rapid decline was prevented by employing a diet only partially deprived of the vitamin. In a few cases a spastic condition of the limbs occurred, accompanied by tremors and convulsions, but in most of the animals ataxia was followed in a few days by paralysis. No degenerative changes were observed in the peripheral nerves, but slight swelling of the myelin sheath and an increased number of nuclei in the sheath of Schwann were observed. In the brain and cord Hofmeister found small capillary haemorrhages and chromatolytic changes of the nerve-cells.

Woollard [1927] and Stern and Findlay [1929] have confirmed the histological findings reported by Hofmeister. The former observed that similar, though less pronounced, changes could be detected in rats receiving daily doses of marmite (a commercial yeast extract) but otherwise starved. The latter workers noted slight chromatolytic changes in the ganglion cells of the cord following uncomplicated vitamin B$_1$ deficiency, while degeneration in the myelin of the peripheral nerves was only seen in cases of long-standing paralysis. These inconspicuous differences are in marked contrast to the striking changes found in birds.

The researches of recent years have not shaken the established fact that human beri-beri is primarily due to deficiency in the diet of the antineuritic vitamin. On the other hand, it is probably unwise to regard the beri-beri problem in the tropics as being solely a question of polished or unpolished rice. The work of McCarrison [1928] suggests that human beri-beri may occur in spite of the presence of a certain amount of vitamin B$_1$ in the diet. From this it follows that relatively undermilled rice may sometimes be associated with the disease, particularly when the diet is deficient in supplementary foods. Human beings rarely live upon rice alone, and the usual consumption of a certain amount of other foodstuffs prevents an absolute correlation between the incidence of beri-beri and the vitamin B$_1$ content of the rice consumed. McCarrison's observation [1924] that the vitamin B$_1$ content of unpolished rice may, by washing, be reduced to that of milled rice, may help to explain certain puzzling features, described by the same author, in the epidemiology of beri-beri in India. Undermilled rice of poor commercial quality may require vigorous washing before it is fit for human consumption.

Clear and convincing evidence has nevertheless accumulated from many lands that the substitution of undermilled for milled rice will cause beri-beri to disappear. Even in India, where, as McCarrison has shown, some facts seem at first sight to clash with the vitamin B$_1$ deficiency hypothesis, the association of beri-beri with milled rice, and its absence when undermilled rice is eaten, is as clear as elsewhere. Infantile beri-beri responds at once to treatment with extracts of rice polishings [Wells, 1921] (see p. 155), but with regard to the effect on adult beri-beri of treatment by vitamin B$_1$ the evidence is not so abundant. Various observers have, however, attested the value in the adult disease of rice polishings, or extracts of rice polishings [Bréaudat and Denier, 1911 ; R. R. Williams and Saleeby, 1915; Jansen and Donath, 1926, 1].

The number of clear-cut clinical experiments on record, in which adult beri-beri was treated by vitamin B$_1$ alone without other dietary alteration, is not large. Failure to secure obvious benefit by means of vitamin B$_1$ extracts may be due to too small a dosage. Moreover, when nerve degeneration is excessive, improvement must necessarily be slow.

The diets on which beri-beri develops are usually deficient in other factors besides vitamin B_1, and some of the symptoms grouped under the heading ' beri-beri' may well be due to other deficiencies. The oedema of wet beri-beri has been ascribed to shortage of protein. In treatment, while stress should be laid on vitamin B_1 as the most important curative agent, it is reasonable to give in addition a good all-round diet containing abundant protein, vitamins, and mineral salts.

PHYSIOLOGICAL SIGNIFICANCE OF THE ANTINEURITIC VITAMIN B_1.

Growth and Maintenance.

As a result of the work which proved the multiple nature of the vitamin B complex, it may be regarded as firmly established that vitamin B_1, in addition to affording protection against polyneuritis, is an essential factor for the normal growth of young rats, and for the maintenance of normal weight and health in adults. Deficiency of this vitamin, as of most other vitamins, is a limiting factor for normal growth and rapidly makes itself felt.

After a period of obscurity, a similar view of the relation of vitamin B_1 to weight maintenance in the pigeon has now become possible. As early as 1911 Schaumann and Chamberlain had noted that, whereas rice-bran or yeast prevented polyneuritis and maintained the weight of birds, the extracts of these substances retained their antineuritic potency but failed to prevent loss of weight. Cooper [1912, 1914, 1, 2], in his investigation of the vitamin B_1 content of foodstuffs, found that the amount needed to restore the weight of rice-fed birds did not correspond to the amount needed to cure polyneuritis, and it was also observed that activated fuller's earth, after treatment with alkali, lost its weight-maintaining properties without sensible deterioration of its antineuritic activity [R. R. Williams and Seidell, 1916]. Funk and Macallum [1916] concluded that the antineuritic and weight-maintenance factors were identical, but they suggested that a larger amount of the vitamin was required for the latter than for the former function. Emmet and McKim [1917] also observed that activated fuller's earth was potent in curing avian polyneuritis, but was much less effective in restoring weight than unmilled rice and other cereals. They recognized the necessity for postulating the existence of two factors, thus confirming the suggestion made originally by Chamberlain and Vedder. This view was not accepted by Seidell [1922, 1] who held that the curative and weight-maintaining properties of his preparations were due to the activity of one substance. The experience of later workers, however, has confirmed the belief that the antineuritic factor does not suffice for the maintenance of body-weight in pigeons when added to a basal diet of polished rice [Kinnersley and Peters, 1925 ; Jansen and Donath, 1926, 1 ; R. R. Williams and Waterman, 1928; R. R. Williams, Waterman and Gurin, 1930; Carter, Kinnersley and Peters, 1930, 1]. In the nutrition of the pigeon, as in that of the rat, the antineuritic vitamin is to be regarded as one of several water-soluble accessory factors required for maintenance of normal weight and health (see p. 121). Lack of this factor, both in the rat and in the pigeon, and presumably in other species, results in decline in weight, as well as in the ultimate development of polyneuritis.

Vitamin B has been found necessary for the growth and maintenance not only of mammals and birds, but also of the frog [Emmett and Allen, 1919; Harden and Zilva, 1920, 2; Billard, 1922], and of insects, *Drosophila* [Northrop, 1917; Bacot and Harden, 1922], and the flour beetle, *Tribolium confusum* Duval [Sweetman and Palmer, 1928].

Storage and Utilization of Vitamin B_1.

Animals possess a definite but limited store of vitamin B_1, which in the case of the rat or the pigeon is exhausted within three or four weeks, as judged by the onset of polyneuritis after this time [Vedder and Clark, 1912; Funk and Macallum, 1915].

The amount of growth which occurs in young animals placed on a vitamin B-deficient diet seems to bear some relation to the vitamin content of the previous diet [Steenbock, Sell and Jones, 1923]. Similarly the administration of an excess of the vitamin B complex to pigeons for some days before placing them on a deficient diet delays the subsequent loss of weight for a time which varies with individual birds [Pilcher and Sollman, 1925]. It has in fact been experimentally shown that the livers of normal rats contain vitamin B, which to a large extent disappears when they are fed on a diet deficient in this vitamin [Osborne and Mendel, 1923]. In man the latent period of beri-beri appears to be not less than 90 days [Fraser and Stanton, 1911] (see p. 250).

Drummond [1918, 1] observed that the length of time over which a rat is able to maintain itself on a diet deficient in vitamin B without serious loss of body-weight is directly proportional to the age at which the restriction is imposed. Adult animals were found to be capable of surviving long periods of deprivation, during which they suffered slow decline of body-weight, though no such feature of the growth curve was seen for young animals. Ultimately both young and adult animals exhibited a rapid decline in weight, followed by death. This led to the belief that the needs of the body for vitamin B are greater during growth than during maturity. As pointed out, however, by Osborne and Mendel [1922, 1], the *rate* of decline in animals possessing undoubtedly different nutritive reserves does not necessarily indicate a difference in the requirement of the vitamin for young and adult animals. They [1922, 1; 1925] found that whereas a daily supplement of vitamin B in the form of 200 mg. of dried yeast gave normal growth in rats, at whatever age the experimental diet was imposed, with doses of 50 mg. of yeast daily the rate of growth was retarded from the beginning of the experiment. With still smaller doses of yeast the larger animals failed in every case even to maintain weight, while the smaller animals failed to give continued growth for any length of time. They concluded that the vitamin B requirement under conditions of growth or maintenance on a diet of constant composition bears some quantitative relationship to the mass of active tissue.

There is some evidence for the view that there is a definite daily utilization of the vitamin [Chick and Hume, 1917–19, 1; Kinnersley, Peters and Reader, 1928]. Not only do symptoms of polyneuritis tend to appear in any given pigeon at a fairly constant date after the commencement of a polished-rice diet, but the duration of the cure following the administration of a given dose of vitamin B_1 is related to the size of the dose. Moreover, the rate of growth of young animals is roughly proportional to the vitamin B content of the diet [Osborne and Mendel, 1917, 2; McCollum and Simmonds 1917; Drummond, 1918, 1].

Loss of Appetite and Inanition.

In his well-known experiments with young rats fed on deficient diets, Hopkins [1912] noted that the food intake became much reduced in the later stages of avitaminosis. He made the important observation that growth is inhibited even when the food intake is more than quantitatively sufficient in calorie value to maintain normal growth. The food, although absorbed normally, is not utilized. Hopkins concluded that the influence of accessory food factors on appetite is secondary to their more direct effect on the growth processes. Diminished food consumption during vitamin B deficiency has been noted in pigeons [Chamberlain and Vedder, 1911, 1, 2; McCarrison, 1921; Kon and Drummond, 1927]. in dogs [Karr, 1920; Cowgill, Deuel and Smith, 1925], and in rats [Funk and Macallum, 1915; Osborne and Mendel, 1917, 2]. Drummond [1918, 1] regarded this as an adjustment in response to the lowered calorific requirement of the animal, a view supported by the fact that polyneuritis develops earlier in animals forcibly fed than in those allowed to feed naturally [Braddon and Cooper, 1914; Marrian, Baker, Drummond and Woollard, 1927]. The significance of loss of appetite in avitaminosis has been discussed by McCarrison [1921] and by Peters [1930, 1, 2]. They take the view that it is protective in its effect on the pigeon, whether by allowing the liberation of essential factors during tissue wasting or in some other manner not at present understood. Kon and Drummond [1927] have suggested that such an explanation may underlie spontaneous cures from head retraction observed in pigeons fed on polished rice.

The inanition resulting from lowered food intake is believed by Drummond and his associates to be responsible for many of the features observed in avitaminosis. Thus fall of body-weight, ruffled feathers, fall of body temperature, and hyperglycaemia are regarded as being due to partial starvation rather than as specific manifestations of lack of vitamin B_1. Pigeons receiving water and 1 g. of marmite daily, but otherwise starved, presented a picture closely resembling that seen in avitaminosis. A number of other observers, whose work is referred to below, have called attention to the fact that many of the features of vitamin B deficiency are closely bound up with the condition of inanition which always accompanies it. It has, indeed, proved extremely difficult, if not impossible, to disentangle the effects of the one from the other [see for example, Simonnet, 1920; 1921]. Nevertheless, avitaminosis is not to be explained merely in terms of inanition. Much evidence has accumulated to show that the vitamin exerts some favourable influence on the metabolism of the animal which is reflected in its continued growth and well-being.

The immediate effect on the appetite of removing either vitamin B_1 or B_2 was well shown in the work of Boas-Fixsen [1931] with adult rats. A decline was noticed within 48 hours, even when the previous diet was entirely adequate, and was greater when vitamin B_1 was removed. These facts argue a very limited capacity for storage of the vitamin, which appears to be excreted day by day chiefly in the faeces.

Relation of Vitamin B_1 to Metabolism.

Much of the literature bearing on the relation of vitamin B_1 to metabolism is conflicting. Attention has been divided between the exact significance of vitamin B_1 for metabolic processes as a whole and its relation to one or other of the main sources of food material. It is important to bear in mind that many of the findings refer to the significance of vitamin B as a whole and require reinterpretation in the light of the multiple nature of this complex.

Many observers have recorded the fall of body temperature in monkeys, rats, and birds during avitaminosis, particularly in the terminal stages, in which there appears to be complete loss of temperature regulation [Eijkman, 1897, 3; Drummond, 1918, 1; Novaro, 1920; Abderhalden, 1920, 2; Cramer, Drew and Mottram, 1921; McCarrison, 1921; Farmer and Redenbaugh, 1925–26, 1; Drummond and Marrian, 1926; Kon, 1927, 1]. In such cases administration of the antineuritic vitamin is followed by a recovery of body temperature within 24 hours.

An indirect relation between vitamin B_1 deficiency and failure in certain oxidase systems was suggested by two studies. Dutcher [1918, 1] observed a diminution in the catalase content of certain organs, while G. M. Findlay [1921, 1] noted that the glyoxalase content of the liver was decreased in the absence of vitamin B, but increased again when it was administered.

Opinion is, however, sharply divided as to whether there is a specific diminution in the oxidative capacity of the tissues due to vitamin B deficiency. In the living animal, associated with the fall in temperature, there occur a lowered basal metabolism and alterations in respiratory exchange, first described by Ramoino [1916] and confirmed by others, but especially stressed by Abderhalden [numerous papers, including some with Schmidt and Wertheimer, 1920–22]. Their view that the changes were specific to vitamin B_1 deficiency was successfully challenged by Drummond and Marrian [1926], whose contention that they were due to the accompanying inanition receives support from the work of Anderson and Kulp [1922] and Gulick [1922; 1924] on poultry and rats respectively [see also Farmer and Redenbaugh, 1925–26, 1; Galvao and Cardoso, 1931]. In comparative experiments with the oxidase systems in isolated tissues from normal and avitaminous animals, it is necessary to distinguish between experiments in which (a) actual oxygen uptake or (b) hydrogen transfer in the presence of dyes is measured. These processes can be carried out either in presence or absence of various substances added as substrates, and have been studied upon muscle, liver and brain tissue, usually obtained from pigeons. Drummond and Marrian [1926] working with liver and muscle did not confirm the claims of Abderhalden *et al.* [1920–22], or of W. R. Hess [1921] and Hess and Messerle [1921] that there was a specific change either of actual oxygen uptake or of dye reduction in presence and absence of succinate ; a similar view was reached by Roche [1925]. This failure to demonstrate changes has not, however, deterred further investigation. Later, Kollath [1929], from a comparison of the effects of vital staining by methylene blue in normal, starving and poly-neuritic pigeons, concluded that in polyneuritis a definite change in the oxidation-reduction potential of certain organs could be demon-strated, associated with changes in cell permeability. This was succeeded by a reiteration by Abderhalden and Vlassipoulos [1930] of the claim that differences in oxygen uptake of pigeon's tissues can be demonstrated in the absence of added substrate. As compared with the normal, an average of 12 observations showed a fall for the liver of avitaminous pigeons of 18 per cent. (not shown by starving birds), and for the brain falls of 12 per cent. for starving and 23 per cent. for avitaminous birds. Using similar methods, Gavrilescu and Peters [1931 ; Gavrilescu, Meiklejohn, Passmore and Peters, 1932, unpublished results] find a slight, statistically insignificant, reduction in oxygen uptake by pigeon's brain without added substrates for avitaminous as compared with normal birds. With added glucose, or more readily with lactate, decreases of 20 per cent. and 40 per cent. respectively were found, more marked in the optic lobes. On the other hand, tissue from avitaminous birds behaved normally in the presence of succinate as substrate. Vitamin B_1 concentrates added in amounts of 1 γ (0·001 mg.) or less per 100 mg. tissue largely restored the oxygen uptake in presence of glucose and lactate, but had little influence on normal brain with added lactate or on avitaminous brain with added succinate. They inferred that the active agent in the concentrates was vitamin B_1. At least these results exclude the possibility that the observed diminution in oxygen uptake was due solely to a diminished amount of tissue substrates. The present position, therefore, is that the deprivation of vitamin B_1 superimposes specific biochemical lesions in the glucose-lactate system upon any changes that may be due to the accompanying inanition. There appears to be some correlation between these specific changes and the opisthotonus symptoms.

The problem of the relation of vitamin B to the quantity and type of foodstuff metabolized has been the subject of a number of investi-gations.

Calorie intake. As regards the total calorie intake, it has been claimed that the vitamin B requirement of an animal is roughly proportional to the total calorie intake × weight $^{5/3}$ [Cowgill, Smith and Beard, 1925 ; Beard, 1925], whereas Plimmer, Rosedale and Raymond [1927] consider that it is simply proportional to the calorie intake ; these relations, however, have been disproved by Roscoe [1931, 1].

Protein intake. Although Funk observed that increase in the ration of protein did not affect the rapidity of onset of polyneuritis, some relation between vitamin B and protein metabolism has been established. Thus the amount of vitamin B required by the rat in order to ensure proper lactation has been found to be proportional to the protein content of the diet [Hartwell, 1922], and in order to obtain normal growth there must also be a definite relation between the vitamin B content of the diet and the protein intake [Drummond, Crowden and Hill, 1922; Reader and Drummond, 1926]. Later, Hassan and Drummond [1927] showed that the vitamin related to protein metabolism is stable to treatment with hot alkali, indicating that vitamin B_1 is not the accessory factor concerned, although vitamin B_2 may be.

Tscherkes [1926] claimed that vitamin B bore a relation both to protein and to carbohydrate metabolism.

Carbohydrate intake. It was first observed by Funk [1914, 1, 2] that polyneuritis in pigeons was the more rapidly produced the greater the amount of carbohydrate ingested by the birds. The difference in the time taken to develop polyneuritis by different individuals was regarded as being determined, in part at least, by the amount of vitamin stored in the body as a consequence of the previous diet, and by the amount and nature of the food eaten during the avitaminous period. Funk's observation was confirmed by Braddon and Cooper [1914], though they did not accept the suggestion that the protection afforded against polyneuritis during starvation was due to the liberation of a supply of the antineuritic substance in the process of tissue wasting. Abderhalden and Lampe [1913] observed that pigeons starved to death did not develop polyneuritis, though this may have been due to the fact that in most cases death from starvation falls within the period required for the development of the disease [Chamberlain and Vedder, 1911, 1, 2]. In a few cases symptoms resembling those of polyneuritis have been observed in starving birds before they have succumbed [Chamberlain, Bloomberg and Kilbourne, 1911; Marrian, Baker, Drummond and Woollard, 1927].

Collazo [1923] found that, after the introduction of considerable amounts of carbohydrate into the crops of normal and avitaminous animals, death invariably occurred in the latter though not in the normal controls. Monosaccharides produced the most toxic, starch the least toxic, effect, while disaccharides occupied an intermediate position. He concluded that carbohydrate metabolism is deranged as a result of the deprivation of vitamin B_1 with the production of toxic substances, and showed [Rubino and Collazo, 1923] that the carbohydrate thus introduced was actually absorbed, but that the liver was unable to store it, the toxic effect not being due to physical reasons as suggested later by Kon [1927, 2].

It has also been claimed that the vitamin B requirement is lower on a high protein than on a high carbohydrate diet [Funk and Collazo, 1925; Randoin and Simmonet, 1924] and can be diminished by substituting part of the carbohydrate of the diet by fat [Evans and Lepkovsky, 1929; 1931].

Carbohydrate metabolism. Disturbance of carbohydrate metabolism when the vitamin B complex is absent has been noted by Randoin and Simonnet [1924] and confirmed by Roche [1931], who found an increase in the ratio C/N of the deproteinized blood filtrates partly caused by hyperglycaemia and partly by the accumulation of intermediate products of carbohydrate metabolism [cf. Kon, 1929; 1931].

Kinnersley and Peters [1929; 1930, 1] have found that the brains of pigeons in the terminal stages of deficiency of vitamin B_1 have an increased lactic acid content. The increased lactic acid appears to be localized in the region of the hind brain, and in this respect differs from the condition after exercise when the raised lactic acid content is general. Fisher [1931], using monoiodoacetic acid [Lundsgaard, 1930] as fixative agent for lactic acid, has shown that the lactic acid content is also raised in the heart, liver, and muscles of the polyneuritic pigeon, returning more slowly after exercise to the normal. Birds cured with marmite behave normally.

Inawashiro and Hayasaka [1928; Hayasaka and Inawashiro 1929–30], in an exhaustive investigation of the metabolism of beri-beri in man, have found that the lactic acid content of the blood is higher than normal and takes longer than usual to return to the initial level after exercise. They think that the resynthesis of lactic acid in the muscles is retarded in beri-beri.

These observations justify the belief that a deficiency of vitamin B_1 induces a fault in the metabolism of lactic acid and agree with the results of the brain studies of Kinnersley and Peters.

Hyperglycaemia. Studies of the blood-sugar level and the respiratory quotient during avitaminosis have contributed further evidence bearing on the theory relating the antineuritic vitamin to carbohydrate metabolism.

Funk and Schönborn [1914] first recorded the fact that pigeons fed on a diet of polished rice developed hyperglycaemia with a corresponding diminution in the glycogen content of the liver, and this has been confirmed as regards the hyperglycaemia by many other workers for the pigeon, and for the rat by Lepkovsky, Wood and Evans [1930] and by Eggleton and Gross [1925]. Since a similar condition was observed in pigeons during starvation [Marrian, Baker, Drummond and Woollard, 1927], it was attributed to inanition.

During avitaminosis B_1 no change occurs in the concentration of non-glucose reducing substances in the blood [Gulland and Peters, 1930] or in the rate of absorption of glucose [Eggleton and Gross, 1925].

While there can be little doubt that inanition is an important contributory factor in the development of hyperglycaemia as well as of certain other features of avitaminosis, it is difficult to accept the view stated by Drummond and his associates, that no relation exists between vitamin B_1 and carbohydrate metabolism, in the light of the evidence of Funk, Braddon, Cooper and later workers.

Relation of Vitamin B_1 to Secretion of Glands.

A considerable literature has accumulated bearing on the relation of the antineuritic vitamin to glandular function. Much of this is conflicting, owing to differences of technique, not infrequently faulty, and to the variety of experimental animals employed. There appears to be no justification for the view that this vitamin is specifically related to the activity of any particular organ of the body. Disorders of function of glands, as of other organs, undoubtedly occur as the result of deprivation of vitamin B_1, but it is probably safer to regard these as local manifestations of a general 'tissue anarchy'.

Nevertheless, a marked feature of vitamin B_1 deficiency is the atrophy and cellular degeneration produced in many organs (intestinal and gastric mucosa, pancreas, salivary glands, and liver), a special feature being the disappearance of lymphoid tissue [see Funk and Douglas, 1914; McCarrison, 1921; Cramer, Drew and Mottram, 1921; G. M. Findlay, 1928].

Digestion. The suggestion that vitamin B might be identical with secretin [Voegtlin and Myers, 1919] has been negatived by the demonstration that extracts containing vitamin B failed to evoke any secretions from the pancreas, liver, or salivary glands [Cowgill and Mendel, 1921; Anrep and Drummond, 1920–21]. On the other hand there is evidence that the flow of gastric juice in dogs deprived of vitamin B_1 is greatly diminished or entirely inhibited [Miyadera, 1921] and that in pigeons the lessened amount of gastric juice is almost free from pepsin [Danysz-Michel and Koskowski, 1922]. Karr, on the other hand [1920], claimed that lack of vitamin B in the dog did not involve disturbances in the digestion and absorption of protein.

The inhibition of the flow of gastric juice in dogs is possibly due to the lack, not of vitamin B_1, but of some stimulating substance which is absent from vitamin-free diets ; thus administration of alcohol produces an immediate flow of gastric juice. Drummond [1918, 1] found that flavouring agents increased the food intake without influencing growth, confirming the original observation of Hopkins [1912] that vitamins stimulated appetite in a manner quite different from the action of flavouring agents.

As regards the effect of vitamin B_1 deficiency on the secretion of specific enzymes, Braddon and Cooper [1914] found that 90–98 per cent. of the starch ingested by polyneuritic pigeons, even on a high carbohydrate diet, was normally digested and absorbed; no change has been observed by a number of workers in the activity of the amylolytic enzymes in polyneuritic pigeons [Tiger and Simonnet, 1921; Rothlin, 1922; Kon and Drummond, 1927; Farmer and Redenbaugh, 1925–26, 2]. Braddon and Cooper also observed a diminution of proteolytic activity in polyneuritic pigeons and were confirmed in this by the experiments of Rosedale and Oliveiro [1928], who examined the enzyme content of the crop, proventriculus, pancreas, and intestine of normal and polyneuritic pigeons and found absence of trypsin and lipase from the latter. Similarly the secretion of pancreatic juice in dogs fed on polished rice was found by Tsukiye and Okada [1922] to be diminished, but was restored on giving vitamin B.

Endocrine glands. The effect of a deficiency of vitamin B on the ductless glands was first examined in pigeons which had died of beriberi by Funk and Douglas [1914], who found a great diminution in size in every case, accompanied by degenerative changes of the cells. R. R. Williams and Crowell [1915] noted great atrophy of the thymus gland in polyneuritic pigeons and to a lesser extent in chickens, but were unable to find any specific relationship between the antineuritic vitamin and the function of the gland.

Adrenal glands. McCarrison [1919], who made a systematic study of the subject, found that the organs of pigeons on a diet deficient in vitamin B lost weight much as in inanition, with the exception of the pituitary and adrenal glands. The adrenals increased to two or three times the weight of those of control birds. The adrenaline content of the enlarged glands was found to be increased proportionately to the size of the organ, while the cortex showed an almost complete absence of lipoids. McCarrison noticed a relationship between this adrenal hypertrophy and the occurrence of hydropericardium in his experimental birds. He regarded the excess of fluid as analogous to 'wet' beri-beri in man, and developed a theory of the cause of oedema in this disease on the basis of excessive adrenaline secretion. The enlargement of the adrenal gland and its increased adrenaline content were confirmed by Kellaway [1921] and by Korenchevsky [1923].

There has been much uncertainty as to the relative parts played by vitamin B deficiency and the associated inanition in the hypertrophy of the adrenal glands. The weight of opinion is in favour of the view that in pigeons the hypertrophy due to avitaminosis B is confined to the cortex [G. M. Findlay, 1921, 1; Stern and Findlay, 1929; Beznák, 1923; Marrian, Baker, Drummond and Woollard, 1927; Marrian, 1928]. The adrenal hypertrophy was found to be greater in cases of uncomplicated vitamin B_1 deficiency than in cases where the bird was deprived of both vitamins B_1 and B_2 [Marrian et al., 1927; Marrian, 1928], thus confirming the finding of G. M. Findlay [1928] with regard to rats. Gross [1923] working with rats found neither hypertrophy of the gland nor increase of adrenaline content as compared with normal animals.

Sexual glands. Deficiency of vitamin B also exerts a powerful influence on the sexual glands. In male animals (monkeys, pigeons, fowls) atrophy of the testis occurs [Funk and Douglas, 1914; McCarrison, 1919; Dutcher and Wilkins, 1921], accompanied by absence of spermatozoa and spermatocytes. Similar changes were observed in the rat by Allen [1919] and Parkes and Drummond [1925], but there is some doubt whether this was due to deficiency of vitamin B or of vitamin E [Mattill, 1926–27]. The testicular degeneration in birds seems to be a true deficiency effect and not due to inanition. The effect of vitamin B_1 deficiency is much more marked than that of vitamin B_2 [Marrian and Parkes, 1928].

In female mice on a diet deficient in vitamin B anoestrus commences abruptly, the normal oestrous cycle ceasing just before decline in weight sets in. Anoestrus is due to the failure to produce oestrin and not to an inability to respond to it on the part of animals suffering from vitamin B deficiency [Parkes, 1928].

Sure [1927, 3; 1928, 2, 3], who has been ineffectively criticized by H. G. Miller [1926–27], finds that the requirement of the female rat for vitamin B_1 and B_2 is three to five times greater for lactation than for normal growth. This increase in the requirement of B vitamins appears to be due to inefficient transfer of vitamin to the milk by the mammary gland. Thus a daily dose of 500 mg. of a yeast concentrate was required by the mother for the normal suckling of a litter of six, whereas a dose of 180 mg. sufficed for successful rearing when 30 mg. was supplied to the mother and the remaining 150 mg. was given to the young directly.

On the other hand Evans and Burr [1928, 1] consider that 'lactation delinquency' is related particularly to the antineuritic vitamin and is in no way due to an inadequate supply of vitamin B_2, the requirement of the lactating animal for vitamin B_1 being five times that for normal growth of the young non-lactating animal.

Relation of Vitamin B_1 to Gastro-intestinal Movements.

Many observers have noted that intestinal atony or stasis results from prolonged vitamin B deficiency in pigeons [Vedder and Clark, 1912 ; McCarrison, 1921 ; Anderson and Kulp, 1922 ; Plimmer and Rosedale, 1926 ; Rosedale, 1929], in rats [Gross, 1924], in monkeys [McCarrison, 1921], and in dogs [Cowgill *et al.*, 1925 ; 1926 ; 1930]. The last-named authors have specially studied the gastric movements and consider that the defective motility of the stomach is a secondary effect due to the condition of anhydraemia which accompanies the vitamin deficiency.   On the other hand, Kon and Drummond [1927] found no delay in the passage of a barium meal through the intestinal canal of polyneuritic pigeons.

Bradycardia.

Carter and Drury [1929] showed that pigeons fed upon a diet of polished rice develop bradycardia and heart block.   This condition is abolished by vagal section or atropine, and can be relieved by giving whole wheat or yeast.   Deprivation of the vitamin B complex in young rats leads to a severe bradycardia which is different from that seen in the pigeon in that it is of 'sinus' origin and is not due to vagal influences [Drury, Harris and Maudsley, 1930].   These authors found that the lowered heart rate could be restored to normal within a few hours after administration of materials rich in vitamin B_1 and the response was found to be roughly graded to the size of the dose given.   It is, however, premature as yet to ascribe these effects to lack of any particular member of the vitamin B complex.

Relation of Vitamin B to Bacterial Infection.

Rats and rabbits fed on diets deficient in vitamin B show no loss of ability to form agglutinins, precipitins, haemolysins, and bacteriolysins [Zilva, 1919, 2 ; Werkman, 1923] and the opsonic index of the serum of such rats were found to be normal [G. M. Findlay and Mackenzie, 1922].   On the other hand a lowered bactericidal action of such rat serum has sometimes been observed [Smith and Wason, 1923 ; G. M. Findlay and Maclean, 1925].   Rice-fed pigeons have a lowered resistance to bacterial infection [G. M. Findlay, 1923, 1] and may develop septicaemia [Barlow, 1930].

Blood Changes in Relation to Vitamin B_1 Deficiency.

Anaemia has been observed in polyneuritic pigeons [Abderhalden, 1921, 1 ; Weill, Arloing and Dufourt, 1922 ; Palmer and Hoffman, 1922–23 ; Barlow, 1930], and in young rats deprived of vitamin B_1 [Sure, 1929 ; Sure and Smith, 1929 ; Sure, Kik and Walker, 1929]. This is sometimes complicated, especially in the later stages of the deficiency, by loss of water from the blood (anhydraemia), a condition which is also seen in inanition due to restricted diet [see Rose, Stucky and Mendel, 1929–30 ; Stucky and Rose, 1929].

A marked fall in the white-cell count, due to a reduction in the number of lymphocytes, has been observed [Cramer, Drew and Mottram, 1921], whilst a large proportion of aged or moribund polymorphs are found in the blood-stream [Happ, 1922].

Excretion of Vitamin B.

Much discussion has centred round the question as to whether vitamin B is excreted unchanged [see Van der Walle, 1922, where the literature is quoted]. Positive results were obtained by Cooper [1914,1] with an alcoholic extract of pigeons' faeces, and by Muckenfuss [1918, 1919] and Gaglio [1919] with urine. Van der Walle has carefully examined the question, and has shown that the undoubted curative effect of normal urine on polyneuritic pigeons is due to the presence of a small amount of the antineuritic vitamin. This possesses the characteristic properties of the vitamin, and disappears from the urine when the diet is deficient in vitamin B_1.

The excretion of the B-vitamins in the faeces would explain the rapid depletion of reserves and the habit of coprophagy which are commonly observed in rats on diets deprived of these vitamins. To diminish access to faeces it is usual, in the study of these vitamins, to maintain the experimental animals in cages provided with bases of wide-meshed wire. Steenbock, Sell and Nelson [1923] found that rats allowed to consume their own faeces might derive as much as half their necessary intake of vitamin B from this source. When coprophagy was prevented it was found necessary to double the vitamin B content of the diet in order to ensure an adequate supply. Although these findings were at first disputed by McCollum, Simmonds and Becker [1925], they have been accepted by later workers [Salmon, 1925; Smith, Cowgill and Croll, 1925]. Heller, McElroy and Garlock [1925] considered that the B-vitamin present in rat faeces was formed by spore-bearing organisms in the intestinal tract, which were capable of synthesizing the vitamin ; these organisms when grown on a synthetic medium, stated to be free of B-vitamins, caused a marked response in growth when fed to rats. Kennedy and Palmer [1928] found a substance present in rat faeces which improved a diet 'complete' in all respects including the antineuritic vitamin ; this substance was soluble in strong alcohol and only moderately heat-stable, which properties resemble those of vitamin B_1 and do not coincide with those of vitamin B_2. The work of Roscoe [1931, 3], however, suggests that both B-vitamins are to some extent present in rat faeces, although much better growth was obtained when the faeces were used to supplement diets already containing either vitamin B_1 or B_2. At present it must be regarded as uncertain whether the B-vitamins present in the faeces are derived from the animal's reserves or from synthesis by micro-organisms in the intestine (see p. 174).

ATTEMPTS TO ISOLATE VITAMIN B_1.

The numerous early claims recording the isolation of the antineuritic vitamin have proved, in the light of later work, to have been premature. Even now the unequivocal isolation of this factor has not been realized, though the preparations of a number of workers [Kinnersley and Peters, 1925, 1927, 1928; Jansen and Donath, 1926, 1, 2 ; 1927 ; Levene, 1928 ; Guha and Drummond, 1929 ; Windaus, Tschesche, et al. 1931] have reached a high degree of activity, and represent a considerable advance upon the work of former investigators. The earlier literature, therefore, need only be briefly reviewed.

Cooper and Funk [1911] found that the curative substance present in an alcoholic extract of rice polishings was precipitated by phosphotungstic acid. The active fraction thus obtained was stated to be free from proteins, carbohydrates, and salts, and to resemble an organic base. Employing the method usually adopted for separating certain organic nitrogenous bases Funk [1911] obtained from the silver nitrate-baryta fraction a crystalline substance melting at 233° C., and having the formula $C_{17}H_{18}O_7N_2$. This substance was curative for pigeons in doses of 20-40 mg. The same process was applied to yeast, milk, and ox brain and led to the isolation of the same substance [Funk, 1912-13, 1]. Funk considered that the chemical properties of the curative substance placed it in the class of pyrimidine bases. Nicotinic acid, which was isolated during the fractionation of yeast and rice polishings, was believed to be a decomposition product of the vitamin [Funk, 1913, 1]. The substances isolated by Funk, however, proved not to be the active vitamin in pure form, but nitrogenous bases contaminated with traces of the vitamin [Barger, 1914; Drummond and Funk, 1914].

Vedder and Williams [1913], using a hydrolysed alcoholic extract of rice polishings, confirmed Funk's observation that the curative activity for avian polyneuritis was precipitated in the pyrimidine fraction, and they concluded that the antineuritic factor is present as a constituent of certain nucleic acids present in rice polishings and yeast. The precipitation of the active substance by silver nitrate and baryta has been confirmed by many workers [Cooper, 1913; R. R. Williams and Saleeby, 1915; Myers and Voegtlin, 1920; Seidell, 1921, 1; Tsukiye, 1922; Jansen and Donath, 1927; Kinnersley and Peters, 1925, 1928; Guha and Drummond, 1929].

Further attempts to isolate the factor were made by Suzuki, Shimamura and Odake [1912], who separated a crystalline picrate which they termed oryzanin; and by Edie et al. [1912], who obtained a crystalline basic substance, torulin, belonging to the pyrimidine group. Abderhalden and Schaumann [1918] attempted to isolate the antineuritic vitamin from yeast, and by precipitation of an alcoholic concentrate with acetone they obtained a crystalline product which they named 'eutonine'. This substance was curative for polyneuritic pigeons in doses of 5 mg., but did not maintain body-weight.

Hofmeister [1920] attempted unsuccessfully to purify the curative substance present in rice-meal by fractional precipitation of an alcoholic extract with potassium bismuth iodide.

Seidell [1916; 1917; 1921, 1; 1922, 1] employed fuller's earth to adsorb the vitamin from autolysed yeast, or from an aqueous yeast extract. The fuller's earth was washed and dried after adsorption, constituting his 'activated solid', which protected pigeons from polyneuritis in doses of 0·1-0·2 g. daily. Baryta extracts the vitamin from the activated solid, and on fractionation of the resulting solution by silver precipitation the vitamin is found to follow the histidine fraction. The final preparation protected pigeons from loss of weight in doses of less than 1 mg. on alternate days. Later Seidell [1924, 1, 2] prepared a crude picrate from an extract of his activated solid. By fractional crystallization from 95 per cent. acetone he obtained a crystalline picrate of an active product having an empirical formula

$C_6H_{18}O_2N_3.C_6H_2(OH)(NO_2)_3$. This product protected pigeons from loss of weight in doses of 2 mg. daily.

A concentrated preparation of the vitamin B complex which has been much used in feeding experiments and as a starting-point for further purification may be made by the method of Osborne and Wakeman [1919]. An acidulated aqueous extract of yeast was submitted to fractional precipitation by alcohol, the fraction thrown out by 80 per cent. alcohol containing the bulk of the activity. After washing and drying, a preparation was obtained which had, weight for weight, sixteen times the activity of the original yeast as tested by growth experiments on rats. A method of concentrating the Osborne-Wakeman fraction has been described by Levene and van der Hoeven [1924; 1925; 1926], which involves a preliminary de-amination with nitrous acid followed by repeated treatment of the extract with small quantities of silica gel at pH 3·0. It is claimed that under these conditions vitamin B_1 is adsorbed by the silica gel almost entirely free from vitamin B_2. The activated gel is extracted with lithium hydroxide at pH 9·8, and the extract fractionated in alcohol and finally precipitated by acetone. The preparation thus obtained, when examined by growth tests on rats, was active for vitamin B_1 in daily doses of 0·07-0·1 mg.

Kinnersley and Peters [1925; 1927; 1928; 1930, 2] employ an aqueous extract of baker's yeast which is treated successively with normal lead acetate, baryta to remove yeast gum, sulphuric acid to remove barium, and mercuric sulphate at pH 2·0 to 3·0. The acid filtrate, from which many impurities have been removed, is brought to pH 7·0 and treated with purified norite charcoal which adsorbs the active factor. The vitamin B_1 can be recovered from the charcoal either by boiling with 50 per cent. alcohol (by volume) acidified with HCl or by boiling successively first with $N/10$ HCl followed by the acid alcohol. In the latter case two different types of extract are obtained of which the first has a curative activity of approximately 0·4 mg. per pigeon day-dose, and the latter 2·0 mg. per day-dose. The extracts so obtained can be freed from metals in aqueous solution with H_2S at pH 4·0, concentrated at pH 3·0, and stored as stable vitamin B_1 solutions after addition of alcohol to 15 per cent. Alternatively they can be used for the preparation of purer concentrates. The methods which have been found most successful have been alcohol fractionation and fractionation with sodium phosphotungstate at varying acidity. Preparations have been obtained with a pigeon day-dose of 0·012 mg. and the purer specimens have been found free from vitamin B_4.

In 1926 Jansen and Donath [1926, 1, 2], working in the laboratory in Batavia in which Eijkman made his fundamental discovery, announced the isolation of the antineuritic vitamin in crystalline form. In their method the vitamin present in an extract of rice polishings is adsorbed on acid clay at pH 5·0, and extracted therefrom with baryta by Seidell's method. The baryta extract, freed from barium with H_2SO_4, is submitted to fractionation with silver nitrate and baryta which precipitates more than 50 per cent. of the vitamin at pH 6·5. The decomposed precipitate is decolorized by norite, and the clear filtrate treated with phosphotungstic acid. The filtrate obtained after decomposition of the precipitated phosphotungstates is evaporated to dryness and extracted with absolute alcohol. Addition of platinic chloride precipitates nearly all the vitamin. The platinum precipitate is decomposed and the filtrate fractionated with alcohol and acetone. The acetone-insoluble fraction is further purified, and the vitamin obtained as a crystalline hydrochloride. It consists of rosettes of small bars, melting at 250° C., the composition $C_6H_{10}ON_2$ being assigned to the free base. Jansen and Donath found that daily doses of 0·002 mg. of the crystals protected rice birds (*Munia maia*) from polyneuritis for three weeks.

Eijkman [1927], and R. R. Williams, Waterman and Gurin [1930], have confirmed the potency of these crystals, and a careful test [Jansen, Kinnersley, Peters and Reader, 1930] has yielded the following results for curative activity—pigeon day-dose, by mouth, 0·009 mg.; by injection, 0·007 mg.; rat day-dose, 0·005 mg.

The application of the methods of Jansen and Donath and others to yeast has led to the isolation of a highly active crystalline compound by Windaus, Tscheche, *et al.* [1931]. The analysis of a crystalline picrolonate (M.P. 229° C.) showed that the substance contained sulphur and led to the tentative formula $C_{12}H_{17}ON_3S$ for the free base. The conversion of the picrolonate into the hydrochloride, melting at 245° C. (Jansen and Donath's hydrochloride melts at 250° C.) entails a loss of 40 per cent. in the yield. The average curative pigeon-day dose, by injection, is stated to be 0·0024 mg.

The sulphur content of Jansen and Donath's crystalline hydrochloride was subsequently demonstrated, and the identity of the crystalline antineuritic preparation from rice with that obtained from yeast seems to be established [Tscheche, 1932].

The acid clay preparation from rice polishings, which is the starting-point of Jansen and Donath's process, is largely used in Java for the cure of beri-beri and forms a satisfactory stable preparation of vitamin B_1. This preparation has been adopted by the (League of Nations) International Vitamin Conference, 1931, as the provisional standard for the antineuritic vitamin B_1 (see Appendix II).

Administration of Compounds of Known Chemical Composition.

Several compounds of known chemical composition have been administered to animals suffering from polyneuritis in the hope, which has not been fulfilled, that some known pure substance might prove to be identical with the antineuritic vitamin. As has already been noted, deprivation of vitamin B_1 is not the only cause of the classical symptom of acute polyneuritis (head retraction) in birds. In view of later experiments the claims as to the alleviation of polyneuritic symptoms by some of the earlier workers must therefore be accepted with caution.

Funk [1912–13, 2] investigated a number of purine and pyrimidine compounds and found that certain of them, adenine, allantoin, yeast- and thymus-nucleic acids among others, exercised a marked though temporary alleviation of the symptoms in polyneuritic pigeons. Schaumann [1908] and Grijns [1909] had failed to find any benefit from the administration of nucleic acid prepared from yeast or katjang-idjo beans. Similarly Drummond [1917] found yeast-nucleic acid and adenine to be inactive.

R. R. Williams [1916; 1917] observed that certain hydroxypyridines exerted an antineuritic effect, but passed readily into a stable isomeric form which was inactive. Trigonelline, betaine, and nicotinic acid, which Funk had suggested to be a decomposition product of the vitamin, produced a similar curative effect. He found, however, that the activity of his preparations disappeared on keeping, and he was unable to reproduce the curative effect in birds receiving a second treatment. Moreover, protective tests with these compounds failed. R. R. Williams and Seidell [1916] obtained from yeast a crystalline material which exerted antineuritic properties. On attempting to purify the substance the antineuritic properties were lost, and the resulting product was found to be identical with adenine. R. R. Williams advanced the theory that the vitamin was liberated in an unstable form by acid and alkaline hydrolysis and readily passed into a stable isomer which was inactive. Reinvestigation of these claims failed to confirm them [Voegtlin and White, 1916–17; Harden and Zilva, 1917; McCollum and Simmonds, 1918; Guha and Drummond, 1929].

Sahashi [1926, 1, 2; 1927] isolated from oryzanin a substance identified as 2 : 6-dihydroxyquinoline, which he found to possess temporary antineuritic properties in doses of 4–15 mg. Later [1928] he stated that 4 (or 5)-glyoxaline methylethylcarbinol in doses of 6 mg. temporarily cured polyneuritic pigeons, although the birds invariably died within 7–10 days. Gulland and Peters [1929] have examined a number of glyoxaline and pyrimidine compounds including those investigated by Sahashi, but with negative results. From its behaviour to silver nitrate and baryta, and from the fact that it gave a strong Pauly reaction, Jansen and Donath [1927] had suggested that their crystalline preparation of vitamin B_1 might contain a pyrimidine or glyoxaline ring. On the other hand Kinnersley and Peters [1928] found that the substance responsible for most of the red coloration with Pauly's reagent did not follow the curative activity on fractionation. Comparative tests of the Jansen-Donath crystals and an active antineuritic yeast preparation showed that both gave an orange colour considerably less intense than that given by an equal amount of histidine [Jansen et al., 1930].

Danysz-Michel and Koskowski [1922] claimed that symptoms of polyneuritis could be suppressed in rice-fed pigeons by the administration of histamine. Abderhalden [1923] and Peters [1924] have also reported cases in which histamine exerted a temporary curative effect, but they lay stress on the fact that the results differ quantitatively and usually qualitatively from the effects produced by the administration of extracts of the antineuritic vitamin. Thus histamine given in daily doses exercised no protection against polyneuritis.

PROPERTIES OF VITAMIN B_1.

The preparation of highly active concentrates of vitamin B_1 in a relatively pure state has clearly emphasized the profound influence exerted by the presence of extraneous material on many of the properties of the vitamin. This is exemplified in its solubility, its stability to heat, and to alkalis, and its relation to various adsorbents. It follows, therefore, that any statement as to chemical or physical properties is valid only in so far as the conditions under which these properties have been determined are accurately defined. Nevertheless, the results of the earlier investigators on the properties of the vitamin as it occurs in natural foodstuffs or in crude extracts have a practical value in problems of dietetics.

Solubility. Eijkman [1906] found that the antineuritic substance was soluble in water, and was not precipitated by moderate concentrations of alcohol. This solvent in varying concentrations has been widely used to extract the vitamin from various natural sources. For the extraction of yeast and rice polishings a 70 per cent. concentration of alcohol was the most effective [Funk, Harrow and Paton, 1923], 95 per cent. alcohol being only an indifferent solvent [Funk, 1912-13, 1; Vedder and Williams, 1913]. The insolubility of crude preparations of the vitamin in the higher concentrations of alcohol has been utilized by Osborne and Wakeman [1919], and Seidell [1926], who employed 80 per cent. alcohol to precipitate their active fractions. Kinnersley and Peters [1927] have demonstrated that while the vitamin is precipitated by alcohol during the early stages of purification, fractions with an activity of 1-3 mg. (pigeon day-dose) which have been freed from alcohol-insoluble material are soluble in absolute alcohol. They also showed that the solubility of the impure vitamin in the higher concentrations of alcohol is largely determined by the hydrogen ion concentration of the solution. Jansen and Donath [1926, 1, 2] found that their crystalline preparation was also soluble in absolute alcohol, and a similar conclusion has been reached by Guha and Drummond [1929], and by R. R. Williams, Waterman and Gurin [1930].

Vitamin B_1 can be readily extracted from yeast and rice polishings by 70 per cent. acetone [Funk, Harrow and Paton, 1923], but is insoluble in pure acetone [Seidell, 1926; Jansen and Donath, 1926, 2; Kinnersley and Peters, 1928]. It cannot be extracted by benzene from wheat embryo or white beans, or from their alcoholic extracts if these are freed from water and alcohol [R. R. Williams and Waterman, 1926], but is removed by benzene from the alcoholic extract if this is not perfectly dry [see McCollum and Simmonds, 1918].

Cooper [1912; 1914, 3] was able to detect distinct traces of the antineuritic factor in an ether extract of egg-yolk, but concluded that this was due to the presence of an ether-soluble substance having a marked adsorptive affinity for the vitamin. This explanation may account for the observation of Myers and Voegtlin [1920] that olive oil and oleic acid removed the antineuritic factor from a solution of autolysed yeast. Vitamin B_1 present in a purified yeast concentrate is not dissolved by ether, ethyl acetate, chloroform, or carbon tetrachloride [Kinnersley and Peters, 1928]. It is soluble in glacial acetic acid [Levine, McCollum and Simmonds, 1922], and in 70 per cent. acetic acid [Funk, Harrow and Paton, 1923].

Stability to heat. There is general agreement that the resistance of vitamin B_1 to heat in faintly acid or acid media is considerable. Most observers have detected little or no destruction of the vitamin after exposure to 100° C. Eijkman [1906] found no destruction of the antineuritic properties of unmilled rice after heating to 100° C. for three hours, and Drummond [1917] observed that yeast or marmite heated for 30 minutes at 100° C. at their natural acidity (pH 4.0-5.0) showed no deterioration of growth-promoting properties for the rat. Chick and Hume [1917–19, 2] made a systematic examination of this question, in which they were careful to avoid certain errors into which some investigators have fallen. In particular they recorded the temperature of the interior of the foodstuff as well as the general temperature of the steamer or autoclave. The former is frequently lower than the latter. They compared the minimal amounts of the unheated and the heated substance required for the cure of poly-neuritis in pigeons. Using wheat embryo and yeast extract they concluded that only slight destruction of the antineuritic vitamin could be detected after heating at 100° C. for 1–2 hours. With higher temperatures there was a progressively increasing degree and rate of destruction, the original potency being reduced to one quarter or less after 2 hrs. at about 129° C. Grijns [1901 ; see also Eijkman, 1906 ; Weill, Mouriquand and Michel, 1916] found that 1–2 hours' exposure to a temperature of 120°C. destroyed the antineuritic properties of unmilled rice, katjang-idjo beans, and buffalo meat, but Eijkman [1906] did not succeed in entirely destroying the protective value of horseflesh under these conditions. Marked destruction of the antineuritic proper-ties of various foodstuffs, such as meat, eggs, yeast extract, and wheat flour when heated for varying periods at temperatures of 110-124° C. has been noted [see Holst, 1907 ; Vedder, 1918 ; Chick and Hume, 1917–19, 2], but dried peas and whole barley appeared to suffer no loss at 118° C. for ten minutes [Holst, 1907].

As most people derive their supply of vitamin B_1 from the cereals in their diet, the practical conclusion to be drawn from the evidence cited is that in the baking of bread or biscuit, a relatively short operation during which the temperature of the interior of the material does not rise above 100° C., no serious diminution in vitamin B_1 content need be apprehended. This proved to be true in the case of wheaten biscuit made from whole flour on which pigeons throve well [Chick and Hume, 1917–19, 2]. Continued heating of foodstuffs at 100° C., however, leads to some loss of the vitamin. In preserving and canning foodstuffs the temperatures employed are frequently much higher than 100° C., and canned foods of all descriptions may contain very little or no vitamin B_1, and, as a practical rule, should therefore be regarded as free from it, unless they have been specially investigated and found to contain it.

Influence of hydrogen ion concentration on the stability of vitamin B_1. Vitamin B_1 resists hydrolysis with acids ; thus there was no diminution in the antineuritic properties of pressed yeast after heating with 20 per cent. sulphuric acid for 24 hours [Cooper and Funk, 1911], and Vedder and Williams [1913] claimed that, after hydrolysis with 50 per cent. sulphuric acid, an extract of rice polishings had an enhanced curative potency. The stability of this vitamin towards acids has been confirmed by many workers [McCollum and Simmonds, 1918; R. R. Williams, Waterman and Gurin, 1929]. Kinnersley and Peters [1928] found that crude antineuritic concentrates stored in 99 per cent. alcohol at pH 1·0–2·0 kept their activity at room temperature for at least three years, but some highly purified preparations gradually lost their activity under these conditions.

The action of alkalis, on the other hand, leads to ready destruction of vitamin B_1 even at low temperatures. Schaumann [1910] and Vedder and Williams [1913] investigated the effect of strong caustic soda; Osborne and Leavenworth [1920-21] showed that the growth-promoting value of yeast was destroyed by treatment with 0·1 N caustic soda for 90 hours at room temperature, whilst Cooper [1913] found that the antineuritic potency of horseflesh was destroyed by treatment with 10 per cent. ammonia at room temperature for 24 hours.

Sherman and Burton [1926], using the rat-growth test, have noted a progressive destruction of the vitamin B complex on heating at 100° C. at decreasing hydrogen ion concentrations. Kinnersley and Peters [1928] found that on heating an antineuritic concentrate (pigeon day-dose 0·059 mg.) for one hour with 0·5 N caustic soda, there was complete destruction of the vitamin. Heating a preparation of activity 3·0 mg. for one hour with 0·1 N soda in the presence of oxygen reduced its activity by approximately 80 per cent., whereas heating it for ten minutes with 0·1 N soda in nitrogen reduced the activity by about 30 per cent. The sensitivity of the vitamin was found to be much increased in the presence of alcohol.

Adsorption of vitamin B_1. Chamberlain and Vedder [1911, 1, 2] were the first to show that the antineuritic vitamin present in an aqueous extract of rice polishings was adsorbed by bone black, and was not removed from the adsorbate by absolute alcohol, water, or ether. Cooper [1913] found that not more than 30 per cent. of the vitamin was removed by this adsorbent, even after filtering an aqueous extract six times through it. Later Peters [1924] showed that the vitamin adsorbed on norite charcoal could be eluted by extraction with 50 per cent. acid alcohol.

Seidell [1916] found that vitamin B_1 was adsorbed by fuller's earth or Lloyd's reagent from a solution of autolysed yeast, and the 'activated solid' resulting from this treatment was found to be highly active in curing avian polyneuritis. Later [1926] he showed that as much as 90 per cent. of the vitamin was adsorbed. Harden and Zilva [1918, 1] also reported a quantitative adsorption of the vitamin by fuller's earth, and by 'dialysed iron' in marked contrast to the behaviour of vitamin C. Jansen and Donath [1926, 1] used acid clay to adsorb the vitamin from an acidified extract of rice polishings in the first stage of their purification process.

A more systematic study has demonstrated the important influence of the hydrogen ion concentration of the medium and of the presence of colloidal impurities on the adsorption of vitamin B_1 by different adsorbents. Emmet and McKim [1917] found that kieselguhr did not adsorb the vitamin, while Zajdel and Funk [1926] obtained only a very incomplete adsorption by colloidal ferric hydroxide at varying hydrogen ion concentrations.

An examination of the adsorption of the vitamin by Lloyd's reagent and silica gel has been made by Levene and van der Hoeven [1924]. Optimum adsorption occurred at pH 4·0. Partial extraction of the adsorbed vitamin was obtained at pH 3·0, but elution was much more complete at pH 9·0. These authors found that silica gel was a much more effective adsorbent for vitamin B_1 than for B_2 and claimed that by the use of this adsorbent in small quantities they were able to prepare antineuritic concentrates virtually free from vitamin B_2. Similar results were obtained by Salmon, Guerrant and Hays [1928, 1, 2]. They showed that the maximum adsorption of vitamin B_1 by fuller's earth was obtained, under their conditions, within the range pH 3·0 — 5·0 with optimum adsorption at pH 4·0. Increasing alkalinity up to pH 9·0 rapidly diminished the amount of vitamin held in adsorption, while at still more alkaline reactions adsorption was negligible. In this respect the antineuritic vitamin was found to behave like an organic electrolyte such as quinine, in contrast to vitamin B_2 which resembled an organic non-electrolyte, showing optimal adsorption at pH 0·08. These workers found evidence of inactivation of vitamin B_1 amounting to as much as 50 per cent. in alkaline solutions, thus emphasizing the importance of employing only weakly alkaline eluents. Kinnersley and Peters [1925; 1927], who use norite charcoal in their preparation of antineuritic concentrates, find that adsorption of the vitamin after the treatment with mercuric sulphate is most complete within the range pH 5·0 — 7·0, and optimal at pH 7·0. They find, however, that the pH of optimal adsorption of the vitamin from crude preparations is modified by the presence of impurities. In the more highly purified fractions the vitamin is most completely adsorbed at pH 9·0 [Peters, 1930, 1, 2].

Miscellaneous properties. The antineuritic vitamin withstands desiccation for long periods of time [Jansen, 1923 ; G. M. Findlay, 1923, 1] as is shown by its abundant presence in dried foodstuffs. It does not appear to be susceptible to oxidation by atmospheric oxygen, in this respect differing sharply from vitamins A and C. Exposure to ozone [Zilva, 1922] has no deleterious effect upon it. Zilva [1919, 1] claimed that exposure to ultra-violet radiation did not destroy the vitamin, a conclusion supported by Hogan and Hunter [1928]. On the other hand, R. R. Williams [1924], Kennedy and Palmer [1929], and Chick and Roscoe [1929, 2] found that longer exposures result in some destruction. Kinnersley and Peters [1928] find that the vitamin in acid solution is stable to hydrogen peroxide, or potassium permanganate, or to heating with 5 per cent. nitric acid. Treatment with nitrous acid is without effect on the vitamin [McCollum and Simmonds, 1918 ; Peters, 1924 ; Levene and van der Hoeven, 1926]. This fact is regarded as strong evidence that the vitamin is neither a primary nor a secondary amine. Vitamin B_1 passes through a parchment membrane [Eijkman, 1906 ; Chamberlain and Vedder, 1911, 2 ; Shiga and Kusama, 1911 ; Drummond, 1917; Seidell, 1922, 1; Zilva and Miura, 1921, 1]. These last observers believe that the vitamin has a molecular weight of the order of 300–350, or that it forms a complex of about this molecular weight with some other substance.

METHODS OF DETECTION AND ESTIMATION OF VITAMIN B_1.

No satisfactory colour reaction, or other chemical test, for vitamin B_1 has yet been discovered, in spite of much effort in this direction. Funk [1913, 1] and Funk and Macallum [1913] found that a pronounced blue colour was given by Funk's crystalline preparation from rice polishings and by various alcoholic extracts of the vitamin in the presence of the uric acid and phenol reagents of Folin and Denis. Eijkman [1927] found that the reaction with the uric acid reagent was given by Jansen and Donath's crystalline preparation of vitamin B_1, but that it was much weaker than that produced by a solution of uric acid of the same concentration. The lack of specificity of this test renders it valueless in identifying vitamin B_1. The same criticism has been made by Bezssonoff [1924, 2] and by Levine 1924–25] of the colour reaction proposed by Jendrassik [1923] as a test for the vitamin.

The biological method of testing for the presence of the antineuritic vitamin, while open to many objections, remains the only one that is as yet satisfactory. The animals which have been most usually employed for this purpose are the fowl, the pigeon, and the rat. The rice bird (*Munia maia*) has also been used.

Experiments with Fowls and Pigeons.

The principal methods adopted in experiments with these animals have been of three types, viz. the protective, the weight maintenance, and the curative.

Protective test. The protective test, in the form originally employed [Eijkman, 1897, 3; Vedder and Clark, 1912; Cooper, 1912; 1914, 1, 2; Chick and Hume, 1917–19, 1; Jansen and Donath, 1926, 1; and later workers], involves an estimation of the daily ration of a particular foodstuff necessary to prevent polyneuritis when added to a vitamin-free diet such as polished rice. The test is open to several objections unless very large numbers of birds are used. In the first place difficulties arise owing to the variability of the times of onset of polyneuritis in different individuals. If a given bird fails to develop symptoms within a specified time, it is always possible that the bird in question might not have become polyneuritic in this time even upon polished rice alone [Peters, 1924], or that polyneuritis might have developed later if the experiments had been prolonged. Thus Vedder and Clark [1912] reported a case of polyneuritis which developed in a pigeon after one hundred days on the experimental diet. There is also the disadvantage that relatively large amounts of the test substance are required and that the experiments are time consuming.

Weight-maintenance test. Another test for the presence of vitamin B_1 [R. R. Williams and Seidell, 1916; Seidell, 1922, 1] is one in which the criterion adopted is the maintenance of the body-weight of the animal on a diet of polished rice, or other vitamin-free diet, when supplemented by the substance under test. Peters [1924] offered the criticism that this criterion is based on the assumption that the factors necessary for the cure of polyneuritis and for weight maintenance are identical. This is now known not to be the case (see p. 121). A further disadvantage of this test for vitamin B_1, when employed over a considerable period of time, as in the experiments of Plimmer and his co-workers [1927], is that the animal may become depleted of some other essential factor which may be absent or deficient both in the test substance and the basal diet.

Curative test. In the curative test the experimental animal is fed on a vitamin B_1-free diet until severe symptoms of polyneuritis have developed. The foodstuff or vitamin concentrate under consideration is then administered in varying doses to separate birds, and determination made of the minimal dose required to effect recovery. In a successful test there is a dramatic recovery from a condition of complete helplessness (see Figs. 26, 27). It is not unusual to see normal gait and flight restored within an hour or two of the administration of the vitamin.

The discovery by Funk [1912–13, 2], and R. R. Williams [1916], that the administration of a number of known chemical substances may be followed by a complete, though temporary, recovery from the classical symptom of head retraction led to the criticism and abandonment of the curative test by various workers. Moreover, head retraction has been shown to develop in certain cases in starvation, even when extracts of the antineuritic vitamin are administered, as a result of 'washing out' the tissues of starving birds by giving large amounts of water by mouth [Chamberlain and Vedder, 1911, 2; Chamberlain, Bloombergh and Kilbourne, 1911; Eijkman and Hoogenhuijze, 1916; Marrian, Baker, Drummond and Woollard, 1927], and in other conditions. The spontaneous cure of head retraction in rice-fed pigeons has been reported by Kon and Drummond [1927]; temporary recovery has also been observed after artificially raising the body temperature of the polyneuritic animal, and as a result of the administration of glucose [Peters, 1924; Roche, 1925].

This test has been reviewed by Kinnersley, Peters and Reader [1928], who have defined the conditions necessary for obtaining reliable and quantitative results. They find that, subject to these conditions, any particular bird tends to develop symptoms of polyneuritis at a constant time (within narrow limits) after the commencement of rice feeding, while the duration of the cure in experiments with their antineuritic concentrates has been found proportional to the dose of vitamin B_1 administered. Although the onset of symptoms varies somewhat from bird to bird, they consider that the test provides a method which is economical in time and material, and which may be relied upon to give fair accuracy in the standardization of antineuritic concentrates. When the curative method is used for the estimation of the vitamin content of natural foodstuffs other difficulties may arise. Thus when the test foodstuff itself is given by mouth after the development of acute symptoms, slowness of digestion or absorption from the alimentary canal may delay the recovery for several days and complicate the interpretation of the experiment. If an extract of the foodstuff is prepared, the inevitably large losses of the curative factor incurred in the extraction process may result in considerable errors. Thus in the case of dried peas the curative dose of the natural material was 10 g., whereas that of the alcoholic extract was the equivalent of 40 g. [Chick and Hume, 1917, 2; 1917–19, 2; see also Cooper, 1912; 1914, 1].

Experiments with Rats.

Growth test. The rat-growth test for water-soluble vitamin B introduced by McCollum and Simmonds [1918], which has been widely employed, particularly in America, involves the determination of the minimum ration of a foodstuff required for normal growth or maintenance when added to a diet complete in all other essential dietary constituents. Many of the earlier workers contented themselves with ascertaining whether the experimental material, when constituting a certain percentage of the diet or a certain daily dose, did, or did not, satisfy the requirements of the animal. Their results, therefore, at best give only a rough idea of the quantitative distribution of what we now know as the antineuritic vitamin in different foodstuffs. Moreover, the failure to recognize the multiple nature of the vitamin B complex frequently led to erroneous or misleading conclusions.

A further source of error which complicated the results of earlier workers with the rat was the failure to prevent coprophagy (see p. 138). It is now usual in the study of the B-vitamins to limit the access of the experimental rats to their own faeces by employing cages with bases made of wide-meshed wire.

The principles underlying the rat-growth test as a quantitative method for the estimation of vitamin B_1 have been examined and defined by Sherman and MacArthur [1927], and by Chick and Roscoe [1929, 1].

Curative test. M. E. Smith [1930] and Kinnersley, Peters and Reader [1930] have introduced a curative test for vitamin B_1, using respectively the young and adult rat as experimental animals. Smith's method consists in the determination of the minimal dose of a test material required to effect a cure of acute polyneuritis in young rats which have been reared after weaning on a basal diet free from the vitamin B complex, supplemented by autoclaved brewer's yeast to provide vitamin B_2 and by cod-liver oil. Under these conditions the animals grow for a time, but subsequently decline in weight and finally, in from 50–80 days, develop typical paralytic symptoms characterized by lameness of the hind- and fore-limbs, inco-ordination, spastic gait, convulsions, and cartwheel and rolling movements. The antineuritic vitamin was usually administered intravenously, and after an injection improvement was noticeable within 3–5 hours and was followed by a cure in 18–24 hours. The duration of the cure appeared to be related to the size of the dose. Subsequently the animal declined in weight, but could be restored by a second injection. The author claimed that the method gave quantitative results when comparing the minimum doses of various antineuritic fractions. Moreover, the vitamin appeared to be specific in relieving the polyneuritic symptoms in the rat, since none of the pure substances tried which have been claimed to produce 'cures' in pigeons was found to be effective on the rat.

In Kinnersley, Peters and Reader's test, adult rats are allowed to fall in weight on a vitamin B_1- free diet (to which vitamin B_2 has been added as alkalized marmite). Upon appearance of symptoms, a dose of vitamin B_1 is given by mouth which takes effect within 30 minutes ; the authors claim that the duration of cure is proportional to the dose administered. Care must be taken to distinguish the symptoms of vitamin B_1 deficiency from those of vitamin B_4 deficiency (p. 167) with which they may be confused.

Vitamin B_2 (Antidermatitis Vitamin[1]).

Symptomatology of Vitamin B_2 Deficiency in the Rat.

Human pellagra is a disease which produces a wide variety of symptoms. To give a rough description, the typical pellagrin shows dermatitis on the face and hands and those parts of the body exposed to sunlight, accompanied by inflammation of the alimentary tract from the mouth to the rectum, and often, in the later stages, by mental disorder and lesions of the central nervous system.

The symptoms observed by Goldberger and Lillie [1926] in albino rats fed on diets containing the antineuritic vitamin but devoid of the heat-stable P-P (pellagra-preventive) factor resembled human pellagra in that certain rats developed symmetrical dermatitis, particularly of the paws, fore-arms, neck, and ears. Depilation occurred in almost all cases. In addition to the skin lesions, the authors describe a tendency for the lids of one or both eyes to adhere together, with an accumulation of dried secretion on the margin of the lids in some instances. Ulceration of the tip of the tongue and at the angles of the mouth occurred in some rats, and diarrhoea in rare cases. The shortest period taken for symptoms to develop was seven weeks. The condition noted by Chick and Roscoe [1927] among rats receiving Peters's antineuritic concentrate from yeast as the sole source of 'vitamin B' appears to be substantially the same. Very similar skin and eye lesions were observed, developing in some animals after about six to eight weeks. Neither stomatitis nor diarrhoea was recorded, but post-mortem examination indicated 'a very unhealthy condition of the whole alimentary tract, especially in the small intestine, which showed signs of inflammation with atrophy of the mucous membrane and often contained blood-stained mucus'.

G. M. Findlay [1928] and Stern and Findlay [1929], who produced a similar 'pellagrous' condition in rats by the method of Chick and Roscoe (i.e. using Peters's concentrate as a source of vitamin B_1), made histological studies of the skin, alimentary tract, adrenals, liver, pancreas, and central nervous system, for the full details of which the original papers should be consulted. The skin condition showed congestion, with invasion of small round cells, followed by the production of flakes of keratinized material on the free surface of the epidermis. Occasionally the whole epidermis was destroyed. Examination of the spinal cord revealed a vacuolation and swelling of the anterior horn cells. No very definite or characteristic lesions were found in other organs of the body.

Sherman and Sandels [1928–29] observed in rats on a vitamin B_2-free diet a somewhat similar condition, but clearly defined dermatitis of the fore and hind paws did not occur. The symptomatology of vitamin B_2 deficiency as recorded by Salmon, Hays and Guerrant

[1] Vitamin G of some American writers.

[1928] agrees well with that described by Goldberger and Lillie and by Chick and Roscoe. Salmon and his colleagues found a 'large coccus' constantly associated with the skin lesions of vitamin B_2 deficiency in the rat, and put forward the idea, which has not been confirmed, that rat 'pellagra' needs a microbic in addition to a dietary cause for its development.

Bing and Mendel [1929], using an extract of rice polishings as the sole source of the vitamin B complex, induced a scabby dermatitis in mice, mostly on the medial surface of the fore and hind legs. Apart from Goldberger's work on black-tongue in dogs, a disease which stands in a somewhat doubtful relation to vitamin B_2 deficiency, this is the only attempt which has been made to investigate the effects of lack of vitamin B_2 in any animal other than the rat.

To sum up, it may be said that skin lesions, often symmetrical, sometimes occur in rats and mice fed on diets devoid of vitamin B_2 but otherwise complete. The symptoms appear after about 6–10 weeks on the deficient diet, during which period growth ceases. Severe conjunctivitis or ophthalmia is constantly recorded, stomatitis occasionally. Red-stained urine is noted by some investigators. Diarrhoea, so marked a symptom in human pellagra, is exceptional in the vitamin B_2-deficient rat. All lesions are curable by foods containing vitamin B_2.

It may be remarked that dermatitis associated with vitamin B_2 deficiency appears to be produced in the rat with some uncertainty. In none of the experiments just recorded did more than a proportion of animals show skin lesions, and several investigators have failed to observe any characteristic symptomatology beyond, perhaps, a condition of general wretchedness. Those who have done much work on vitamin B_2 are puzzled by the changeable nature of the lesions occurring in the vitamin B_2-deficient animal and by the frequent failure to produce any characteristic skin symptoms. Complete cessation of growth without any accompanying decline in weight is, however, a constant feature of young rats provided with vitamin B_1 but deprived of vitamin B_2.

SEPARATION OF VITAMIN B_2 FROM VITAMIN B_1.

Naturally occurring substances containing one B-vitamin tend as a rule to contain the other, though in some there are marked quantitative differences. An exception exists, however, in egg-white, which, according to Chick and Roscoe [1929, 1], contains vitamin B_2 without admixture of vitamin B_1. In order to investigate the properties of either vitamin it has usually been necessary to work with material containing both, such as yeast, and attempts have been made to obtain a separation of vitamin B_2 from vitamin B_1 without loss of potency.

Separation by heat. The relative stability of vitamin B_2 to heat enables fractions free from vitamin B_1 to be easily prepared, but the application of heat sufficient to destroy the antineuritic vitamin does not leave vitamin B_2 unimpaired [Chick and Roscoe, 1929, 2].

Separation by adsorption. Salmon, Guerrant and Hays [1928, 1] attempted to effect a separation of the B-vitamins by selective

adsorption on fuller's earth.   When an extract of soya-bean leaves
was treated with a very small quantity of fuller's earth, vitamin B_1
was adsorbed with a very small admixture of vitamin B_2; according
to Narayanan and Drummond [1930], however, fuller's earth
effectively adsorbed vitamin B_2 also, from a solution containing very
little vitamin B_1, at pH values from 6·8 to 0·01.   The removal of the
vitamin became more nearly complete as the acidity was raised.

At neutral or slightly alkaline reactions vitamin B_1 is probably
more strongly adsorbed by norite charcoal than vitamin B_2 [Peters,
1924 ; Narayanan and Drummond, 1930].

Separation by lead acetate precipitation.   The antineuritic concentrate
prepared from yeast by Peters's method [1924] is free from the
vitamin B_2 present in abundance in the original yeast.   Chick and Roscoe
[1929, 2] attempted to determine at what stage of the process vitamin
B_2 is removed.   It was found that during precipitation of the original
aqueous yeast extract by lead acetate a considerable amount (roughly
one-half) of the vitamin B_2 was carried down with the precipitate,
when the precipitation took place at a pH of about 4·5–4·7.   At
neutral or slightly alkaline reactions precipitation with lead acetate
removed vitamin B_2 more nearly completely from solution, but the
further the reaction was carried towards alkalinity the more vitamin B_1
was precipitated also.

PROPERTIES OF VITAMIN B_2.

Heat-stability.   Almost all the investigators who have attempted
to unravel ' water-soluble vitamin B ' into its component parts have
used autoclaved yeast as a source of vitamin B_2, it being assumed
that the antineuritic vitamin is destroyed by being exposed for a few
hours to temperatures of 120°–130° C. [Grijns, 1901 ; Eijkman,
1906 ; Chick and Hume, 1917–19, 2].   Vitamin B_2 is often referred
to as the 'heat-stable factor' in the vitamin B complex.   Its heat-
stability is, however, only relative, depending largely on the reaction
at which heating takes place.   Chick and Roscoe [1927] found that
brewer's yeast when heated at 120° C. for five hours at its normal pH
of about 4·5–5·0 loses half its vitamin B_2 potency.   Subsequently,
R. R. Williams, Waterman and Gurin [1929] investigated the
destruction of vitamin B_2 in brewer's yeast heated for six hours at
different reactions at 120°C.   They concluded that at this temperature
much vitamin B_2 survived if the reaction were that natural to yeast
(pH about 4·5), and more if it were more acid (pH 1·6–2·0).   If the
reaction were acid some vitamin B_1 was also found to survive this
temperature.   At pH 8–14 both vitamins were destroyed.   Similar
results have been recorded by Chick and Roscoe [1930].   At pH 5·0
about 50 per cent. of the original vitamin B_2 was lost when the yeast
was heated for 4–5 hours at 123° C.   When an aqueous yeast extract,
at a pH of 8·3–10, was subjected to 122°–125° C. for 4–5 hours, between
75 and 100 per cent. of the original vitamin B_2 was lost ; on heating
for 2 hours at 98°–100° C. (pH 8·3) the loss was about 50 per cent.;
at room temperature for ten days (at pH 8·3), 30 per cent.

The constituent of the B-vitamin complex which is able to correct
the deleterious effect of excessive protein (70 per cent.) in a diet

[Hassan and Drummond, 1927 ; Hartwell, 1928] is now generally supposed to be identical with vitamin B_2. This factor, as contained in marmite, was found to survive heating in ' strongly alkaline' solution for 1 hour at 120° C. (Hassan and Drummond), a result which has been confirmed by Reader [1929, 2].

The discrepancy between this result and that obtained by Chick and Roscoe suggests that the stability of vitamin B_2 to high temperatures may be influenced by other factors than the pH, for example, by the salt content of the solution.

Since a number of investigators have shown that there are other factors in the vitamin B complex in addition to vitamins B_1 and B_2, factors which are necessary for the continued growth of rats or for the maintenance of weight in pigeons [R. R. Williams and Waterman, 1927–28 ; 1928 ; Hunt, 1928, 2 ; Reader, 1929, 2] the sensitivity of vitamin B_2 to heat and alkali under various conditions is of considerable importance. If it be assumed that vitamin B_2 survives unchanged on heating, whatever the reaction, the danger arises that an unrecognized shortage of this vitamin may be mistaken for lack of an unknown factor. The existence of other B-vitamins cannot be satisfactorily proved unless the most rigid precautions are taken to exclude a quantitative deficiency of vitamins B_1 and B_2.

Solubility. The antineuritic vitamin has long been known to be soluble in alcohol in strengths ranging from 88 per cent. to absolute [Fraser and Stanton, 1911]. Drummond [1917] found that ' watersoluble vitamin B ' could not be satisfactorily extracted with absolute alcohol, but succeeded with 70 per cent., an observation readily explained in the light of later knowledge that the second factor in the vitamin B complex is relatively insoluble in strong alcohol.

Goldberger, Wheeler *et al.* [1926] in the course of their demonstration of the dual nature of vitamin B, found that an 18 per cent. alcoholic extract of whole maize was deficient in vitamin B_2, though rich in the antineuritic factor. It was observed by Salmon, Guerrant and Hays [1928, 1] that the vitamin B_2 contained in an extract from soya-bean leaves was precipitated by 82·7 per cent. alcohol. Similarly, Sherman and Sandels [1928–29] found vitamin B_2 to be insoluble in 95 per cent. alcohol, an observation confirmed by Chick and Roscoe [1929, 2]. It was noted by both these latter groups of workers that the vitamin B_2 recovered from the residue insoluble in strong alcohol was reduced in amount, a fact suggesting that alcohol in high concentrations had a destructive effect upon it. Narayanan and Drummond [1930], on the other hand, found vitamin B_2 to be very soluble in 50 per cent. alcohol, which extracted about 88 per cent. of the vitamin B_2 originally present in a yeast fraction.

Dialysis. Vitamin B_2 dialysed through a cellophane membrane, permeable also to vitamin B_1, at a pH of about 3·0 [Chick and Roscoe, 1929, 2]. Zilva and Miura [1921, 1] observed that 'water-soluble vitamin B ' passed a collodion membrane of such permeability as to permit diffusion of semi-colloidal substances such as methylene blue and safranine.

Susceptibility to ultra-violet irradiation. Hogan and Hunter [1928] reported that the vitamin B_2 present in yeast was destroyed by an exposure to ultra-violet irradiation which left vitamin B_1 unimpaired.

In attempting to repeat this work, Chick and Roscoe [1929, 2] confirmed the susceptibility of vitamin B_2 to damage by ultra-violet radiation, but found that irradiation of a yeast extract for six hours at a distance of 40 cm. destroyed only about half the vitamin B_2 originally present. Its content of vitamin B_1 suffered also, so that ultra-violet irradiation does not provide a satisfactory method of separating vitamin B_1 from vitamin B_2.

Action of nitrous acid on vitamin B_2. Vitamin B_2, like vitamin B_1 [Peters, 1924], does not appear to be susceptible to the action of nitrous acid, so that its activity cannot depend on the presence of amino-nitrogen. Levene [1928] reported that vitamin B_2 was destroyed by de-amination, but the results of other workers are opposed to this view. Chick [1929] found that de-amination had no effect on the vitamin B_2 activity of a yeast extract, and later Narayanan and Drummond [1930] recorded a similar result, which is in accord with the observation of McCollum and Simmonds [1918] that 'water-soluble vitamin B' is resistant to the action of nitrous acid.

It will be seen that the literature concerning the properties of vitamin B_2 is full of contradictions. The probable explanation lies in the fact that, in common with the other recently described members of the vitamin B complex, vitamin B_2 is not yet a well-defined chemical entity. Its solubility and precipitation limits, and also its stability to heat, are influenced greatly by the circumstances under which the tests are made, including not only the pH, but also the presence of other substances, mineral salts, adsorbents, &c. Doubtless these discrepancies will be cleared up as the result of further investigations.

Methods of Estimation of Vitamin B_2.

Two methods have been described for the estimation of vitamin B_2. In both the rat is used as the experimental animal; in one the criterion adopted is the cure of dermatitis developed in absence of this vitamin, and in the other the restoration of growth. Only the latter can as yet be used with any degree of accuracy.

Curative test. Goldberger and Lillie [1926] and Chick and Roscoe [1927] showed that the dermatitis which developed in rats on diets deficient in vitamin B_2 could be cured by the administration of this vitamin, and the latter workers [1928] investigated the dermatitis-curing effect of the substances tested by them for content of vitamin B_2 by other methods [see also Aykroyd and Roscoe, 1929 ; Chick and Copping. 1930, 1 ; Chick, Copping and Roscoe, 1930 ; Roscoe, 1930]. It is, however, difficult to obtain quantitative results, as there is a great variation in the time elapsing before symptoms develop and in their type and severity, as well as in the general condition of the animal. It was found, however, that, with the substances tested, the curative value ran parallel with the growth-promoting potency, slightly less of any material being needed to cure symptoms than to promote good growth.

Leader [1930], Sherman and Sandels [1931] and Sure and Smith [1930–31] obtained symptoms of dermatitis with greater frequency when the diet contained some vitamin B_2 than when it was entirely deficient. When the dermatitis developed on diet containing only a small amount of vitamin B_2 it seems possible that the symptoms may have been due to a partial lack of the vitamin; but when, as in the cases observed by Sure and Smith, the rats received as much as 10 per cent. of autoclaved yeast in their diet, grew normally, but yet developed symptoms of dermatitis, it would seem that the symptoms were not the same as those observed by other workers with vitamin B_2-deficient animals, or else that the factors preventing dermatitis and promoting growth were not identical. In either case experiments based on the cure of symptoms so obtained cannot be used for accurate quantitative estimation of vitamin B_2.

Growth test. In this test comparison is made between the amounts of different materials needed daily by young rats to promote growth, at a given standard rate, when these are administered as additions to basal diets adequate in all respects and lacking only in vitamin B_2. These methods differ one from another in the form in which the vitamin B_1 is supplied. Both yeast and the cereal embryos (which contain relatively more vitamin B_1 than B_2) have been used as the starting-points for purified vitamin B_1 concentrates suitable for use in these tests.

Goldberger and Lillie [1926] used an alcoholic extract of corn meal and also an adsorbate on fuller's earth from yeast extract [Seidell, 1922, 3] as sources of vitamin B_1. The former contained only small amounts of vitamin B_2 but the latter contained sufficient B_2 for good growth if the dose was large.

Chick and Roscoe [1927] used the vitamin B_1 concentrate prepared from yeast by the method of Peters [1924; Kinnersley and Peters 1925], which is obtained by extraction with acid alcohol from a charcoal adsorbate. This extract which is free from vitamin B_2 was also used by Narayanan and Drummond [1930].

In the method of Chick and Roscoe, young rats about 40 g. in weight, immediately after weaning, receive an experimental diet in which the caseinogen providing the protein is specially purified. Vitamins A and D are supplied by a daily ration of cod-liver oil and vitamin B_1 by 0·1 c.c. ($\equiv$ 0·6 g. dried yeast) of Peters's concentrate. On this diet the body-weight should remain constant indefinitely, but on addition of a source of vitamin B_2 growth is immediately resumed. Determination is made of the minimum dose required daily to restore growth to the extent of about 12 g. weekly increase in weight, over a period of about five weeks.

Evans and Burr [1928,1] and Hetler, Meyer and Hussemann [1931] used 'tiki-tiki', an alcoholic extract prepared from rice polishings for the treatment of beri-beri in the Philippines (p. 127). The extent of growth which occurred when more than a minimal amount of this extract was given showed, however, that vitamin B_2 was present. The former workers considered that this was contained in the unpurified caseinogen and starch of the basal diet, but the latter workers that it was contained in the tiki-tiki.

Guha and Drummond [1929] prepared vitamin B_1 concentrates using adsorbates on charcoal and fuller's earth from an alcoholic extract of wheat germ. These were used by Guha [1931, 2, 3] in vitamin B_2 tests, as also was an aqueous alcoholic extract of yeast fractionated with normal lead acetate [Guha, 1931, 1]. The latter preparation, however, contained some vitamin B_2.

R. R. Williams, Waterman and Gurin [1929] in their tests for vitamin B_2 used as source of vitamin B_1 an activated fuller's earth preparation from yeast, described by them in 1928 and shown to contain no vitamin B_2.

DISTRIBUTION IN FOODSTUFFS OF THE VITAMIN B COMPLEX.

The (Antineuritic) Vitamin B_1.

The distribution of the antineuritic (antiberi-beri) vitamin B_1 was first studied systematically by Cooper [1912; 1914, 1, 3] at the Lister Institute, using as criterion the prevention or cure of polyneuritis in pigeons on a diet of polished rice. In response to war-time needs this work was rendered more complete by other workers in the same Institute [Chick and Hume, 1917, 1, 2; 1917–19, 1]. A summary of the chief results obtained is given in Tables IX and X.

TABLE IX.

Showing approximately relative values of the more important foodstuffs (weight for weight) in natural condition for prevention of beri-beri.
(Value of wheat germ taken as equal to 100.)

Substance.	Value.	Approximate water content. Per cent.
Wheat germ	100	10 to 13
Wheat bran	25	10 to 13
Rice germ	200	10 to 13
Yeast (pressed)	60	70
Peas (dried)	40	12
Lentils	80	10
Egg yolk	50	70
Ox liver	50	70
Ox muscle	11	75
Potatoes	4.3	80

Of subsequent work using the growth of rats as criterion, only that which has been done since the discovery of the complex nature of vitamin B and in which due provision of vitamin B_2 has been made in the basal diet can now be accepted to indicate the distribution of the antineuritic vitamin apart from other members of the vitamin B complex [Salmon, 1927; Aykroyd and Roscoe, 1929; Roscoe, 1930; 1931, 1, 2; Aykroyd, 1930, 2].

Vitamin B_1 is widespread and has been detected in almost all the natural foodstuffs examined except egg white, honey, and the endosperms of cereals. Yeast, eggs, liver, and the embryos of cereals are the richest known sources, and green-leaf vegetables must be regarded as potent if dry weights are considered. Milk, meat, and fish are poor in this vitamin; the roes of fish, however, like the eggs of birds, are rich sources.

Cereals. The most important practical result emerging from the work on vitamin B_1 is the fact that among its chief sources are to be

TABLE X.

Preventive Experiments.

MINIMUM DAILY RATION WHICH MUST BE ADDED TO A DIET OF POLISHED RICE TO PREVENT ONSET OF POLYNEURITIS (BERI-BERI) IN A PIGEON OF 300 TO 400 G. WEIGHT.

Substance.	Daily Ration.		Observer.	Notes on Results.
	Natural Foodstuff. (g.)	Dry Weight. (g.)		
Wheat germ, sample R.I., free from bran	1.5	1.3	Chick and Hume [1917, 1, 2 1917–19, 1]	Complete protection.
Wheat bran, sample R.I., free from germ	More than 1.5	More than 1.4	,,	No protection with 1.5 g. daily. Polyneuritis occured in same time as in control birds.
,, ,,	More than 2.5	More than 2.2	,,	Small degree of protection. Mean time of onset delayed about 2 weeks.
Yeast extract, commercial sample A	{ 0.5, 1.0	0.35, 0.7	,,	Protection not secured in all cases.
Pressed yeast	2.5	0.5	,,	Protection.
Lentils	—	3.0	Cooper [1912, 1914, 1, 3]	,,
Barley, unhusked	3.7	3.2	,,	,,
Barley, husked	5.0	4.5	,,	,,
Egg yolk	3	1.5	,,	,,
Ox muscle	20	5.0	,,	,,
Ox heart muscle	5	1.7	,,	,,
Ox brain	6	1.2	,,	,,
Ox liver	3	0.9	,,	,,
Sheep brain	12	2.5	,,	,,
Fish muscle	More than 10	More than 2	,,	Protection not secured with these amounts.
Cheese	More than 8	More than 5.6	,,	
Cow's milk	More than 35	More than 8.5	,,	

numbered the cereals and edible pulses. In the case of the cereals an interesting differentiation has been established [Chick and Hume, 1917–19, 1] between the different constituents of the grain, the largest deposit of the antineuritic factor being found in the embryo or germ, the bran (*pericarp* and *aleurone layer*) coming next in order of importance (see Fig. 29 a, b). The endosperm, especially when deprived of the aleurone layer (as is customary in the preparation of white wheaten flour or 'polished' rice), is deficient in the antineuritic factor, and if employed too exclusively as a diet will occasion polyneuritis in birds or beri-beri in man [see also Edie and Simpson, 1911]. The experimental work on cereals has been done chiefly with rice and wheat, but there is confirmatory evidence in the case of maize and rye, and no reasonable doubt exists that, as a rule, among cereals, the anti-beri-beri factor is chiefly concentrated in the embryo.

The potency of the cereal embryo in curing avian polyneuritis was found to be very great. Chick and Hume found that 2·5 g. (and occasionally 1 g.) of wheat germ was sufficient to cure a pigeon showing fully developed symptoms ; in case of rice and maize embryo, cures were obtained with amounts varying from 0·5 to 1 g. and from 1 to 3 g. respectively.

The prevailing opinion, based on observation of rice-eating populations consuming decorticated rice, has located the principal deposits of the substance preventing beri-beri in the wall of the husked grain, and in the outer layer (aleurone layer) of endosperm, which is removed during steam milling. This view was based upon the connexion between beri-beri and decorticated rice, and the prevention or cure of the disease effected when rice bran or its extracts were added to the diet. A truer explanation recognizes the richer source of the vitamin to be the germ removed with the bran. In the case of wheat and rice the germ, weight for weight, was found to be respectively five times and ten times as potent as the bran in the cure of polyneuritis.

The wheat grain has also been investigated by Bell and Mendel [1921–22; 1922; see also Osborne and Mendel, 1919, 2] who used growth of mice as criterion for the presence of the vitamin B complex and found that the embryo contained about one-sixth of the total amount in the grain. White flour (American patent flour) contained no appreciable amount of vitamin B_1 ; low grade flour and bran were about twice as rich, and standard middlings, which contained most of the embryo, four times as rich as the unmilled grain ; the remaining grades (first and second clear) were about equal to the unmilled grain. It must be remembered that in the preparation of bread yeast is added, and this will introduce a small amount of vitamin B_1 ; the amount of yeast added is usually less than 1 per cent. of the flour.

Pulses. The foodstuffs next in importance to the cereals in prevention of beri-beri are the pulses. Grijns [1901] and others have demonstrated the value of certain beans ('katjang-idjo', *Phaseolus radiatus*) in prevention and cure of avian polyneuritis or human beri-beri. Dry peas and lentils were found to occupy a high place in the series of foodstuffs collected in Table IX. Experiments with rats confirm the results which have been obtained with pigeons [see

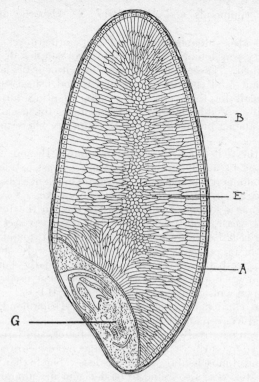

Fig. 29 a.[1] Diagram of a longitudinal section through a grain of wheat, showing :
B, pericarp, forming the branny envelope ; A, aleurone layer of cells forming the
outermost layer of the endosperm removed with the pericarp during milling ; E,
parenchymatous cells of the endosperm ; G, embryo or germ.

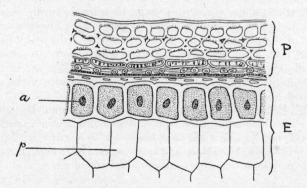

Fig. 29 b.[1] Cross-section through the branny envelope and outer portion of the
endosperm of wheat grain, showing : P, the pericarp ; E, endosperm, consisting of
a, layer of aleurone cells, and p, parenchymatous cells.

[1] Reproduced, with the permission of the Controller of H.M. Stationery Office,
from Figs. 1 and 2 in Dr. J. M. HAMILL's 'Report to the Local Government Board
on the nutritive value of bread made from different varieties of wheat flour', 1911.

McCollum, Simmonds and Pitz, 1917, 2; Osborne and Mendel, 1919, 1].

Eggs are also valuable sources of the antiberi-beri factor, and this property was found unimpaired in two samples of dried hen's eggs examined. These large deposits of antineuritic factor in the seeds of plants and eggs of animals (birds and fishes) suggest a due provision made for the wants of the young offspring during the early period of life. Vedder [1913, p. 61] mentions the usual prevalence of beri-beri among pregnant women in countries where the disease is endemic.

Yeast is the richest known source of vitamin B_1 and is unaffected in this respect by autolysis and extraction. Yeast extract A (Table X) was a commercial preparation (marmite) much used as a substitute for meat extract in preparation of soup cubes, &c. Yeast has been largely used as a source of vitamin B for rats, in the form of fresh yeast, dried yeast, autolysed yeast, and yeast extract. Kennedy and Palmer [1922, where the literature is quoted] found yeast to be very variable in potency. Satisfactory results were obtained with about 0.6 g. fresh brewer's yeast administered daily, but even then reproduction was not normal. Other observers have used such quantities as 3.6 per cent. of dried yeast in the diet, 0.1–0.2 g. dried yeast daily, or an equivalent amount of extract [Drummond, 1917; see Osborne and Wakeman, 1919].

Meat is comparatively deficient in this factor, and large quantities were required for curing or preventing pigeon polyneuritis. This was specially true of muscle-fibre which was less valuable than heart, liver, or brain. Meat was also found to be deficient in vitamin B as tested on rats [Osborne and Mendel, 1917, 2], and in this case also the heart, liver, and brain were found to be more efficacious.

Vegetables and Fruits. Of the green-leaf vegetables tested, watercress and lettuce proved to be about twice as rich as cabbage and spinach and not inferior to egg-yolk or the embryo of cereals, if dry weights are compared. Of the ' root vegetables ' examined, carrot is the richest and about equal to cabbage or spinach, turnip is less rich and potato by far the poorest [Roscoe, 1931, 2]. The lower water-content of the potato and the larger quantities ordinarily consumed, however, give it an enhanced importance as a source of vitamin B_1 in an ordinary diet.

There are as yet few trustworthy quantitative studies on the vitamin B_1 content of fruits.

Milk. Fresh cow's milk is often so poor in vitamin B_1 that it has proved difficult to administer sufficient amounts to the experimental animals (Table X), and it has been necessary to test the dried product. Studies on human milk [Macy and co-workers, 1927; 1930] have shown it to be even poorer than cow's milk in antineuritic vitamin (see p. 164).

The (*Antidermatitis*) Vitamin B_2.

In general vitamin B_2 has been found to accompany vitamin B_1 in ordinary foodstuffs. Hen's egg white, which contains the former and is devoid of the latter [Chick and Roscoe, 1929, 2], appears to be unique in this respect. The quantitative distribution of these two vitamins, however, shows many differences and these were put forward as an argument in favour of the multiple nature of the 'water-soluble B' vitamin many years before the separate existence of vitamins B_1 and B_2 was demonstrated [see for example Mitchell, 1919].

Vitamin B_2 is frequently found to accompany the proteins of 'high biological value', probably in an adsorbed state, and in some cases is removed only with difficulty, e.g. from caseinogen [Chick and Roscoe 1927]. The richest known sources are liver, yeast, milk, and green-leaf vegetables if dry weights are compared. Egg yolk, egg white, and meat (ox muscle) are inferior.

Meat and milk are much richer in vitamin B_2 than in the anti-neuritic vitamin, but the reverse is true of egg yolk and green vegetables. The potency of green vegetables in this vitamin appears to run parallel with the degree of greenness of the leaf. Egg white has proved very useful in the study of the vitamin B complex as pro-viding a source of vitamin B_2 unaccompanied by vitamin B_1.

In the cereals and their components there are also marked differences in the distribution of vitamins B_1 and B_2. Wheat embryo, one of the richest sources of the former, is relatively poor in the latter, inferior in this respect to meat and milk. The endosperms of wheat and maize on the other hand, while devoid of vitamin B_1, have been found to contain small but appreciable quantities of vitamin B_2.

The distribution of vitamins B_1 and B_2 is shown in Table XI. The vitamin B_1 content of a foodstuff, as there stated, is estimated from pro-tective and curative pigeon tests (see p. 147) or from growth experiments on rats in which the remainder of the vitamin B complex was supplied and vitamin B_1 was the only limiting factor. The results given for the vitamin B_2 contents depend on experiments expressly designed to estimate the vitamin B_2 content of a foodstuff. The distribution of Goldberger's P-P and the blacktongue-preventive factors is not included here (see p. 183).

Most of the work on the distribution in nature of the B-vitamins has been concerned with the whole complex. In column 6 of Table XI is given an estimate of the richness in this multiple factor of foodstuffs whose relative content of vitamins B_1 and B_2 is still unknown.

The values given refer to substances in the fresh natural state. It should be noted that the drying of natural foodstuffs which have a high water-content, e.g. fruits and vegetables, increases their content of B-vitamins relative to bulk. The temperature required to preserve foods by canning may seriously affect vitamin B_1. The heat neces-sary for cooking, e.g. boiling of vegetables or stewing of meat, on the other hand, does not of itself as a rule impair the vitamin B_1 potency of the foodstuff concerned, but loss tends to occur through diffusion of the vitamin into the cooking water [Roscoe, 1930].

In the following table o indicates either that the vitamin in ques-tion has not been detected, or that it is present in very small amount; + that the material contains the vitamin; + + that it is a good source; and + + + that it is a rich source.

TABLE XI.

Distribution of Vitamins B_1 and B_2 in Foodstuffs.

Substance.	Vitamin B_1.	References.	Vitamin B_2.	Refs.	Water-soluble Vitamin B.	References.
Cereals and Cereal Products.						
Barley (unhusked) . . .	+ +	1, 2	.	.	+	3, 4, 5
„ (husked) . . .	+ +	1				
Buckwheat.	+	2				
Custard powders and egg substitutes.	.		.	.	o	6
Dari	+ +	2				
Maize, whole	+ +	2, 85	+	7, 85		
„ embryo	+ + +	20, 21	+	7		
„ endosperm . . .	o	2	o	7		
Gluten	o	2				
Malt	+	4	.	.	+	4, 9, 5, 11
„ extract (commercial) .	+	12, 13, 14	.	.	+	11, 13, 14
Millet	+ +	2	+	15		
Oats, whole	+	2, 16, 17	.	.	+	17, 18
Rice, whole.	+ +	22	+	15		
„ embryo	+ + +	20, 21				
„ bran	+ +	19, 20, 21				
„ polished	o	.	o			
„ starch	o	.	o			
'Parboiled' rice, whole . .	+ +	22				
„ „ polished .	+ +	22				
Rye	+ +	2				
Wheat, whole	+ +	2, 84, 85	+	7, 84		
„ germ	+ + +	2, 20, 21, 75	+ +	7		
„ bran	+ +	2, 19, 20, 21	+ +	7		
„ middlings . . .	+ +	2	+ +	7		
„ flour, refined (endosperm)	o	21, 22, 23	o	7		
Legumes.						
Beans, green string . . .	.	.	.	.	+	24
„ haricot	+ +	2				
„ kidney	.		.	.	+ +	25
„ mongo	.		.	.	+ +	26
„ Soy	+	2, 27	+	27		
„ velvet	+ +	27	+	27		
„ katjang-idjo (*Phaseolus radiatus*). . . .	+ + +	19				
Lentils	+ +	1, 2	.	.	+ +	28, 48
Peas, fresh	.	.	.	.	+ +	29
„ dry	+ +	2, 21, 30	+ +	7		
Other Seeds.						
Coffee beans, fresh . . .	+	2				
Cotton seed	.	.	.	.	+	
Nuts.						
Almond	+	2	.	.	+	32
Brazil-nut	.	.	.	.	+	32
Chestnut	+	2	.	.	+	32
Coco-nut	.	.	.	.	+	32
Filberts	+ +	12	.	.	+	32
Hazel	+ +	2	.	.	+	32
Hickory-nut	.	.	.	.	+ +	32
Pea-nut	+ +	2, 30	.	.	+	34
Pecan	.	.	.	.	+ +	32
Pine	.	.	.	.	+ +	32
Walnut, black	.	.	.	.	+	32
„ English	.	.	.	.	+	32

Substance.	Vitamin B_1.	References.	Vitamin B_2.	Refs.	Water-soluble Vitamin B.	References.
Vegetables.						
Artichokes					+ +	35, 36
Asparagus					+ +	38
Bamboo shoots					o	
Beet, leaves and stem					+	37
„ root					+	37
„ sugar, root					o	39
Bilimbi (*Averrhoa carambola*)					+	6
Cabbage, green leaves	+ +	40	+ +	40		
„ etiolated „	+ +	40	+	40		
Carrots	+ +	41	+	41		
Cauliflower					+	42
Celery					+	38
Clover					+ +	37, 38
Dandelion					+ +	38
Dasheen (*Caladium colocasia*)					+	39, 43
Duhat (*Eugenia jambolana*)					+	6
Lettuce	+ +	40	+	40		
Lucerne (Alfalfa)					+ +	37, 38
Mushroom					+	44
Okra					+	35
Onion	+	40	+	40		
Parsley					+ +	38
Parsnips					+ +	29
Pollen	+ +	45				
Potatoes, raw	+ +	41	+	41		
„ peel	+ +	21				
Pumpkin					+	46
Radish					+	47
Rape leaves	+	27	+ +	27		
Spinach	+	40	+ +	40		
Sugar cane					o	59
Swede					+	39
Sweet potato					+	49
„ leaves					+	35
Timothy grass					+	37, 38
Turnips	+	41	+	41		
„ greens					+ +	50, 51
Velvet bean, leaves	+	27	+ +	27		
Watercress	+	40	+ +	40		
Fruits.						
Alligator pear (Avocado)					+	35, 52
Apple	+	41	+	41	+	53, 29
Banana	+	54	+	54		
Breadfruit					+	59
Cherry					+	54
Currant	o	21				
Date	+	21				
Grape					+	29, 53
Grape fruit					+	53
Green pepper					+	55
Lemon juice					+	29, 53
Lime juice	+	56				
Melon, cantaloup					+	29, 51
Orange juice	+	8	+		+	9, 29, 53, 58
Paw-paw (Papaya)					+	60
Peach					+	29, 61
Pear					+	54, 53
Prune					+	53, 29
Raisin					+	62
Strawberry					+	63
Tomato	+		+		+ +	29, 53, 64, 65

Substance.	Vitamin B₁.		Vitamin B₂.		Water-soluble Vitamin B.	
		References.		*Refs.*		*References.*
Meat and Fish.						
Oysters			.	.	+ +	68
Clams	.	.	.	.	o	69
Blood	o	70	+	66		
Fish muscle (hake) . . .	+	1	.	.	o	67
,, roe	+	21	.	.		
Meat, lean beef, mutton and pork	+ +	1, 30, 75	+ +	7		
Ox brain	+ +	12, 56				
,, heart	+ +	1				
,, kidney	.	.	+ + +	74		
,, liver	+ +	12 75	+ + +	7		
,, testes	+	19				
Pig brain			.	.	+	72
,, heart			.	.	+	72
,, kidney			.	.	+	72
,, liver			.	.	+ +	71, 72
Sheep brain	+ +	12				
,, pancreas (sweetbreads)	.	.	.	.	+ +	73
Milk and Milk Products.						
Milk, cow's, fresh . . .	+	12,30,76,79	+ +	7, 79		
,, ,, dried . . .	.	.	.	.	+ +	29
,, ,, sterilized . .	.	.	.	.	+	6
,, ,, boiled . . .	.	.	.	.	+	6
,, ,, pasteurized . .	.	.	.	.	+	82
,, ,, condensed . .	+	83	.	.	+	6
,, ,, skimmed (dried)	+	77	.	.	+	82
,, goat's	.	.	.	.	+	
,, human	+	80, 81	+	80, 81		
Cheese	o	12	+	7		
Eggs, Hen's.						
,, White	o	86	+ +	86		
,, Yolk	+ +	1, 86, 75	+	7		
Miscellaneous.						
Beer (stout)	o	57	+	57		
Sugar	.	.	.	.	o	6
Tea	.	.	.	.	o	6
Honey	o	45, 88	o	88		
Molasses, beet	.	.	.	.	+	87
,, cane	.	.	.	.	+ +	87
Yeast, brewer's . . .	+ + +	.	+ + +			
,, dried . . .	+ + +	.	+ + +			
,, extract (marmite) .	+ + +	.	+ + +			
,, autolysed . . .	+ + +	8	+ + +			
,, autoclaved . . .	o		+ +			

1. Cooper, 1912
2. Plimmer, Rosedale, Raymond and Lowndes, 1927
3. Steenbock, Kent and Gross, 1918
4. Harden and Zilva, 1924
5. Southgate, 1924, 1
6. Med. Res. Coun. Report, 1924
7. Aykroyd and Roscoe, 1929
8. Kinnersley and Peters (unpublished)
9. Cooper, 1914, 1
10. Stammers, 1924, 2
11. Bacharach and Allchorne, 1928
12. Cooper, 1914, 1
13. Randoin and Lecoq, 1927, 2
14. Randoin and Lecoq, 1926, 2
15. Aykroyd, 1930, 1
16. McCollum and Kennedy, 1916
17. Smith and Hendrick, 1926
18. McCollum, Simmonds and Pitz, 1917, 1
19. Schaumann, 1910
20. Chick and Hume, 1917-19, 1
21. Chick and Hume, 1917, 1
22. Aykroyd, 1932
23. Ohler, 1914
24. Quinn, Butris and Milner, 1927
25. McCollum, Simmonds and Pitz, 1917, 2
26. Santos, 1922
27. Salmon, 1927

28. Jones and Murphy, 1924
29. Sherman, 1926
30. Vedder and Clarke, 1912
31. Osborne and Mendel, 1917, 1
32. Cajori, 1920
33. Johns, Finks and Paul, 1919
34. Daniels and Loughlin, 1918
35. Santos, 1922
36. Morgan and Stephenson, 1923
37. Osborne and Mendel, 1919, 3
38. Osborne and Mendel, 1922, 2
39. Steenbock and Gross, 1919
40. Roscoe, 1930
41. Roscoe, 1931, 2
42. Russell, Morrison and Ebling, 1926
43. Miller, C. D., 1927
44. Orton, McCollum and Simmonds, 1922
45. Dutcher, 1918, 2
46. Morgan and Francis, 1924
47. Morgan, 1924
48. Eddy, Kohman and Carlsson, 1926
49. Blackberg, 1928–29
50. Burton, 1928
51. Newton, 1928
52. Weatherby and Waterman, 1928
53. Osborne and Mendel, 1920, 2
54. Kansas Agr. Exp. Sta. Report, 1926–28
55. Quinn, Burtis and Milner, 1927
56. Funk, 1912–13, 1
57. Aykroyd (unpublished)
58. Willimott, 1928

59. Miller, C. D., 1929
60. Miller, C. D., 1926
61. Kohman, Eddy, Carlsson and Halliday, 1926
62. Dutcher and Outhouse, 1922–23
63. Kohman, Eddy and Halliday, 1928
64. Sherman and Grose, 1923–24
65. House, Nelson and Haber, 1929
66. Kollath, 1930
67. Drummond, 1918, 2
68. Jones, Murphy and Nelson, 1928
69. Jones, Nelson and Murphy, 1928
70. Hoagland, 1923
71. Osborne and Mendel, 1917, 3
72. Osborne and Mendel, 1918
73. Eddy, 1916
74. Hoagland and Snider, 1930
75. Chick and Copping, 1930, 2
76. Gibson and Concepcion, 1916
77. Johnson and Hooper, 1921
78. McCollum and Davis, 1915, 2
79. Hunt and Kraus, 1928
80. Macy, Outhouse, Graham and Long, 1927, 2
81. McCosh, Macy and Hunscher, 1931
82. Johnson, 1921
83. Daniels and Brooks, 1927–28
84. Sherman and Axtmayer, 1927
85. Hunt, 1928, 1
86. Chick and Roscoe, 1929, 1
87. Nelson, V. E., Heller and Fulmer, 1925
88. Hoyle, 1929

Vitamins B_3 and B_5.

The literature of the last 20 years dealing with the behaviour of pigeons fed on polished rice supplemented with yeast extracts and other sources of the antineuritic vitamin exhibits much disagreement as to whether full maintenance of weight can be induced by addition of the antineuritic vitamin alone. Thus Emmett and McKim [1917] showed that there were quantitative differences between the amounts required to cure polyneuritis and to give full nutrition when the birds were treated respectively with a yeast concentrate or the original yeast. Evidence related to the same question was early presented by Cooper [1913], who found that potency to prevent polyneuritis and to protect against loss of weight did not run parallel in a series of foodstuffs. Hence some workers held that curative and weight-maintenance factors in the pigeon were different, though others [e.g. Seidell, 1922 1,] used weight maintenance upon polished rice as a means of testing for 'vitamin B'. Kinnersley and Peters [1925] found that one of the most potent antineuritic concentrates obtained by them up to that time (daily dose 0.08 mg.) did not arrest loss of weight in pigeons fed upon polished rice when given in sufficient amounts to protect against polyneuritis for at least 44 days. Somewhat later Jansen and Donath [1926, 2], finding that their crystalline vitamin B preparation could protect against loss of weight as well as against polyneuritis if supplemented by meat powder and cod-liver oil, considered that any factor required, other than the antineuritic vitamin, was protein in character. A step towards clearing up these difficulties was taken when R. R. Williams and Waterman [1927–28; 1928] showed that pigeons upon an artificial diet or on polished rice did not gain in weight when vitamin B_1, adsorbed upon fuller's earth, was administered, or when this was supplemented with autoclaved yeast containing vitamin B_2. When, however, instead of the latter, air-dried yeast was given, the birds at once improved in condition and attained a maximum weight-level. The same effect was produced by whole wheat. They interpreted this to show that yeast contained in addition to the antineuritic vitamin B_1 a thermolabile factor which was not adsorbed by fuller's earth. Special experiments were made to show that the unknown factor in unheated yeast was not vitamin A, D, or E. The essential facts have been confirmed [Peters, 1930, 1, 2] and vitamin B_3, as it is now called, has been found to be present in whole wheat, in wheat germ and in other foodstuffs, as well as in yeast [Eddy, Gurin and Keresztesy, 1930].

It can be considered an established fact that a pigeon whose weight has fallen upon a polished-rice diet does not rise in weight even when receiving very large doses of vitamin B_1 concentrates. Many such concentrates, though not all, however, have been found to stabilize the weight at about 80 per cent. of the maximum possible. The recognition of the special entity, vitamin B_3, described above as necessary for rising nutrition under these experimental conditions, does not clear up completely the discrepancy between the effect of different vitamin B_1 concentrates. It appears that for maintenance at some intermediate weight, vitamin B_1 alone is not sufficient. Experiments by Carter, Kinnersley and Peters [1930, 1, 2] and simultaneous work by R. R. Williams, Waterman and Gurin [1930], using both their own preparations and one of Jansen and Donath, indicate that some highly purified vitamin B_1 preparations in comparatively large doses cannot alone maintain weight in pigeons feeding upon polished rice. The missing entity, present in some vitamin B_1 preparations from yeast and absent from others, is considered by Carter, Kinnersley and Peters [1930, 2] to be distinct from the other factors of the vitamin 'B complex' including vitamin B_3 and vitamin B_4. It has been provisionally termed vitamin B_5 and is present in whole wheat, yeast and marmite, and in the acid alcoholic extracts from the norite charcoal in the Kinnersley-Peters method of extraction of vitamin B_1 from yeast. It is adsorbed upon fuller's earth together with vitamin B_1 and is more stable in alkaline solution than vitamins B_1 and B_4 under the conditions so far investigated. Its characteristic effect is that given together with vitamin B_1 to pigeons losing weight on a diet of polished rice, it arrests this loss, but does not produce an increase, for which vitamin B_3 is also necessary. Vitamins B_3 and B_5 appear to be more readily stored than vitamin B_1.

Randoin and Lecoq have repeatedly claimed that pigeons need in addition to the antineuritic vitamin a factor *d'entretien*, thought to be more stable to heat than the antineuritic. As the pigeons were not allowed to feed naturally, it is difficult to relate this work with the foregoing, but it would appear that the vitamin B_5 factor is here indicated, though Lecoq [1931] considers this factor *d'entretien* to be identical with vitamin B_3 [see also Hauge and Carrick, 1926, 1].[1] The stability of

---

[1] It is possible also that the claim of Rosedale [1929], that a curative factor for

vitamin B_5 to heat and alkali suggests a possible identity with factor Y (see below). We may summarize briefly by pointing out that though knowledge about these newer vitamin B factors has not yet reached the same level of certainty as that about those which have been longer known (there are as yet no definite pathological lesions known to be attached to their deficiency), it is impossible to ignore the cumulative evidence in favour of their existence available at the present time.

Vitamin B_4.

Reader [1929, 2] showed that rats on a basal diet with the addition of alkaline autoclaved marmite (120° C. for 1 hour at pH 9) as a source of vitamin B_2 did not grow at the normal rate when vitamin B_1 was added in the form of Peters's concentrate, but did so when unheated marmite was added. The existence of a thermolabile factor in addition to vitamin B_1 was thus indicated. This factor [Reader, 1930, 1, 2] was found to accompany vitamin B_1 in the Kinnersley and Peters process for the concentration of that vitamin as far as the stage at which mercuric sulphate is added. The precipitate then produced, which was almost free from vitamin B_1, contained the vitamin B_4. This could be further concentrated by decomposing the mercury precipitate with sulphuretted hydrogen, concentrating *in vacuo* and removing the precipitates formed by the successive addition of 50 per cent. alcohol at pH 4·5 and of 80 per cent. acetone to the concentrated filtrate from the former.

Vitamin B_4 can be estimated by a curative method on adult rats which have been made polyneuritic by deprivation of vitamins B_1 and B_4 and have then received doses of vitamin B_1 free from vitamin B_4 (see p. 140) [Reader, 1930, 2]. In these circumstances the polyneuritic symptoms disappear, but the animal remains in a condition of muscular weakness, with spastic gait, swollen red paws, and a tendency to sit in a hunched position, these symptoms forming the syndrome characteristic of vitamin B_4 deficiency. Administration of vitamin B_4 causes the disappearance of these symptoms and restores growth. The daily dose required of the purest preparation so far obtained was 0·4 mg., but a crystalline specimen of vitamin B_1 from rice polishings [Jansen *et al.*, 1930] was found to be effective as B_4 in a dose of 0·002 mg. per diem.

Factor Y.

The existence of Factor Y [Chick and Copping, 1930, 2] was deduced from the results of comparative experiments on the growth of young rats receiving a basal diet in which vitamin B_1 was provided by minimal doses of Peters's purified concentrate from yeast, while vitamin B_2 was supplied respectively as an autoclaved yeast extract or a preparation from egg white. Growth was consistently found to be superior in the former case. This fact indicated that a heat-stable dietary factor, in addition to vitamin B_2, was present in autoclaved yeast extract more abundantly than in egg white; this factor was provisionally called factor Y. Its distribution was studied by a series of comparative tests similar to the above in which the vitamin B_1 in

intestinal stasis is present in the lead acetate precipitate from rice-polishing extract, is to be explained in terms of one of these factors.

the diet was provided by minimal doses of various foodstuffs [Roscoe, 1930; Chick and Copping, 1930, 2]. Factor Y was found to be absent from, or present in small amounts in, onion, meat (ox muscle), wheat embryo, and egg white and present more abundantly in yeast and watery yeast extracts (even after strongly heating at 120-125° C. in alkaline solution for 4 hours at pH 9–10), ox liver, egg yolk, and green-leaf vegetables, i.e. in foods known to possess the highest nutritive values.

Its great resistance to heat and alkali distinguishes this dietary factor from all other known constituents of the vitamin B complex.

Growth Factors for Yeasts and Bacteria, and their Relation to the Vitamin B Complex.

The evidence which is available seems to suggest the existence of a number of growth factors for yeasts and bacteria. In certain species growth appears to be dependent on the presence of the appropriate factor, whereas in others growth can occur in a synthetic medium containing only a small number of known chemical compounds. It appears, further, that certain organisms possess the ability to synthesize certain of the B-vitamins as judged by animal tests, whereas in other cases no such synthesis can be demonstrated.

GROWTH FACTORS FOR YEASTS.

Wildiers [1901] first observed the fact that when a synthetic medium containing only well-defined substances was inoculated with yeast no growth occurred unless the inoculation were a large one. He explained the phenomenon by supposing that the yeast required some unknown substance for its development which was not present in synthetic media, but was present in ordinary beer wort and in all growing cultures of yeast. He termed this substance 'bios', and made a number of observations on its chemical and physical properties. He believed that yeast did not itself produce bios but was entirely dependent on outside sources for its necessary supply.

In order to avoid confusion of thought in this field, it has been decided to retain the term 'bios' for growth-promoting factors for yeast. Even this limitation leaves the difficulty that the term is still used in a different sense by different workers; some imply a growth stimulant, others an essential factor for growth, while others again refer to a factor stimulating the production of carbon dioxide. As these effects are not necessarily physiologically equivalent, caution is required in interpreting the literature. In addition it is not clear that due attention has always been paid to the need for accurate adjustment of media, temperature, &c., and the distinction of the effects of such factors from that of bios.

Interest in this question has centred mainly round three problems, viz:

The relation of bios to the growth of the yeast cell.

The relation of bios to vitamin B_1, and the use of yeast growth as a criterion in tests for vitamin B_1.

The synthesis of vitamin B_1 by yeast.

The Relation of Bios to the Growth of the Yeast Cell.

For a discussion of the early literature the review of Tanner [1925] should be consulted.

Pringsheim [1906] examined the phenomenon discovered by Wildiers critically and came to the conclusion that the failure of small inoculations to grow in mineral solutions is due to the inability of the yeast to adapt itself rapidly enough to the new medium.   When a larger inoculation is made some of the cells bud at the expense of material derived from other cells which die, and at the same time partially make use of the inorganic constituents of the medium.   Subsequently they become adapted to assimilate this, and thereafter grow normally.

According to Wright [1922] yeast, growing in a synthetic medium to which lemon juice has been added, multiplies at the expense of the lemon juice until a certain concentration of cells is attained, after which the ammonium salt of the medium is utilized. Wildiers's bios, on this view, would be simply a source of suitable nitrogen. Certain yeasts, according to Ide [1906], never seem to acquire the power of rapid growth in synthetic media.

A fact of fundamental importance is that different species and strains of yeast behave very differently in respect to their need for bios.   This may be deduced from the work of Bachmann [1919], Lucas [1924], Copping [1929], and Fulmer, Nelson and White [1923], the last named having used a yeast which grew well on an artificial medium in which a synthetic sugar, methose, replaced sucrose.

The answer to the question whether bios acts simply as a stimulant to growth [Macdonald and McCollum, 1920–21 ; Macdonald, 1923] or is indispensable for growth [Funk and Dubin, 1921 ; Willaman and Olsen, 1923] is probably different for different species of yeast.   Peskett [1927–28] found that there appears to be a critical concentration of bios, in the presence of which a small seeding of yeast will attain the same ultimate cell concentration as a large seeding.   In the presence of concentrations of bios below this critical value this is not the case.

There seems, therefore, no reason to suppose, at any rate in the case of certain strains of yeast, that bios is a substance '*indispensable au developpement de la levure*', as believed by Wildiers, but rather that it acts as a stimulant to the growth of the yeast cell.   For some yeasts, however, bios appears to be an essential factor for growth.

Concentration of Bios.

Meanwhile much effort has been devoted to the isolation of bios and to the study of its chemical properties.   Recent work has tended to emphasize the complexity of the bios effect, and evidence, still somewhat conflicting in character, has been forthcoming in support of the view that more than one factor is concerned.

Thus it was found by Fulmer and Nelson [1924], and Fulmer, Duecker and Nelson [1924] that, in alcohol fractionation of an aqueous extract of alfalfa, the fraction obtained with 40 per cent. alcohol and the residue obtained after repeated extraction with 95 per cent. alcohol provided a much better growth stimulus to *S. cerevisiae* when both were present than when either was present alone.

Much work has been done on the fractionation of bios [W. L. Miller, 1924; Lucas, 1924; Deas, 1924; Sims, 1924; Eastcott, 1924; 1928]. Two fractions, bios I (precipitated by baryta) and bios II (not precipitated; adsorbed by charcoal and yeast) have been obtained from malt combings and rice polishings, and found to be separately inactive but active in combination. Neither promoted the growth of rats or cured avian polyneuritis. Bios I, which has also been isolated from tea-dust, was found to be inactive inositol. Whether this substance bears a relation to yeast growth similar to that claimed by Reader [1929, 1] for mannitol to the growth of *Streptothrix corallinus* remains uncertain. Narayanan [1930] failed to obtain any growth stimulus for *S. cerevisiae* with inositol.

A crystalline material, melting at 223° C. and having bios activity, has been isolated from yeast extract by a method involving its selective adsorption or precipitation by ferric oxide hydrosol at pH 5·3, and subsequent removal of the iron by baryta [Eddy, Kerr and Williams, 1924]. The crystals had an empirical formula $C_5H_{11}ON_3$, were soluble in water, acids, and alkalis, and in alcohol up to 80 per cent. concentration. Later, by conversion into the inactive sulphonamide and hydrolysis of this back to the original active compound, these authors brought further evidence that the activity of their factor, which they termed α–bios, was not due to traces of an adherent potent substance [Kerr, Eddy and Williams, 1925–26]. By the use of phosphotungstic acid and subsequent treatment with fuller's earth, two fractions were obtained from yeast extract [R. J. Williams, Wilson and Ahe, 1927] which exhibited marked bios activity in combination, but little or no action independently. In later work, Kerr [1927–28], by a method of electro-dialysis, succeeded in separating a β-bios and a γ-bios which resembled the bios II of Miller and Lucas.

Narayanan [1930] found that samples of Eddy's α- and β-bios were considerably less active in stimulating the growth of *S. cerevisiae* than his own preparations. He observed that the bios activity was precipitated by phosphotungstic acid and platinic chloride, but not by lead acetate. In agreement with Peskett and O'Brien [1930] no evidence was obtained in favour of the complex nature of bios.

The Relation of Bios to Vitamin B_1, and the Use of Yeast Growth as a Test for Vitamin B_1.

The employment of yeast growth as a test for the antineuritic vitamin was based on the assumption of the identity of this vitamin with Wildiers's bios. R. J. Williams [1919] was led to this view by his observation that the growth of yeast was markedly stimulated by the addition to his synthetic medium of extracts known to contain the antineuritic vitamin, and his suggestion was supported by the close similarity of these two factors in their behaviour to phosphotungstic acid, to acids and alkalis, and to heat.

Several modifications of the test were proposed [Bachmann, 1919; R. J. Williams, 1920; Funk and Dubin, 1920; Swoboda, 1920; Eddy and Stevenson, 1919–20, 1, 2, 3; 1920], but its reliability was not firmly established. Thus Funk and Dubin found that the growth of yeast varied directly with the dose of the antineuritic factor when small concentrations were employed, but that with higher concentrations of vitamin this relationship did not hold good, suggesting the presence of inhibitory factors. E. W. Miller [1920] reported large variations in the growth of colonies maintained under identical conditions, while Whipple [1920] found that salts and nitrogenous organic substances present in the vitamin extract introduced complicating factors.

A further study of the question revealed many discrepancies between the results of tests for vitamin B_1 obtained by animal experiments and by yeast growth respectively. These concerned the heat-stability of the factors involved [see E. W. Miller, 1920; R. J. Williams, 1919; Eddy and Stevenson, 1920; Emmett and Stockholm, 1920; Souza and McCollum, 1920; Funk and Paton, 1922], their occurrence in various materials such as commercial glucose and hydrolysed meat extract [Souza and McCollum, 1920] and various vegetables [R. J. Williams, 1921; Eddy, Heft, Stevenson and Johnson, 1921], behaviour to adsorbents [Funk and Dubin, 1921; Fränkel and Scharf, 1921], production by moulds [Hoet, 1922], and presence in the tissues of animals deprived of vitamin B [Heaton, 1922]. It was also found that the bios I and II of Miller and his colleagues had no antineuritic potency [Deas, 1924].

While the evidence is overwhelmingly against the suggested identity of bios and vitamin B_1, the possibility raised by Eddy that vitamin B_1 might be one factor related to the growth of yeast has not yet received a final answer. According to R. J. Williams, Warner and Roehm [1929] certain yeasts require for growth one factor only which is not adsorbed by fuller's earth or precipitated by phosphotungstic acid, while other species need at least two factors, one of which resembles vitamin B_1 in its chemical and physical properties, the other being similar to or identical with bios. In the Jansen-Donath technique for the isolation of vitamin B_1, the activity at various stages up to the final precipitation by acetone as judged by the yeast test gave good agreement with the results of animal tests, but beyond this stage discrepancies appeared [R. J. Williams and Roehm, 1930; Narayanan, 1930]. The final crystalline product, however, showed a high degree of potency in stimulating yeast growth.

Synthesis of Vitamin B_1 by Yeast.

The synthesis of vitamin B by yeast was demonstrated by V. E. Nelson, Fulmer and Cessna [1921], who found that after subculture for a year in a purely synthetic medium the yeast thus obtained promoted growth of young rats. Harden and Zilva [1921] also showed that various strains of yeast grown under similar conditions cured polyneuritis when administered to pigeons. Eijkman, Hoogenhuijze and Derks [1922], on the other hand, found that yeast grown on a synthetic medium had no curative action on avian polyneuritis whereas yeast cultured on natural wort was highly active. The liquid separated from the yeast at the end of fermentation was inactive. It was concluded that yeast does not synthesize the antineuritic factor but that it abstracts it from the medium when this contains the

factor or the products of its break-down. Similar results were
obtained by Southgate [1924, 2].

Funk and Freedman [1923] concluded that the synthesis of the
antineuritic vitamin by yeast is determined by the presence of bios in
the medium. This has been confirmed by Macdonald [1922], Heller
[1923], Hawking [1927], and Peskett [1927].

Hoet, Leclef and Delarue [1924] found that of the organisms
Monilia candida, Torula rosea, and *Mycoderma cerevisiae* only the
first is capable of synthesizing the antineuritic factor. The observation that different strains may vary in their ability to form vitamin B_1
may account for the negative results of Eijkman and his co-workers,
and of Southgate.

BACTERIAL REPRODUCTION AND GROWTH FACTORS.

Much discussion has taken place with regard to the question
whether bacteria require growth stimulants of the nature of vitamins,
and further whether they are capable of synthesizing vitamins.
The general question can only be dealt with summarily here and for
further details the reader is referred to the Medical Research Council
System of Bacteriology, vol. 1, p. 252; vol. 2, *passim.*

The conclusion to be drawn from the large amount of experimental
work which has been done on this subject may be summarized briefly
as follows.

Some bacteria (Group 1), e.g. *B. coli, B. pyocyaneus,* &c., can be
cultivated continuously on purely synthetic media, whilst others
(Group 2), e.g. *Staph. pyogenes albus, C. diphtheriae, Meningococcus,*
&c., can only be cultivated continuously in such media when certain
pure amino-acids are added.

The *haemolytic streptococci and pneumococci* (Group 3), on the
other hand, do not grow on synthetic media and require a growth-
promoting factor. This occurs in ordinary beef broth and in many
animal and vegetable extracts, fruit juices, &c. [see Hosoya and Kuroya,
1923, 1, 2; Weichardt, 1920; Davidsohn, 1924; Leichtentritt and
Zielaskowski, 1922; Reader, 1928]. This growth factor appears to
be more stable to heat and alkali than vitamin B_1, less so than bios.

Finally the *haemophilic bacteria,* e.g. *B. influenzae* Pfeiffer (Group
4), require a still more complex medium containing two unknown
factors [Fildes, 1921; Thjötta and Avery, 1921]. The first of these
(the V or vitamin factor) is very easily inactivated by heat or alkali,
occurs in many vegetable extracts and is synthesized by many bacteria.
The second (the X factor) contains iron and occurs in blood, but is
also present in potato and is produced by certain bacteria; in blood
it is thermostable.

The interesting observation has been made by Reader [1927] that
Sarcina aurantiaca and two strains of streptothrix can be grown on a
suitable synthetic medium, but that growth is greatly enhanced by
the addition to the medium of traces of a tryptic digest beef broth.
The growth stimulant present has been shown to be an organic,
water-soluble, and dialysable substance which is not precipitated by
either normal or basic lead acetate. It is found in muscle, serum,
wheat embryo, and in some antineuritic yeast concentrates having an

activity of 0·01 mg. (pigeon day-dose). The factor is not inactivated by alkali [Reader, 1928 ; Peters, Kinnersley, Orr-Ewing and Reader, 1928], indicating that it is not identical with vitamin B_1 though possibly related to it. It has been shown that the Jansen-Donath crystals of the antineuritic vitamin produce maximal growth of the streptothrix in concentrations as low as $4·2 \times 10^{-4}$ mg. per 100 c.c. of medium [Jansen, Kinnersley, Peters and Reader, 1930]. Reader [1929, 1] observed that the addition of mannitol to the synthetic medium containing a small amount of an antineuritic concentrate produced a marked stimulant action on the growth of the streptothrix. Other polyhydric alcohols, including inositol, were inactive. It was concluded that mannitol acted as a specific source of food supply rather than as an additive growth stimulant.

It was further shown [Orr-Ewing and Reader, 1928] that the meningococcus could be grown successfully on a medium devoid of the streptothrix factor, but that in the course of its growth this factor was synthesized.

There is therefore no conclusive evidence to support the view that bacteria require the presence of vitamin B_1 as such for normal growth. On the other hand the synthesis of the vitamin by many, though not by all, species of bacteria has been attested by a number of observers. The subject is of much interest with respect to the possible synthesis of B-vitamins in the alimentary canal of animals on vitamin-free diets. There is some doubt about the synthesis of vitamin B_1 by *B. coli* [see Damon, 1921; Kuroya and Hosoya, 1923], but positive results have been obtained with *B. influenzae* Pfeiffer, *Mycobact. smegmatis*, *Mycobact. phlei*, and *Mycobact. moelleri* [Damon, 1923; 1924], *B. vulgatus* [Scheunert and Schieblich, 1923], negative with *B. paratyphosus*, *B. subtilis* (a large amount of which was administered) [Damon, 1921], *B. adhaerens* and *B. friedländer* [Damon, 1923; 1924].

Sunderlin and Werkman [1928] found that the growth of rats was stimulated by the addition to the diet of cultures of *Torula rosea*, *Oospora lactis*, *B. adhaerens*, *B. coli*, *B. subtilis*, *B. mycoides*, *Azotobacter chroococcum*, *Rhizobium leguminosarum*, and by *Actinomyces*.

Bechdel, Eckles and Palmer [1926] found that calves could be grown to maturity on a diet carrying insufficient vitamin B to support the growth of rats. This fact was later shown by Bechdel, Honeywell, Dutcher and Knutsen [1928] to be due probably to the synthesis of vitamin B by a flavobacterium present in the rumen of the animals. Both the alcoholic extract of the contents of the rumen of a cow fed on a diet low in vitamin B and cultures (on a medium free from vitamin B) of a flavobacterium, which was abundantly present in the rumen contents, protected rats against deficiency of the vitamin B complex.

Refection.

Refection is the term used to describe a remarkable condition in which rats can exist and grow normally without any supply of the vitamin B complex in their diet [Fridericia *et al.*, 1927; Roscoe, 1927, 2]. The condition may occur spontaneously in rats on synthetic diets containing the B-vitamin complex, or on those deprived of it (Fridericia *et al.*) or of its constituents (Roscoe). In the last instance the symptoms of deficiency of vitamin B_1 (polyneuritis) or of vitamin B_2 (dermatitis) are rapidly cured. Normal growth to maturity may take place and breeding for two generations of refected rats has been recorded (Fridericia *et al.*).

The condition is infectious. It can be transmitted by feeding the faeces of refected rats and may also spread in the absence of direct contact, unless the refected animals are kept strictly segregated. These facts have led Fridericia to postulate a virus of refection.

The most noticeable feature of refected rats, apart from their satisfactory growth and generally good condition, is the presence in the faeces of a large proportion (up to 60 per cent.) of undigested starch. In some cases as much as 45 per cent. of the starch of the diet may be thus excreted in the faeces. The growth of the animal appears to some degree to be related to the amount of starch excreted, and this starch has been found to be very resistant to the action of amylase or ptyalin. The phenomenon of refection has only been recorded with diets containing raw starch; when the carbohydrate is present as cooked starch (Roscoe) or as sugar (Fridericia) refection has not been observed.

The faeces of refected rats appear to be richer in B-vitamins than those of other rats deprived of these vitamins. This suggests that in the refected state the vitamin B complex is synthesized in the intestinal tract, owing (according to Fridericia) to the presence of an infecting micro-organism, probably identical with that transmitting the condition from rat to rat. All attempts to isolate any micro-organism, however, have so far been unavailing and attempts to induce refection by systematic feeding with small doses of various living yeasts have also been unsuccessful [Roscoe, personal communication].

Mendel and Vickery [1928–29] have reported their repeated failure to produce refection in rats and the condition has not as yet been observed in the United States. It seems possible that its occurrence in European laboratories may be due to a chance infection of the intestine with some wild yeast derived from the particular sample of starch incorporated in the diet. The use of potato starch appears to favour the occurrence of refection [Kon and Watchhorn, 1928; Roscoe, personal communication], but in the United States this was also used without success.

The non-specific nature of the protection afforded in refection is shown by the power to correct a deficiency of the complete yeast B-vitamin complex and is another reason for supposing that the protective mechanism may be concerned with growth of a yeast or other micro-organism in the animal's intestine. An interesting case is described by Boas-Fixsen in her investigation of the pathological state induced by feeding young rats on dried egg white as sole source of protein (Boas, 1924, 1, 2; 1927; Boas Fixsen, 1931). This condition, which includes severe dermatitis, as well as nervous affections, develops on diets containing marmite, but can be cured or prevented by whole yeast and by many foodstuffs known to be rich in the vitamin B complex. In the course of her work spontaneous cures took place resembling refection, marked, in this case also, by the excretion of bulky faeces containing undigested starch. The refected condition could be transmitted to unrefected rats on the egg white diet by feeding them with these faeces or equally with the white faeces from rats which had become refected on diets deprived of all B-vitamins.

A condition resembling refection has been noticed in pigeons fed on a diet deprived of B-vitamins consisting of autoclaved rice and dhal (legumes); it differs, however, from that described by Fridericia and his co-workers and by Roscoe in the fact that it was developed on a cooked diet and could not be transmitted to unrefected birds by feeding the bulky faeces excreted [Taylor and Thant, 1928].

CHAPTER VII

PELLAGRA AS A VITAMIN DEFICIENCY DISEASE.

HISTORY.

THE records of pellagra do not extend far back into medical history. The disease, which possesses very characteristic and easily recognized symptoms, was apparently unknown to the physicians of antiquity, a fact ascertained and used in controversy many years ago. Its scientific history dates from the treatise written by the Spaniard, Casal, in 1735, which was not fully published until 1763. It is interesting to note that Casal gave a full description of the very poor diets customary in the pellagrous districts of Andalusia, and actually ascribed the disease to faulty nutrition.

A few years later pellagra was recognized and received its name in Italy, where it has ever since been prevalent. Early in the nineteenth century it was observed in France and subsequently it spread eastward across Europe, afflicting Hungary, Rumania, Turkey, and Greece. In 1847 pellagra was recorded in Egypt by Pruner, and towards the end of the century Sandwith [1898] gave a full account of the condition in that country. Recently the disease has been reported from more southerly countries in the African Continent, such as Rhodesia and Nyasaland.

In the United States, pellagra first became seriously evident about 1909 [Wood, 1920]. Within a few years of its recognition it became a terrible scourge among the negroes and poor whites of the Southern States, 170,000 cases being recorded in 1917, with a high mortality [McCollum and Simmonds, 1928]. Of recent years the American outbreak has become milder in form and somewhat lessened in prevalence, but in the cotton-growing districts of the Southern States pellagra remains a very serious menace.

Vedder [1916], in supporting the dietetic origin of pellagra, which was suggested by Funk [1912], pointed out some suggestive analogies between that disease and beri-beri. It is interesting to note that in both cases the theories of their aetiology have run a similar historical course. Before the time of Pasteur and the germ theory of disease many physicians unhesitatingly ascribed to beri-beri and pellagra an origin in poor and monotonous diet. Later, when microbes were at the height of their popularity, a new bacterial cause of both scourges was discovered by enthusiasts almost annually. Of recent years it has again become clear that the origin of beri-beri and pellagra must be sought in faulty nutrition, but while there is good evidence that beri-beri is related to deficiency of vitamin B_1, the exact relation between pellagra and dietary error still remains to be demonstrated beyond question.

An enormous amount of human effort has been expended in the study of this formidable disease, and some early work on the subject has considerable interest and value. The voluminous early literature has been collected by Harris [1919] to whose book those interested should refer. Among a number of shrewd investigators the French physician Roussel [1845; 1866] stands out. Roussel realized clearly the value of milk in the treatment of pellagra, a fact recorded by Casal and many others, and recommended that pellagrins should be given broth, meat, eggs, and fish. He pointed out the very important fact, which can be further developed to-day, that the history of the spread of pellagra in Europe is the history of the introduction of maize as a staple food. Brought from America, maize reached Spain first, then Italy, and later France, and thence its use spread gradually eastward. Pellagra followed it across Europe into Africa, where maize, first used in Egypt, is now tending to displace millet as the most widely used cereal. On the other hand, the apparently sudden outbreak of pellagra in the United States, where maize has long been used, has never been quite satisfactorily linked to a change of dietary habits either as regards maize or other foodstuffs.

A connexion between pellagra and chronic alcoholism has been noted by several observers [Klauder and Winkelman, 1928; Sweitzer, 1928; Kumer, 1931].

THE OCCURRENCE OF PELLAGRA ON DIETS CONSISTING CHIEFLY OF CEREALS OTHER THAN MAIZE.

Many observers in the last century were impressed by the intimate connexion between maize and pellagra. Pellagra has been called ' zeism ', and at one period research resolved itself into an effort to demonstrate a pellagra-producing poison in maize. There are, however, a number of well-authenticated instances of the appearance of the disease on other staple foods. Stannus [1911–12; 1913–14] and Sheppard [1912] have reported its occurrence on rice, W. H. Wilson [1921] on millet, and Siler, Garrison and McNeal [1913] recorded its prevalence in a district where wheat flour was the most widely used cereal. A few cases [Sambon, 1913] in persons who had never eaten maize have been reported in the British Isles.

Such observations must be taken into account in an aetiological inquiry, but perhaps too much can be made of them. It should never be forgotten that pellagra is *almost* exclusively a maize eater's disease and that its occasional appearance among a population consuming other cereals attracts attention by its very rarity.

THE PREVENTION OF PELLAGRA BY DIETARY ALTERATIONS.

Goldberger was appointed in 1913 by the U.S.A. Bureau of Public Health to investigate the outbreak of pellagra in the Southern States, which was just then assuming grave proportions. He appears [1914] to have been struck at the outset by two observations, which he made the basis of his researches. One was the prevalence of the disease among the very poor, the other, the immunity of doctors and attendants in asylums where pellagra was rife.

The latter fact at once excluded the theory that pellagra is primarily an infectious, microbe-borne disease. With regard to diet, however, the patients were definitely worse off than the staff. Goldberger gained the impression that their dietary, and the dietary

of other pellagrins in the cotton-milling districts, differed from
that of individuals and populations without pellagra in being
mainly composed of cereals and almost devoid of animal protein.

An example on a small scale of the incidence of the disease
throughout the general population was discovered at an orphanage
in Missouri in which pellagra was found to be confined to one age
group, which, in comparison with the rest, had a diet very short of
fresh meat and other animal protein [Goldberger, Waring and
Willets, 1915]. Acting on the observation that pellagra does not
occur when liberal amounts of animal protein are eaten, Goldberger
and his colleagues attempted preventive experiments, made possible by the recurrent nature of the disease. In two orphanages
containing large numbers of pellagrous children recurrence was
prevented by adding milk and eggs to the poor diet, composed
mainly of maize and other cereal foods. In other similar institutions under observation no dietary change was made, with the
result that pellagra recurred in 40 per cent. of the former year's
victims.

Goldberger, Wheeler and Sullivan [1915] restricted 11 convicts
working on a prison farm, who were offered a pardon on the conclusion of the experiment, to a diet mainly composed of maize
endosperm for 6 months. After $5\frac{1}{2}$ months, 6 were found to be
suffering from a condition closely resembling pellagra. In the following year Goldberger [1916] and a number of his colleagues in
reply to critics, demonstrated on themselves the impossibility of
transmitting pellagra by inoculation with the secretions of pellagrins.
In support of the dietetic theory a careful study of the epidemiology
of the disease in certain villages in South Carolina [Goldberger,
Wheeler and Sydenstricker, 1920] showed that 'increasing supplies of milk and fresh meat were associated, one independently of
the other, with a decreasing pellagra incidence'.

Simultaneous work by W. H. Wilson in Egypt confirmed Goldberger's observation that dietary measures can prevent pellagra. Wilson
[1921], adopting the hypothesis that the cause of pellagra is to be
found in a shortage of proteins of high biological value according
to Thomas's [1909] figures, showed clearly that pellagra may be
cured and prevented by the addition of milk or meat to the high
cereal diet with which he found the disease associated. Boyd and
Lelean [1919], working in co-operation with Wilson in Egypt, reached
conclusions similar to his with regard to the causation of pellagra.

The Amino-Acid Deficiency Theory.

There is thus sound evidence that certain types of foodstuffs, taken
in adequate amounts, will avert pellagra. Goldberger [1922],
following Wilson and others, at first identified the preventive
agent with proteins of 'high biological value,' a value connected
with their content of the more important amino-acids. There was
considerable evidence in favour of the amino-acid deficiency theory
of pellagra. Kossel and Kutcher [1900], Osborne and Harris [1905],
and Wilcock and Hopkins [1906] had demonstrated that zein, the
principal protein of maize, is deficient in lysine and tryptophan.

Thomas [1909] defined 'biological value' as the number of parts of body nitrogen replaceable by 100 parts of the nitrogen of the foodstuff tested, and by experiments on himself worked out values for the proteins of a number of common food substances. His method consisted in consuming a nitrogen-free diet for a few days until his nitrogen output fell to a low figure, taken to represent only endogenous metabolism, and then testing the power of various foods, fed as additions to the nitrogen-free diet, to replace the nitrogen lost in tissue destruction. Thomas assigned to maize the low value of 30 as compared with rice 88, wheat flour 39·5, ox muscle 105, and milk 100.

On the basis of Thomas's figures W. H. Wilson [1921] showed that diets associated with pellagra in Egypt and elsewhere usually contained only protein of low biological value. He suggested that pellagra is liable to occur when the biological value of the protein consumed daily falls below a value equal to that of 40 to 45 g. of meat protein, and demonstrated that the diets of pellagrins are usually below this figure.

The amino-acid deficiency theory rests, however, on shaky foundations. It is difficult to accept Thomas's results as absolute, since they have not been confirmed either for man or the lower animals. Martin and Robison [1922] pointed out the difficulties underlying determinations of biological value and subjected Thomas's results to criticism, for the details of which their original paper should be consulted. Taking great care to avoid fallacies they attempted to estimate by experiments on themselves the biological value of the proteins of milk and whole wheat. Their value for wheat (35, C.J.M., and 31, R.R.) agreed fairly well with that of Thomas for wheat flour (39·5), but in the case of milk the difference was large (50, C.J.M., and 100, Thomas).

McCollum [1911], using Thomas's method and working with pigs, had found previously that zein could cover 73 per cent. of the animals' nitrogen expenditure. Using the pig as the experimental animal Hart and McCollum [1914] found the growth value of the proteins of the wheat, maize, and oat kernels roughly equal. These growth experiments, being probably complicated by unrecognized vitamin deficiences, are, however, difficult to interpret. It may be remarked that Thomas's work, which was performed before the importance of the vitamins was realized, is also subject in this respect to criticism.

Later work of McCollum, Simmonds and Parsons [1921], in which young rats were reared to maturity on diets containing protein from one source only, assigned to maize a low value and showed that the foodstuffs may be arranged as follows in descending order as regards the biological value of the constituent proteins:
(1) Ox kidney;
(2) Whole wheat;
(3) Milk; ox liver;
(4) Ox muscle; barley; rye;
(5) Maize; oats;
(6) Soy bean; navy bean; pea.
In this series the low position of maize is noteworthy, and a

similar result was obtained by Mitchell [1924], who also used the rat as experimental animal, but employed the method of nitrogenous exchange for determining the biological value of the proteins investigated.

At present a fresh survey of the 'biological value' of proteins, with fuller recognition of the role played by the vitamins, is required. Until this is available and more trustworthy figures have been obtained for the biological value of the proteins of maize compared with those of other cereals, it is difficult to assess the importance of amino-acid deficiency as a factor in the causation of pellagra.

THE PELLAGRA-PREVENTIVE FACTOR.

Funk [1912; 1913, 2] was the first to suggest that pellagra, like beri-beri, might be due to a vitamin deficiency, and advanced the theory that in the milling of maize a dietary factor is removed whose absence leads to pellagra.

Voegtlin, Neill and Hunter [1920] administered to pellagrins a 95 per cent. alcoholic extract of ox liver in daily doses equal to 1 kg. of fresh liver. They claimed that the extract, which was almost free from amino-nitrogen, produced as good a therapeutic effect as 'a diet containing a considerable quantity of milk, eggs, and meat'. It was recorded by the same observers that alcoholic extracts of rice polishings and yeast failed to produce parallel results, which suggested that the curative substance was not 'water-soluble vitamin B'.

Goldberger [1922] at first believed that amino-acid deficiency was the cause of pellagra, but, in the course of clinical observations to discover which foods could prevent pellagra, he obtained evidence pointing in another direction. These experiments consisted in making clear-cut additions to the dietary in certain asylums in which pellagra recurred regularly, a dietary mainly composed of maize and short of animal protein, and observing the effect of these additions on the incidence of pellagra in the following spring. By this work the value of milk and meat in both prevention and treatment was further confirmed [Goldberger and Tanner, 1924]. Gelatin, butter, and cod-liver oil were found to be without preventive effect. Supplements of dried soy beans and cowpeas, legumes containing a high proportion of vegetable protein, did not lower the proportion of recurrences [Goldberger and Tanner, 1925]. Addition to the diet of a liberal allowance of caseinogen, previously purified by repeated washings in acidulated water, had no effect in preventing the systemic lesions of pellagra, though it appeared to have some power to avert the appearance of the characteristic dermatitis, an observation difficult to reconcile with the theory that animal proteins, or proteins of supposed high biological value, are all-important in the prevention of pellagra. Having at about this time accidentally discovered that yeast was effective in preventing and treating experimental blacktongue in dogs, a condition thought to be analogous to pellagra, Goldberger and Tanner tried the effect of yeast as a prophylactic in the human disease. It was found that 30 g. daily of dried brewer's yeast gave complete protection. This would supply less than 15 g. of protein, and later it was discovered by Goldberger and his co-workers [1926] that a commercial preparation made from an acid extract of yeast, which contained very little protein-nitrogen, given in doses of 15 g. per diem, was equally effective. This confirmed the earlier observation of Voegtlin, Neill and Hunter [1920] referred to above (p. 180). A non-protein 'P-P' (pellagra-preventive) factor was therefore postulated in yeast and other foodstuffs possessing similar preventive properties.

Subsequently the 'P-P' factor was found by Goldberger and Wheeler to be present in tomato juice [1927, 1], wheat germ [1927, 2] and canned salmon [1929]. Carrots and turnips [1927, 1] and Virginian cowpeas [1927, 2] were found to be poor sources of the factor.

As the result of the extension of these investigations to experimental work on rats, Goldberger and his colleagues were able to identify their pellagra-preventive dietary factor with a vitamin contained in the yeast vitamin complex, differing from the antineuritic vitamin in its stability to heat and in its distribution in foodstuffs. This vitamin is now known as vitamin B_2 and by some American authorities as vitamin G. The therapeutic value of yeast in pellagra has since been confirmed by other observers in U.S.A. and elsewhere. In Russia, Tcherkes [1929], investigating a severe outbreak of pellagra in the Ukraine, recorded that a daily allowance of 45 g. of yeast, 1·5 litres of milk, or 200 g. of meat was of great effect in clearing up the symptoms of pellagra.

Carley [1930] tried the effect of dried brewer's yeast on a number of negro pellagrins in Mississippi. He states that 1 oz. per diem assisted in alleviating the symptoms, and that a similar daily dose, continued over a period of six months, was extremely effective in preventing recurrence.

EXPERIMENTAL BLACKTONGUE IN DOGS.

Chittenden and Underhill [1917] observed in dogs given a diet composed of wheat-flour biscuits, peas, and cotton-seed oil, a pathological syndrome which they suggested might be the analogue of human pellagra. In periods ranging from one to six months the dogs showed necrosis and gangrene of the tongue and buccal mucous membrane, accompanied by a bloody diarrhoea. Death usually ensued. The inclusion in the diet of large amounts of peas or small amounts of lean meat delayed the appearance of these symptoms.

Wheeler, Goldberger and Blackstock [1922] suggested that the disease produced experimentally by Chittenden and Underhill was identical with 'blacktongue' (canine typhus, Stuttgart epizootic, &c.), a canine disease well known to veterinarians, so named because the affected animal develops necrotic areas on the tongue. Pellagra and blacktongue appear to have a similar geographical distribution in the United States, and Wheeler and his colleagues further suggested that blacktongue occurring spontaneously is, in reality, canine pellagra.

Later, Goldberger and his collaborators [1925; 1926; 1928, 1, 2] produced in dogs by dietary means a disease which they called 'blacktongue'. The diets of the dogs were modelled on those found to be associated clinically with human pellagra, and on that used in the prison farm experiment (p. 178) [Goldberger, Wheeler and Sullivan, 1915]. It was found that blacktongue and pellagra, developing on similar diets, could be prevented by similar foodstuffs, and the two conditions were accepted as analogous by the American workers. A wide study of the distribution of the blacktongue-preventive factor was undertaken with the purpose of acquiring practical information of use in the prevention of pellagra [Goldberger, Wheeler, Lillie and Rogers, 1928, 2; Goldberger, Wheeler, Rogers and Sebrell, 1930]. It was found that the blacktongue-preventive factor in yeast was thermostable [Goldberger, Wheeler, Lillie and Rogers, 1928, 1], and this observation was used to link up human pellagra with rat 'pellagra', the latter being associated with lack of the relatively thermostable vitamin B_2.

Though the possibility of producing a pellagra-like disease in dogs was first suggested to Goldberger by Chittenden and Underhill's experiments, it soon appeared that the two groups of investigators were dealing with different conditions. Underhill and Mendel [1925] discovered that their syndrome could be relieved by a number of substances containing carotene. Carrots and yellow butter, which Goldberger had found lacking in the pellagra and blacktongue-preventive factors, cured their experimental disease, while yeast, though rich in the P-P factor, was without effect. Underhill and Mendel [1928] later recorded that crystallized carotene possessed curative properties, a significant observation in the light of the discovery that carotene and vitamin A have similar physiological actions (see p. 39). The food-mixture given by Underhill and Mendel to their dogs lacked vitamin A, and this deficiency may have caused many of the symptoms observed, while the diets employed by Goldberger, modelled on those associated with human pellagra, contained that vitamin. It would seem that the two groups of investigators had been dealing with only superficially similar pathological conditions, which were associated in reality with a deficiency of different food factors. It is possible that Underhill and Mendel's syndrome may have been caused by lack of vitamin A and by other serious dietary deficiencies, though on the other hand it was recorded that cod-liver oil would not cure the affected dogs [Underhill and Mendel, 1925].

THE RELATION BETWEEN VITAMIN B_2, THE P-P FACTOR, AND THE BLACKTONGUE-PREVENTIVE FACTOR (GOLDBERGER).

Aykroyd and Roscoe [1929] pointed out that the distribution in foodstuffs of the P-P factor, the blacktongue-preventive factor, and vitamin B_2 as determined by themselves showed fair agreement. Table XII shows the correspondence.

TABLE XII.

Comparison of the Preventive Value of Various Foodstuffs for Vitamin B₂-Deficiency in Rats, for Pellagra in Man, and for Blacktongue in Dogs.

The percentages refer to the proportions present in the diet.

Material.	Vitamin B_2. Rat.	P-P Factor. Man.	Blacktongue-preventive Factor. Dogs.
Maize endosperm	Very poor.	Associated with pellagra in U.S.A. and Italy.	. . .
Wheat flour	Very poor.	Associated with pellagra in U.S.A.	Used in basal diet to produce the disease.
Whole maize	Poor. Growth less than half the normal.	Traditionally associated with pellagra.	No preventive action; used in basal diet to produce the disease.
Whole wheat	Poor, but better than maize.	. . .	66 % delayed onset of the disease; no protection.
Peas	30–40 % needed for good growth ('Clipper' dried peas).	30–35 % (168 g. daily), incomplete protection (Virginian cowpea).	58 %, slight protection; 73 %, almost complete protection (Virginian cowpea).
Wheat germ	15–30 %, good growth.	30 %, protection almost complete.	31 %, protection almost complete.
Fresh milk	5–10 % milk solids, good growth.	20 % solids (1,200 g. buttermilk daily) protected.	250–300 c.c. skim milk daily protected.
Lean meat	7–10 % (dry weight), good growth.	10 % (dry weight, 50 g. daily) protected.	11 % (dry weight) protected.
Dried yeast	1–3 % good growth,	7 % (30 g. daily) protected.	5 % protected.
Liver	1–2 % (dry weight) ox liver, good growth.	Alcoholic extract of ox liver effective in treatment.	11 % dried pork liver protected.
Dried egg yolk	7–15 %, good growth.	. . .	17 % protected.

Apart from similarity of distribution, other evidence points to the identity of vitamin B_2 and the P-P factor. As previously recorded, a diet deficient in vitamin B_2 often produces a pellagra-like syndrome in rats and mice. Experimental blacktongue in dogs (also a pellagra-like condition) develops on diets similar to those associated with human pellagra and the factor which prevents its occurrence is, like vitamin B_2, relatively thermostable.

It is not justifiable, however, to assume that pellagra and vitamin B_2 deficiency are synonymous. Evidence against the identity of vitamin B_2 with the P-P factor, and the analogy between human pellagra and rat dermatitis, is the fact that this last disease requires a highly purified diet for its development. Again, it has been shown by Aykroyd [1930, 1] that maize, millet, and rice, the last two of which are rarely associated with pellagra, are all three equally low in their vitamin B_2 content. This observation weakens the theory that pellagra is due solely to a deficiency of vitamin B_2.

Pellagra and Beri-beri.

Diets composed almost exclusively of milled rice or refined wheat flour are commonly found among populations liable to beri-beri, but this disease is rarely recorded among maize-eaters. It is possible that there is enough vitamin B_1 in their diet to enable them to subsist long enough on this defective cereal to develop pellagra, supposing the latter disease to be due to vitamin B_2 deficiency and to occur after a longer depletion period than beri-beri. It could also be argued that the exclusive eater of milled rice and refined wheat flour, whose diet is deficient in both B vitamins, does not get pellagra because he succumbs first to beri-beri. Against such a theory is the observation that 'parboiled' rice, which contains vitamin B_1 [Plimmer *et al.*, 1927], usually confers immunity from beri-beri [Fraser and Stanton, 1911] and is almost never associated with pellagra, though it does not compare favourably with whole maize and maize endosperm as a source of vitamin B_2 [Aykroyd, 1930, 1].

The Maize Toxin Theory of Pellagra.

Lombroso's theory that a poison produced in deteriorated maize is the cause of pellagra—a theory still held officially in Italy—was the starting-point of numerous investigations in the last century. In spite of considerable effort, however, no conclusive experiment in proof was put forward. At a somewhat later period the 'photo-dynamic' theory attracted adherents. It has long been known that the skin lesions of pellagra occur on parts of the body exposed to sunlight, and Aschoff [1905] suggested that this might be explained by the presence of a photo-sensitizing substance in maize analogous to that supposed to exist in buckwheat. It is said that white hogs and sheep which consume buckwheat develop skin lesions on the parts exposed to sunlight.

Horbaczewski [1910; 1912] attempted to demonstrate the presence of a photo-sensitizing substance in maize by experiments on white mice and rats. White mice fed on maize polenta and milk developed dermatitis, when exposed to sunlight, in periods ranging from two weeks to six months. Dermatitis was also recorded in a number of rats given a diet of wheat flour and milk to which an alcoholic extract of maize was added. Subcutaneous injection of maize extracts into mice resulted in death in two or three hours in animals exposed to light, while in the dark they survived for twenty to thirty hours. An attempt to repeat Horbaczewski's observations on rats has proved unsuccessful [Aykroyd, 1931, unpublished results].

It is difficult to assess the value of Horbaczewski's work. His papers contain some contradictions, and some experiments are imperfectly controlled and need confirmation. Nevertheless, the possibility that maize contains a positive 'pellagra-producing' factor, perhaps operative only in the absence of the P-P factor, should not altogether be lost sight of. It is conceivable that the action of the P-P factor might be to neutralize a toxin rather than to make up a deficiency, just as vitamin D 'neutralizes' the anti-

calcifying effect of certain cereals though it also makes up a
deficiency. Since it has been found that maize does not greatly
differ from other cereals as regards its vitamin B_2 content, the
epidemiology of pellagra cannot at present be explained in terms
of a deficiency of this vitamin. If, however, a positive toxic factor
could be demonstrated in maize, this difficulty would be overcome.

The Present Position of Pellagra Research.

Though a considerable number of points remain obscure, from
the practical point of view much useful knowledge about pellagra
has been obtained in the last twenty years. Pellagra is unques-
tionably associated with a poor and monotonous diet, and its
appearance can be prevented by suitable dietary alterations. The
observations of Goldberger, Wilson, and others should be of the
utmost value to administrators and medical men in actual contact
with the disease. The efficiency of yeast, for example, in prevention and in cure of milder cases, has been conclusively demonstrated. Yeast is cheaper than milk and meat, also efficient
pellagra-preventives, but is often a difficult addition to make to
a human dietary. The important question of the attitude to
be adopted towards the consumption of maize by pellagrins or
potential pellagrins remains unsettled. It is, however, interesting
to recall that in the last century the French physicians concerned
with pellagra directed their efforts mainly to the elimination of
maize from the diet of the people. Their campaign was ultimately
successful and the use of maize in France was discontinued. The
simultaneous disappearance of pellagra naturally appeared to be a
complete justification of the policy.

CHAPTER VIII

VITAMIN C, THE ANTISCORBUTIC VITAMIN.

SCURVY has for many centuries been regarded as a disease due to dietetic errors, and rightly so. It was common knowledge in olden times, especially among seafaring folk, that scurvy occurred after deprivation for long periods of fresh foodstuffs, and that it could be prevented and rapidly cured when fresh vegetables and fruits were available. Thus Bachstrom in 1734 (*Observationes circa scorbutum; eiusque indolem, causas, signa et curam*) wrote as follows:

'From want of proper attention to the history of the scurvy, its causes have been generally, though wrongfully, supposed to be cold in northern climates, sea-air, the use of salt meats, etc., whereas this evil is solely owing to a total abstinence from fresh vegetable food and greens; which is alone the true primary cause of the disease. And where persons, either through neglect or necessity, do refrain for a considerable time from eating the fresh fruits of the earth, and greens, no age, no climate or soil are exempted from its attack. Other secondary causes may likewise concur, but recent vegetables are found alone effectual to preserve the body from this malady; and most speedily to cure it, even in a few days, when the case is not rendered desperate by the patients being dropsical or consumptive' (translation given by Lind [1757, p. 394]).

Other theories of the aetiology of scurvy dating from more recent times include, firstly, that of bacterial origin, which has been frequently advanced from different sources, and, secondly, the suggestion that the cause is chronic poisoning from putrefying meat or fish. Many adherents of the former theory [e.g. Coplans, 1904; Jackson and Moody, 1916] have brought forward some experimental support for their view, the explanation being, doubtless, that any animal in a scorbutic condition, due to dietetic deficiency, will be a ready prey to a secondary infection. The second view, first advanced by Torup [quoted by Jackson and Harley, 1900, 1] and supported by the work of Jackson and Harley [1900, 1, 2], received wide acceptance in recent times, especially among the leaders of some Arctic expeditions, with the result that the nature of the stores taken and diet arranged was modified accordingly. There is, however, little, if any, support for this view in the final experience of the expeditions, and the interpretation placed by Jackson and Harley upon their experimental results has not been accepted by their scientific colleagues [Holst and Frölich, 1912, p. 42].

A diet deprived of all antiscorbutic foods is generally one which affords an acid ash, and it was suggested by Wright [1900; 1908] that scurvy was caused by a condition of acidosis brought about by a diet deficient in organic salts of sodium and potassium. Wright found a decrease in the alkalinity of the blood of scurvy patients, some of whom responded favourably to treatment with alkalis, whereas Lamb [1902] was unable to confirm this. The oicarbonate of the blood and plasma of scorbutic guinea-pigs is somewhat lower than that of normal guinea-pigs [Hess and Killian, 1918–19; Lepper and Zilva, 1925], but can be brought up to normal by the addition of sodium citrate to the diet without alleviation of the scorbutic symptoms. Moreover, scurvy can be cured by the administration of daily doses of concentrated fractions of lemon juice which contain only about 1 mg. of solid matter.

The pH of the blood of guinea-pigs does not decrease in scurvy (Lepper and Zilva), thus showing that acidosis does not occur.

The idea that experimental scurvy in guinea-pigs was due to chronic constipation [McCollum and Pitz, 1917; McCollum, 1918; Pitz, 1918] has been found to be erroneous [Chick, Hume and Skelton, 1918, 1, 2; Cohen and Mendel 1918; Cohen, 1917–18; Hess and Unger, 1918, 1; Harden and Zilva, 1918, 3] and has been abandoned by its originators.

Systematic experimental work on scurvy dates from the early part of the present century, when Axel Holst and his colleagues at the University of Christiania made a careful study of guinea-pig scurvy, its aetiology, symptoms, and methods of prevention and cure, and decided that it offered a complete analogy with the human disease. One or two centuries previously, when scurvy was an everyday occurrence and the common dread of all seamen, rough 'experiments' were from time to time made upon the human material so unfortunately provided. Thus Lind, in the middle of the eighteenth century, published the following account of an 'experiment', which expresses, as the result of his own careful observation, what became the common knowledge of his own day.

'On the 20th May, 1747, I took twelve patients in the scurvy, on board the "Salisbury" at sea. Their cases were as similar as I could have them. They all in general had putrid gums, the spots, and lassitude, with weakness of their knees. They lay together in one place, being a proper apartment for the sick in the fore-hold; and had one diet common to all, viz., water-gruel sweetened with sugar in the morning, fresh mutton-broth oftentimes for dinner; at other times light puddings; boiled biscuit with sugar, etc., and for supper, barley and raisins, rice and currants, sago and wine, or the like.

'Two of these were ordered each a quart of cyder a day. Two others took twenty-five drops of elixir vitriol, three times a day, upon an empty stomach; using a gargle strongly acidulated with it for their mouths. Two others took two spoonfulls of vinegar three times a day upon an empty stomach; having their gruels and their other food well acidulated with it, as also the gargle for their mouths. Two of the worst patients, with the tendons under the ham rigid (a symptom none of the rest had), were put under a course of sea-water. Of this they drank half a pint every day, and sometimes more or less, as it operated by way of gentle physic. Two others had each two oranges and one lemon given them every day. These they ate with greediness, at different times upon an empty stomach. They continued but six days under this course, having consumed the quantity that could be spared. The two remaining patients took the bigness of a nutmeg three times a day of an electary recommended by an hospital-surgeon, made of garlic, mustard-seed, *rad-raphan*, balsam of *Peru*, and gum myrrh; using for common drink, barley-water well acidulated with tamarinds; by a decoction of which, with the addition of *cremor-tartar*, they were gently purged three or four times during the course.

'The consequence was, that the most sudden and visible good effects were perceived from the use of the oranges and lemons; one of those who had taken them being at the end of six days fit for duty. The spots were not indeed quite off his body, nor his gums sound; but without any other medicine, than a gargarism of *elixir vitriol*, he became quite healthy before we came into Plymouth, which was on the 16th June. The other was the best recovered of any in his condition; and being now deemed pretty well, was appointed nurse to the rest of the sick.

'Next to the oranges, I thought the cyder had the best effects. It was indeed not very sound, being inclinable to be aigre or pricked. However, those who had taken it were in a fairer way of recovery than the others at the end of the fortnight, which was the length of the time all these different courses were continued, except the oranges. The putrefaction of their gums, but especially their lassitude and weakness, were somewhat abated, and their appetite increased by it.

'As to the *elixir of vitriol*, I observed that the mouths of those who had used it by way of gargarism, were in a much cleaner and better condition than many of the rest, especially those who used the vinegar; but perceived otherwise no good effects from its internal use upon the other symptoms. I indeed never had a great opinion of the efficacy of this medicine in the scurvy, since our longest cruise in the "Salisbury" from the 10th August to the 28th October, 1746; when we had but one scorbutic case in the ship. The patient was a marine (one Walsh), who after recovering from a quotidian ague in the latter end of September, had taken the *elixir vitriol*, by way of a restorative for three weeks; and yet at length contracted the disease, while under a course of medicine recommended for its prevention.

'There was no remarkable alteration upon those who took the electary and tamarind decoction, the sea-water, or vinegar, upon comparing their condition, at the end of the fortnight, with others who had taken nothing but a little lenitive electary and *cremor-tartar*, at times, in order to keep their belly open; or a gentle pectoral in the evening, for relief of their breast' [Lind, 1757, p. 56].

Holst and Frölich [1907; 1912] showed that scurvy could be induced in guinea-pigs by removing the greenstuff from the ordinary diet of grain and cabbage leaves, and by giving a diet consisting of grain and water only. It proved immaterial what grain was used, and the experiments included uncooked maize, oats, barley, and rice, as well as wheat and rye in the form of bread. In all cases this diet caused severe scurvy from which the animals died in from twenty to forty days, showing the haemorrhages and bony changes characteristic of the disease. By supplementing the scurvy diet with fresh vegetables, fruits, and fruit juices, these observers were able to maintain the animals in health. For example, scurvy was prevented by a daily ration of 30 g. of fresh raw cabbage, dandelion leaves, sorrel, carrot, or cranberries. When these antiscorbutic materials were heated, their value was reduced by an amount depending on the temperature and time of heating; after heating at 100° C. for one hour (and in some cases for half an hour) the same ration was found inadequate to prevent scurvy. A similar result was obtained with dried materials; rations equivalent to 30 g. of raw carrot, dandelion leaves, or cabbage leaves failed to prevent scurvy when in the dried condition, and equally disappointing results were obtained with dried potatoes. The antiscurvy substance originally present in the expressed juices of vegetables suffered a similar fate rapidly on keeping, but the expressed juices of acid materials, e.g., lemons or sorrel leaves, were found to be more stable in this respect.

A further result of first-class importance was obtained by Fürst [1912] also working in Holst's laboratory, He found that, whereas dry cereals or pulses, e.g., oats, barley, lentils, peas, beans, were unable to prevent scurvy in the dry condition, if soaked in water and allowed to begin germination for 2–3 days they acquired antiscurvy properties. This result was confirmed by Chick and Hume [1917, 1], and Chick and Delf [1919] as regards pulses. In the case of cereals it was called in question by Weill, Mouriquand and Péronnet [1918], but has since been frequently confirmed (see Table XIII, p. 205).

Even this important result had been anticipated as long ago as 1782, for we find in 'An account of the Diseases of India as they appeared in the English Fleet' (by Charles Curtis, formerly Surgeon of the Medea Frigate, Edinburgh, 1807) the following passage (p. 41):

'With regard to sea-scurvy, reports and accounts have been published, as if this had been cured at sea, by lime or citron juice, lemon rob, nitre dissolved in vinegar, nitric acid and all which I would suspect to be rather something hyperbolical. But there is a plan for this purpose recommended by a *Mr. Young of the Navy*, which from its practicability and perfect conformity to known and established principles, is highly deserving of attention, and of being recorded in such a publication. It proceeds upon the well-known fact, that nothing more is necessary for the cure of this disease in any situation where there is tolerably pure air, than—not dead and dried, but fresh vegetable diet, greens or roots, in sufficient quantity. To be sure, we cannot have a kitchen garden at sea, and a short and scanty crop of greens can only be raised on board ship; *but beans and pease, and barley and other seeds brought under the malting or vegetating process, are converted into the state of a growing plant, with the vital principle in full activity throughout the germ and pulp* and if eaten in this state without any sort of preparation, except that of separating or rejecting the husks, cannot fail to supply precisely what is wanted for the cure of scurvy, *viz.*, fresh vegetable chyle.

'For this purpose, besides the articles mentioned, which may all be employed, he gives the preference for gram, an East Indian grain, chiefly used in the feeding of horses. The malting process is to be performed in shallow frames of wood, constructed so as to preserve the water for successive operations; and a little experience will readily lead to the proper degrees of heat and moisture for conducting it successfully.'

From the researches of Holst and his colleagues we are enabled to make the following generalization. The antiscorbutic accessory factor is found in nature associated primarily with living plant tissues in which active metabolic processes are still proceeding. When these active processes cease or are greatly reduced, as in seeds, the antiscurvy vitamin also disappears. In the case of seeds it is created anew during germination. The distribution of this factor thus presents a marked contrast with that of the anti-beri-beri factor, of which one of the principal sources is found in dry seeds.

EFFECTS OF VITAMIN C DEFICIENCY.

Guinea-pigs as Experimental Animals.

The symptoms of severe scurvy in guinea-pigs are briefly the following. Tenderness and swelling of the joints are the earliest sign, and the animal will frequently adopt a position (scurvy position), in which it rests on its side, while the affected member is held twitching in the air. In other cases the animal lies down with the side of its face upon the floor of the cage indicating that its gums and jaw have become tender ('scurvy face-ache position', see Fig. 30). Later on the teeth become loose, solid food is refused, and death may occur a few days later. In cases where the antiscorbutic given is only adequate for partial protection, the animal will usually live on for a considerable time, exhibiting swollen and painful joints, but growing up and enjoying a measure of health and spirits depending on the degree of protection afforded [see Delf, 1918].

In animals dying from scurvy the principal lesions at the post-mortem examination show close analogy with those characteristic of the human disease. Haemorrhages occur in any position, but are most frequent in the limbs. In cases where they occur in the intestinal tract blood is frequently passed in life, and death occurs suddenly. Rarification of the long bones is almost invariably present, and these frequently show fracture in the neighbourhood of the junction of shaft and epiphysis. The ribs are swollen and often fractured at the juncture of bone with cartilage. The teeth are loose and can easily be removed.

The histological changes produced at the rib junctions in the guinea-pig are very striking. These changes are gradually produced and become progressively more extensive as the period of deficient diet increases. Tozer [1918; 1921, 1, 2] distinguishes 'incipient', 'mild', 'chronic', and 'acute' scurvy, and these various degrees are illustrated by Fig. 31, ii–vi, the normal condition being shown in Fig. 31, i. No macroscopic changes occur for the first seventeen days, but about this time, even when the rib remains flat and normal in appearance, microscopic changes are apparent. 'The most noticeable departures from the normal are a variable amount of irregularity of the junction as a whole, slight disarrangement, and usually shortening of the rows of cartilage cells and of the trabeculae; an increased amount of blood in the marrow cavity, and a reduction

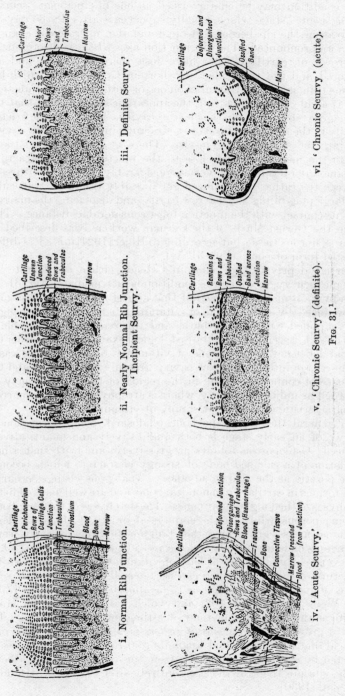

i. Normal Rib Junction.

ii. Nearly Normal Rib Junction. 'Incipient Scurvy.'

iii. 'Definite Scurvy.'

iv. 'Acute Scurvy.'

v. 'Chronic Scurvy' (definite).

vi. 'Chronic Scurvy' (acute).

Fig. 31.[1]

[1] Reproduced by permission from the *Biochemical Journal*, 1918, 12, p. 446.

in thickness of the bone, especially near the junction' (Fig. 31, ii)·
This condition may be characterized as one of 'incipient' scurvy.
In the 'acute' stage which usually supervenes after 18–35 days of
deprivation the rib becomes swollen and the 'microscopic changes
are more pronounced. The rib junction as a whole is disorganized,
the rows of cartilage cells have lost their alignment and are
scattered, and the trabeculae are shortened. The bone, which has
become thin, is usually fractured on one or both sides of the junction,
and, as a rule, quite close to it, the appearances suggesting that the
cartilage is telescoped into the marrow cavity. There is haemorrhage,
usually in the neighbourhood of the fracture, into the marrow cavity,
and into the surrounding muscles. There is also a mass of tissue
within the marrow cavity close to the junction and the fracture.
The amount of this tissue varies considerably, from a few threads
between the rather disorganized and possibly fractured trabeculae
to a large plug filling the marrow cavity, and displacing the marrow
from its contact with the junction for a considerable distance.' This
tissue, the 'Gerüst Mark' of the German workers, was described by
Tozer as fibrous tissue, but according to Höjer [1924] it is a less differentiated form of bone' (Fig. 31, iv).

Partial deprivation of vitamin C leads either to 'definite' or
'chronic' scurvy, in which the condition is intermediate (Fig. 31, iii,
v, and vi). It may be pointed out that almost identical changes may
be produced by deprivation of vitamin A when the guinea-pig is
well supplied with antiscorbutic, and this renders it impossible in
mild cases to ascertain from the histological examination whether the
partial deficiency has been one of vitamin C or A. In acute cases,
haemorrhage into the marrow cavity, fracture of the bone, and the
presence of connective tissue in the region of the junction may be
regarded as indicating scurvy, whereas atrophy of the bone marrow
is characteristic of a deficient supply of vitamin A.

In general the membrane bone (endosmal bone) formation in
scurvy of an early stage is both qualitatively and quantitatively
reduced. Osteoporosis follows progressively 'and with that a new
formation of a calcified bone of spongy character' which becomes
more porotic as the scurvy advances. Analogous changes occur in
bone formed in cartilage (enchondral bone) and are well marked in the
epiphyses of the long tubular bones. The diaphyses of the long bones
become porous, whilst at the epiphyseal junctions shapeless dense
columnar masses are formed, the 'Trümmerfeldzone' of the German
workers, which are entirely lacking in collagen fibrils [Höjer, 1924].

A very early symptom of lack of vitamin C is the change in the
structure of the teeth, which can be detected when the other scorbutic symptoms are so slight as to be almost unrecognizable [Zilva
and Wells, 1919] (see p. 102) and which has been used by Höjer
[1926] as the basis of a method of estimation of vitamin C. The
rate of growth of the incisors of guinea-pigs, which in animals on a
normal diet is constant and amounts to 0·75 mm. a day, is greatly
affected by removal of vitamin C from the diet and in total absence
of the vitamin the growth ceases entirely after 15–20 days [Dalldorf
and Zall, 1930].

The characteristic effect of scurvy on the tissues other than bones is atrophy. Thus a general atrophy of the connective tissue occurs, specially attacking the collagen fibrils, and of the vascular walls, whilst the muscular and lymphoid tissue, the liver, salivary glands, adrenals, and kidneys undergo an atrophy combined with necrosis. These changes may be traced at a very early stage of the latent period of the disease [Höjer, 1924; see also Meyer and McCormick, 1927–28; K. D. Harris and Smith, 1928]. According to McCarrison [1921] and Brouwer [1927], however, the adrenals are enlarged; the lipoid content of their cortex is reduced [Peiper, 1922].

With regard to other histological effects of vitamin C deficiency, it may be noted that no marked change occurs in the blood picture [Bedson, 1921; Herzog, 1921; G. M. Findlay, 1921, 2], while the endothelium of the capillaries becomes swollen and degenerated, and there results a stagnation of blood in the capillaries which appears to be one of the factors leading to deficient oxygenation of the tissues and thus to death [G.M. Findlay, 1921, 1]. Both in acute and chronic scurvy definite lesions of a degenerative character occur in the bone marrow of guinea-pigs, and, possibly owing to these, guinea-pigs with chronic scurvy are less resistant to infection than normal animals [G. M. Findlay, 1923, 2]. On the other hand Zilva [1919, 2] found no diminution in the power to form agglutinins and amboceptor in scorbutic guinea-pigs.

The changes in the bone marrow and liver of scorbutic guinea-pigs persist for a long time after the animal has received a complete diet and consequently the symptoms of scurvy recur very rapidly when such animals are again deprived of vitamin C [Mouriquand, Michel and Bernheim, 1924, 1, 2].

Monkeys as Experimental Animals.

In many ways monkeys are more suitable animals to use than guinea-pigs for testing the antiscorbutic value of foodstuffs, since they are capable of taking much larger doses of substances of low antiscorbutic potency, whilst their daily requirement of antiscorbutic vitamin is almost exactly the same as that of guinea-pigs (see p. 195). Monkeys have proved, for example, of special value in the testing of milk, the protective dose of which for guinea-pigs is just at or beyond the receptive capacity of this animal. A convenient basal diet for monkeys consists of boiled polished rice (100 g. dry weight), wheat germ 30 g. and autoclaved milk 200 c.c. daily [Barnes and Hume, 1919, 1, 2; Harden and Zilva, 1919]. In experiments with milk, part of the autoclaved milk is replaced by the milk to be tested. On this diet monkeys develop scurvy in about 8–10 weeks, with symptoms closely resembling those of human scurvy. Such are sponginess and bleeding of the gums with loosening of the teeth (usually the earliest sign), and haemorrhage under the periosteum, into the orbit, and in almost any part of the body. There is weakness and ultimately almost complete powerlessness of the hind limbs, a condition which is characteristic of infantile scurvy and is apparently the result of haemorrhages into the hip and knee joints. The bones also become fragile and there is enlargement and disruption of the rib junctions. When the disease is far advanced the whole body and limbs are tender. The effect of antiscorbutic deficiency upon the weight of the monkey is similar to that observed with guinea-pigs. Various genera and species have been successfully employed, but *Macacus rhesus* is probably the most suitable, although there is great individual variation.

ORIGIN AND PHYSIOLOGICAL FUNCTION OF VITAMIN C.

Origin.

The only important fact known about the origin of this vitamin is that it is produced during the germination of seeds [Fürst, 1912]. As regards its function in the plant or the nature of its precursor in the seed nothing has so far been ascertained. Its high concentration in such different parts of the plant as the leaves (cabbage), the fruit (lemons, &c.), and the root (swedes) renders it difficult to draw any definite conclusion either as to its function or mode of origin.

Requirements of Different Animals.

Animals derive vitamin C—directly or indirectly—from the vegetable kingdom. Different species of animal, however, vary greatly in their susceptibility to scurvy and in the amount of antiscorbutic vitamin which they require for growth and maintenance. Thus, while human beings, monkeys, and guinea-pigs are susceptible to scurvy, rats, mice, and adult rabbits do not show the characteristic symptoms of the disease, in spite of deprivation of vitamin C. It appears, however, that the difference between these two classes is one of degree only. It has been shown [Harden and Zilva, 1918, 4; Drummond, 1919, 1] that rats existing on a scorbutic diet do not thrive so well, and are not so fertile, as those which receive some antiscorbutic material, although Hartwell [1930] could not confirm this. Parsons [1920] has shown that the liver of the rat, and, to a much less extent, the muscle, contains vitamin C even when the animal has been kept for a long time on a scorbutic diet, and that this was also the case in the offspring of such rats reared on the same diet [Parsons and Hutton, 1924; Lepkovsky and Nelson, 1924]. It is evident that the rat requires vitamin C, but only in very small amounts compared with such animals as the guinea-pig and monkey. It is of interest that another rodent, the prairie dog of North America (*Cynomys ludovicianus*), resembles the rat, a young animal of 169 g. growing to a weight of 690 g. in six months when maintained on a diet (soy-bean flour and butter) on which guinea-pigs acquired scurvy in 2–3 weeks [McCollum and Parsons, 1920]. The rabbit receiving a scorbutic diet of oats, beans, and water generally loses weight and dies, but does not develop the characteristic symptoms of scurvy. Female rabbits became pregnant, but the young were born dead, and showed typical haemorrhages and bone lesions [G. M. Findlay, 1921, 3]. The addition of swede juice to the diet produced a great improvement in the condition of the animals.

The fowl is also able to subsist on a scorbutic diet and like the rat possesses under these conditions a store of vitamin C in the liver [Carrick and Hauge, 1925, where the literature is quoted; Hauge and Carrick, 1926, 2]. Calves [Thurston, Eckles and Palmer, 1926; Thurston, Palmer and Eckles, 1929] and pigs [Hughes, Aubel and Lienhardt, 1928] also thrive without any obvious source of vitamin C, although well-developed scurvy has been occasionally observed in pigs [Plimmer, 1920; Zilva, Golding and Drummond, 1924]. It is still doubtful whether these animals acquire the vitamin C contained in their livers by the accumulation of traces from their food or by chemical change from some source of which guinea-pigs are not able to avail themselves. Even among the animals which are subject to typical scurvy there are great differences in requirement. Thus, for protection from scurvy, a monkey weighing 2–3 kg. requires about the same daily dose of orange juice, 1·5 c.c. [Harden and Zilva, 1919, 1920, 1], or milk, 100–150 c.c. [Barnes and Hume, 1919, 2], as a guinea-pig of 250–300 g. A child of 8–10 kg. requires about 500 c.c. of milk or 10–15 c.c. of orange juice per day, so that its requirements are approximately the same as those of the monkey per unit of weight, whereas those of the guinea-pig are 5–10 times greater.

Göthlin [1931] has made use of a blood capillary resistance test (p. 266) to ascertain the minimum dose of antiscorbutic substances, such as orange juice, required to preserve a normal capillary resistance in adults. This was found by experiments on patients in an asylum, who were artificially fed, to be about 0·7–1·0 c.c. orange juice per kg. per day; or 42–60 c.c. for an adult weighing 60 kg.

To protect a young guinea-pig from the ordinary symptoms of scurvy a daily dose of 1·5 c.c. orange juice is needed, whilst 3 c.c. are required to prevent degeneration of the dental pulp. Assuming that the dose required to preserve normal capillary resistance is of the same order as that required to prevent degeneration of the dental pulp, it would follow that an average adult would require 14–20 times as much antiscorbutic as a guinea-pig. The requirements of a human adult for other foodstuffs can be roughly calculated by the use of these factors from the experimentally determined values for the guinea-pig, provided that the foodstuffs are such that their vitamin C is as readily absorbed in the human digestive tract as in that of the guinea-pig. On this basis a man would require per diem about 1000 c.c. milk, 200 g. of boiled new potatoes, 350 of old; 400 c.c. of carrot juice, 60 c.c. of tomato juice, &c.

Storage and Excretion.

Although vitamin C is present in muscle and tissue, it does not appear to be stored in the animal body to the same extent as vitamin A. Experiments with guinea-pigs [Hess, 1920, p. 75; Harden and Zilva, 1918, 2] show that a previous period during which large doses of orange or lemon juice (freed from acid) are administered, does not in any way increase the time necessary for the development of scurvy on a deficient diet. Some idea of the relative amounts stored by the guinea-pig and monkey may be gathered from the fact that although the daily requirements are the same, the guinea-pig develops scurvy in three weeks, the monkey in two months: in the human being the period of development is six to eight months (p. 267).

No evidence of excretion of the antiscorbutic vitamin in the urine has been obtained [Van der Walle, 1922].

Effect of Vitamin C Deficiency on Metabolism.

In spite of much experimental work, it has not been found possible to establish any definite relation between the onset of scurvy and disturbed metabolism. As the disease progresses all the metabolic processes of the animal are disturbed, owing to the state of inanition which supervenes, and the changes reported by many observers must be attributed to this cause. If, however, any metabolic disturbance precedes or accompanies the onset of scurvy it should reveal itself in the guinea-pig in the early stages of the vitamin C deficiency, since scorbutic lesions are sometimes in evidence by the tenth day and microscopic changes in the teeth can be detected still earlier [Zilva and Wells, 1919].

Acting on this principle Shipp and Zilva [1928, 2] and Humphreys and Zilva [1931] have investigated the metabolism of nitrogen, calcium, and phosphorus by making daily observations of the intake and output of these elements by guinea-pigs on a scorbutic diet. The results for these three series of experiments were similar. No definite indications of a disturbed metabolism were found in the early stages of the disease. When the intake of food was diminished as the disease progressed disturbances occurred, the balance in every case becoming negative. Similar results were obtained in Japan by Nagayama and his co-workers, who also found no disturbance of carbohydrate metabolism [Nagayama, Machida and Takeda, 1928; Nagayama and Sato, 1928; Nagayama and Munehisa, 1929]. The experiments of Baumann and Howard [1917] on the metabolism of calcium, phosphorus, and nitrogen are vitiated by the low intake of the elements in question by the experimental animals, so that their conclusion that the negative balance observed is characteristic of scurvy cannot be accepted. Jarussowa [1928], whose animals were forcibly fed, observed a negative balance of nitrogen, but this did not become evident until the 24th day, long after the symptoms of scurvy had been manifested.

The calcium and phosphorus contents of the blood of guinea-pigs are very variable, but no definite change occurs in scurvy [Palladin and Ssawron, 1924; Edelstein and Schmal, 1926; Shipp and Zilva, 1928, 2]. The fall in blood-phosphorus noted during scurvy by Euler and Myrbäck [1925] was probably an accidental variation. No change in the calcium and phosphorus of the serum of guinea-pigs suffering from scurvy was found by Nagayama and Munehisa [1929].

The fatty tissues undergo no marked change in scurvy, but the cholesterol is decreased in lungs and testes, slightly in muscle and largely in the adrenals [Nagayama and Tagaya, 1929; Igarashi and Tagaya, 1929].

The excretion of lactic acid in the urine of scorbutic guinea-pigs was found to run parallel to that in the urine of controls kept on a restricted normal diet so that they lost weight at the same rate as the scorbutic animals, and no specific effect of scurvy was detected [Shipp and Zilva, 1928, 1].

According to Palladin and his colleagues, deprivation of vitamin C is accompanied by a rise in the blood-sugar and blood-amylase, which attains its maximum at the end of the second week and then gradually falls off [Palladin, 1924]. This change in the blood-sugar due to scurvy could not be confirmed by Lepper and Zilva (unpublished results). Other blood ferments (catalase, protease, esterase, and peroxidase) are scarcely affected in the early stages of vitamin C deficiency [Palladin and Normark, 1924]. The creatine of the muscles steadily increases, whereas in starvation it first increases and then decreases [Palladin and Kudrjwzewa, 1924]. At the same time creatine appears in the urine and steadily increases in quantity, as does also the proportion of creatine- and creatinine-N to the total N of the urine. Near the end of the scorbutic period, as death approaches, the muscles contain comparatively little creatinephosphoric acid, whereas the lactacidogen is increased [Palladin and Epelbaum 1929].

CONCENTRATION OF VITAMIN C.

The methods employed are based on the facts that the greater part of the vitamin is precipitated by basic lead acetate [Zilva, 1924, 3], i.e. by lead acetate in the slightly alkaline region, and that impurities can be previously precipitated by treatment with the normal salt [Bezssonoff, 1922, 1; Zilva, 1925], with alcohol [Harden and Zilva, 1918, 2; Zilva, 1924, 3], and by fermentation of the sugars in the solution with yeast [Zilva, 1924, 1; Lepkovsky et al., 1925; Grettie and King, 1929]. Owing to the great instability of the vitamin (see p. 199) and the variations in the character of the medium, preparations of very variable activity are often obtained even from the same natural source.

Lemon juice forms one of the best sources for the concentration of vitamin C. Chemical and physical studies have afforded some information as to the conditions governing the concentration of the active principle [Zilva, 1924, 1, 3; 1925; 1927, 1, 2; 1928; 1929; 1930; Daubney and Zilva, 1926; Hoyle and Zilva, 1927]. The best results were obtained by Zilva by using the following procedure. The bulk of the organic acids are removed from the lemon juice by the addition of an excess of precipitated chalk and the mixture is allowed to stand for about one hour. The liquid is then filtered through a Büchner funnel and a saturated solution of normal lead acetate is added. The proper quantity to be used can only be ascertained by trial and must be such that the final preparation has a reducing power to phenolindophenol (0·02 per cent. solution) of not less than 6 c.c. for an equivalent of 5 c.c. of the original decitrated juice (see p. 199). The quantity varies greatly with the individual sample and unless the right amount of the reagent is used at this stage, there may be a great loss of activity in the final preparation. After immediate filtration through a Büchner funnel or centrifugation, the liquid (pH 5·0 — 5·4) is brought to pH 7·2 — 7·4 by addition of a 6 per cent. solution of ammonia. The precipitate which contains the vitamin is quickly centrifuged and taken up in 10 per cent. acetic acid. The lead is then removed by the addition of just sufficient saturated magnesium sulphate (3–5 c.c. for 50 c.c. of decitrated juice) and subsequently of 2 volumes of 96 per cent. alcohol. After filtration the solution is concentrated to a small volume in order to remove the greater part of the acetic acid. An equivalent of 1·5 c.c. of the original juice (i.e. a daily protective dose for a guinea-pig), prepared daily in small quantities and administered very soon after preparation to young guinea-pigs, is sufficient to keep the animals alive for periods of about 60 days, although scorbutic symptoms may be present. Considering the risk of loss in activity involved in the manipulation, it would appear that the greater part of the antiscorbutic potency of the juice can be obtained in the final fraction by this procedure.

The active lead precipitate may be dissolved in acetic acid and reprecipitated at pH 7·2 — 7·4 [Grettie and King, 1929; Sipple and King, 1930]. Care must, however, be taken that the minimum amount of acetic acid is used, and it is found that the reprecipitation does not necessarily lead to further concentration, as the loss of activity may more than balance the removal of inactive matter [Zilva, 1931]. Grettie and King [1929] and Sipple and King [1930] have also introduced several minor modifications into the process without materially increasing the degree of concentration.

It is possible by the above method to effect such a concentration that the protective dose for a guinea-pig (the equivalent of 1·5 c.c. of lemon juice) may contain about 0·5–1 mg. of solid matter, whereas 1·5 c.c. of the original juice contains about 135 mg. The result depends on the character of the juice, since the same procedure may yield different figures with different samples.

The purest fraction so far obtained is undoubtedly a complex mixture of substances. Concentrated preparations have been found to contain phosphorus, nitrogen [Zilva, 1924, 3], amino-compounds and amides [Zilva, 1925], iron, sulphur [Hoyle and Zilva, 1927], and iodine, the last of which can be separated from the active principle by dialysis [Daubney and Zilva, 1926]. These preparations possess strong reducing properties (see p. 199), give a faint coloration with ferric chloride and a faint cloudiness with bromine water [Grettie and King, 1929]. The amide nitrogen has no relation to the antiscorbutic activity of the lemon juice [Zilva, 1925] and probably the other substances mentioned above are also impurities.

The process detailed above for lemon juice can be applied to swede juice [Zilva, 1925]. Bezssonoff [1925] used a similar method with cabbage juice in which the active principle was reprecipitated several times with lead acetate and extracted with alcohol and with acetone. He claimed to have obtained a crystalline material which was protective for adult guinea-pigs in doses of 2 mg. Zilva [1930] was unable to confirm this work.

The statement has been made by Rygh et al. [1931; 1932, 1, 2;

Laland, 1932] that substances possessing high antiscorbutic activity can be obtained from an opium alkaloid, narcotine, by ultra-violet irradiation or by chemical methods. Unripe *Citrus* fruits are said to contain narcotine, which disappears on ripening, giving rise to vitamin C.

Partial demethylation of narcotine (from opium) yielded an *o*-diphenol which, it is stated, possessed a high degree of antiscorbutic activity.

A repetition of the experiments with partially demethylated narcotine by Smith and Zilva [1932] has yielded negative results and the conclusions of Rygh *et al.* cannot be considered as established.

CONDITIONS OF STABILITY OF VITAMIN C.

Vitamin C is very sensitive to oxidizing agents and to air [Delf, 1920; Hess, 1920; Hess and Unger, 1920–21; Zilva 1921; 1922; Dutcher, Harshaw and Hall, 1921]. Inactivation takes place rapidly in alkaline solution in the presence of air [Holst and Frölich, 1912; Harden and Zilva, 1918, 6; Hess and Unger, 1919], but not under anaerobic conditions [Zilva, 1923, 1]. Thus at pH 12·5 decitrated lemon juice lost 80 per cent. of its potency on exposure to air for half an hour and the whole of it in 3 hours, whereas when preserved anaerobically for 24 hours it had not appreciably decreased in potency. The antiscorbutic activity of a juice at pH 2·2 (the natural acidity of lemon juice) was decreased by aeration for 1 hr. at 100°, but to a much less extent than that of juice at pH 6·2 − 6·6.

Evidence is accumulating to show that the inactivation is not direct. Lemon juice, and other sources of vitamin C, and active preparations derived from them, possess reducing properties. Even the purest antiscorbutic fractions reduce ammoniacal silver nitrate in the cold and decolorize potassium permanganate [Zilva, 1924, 3]. Conditions favourable to the preservation of the vitamin are favourable to the preservation of these reducing properties of the active solution, but the destruction of the antiscorbutic activity and of the reducing properties proceed at different rates [Connell and Zilva, 1924, 1]. Phenolindophenol is also rapidly reduced in the air to its leuco-base by decitrated lemon juice and other sources of vitamin C, and by using this indicator Zilva [1927; 2; 1928; 1929; 1930] studied titrimetrically the behaviour of the reducing power of active solutions in relation to their antiscorbutic activity. The reducing capacity, like the antiscorbutic factor, is destroyed in alkaline medium in the presence of air, and when the active solution is aerated. When, however, phenolindophenol is added to decitrated lemon juice until the indicator is no longer reduced and the solution administered to the test animals *immediately*, no very appreciable loss in antiscorbutic activity is detected, but if this solution is administered after a few hours, the presence of the vitamin cannot be detected. If the quantity of the indicator is insufficient completely to destroy the reducing capacity, the leuco-compound formed is re-oxidized in the air, and the resulting colour base is again reduced by the active solution until the reducing power is entirely destroyed.

That this reducing substance is not the vitamin itself is also shown
by the fact that the precipitate formed in decitrated lemon juice by
normal lead acetate at pH $5.0-5.4$ (which is antiscorbutically inactive) reduces phenolindophenol even more readily than the active
fraction obtained with the same reagent at pH $7.2-7.4$ [1927, 2].
The latter fraction, which has a lower reducing capacity than its
equivalent of decitrated lemon juice, is also less stable than the
original juice [1928] and when its reducing capacity for the indicator
falls below a certain level it loses its antiscorbutic activity [1930].

All this evidence suggests that the ' phenolindophenol-reducing
principle ' exerts a protective action on the vitamin. It is not yet
known whether the inactivation of the antiscorbutic factor which
takes place rapidly in the absence of the reducing principle is itself
due to oxidation or to some other change. There is the possibility
that vitamin C is composite in the sense of an enzyme and co-enzyme,
but experimental evidence so far obtained does not support this
view. Thus if the ' phenolindophenol-reducing principle ' obtained
by precipitation with normal lead acetate, which is free from vitamin
C, is added to the ' active ' fraction in which the reducing power
and consequently the antiscorbutic potency have been destroyed by
mild oxidation, the vitamin activity is not restored [1930].

Zilva's results with respect to the behaviour of the reducing
substance to colouring matters have been confirmed by Tillmans
and P. and W. Hirsch [1932, 1, 2], but they claim, in disagreement
with him, to have found that the reducing power and antiscorbutic
potency of lemon juice and preparations from it are always proportional. When the reducing power is completely removed by the
addition of a colouring matter they ascribe the residual antiscorbutic
power to the action of the primary oxidation products formed.
On standing and on further oxidation these are slowly converted
into some substance or substances without antiscorbutic potency.
They conclude that the action of vitamin C is due to the reducing
substance and its primary oxidation products.

Zilva, however, as explained above, has frequently obtained fractions of high reducing power which were devoid, or almost devoid,
of antiscorbutic potency and these observations invalidate the
conclusions drawn by Tillmans and P. and W. Hirsch from their
experiments.

Another series of observations made by Zilva in these investigations has a bearing on the destruction of the reducing power and
the inactivation of vitamin C. If decitrated lemon juice in neutral
or acid medium is heated in an autoclave anaerobically at 115° C.
for one hour, a certain degree of diminution takes place both in
the antiscorbutic activity and in the capacity for reducing phenolindophenol, although the reducing capacity for iodine is increased by
this treatment [1929]. Such heated juice when stored under neutral,
but not acid, conditions loses its vitamin C and phenolindophenol-
reducing capacity much more quickly than unheated lemon juice
[1927, 1928]. The autoclaved juices are also capable of oxidizing
p-phenylenediamine [1929]. The addition of autoclaved to unheated
decitrated juice also accelerates the destruction both of the 'phenolindophenol-reducing principle ' and of the vitamin, as also does the

addition of an ethereal extract from autoclaved decitrated lemon juice, or of quinol, quinhydrone, benzoquinone [1929; 1930] or catechol (unpublished results). It would therefore appear that in the process of autoclaving a substance is formed, possibly of a phenolic character, which promotes the destruction (either directly or after previous oxidation by exposure to air) of the 'phenolindophenol-reducing principle' and eventually of the vitamin. It is also probable that the reducing properties of antiscorbutic solutions may be due to several substances, some of which, like the 'phenolindophenol-reducing substance', may act as protective agents for the vitamin, whilst others such as the 'phenolic substances' may, under certain conditions, acquire inactivating properties.

Decitrated lemon juice can be preserved aerobically at pH 1·0–0·6 or at pH 7·0 for a week with no significant loss of potency [Zilva, 1930]. It is stated by J. Williams and Corran [1930] that the potency of acidified lemon juice at a lower pH than 1·8 (pH 1·1, 1 and 0·6) disappears completely in 7–8 months at 15–18° C. The latter authors have also found that antiseptics, in concentrations capable of preserving lemon juice at ordinary temperatures from mould growth, &c., have, as a rule, a very deleterious effect on the stability of vitamin C.

Bezssonoff [1921, 2; 1922, 2; 1923] found that vegetable extracts containing vitamin C give with a solution of phosphomolybdotungstic acid a blue coloration which is also given in great intensity by quinol. He traced a marked parallelism between the antiscorbutic potency of such extracts and the intensity of the blue reaction and suggested that the antiscorbutic substances probably contained an unstable radical which could be split off in the form of quinol and that this reaction could be utilized as a test for vitamin C. On the other hand, it was found by Kay and Zilva [1923], that although the parallelism found by Bezssonoff undoubtedly exists in many cases, the substance giving the blue coloration can be removed by adsorption with fuller's earth from lemon juice, leaving a liquid which gives no reaction with the reagent but possesses antiscorbutic properties. Further, substances not containing vitamin C, such as yeast, gave a positive reaction. Wedgewood and Ford [1924] have also found that the colour reaction is not specific for vitamin C. It is more likely that the colour is given by some phenolic substances accompanying the antiscorbutic factor in its natural sources, since the reagent is a modification of Folin's reagent for phenol.

Our present knowledge of the conditions of stability of vitamin C makes it plain that the preparation of active concentrates by chemical fractionation on a large scale and the preservation of the activity of such preparations are at present impracticable. It is, however, possible to concentrate natural antiscorbutic juices under carefully controlled conditions without incurring great losses of the vitamin and also to preserve such preparations for a considerable time (see p. 255).

CHEMICAL AND PHYSICAL PROPERTIES OF VITAMIN C.

As already mentioned the purest preparation of vitamin C so far obtained is a complex mixture. Information is, however, available concerning the physical and chemical behaviour of the active principle under various conditions.

Vitamin C dissolves readily in water and in all strengths of alcohol [Harden and Zilva, 1918, 1; Hess and Unger, 1918, 2; Hart, Steenbock and Lepkovsky, 1922]; in methyl alcohol, but not in butyl alcohol, light petroleum, &c. [Hart, Steenbock and Lepkovsky, 1922]. It diffuses through a collodion membrane of such permeability that it permits the passage of methylene blue, neutral red, and safranine; membranes of lower permeability do not allow its diffusion [Zilva and Miura, 1921, 1]. The diffusion proceeds differently from that of the sugar and the nitrogenous substances present in decitrated lemon juice [Connell and Zilva, 1924, 2]. The 'phenol-indophenol-reducing substance' dialyses, like the vitamin [Zilva, 1928]. Lemon juice can be filtered through a Berkefeld filter without loss of potency [Harden and Zilva, 1918, 1], but the vitamin C is partially retained by a Chamberland candle [Ellis, Steenbock and Hart, 1921]. It is not adsorbed from neutral solution by fuller's earth [Harden and Zilva, 1918, 1], or by colloidal ferric hydroxide (dialysed iron), but is taken up from orange juice by blood charcoal [Ellis, Steenbock and Hart, 1921]. When decitrated lemon juice is treated with adsorbents such as 'norite' or fuller's earth, a varying degree of diminution takes place in the vitamin C content of the supernatant solution, which is probably due to oxidative changes associated with the adsorbent [Zilva, unpublished results]. No convincing evidence of the existence of more than one antiscorbutic principle has hitherto been advanced, although the early investigators were led by the varying behaviour of different foodstuffs towards heat and drying to suggest that several such substances might exist. The experimental evidence in favour of this idea adduced by Scotti-Foglieni [1926, 1; 1927; 1928], Bezssonoff [1926, 2; 1927], and Randoin and Lecoq [1927, 1] is open to criticism, and has not been confirmed.

The effects of heat and oxidation on vitamin C have already been discussed (p. 199).

ESTIMATION OF VITAMIN C IN FOODSTUFFS.

The researches of Holst and his co-workers on the distribution of vitamin C were continued in 1916 at the Lister Institute, with the aim of making a more complete survey of the commoner foodstuffs and assigning to each some quantitative value as regards antiscurvy properties [Chick and Hume, 1917, 1]. Young, growing guinea-pigs (about 350 g. weight) were employed, the methods used being in essential those of Holst and his colleagues. The principal modification was the substitution of water in the scurvy diet of oats, bran and water by a daily ration of about 60 c.c. of strongly heated milk (autoclaved at 120° C. for one hour), to supply vitamin A [see Hume, 1921]. This addition of milk very greatly improves the general condition of the experimental animals, although the onset of scurvy is not thereby seriously influenced.

Another suitable diet is that used by Zilva [Bracewell, Hoyle and Zilva, 1930, 2] consisting of—

Bran	6 parts by volume
Barley meal	2 ,, ,, ,,
Middlings	3 ,, ,, ,,
Fishmeal	1 ,, ,, ,,
Crushed oats	4 ,, ,, ,,

which was offered *ad lib.*, along with 40–60 c.c. of milk reconstituted from a dried powder and autoclaved.

The use of autoclaved milk in the basal diet in such experiments has been criticized on insufficient grounds by Hess and others for the reason that such milk might retain a small and variable amount of antiscorbutic. To avoid the use of milk Sherman and his colleagues employed a ration of oats, 59 per cent.; skimmed milk powder heated in open trays at 110° C., 30 per cent.; butter fat, 10 per cent.; and salt 1 per cent. This diet they found to be taken well by the animals [Sherman, La Mer and Campbell, 1921; 1922]. Eddy later [1929] substituted 1 per cent. of cod-liver oil for the equivalent amount of butter fat and added yeast, so as to ensure a good supply of vitamins D and B. Other scorbutic diets which have been suggested to avoid the use of milk are those of Lopez-Lomba and Randoin [1923, 1, 2]—meat peptone, starch, yeast, butter fat, salt mixture, and filter paper—and of Bezssonoff [1926, 1]—oats, bran, yolk of egg, and yeast.

On a diet deprived of vitamin C, but containing all other essential elements, the guinea-pig shows normal growth for the first 15–20 days of the experiment; with onset of scurvy symptoms, about the twentieth day, the weight of the animal begins to decline, death from acute scurvy ensuing about the thirtieth to fortieth day.

To obtain quantitative results it is necessary to determine the minimal amount of the various foodstuffs that must be added daily to the 'scurvy' diet in order to prevent occurrence of scurvy. When this minimal amount (or more) is consumed, growth does not cease about the twentieth day, but the animal continues to grow in good health without symptoms of scurvy. As a general rule the animals should be kept under observation during three months.

In assessing the results of such experiments several interdependent factors have to be considered, namely, duration of test period, extent of growth, cause of death, first appearance of scorbutic symptoms, and degree of scurvy at death as determined by postmortem examination. The relative importance of these observations in the assessment of the potency of a dose often varies with the condition of the individual animals.

Sherman and his colleagues attempted to institute a quantitative estimation of relative antiscorbutic potency based on the amounts of two or more materials required to provide the same *degree* of protection. Their experiments were made with filtered juice of canned tomatoes, and were employed for estimating the loss of antiscorbutic potency undergone by this on further heating. A detailed tabulation was made of the symptoms produced by the specific doses of the juice and these were compared with the symptoms of the animals receiving the heated juice. Thus 3·9 c.c. of juice heated for an additional hour at 100° C. produced symptoms judged to be of the same degree of severity as those present in the animals receiving 2 c.c. of original juice, so that the relative antiscorbutic power of the former juice was in this case $\frac{2}{3·9}$ or about 50 per cent. [see also Kenny, 1926].

The chief source of uncertainty in such quantitative experiments has not been found to lie in the nature of the basal diet used, but in the clinical variations of the individual experimental animals and in the indefinite nature of the 'end-point'. Complete protection from scurvy as used by some observers or a 'definite degree of partial protection', as employed by Sherman, are in practice equally difficult to define with accuracy, and it is rarely that differences of less than about 50 per cent. of the dose can be shown to have a definite effect.

Höjer's method. An entirely different principle is employed by Höjer [1926], who determines the degree of scurvy by means of a histological examination of the teeth. His method consists in giving daily doses of the material to be tested, two control animals being kept on the basal diet alone and two on the basal diet with a fully protective dose of a known antiscorbutic. After a period of 10–14 days all the animals are killed. The lower jaw is examined histologically and from a consideration of the changes (see p. 102) Höjer claims not only to be able to determine the minimum fully protective dose with an error of not more than 10 per cent., but to determine quantitatively with moderate accuracy the degree of protection afforded by doses which only afford partial protection. This method has the advantage that it only requires three weeks for a determination in place of the 2–3 months required by the older method. The dose required for complete protection as judged by this method is about twice as large as that required by the usual method [see Goettsch, 1928].

A modification of Höjer's method has been described by Key and Elphick [1931] in which, using the same criterion, four degrees of scurvy are distinguished, the antiscorbutic potency being determined in terms of the dose of a standard antiscorbutic substance which would induce the same degree of scurvy.

As a material to be used as a standard of reference in the biological estimation of vitamin C, the (League of Nations) International Vitamin Conference [1931] has adopted fresh lemon juice, this source of the vitamin having been found remarkably constant. This should be decitrated and used immediately (see Appendix II).

DISTRIBUTION OF VITAMIN C IN FOODSTUFFS.

Tables XIII and XXI (see Appendix I) show the approximate antiscorbutic values of a series of foodstuffs, the values being based upon the minimal protective doses as determined for guinea-pigs.

The sign + indicates that the vitamin is present, + + that the material is a good source, and + + + that it is a rich source of the vitamin; o indicates that the vitamin has not been detected by the method employed.

TABLE XIII

Distribution of Vitamin C in Foodstuffs.

Foodstuffs.	Antiscorbutic value.	References.
Cereals.		
Wheat, whole grain	o	1
Germ		
Bran	o	
Endosperm, e.g. white wheaten flour, polished rice	o	
Germinated Kafir corn (*Sorghum vulgare*)	+	2
Barley	o	3
,, sprouted	+	3, 4
Malt, green	+ +	5
,, kilned	o	6
,, extract	o	7, 8, 9
Oats	o	3
,, sprouted	+	3
White flour and bread	o	1
Maize (young cobs, green mealies)	+	10
Vegetables.		
Asparagus, raw	+ + +	11
,, boiled	very low	11
Beetroot	+	13, 32
,, juice	+	12
Cabbage, raw, fresh green leaves	+ + +	14
,, cooked 1 hr. at 100° C.	+	14
,, dried	+	15
,, canned	+ +	11, 16, 17
Sauerkraut	o to + +	11, 42, 43, 44
Carrot, young raw	+ +	11, 18
,, old raw	+	18
,, young cooked	+	18
,, old cooked	+	18
,, dried	+	18
,, juice	+	12
,, young canned	o	19
Cauliflower, raw	+ + +	11
,, boiled	+ +	1, 11
Celery, raw	+ +	11
Cucumber	+ +	20
Dandelion	+	1
Endive	+	1
Lettuce	+ + +	1, 11
Mangold leaves	+ + +	11, 21
Mangold	+	
Onion	+ to + +	22
Pepper, green	+ + +	23
Potato, raw	+ + to + + +	11, 24
,, cooked 1 hr. at 100° C.	+	11, 24
,, cooked 15 mins	+ +	11, 24
Pumpkin, juice and pulp	+	2
Rhubarb	+ +	11, 25
Sorrel	+	1

Foodstuffs.	Antiscorbutic value.	References.
Vegetables (*cont.*)		
Spinach, raw	+ + +	11, 19, 26, 27, 28
,, cooked	+ to + +	11, 19, 26, 27, 28
,, canned	+ to + +	19, 26, 27, 28
Sugar cane juice	o	2
Swede (Rutabaga) juice	+ + +	12, 29, 30
Sweet potato juice	+ +	2, 41
Turnip tops	+ +	31, 33
,, root	+ +	13, 32, 33
Vegetable marrow juice	+ +	2
Watercress	+ + +	34
Desiccated vegetables as a class	o to +	1
Pickled cabbage	o	22
Legumes.		
Beans, green pods		
,, runner		
,, string	+ to + +	16, 23, 11
,, French		
,, ,, canned	doubtful	16
,, haricot	o	11
,, ,, sprouted	+ +	35
Cow peas (*Vignum sinense*) sprouted	+ + +	2
Lentils soaked	+	36
,, germinated	+ +	36
Peas, green, raw	+ + +	11, 37
,, ,, canned	+ +	11, 37
,, dried and then soaked	+	35, 36
,, germinated	+ +	35, 36
Soy beans	o	3
,, sprouted	doubtful	2
Mushrooms	o	11, 39, 40
Tea infusion, green	+ +	49
,, ,, black	very low	49
Eggs.		
Fresh, whites	o	22, 38
,, yolks	o	22, 38
Dried	o	22
Meat, etc.		
Muscle, lean	very low to +	45, 46
Liver, rabbit or pig	+ +	47
,, chicken	+	48
Meat juice, raw	very low	22
,, canned	o	22
Oysters	+	50
Milk.		
Cow's, whole, raw	+	51, 52, 53, 54, 55
,, whole, pasteurized	probably lower than raw, depending on the method used.	56
,, whole, rapidly scalded	very little less than raw.	58
,, ,, sterilized at 120° C.	about 50% of value of raw milk.	51, 52, 59
,, condensed, sweetened	+	60
,, ,, unsweetened	50% value of raw milk.	59
,, whole, dried	o to +	58, 61, 62, 63
,, ,, raw irradiated	o to +	64, 65
,, dried ,,		
,, skim, raw	+	57
,, ,, dried	o to +	57

Foodstuffs.	Antiscorbutic value.	References.
Milk (*cont.*)		
Goat's, raw	+	66, 67
Human, raw	o to +	68, 69
Lactic acid milk	+	70, 71
Lactose	o	72
Beer.		
Kafir, as drunk in turbid condition containing residues of malt and yeast	+	2
Spruce infusion	+	73
Pale ale	o	5, 6
Honey	o	75, 76, 77
Fruits.		
Almonds, sprouted	+	35
Apples, raw	+ to + + (depending on variety).	78, 11, 79
„ baked	same as raw	79
„ canned	+ to + +	80
„ dried	very low	78
„ concentrated juice	+	81
Apricot, fresh	o to +	11, 113
„ dried	o	113
„ sulphured and dried	+	113
Bananas, raw	+ +	78, 82
„ baked	+ to + + }	78, 83
„ dried	o to + }	
Blackberry	+ +	11
Bilberry (*Vaccinium myrtillus*)	+	11
Cherries	+ to + +	11
Cloudberries (*Rubus chamemorus*)	+	1
*Cocum (dried)	+	85
Currants, fresh	+ +	11
Cranberry (juice)	very low	1
Gooseberries	+ +	11
Grape	very low	11, 12
„ juice dried	o	84
„ „ concentrated	o	2
Grape fruit juice	+ + +	82, 86
„ „ „ dried	+ +	84
Lemon juice, fresh	+ + +	87, 88
„ „ concentrated or dried	+ + +	89, 90
„ „ preserved	o to + +	88
„ „ tablets	+ +	91
„ peel (flavedo)	very low	92
Lime juice, fresh	+ +	87, 88
„ „ preserved	o to +	87
„ „ concentrated	+	81
Mango, fresh	+ + to + + +	116
* „ dried (Amchur)	low	85
Melon (cantaloup)	+ +	105
Mulberry	+	1
Naartje (*Citrus nobilis* Lourerio)	+ + +	2
Orange juice, fresh	+ + +	88, 12, 86
„ „ dried	+ + +	93, 84
„ „ concentrated	+ + +	94, 95
„ marmalade	very low	2
„ peel	+ +	96
„ „ dried	+	96
„ „ outer	+ +	97
„ cake (dried minced orange)	o to +	2
Paw-paw (*Carica papaya*)	+ + +	2, 98
Peach and peach juice	+ to + +	2, 11
„ canned	+ to + +	99, 100

*Dried fruit much esteemed as antiscorbutic by natives of India.

Foodstuffs.	Antiscorbutic value.	References.
Fruits (*cont.*)		
Peach, dried	+	101
Pear	+	11, 100
,, canned	o to +	100, 102, 115
Pineapple fruit and juice	+ +	2, 103
,, canned	+ +	103
Plums	very poor to + +	11
Prickly pear (*Opuntia decumana*)	+ +	2
Prunes, fresh	+	113
,, dried	o	96, 113
,, sulphured and dried	+	113
Raisins	o	104
Raspberry	+ +	1, 11
,, juice dried	o	84
Strawberry, raw and preserved	+ + to + + +	11, 106
*Tamarind, dried	low	85
Tomato, raw	+ + +	2, 107, 108, 109, 110, 111
,, dried	+ +	2, 107
,, canned	+ + to + + +	111, 110, 112
Commercial dried fruits, except some peaches	o	101, 113, 114

*Dried fruit much esteemed as antiscorbutic by natives of India.

References to Table XIII.

1. Holst and Frölich, 1912
2. Delf, 1921
3. Cohen and Mendel, 1918
4. McClendon and Cole, 1919
5. Harden and Zilva, 1924
6. ,,   ,,   1918, 5
7. Gerstenberger, 1921
8. McClendon *et al.*, 1919
9. Randoin and Lecoq, 1927
10. Delf, unpublished
11. Scheunert, 1930
12. Chick and Rhodes, 1918
13. Russell and Morrison, 1922
14. Delf, 1918
15. Delf and Skelton, 1918
16. Campbell and Chick, 1919
17. Eddy and Kohman, 1924
18. Hess and Unger, 1919
19. Remy, 1928
20. Embrey, 1923
21. Boock and Trevan, 1922
22. Chick and Hume, 1917, 1
23. Quinn, Burtis and Milner, 1927
24. Givens and McClugage, 1920
25. Pierson and Dutcher, 1920
26. Eddy, Kohman and Carlsson, 1925
27. Pierson, 1926
28. S. Dakota Agri. Exp. Station, 1927
29. Delf, 1920
30. Delf, 1925
31. Burton, 1928
32. Scheunert, 1927
33. Shorten and Ray, 1921
34. Coward and Eggleton, 1928
35. Fürst, 1912
36. Chick and Delf, 1919
37. Eddy Kohman, and Carlsson, 1926
38. Dougherty, 1926
39. Hara, 1923
40. Steidle, 1924
41. Peck, 1924
42. Wisconsin Agr. Exp. Station, 1929
43. Ellis, Steenbock and Hart, 1921
44. Wedgewood and Ford, 1924
45. Dutcher, Pierson and Biester, 1920
46. Medes, 1926
47. Parsons, 1920
48. Hart, Steenbock, Lepkovsky and Halpin, 1925
49. Mattill and Pratt, 1928–29
50. Randoin, 1923
51 and 52. Chick, Hume and Skelton, 1918, 1, 2
53. Barnes and Hume, 1919, 1, 2
54. Kieferle and Zeile, 1926
55. MacLeod, 1927
56. Hess and Fish, 1914
57. Johnson and Hooper, 1922
58. Munsell and Kifer, 1929
59. Hart, Steenbock and Smith, 1919
60. Hume, 1921
61. Jephcott and Bacharach, 1921
62. Cavanaugh, Dutcher and Hall, 1924
63. Supplee and Dow, 1926
64. Hottinger, 1927, 2
65. Supplee and Dow, 1927
66. Hunt and Winter, 1922
67. Meyer and Nassau, 1924
68. Hess, 1920–21
69. Meyer and Nassau, 1925
70. Stevenson, 1920
71. Göthlin, 1931
72. Harden and Zilva, 1918, 3
73. Appleton, 1921
74. Southgate, 1924, 1
75. Faber, 1920

76. Hoyle, 1929
77. Kifer and Munsell, 1929
78. Givens, McClugage and Van Horne, 1922
79. Bracewell, Hoyle and Zilva, 1930, 1, 2
80. Kohman, Eddy and Carlsson, 1924
81. Robison, 1919
82. Jansen and Donath, 1925
83. Eddy and Kellogg, 1927
84. Givens and Macy, 1921
85. Chick, Hume and Skelton, 1919
86. Bracewell and Zilva, 1931
87. Chick, Hume and Skelton, 1918, 3
88. Davey, 1921
89. Harden and Zilva, 1918, 2
90. Zilva, 1924, 2
91. Bassett-Smith, 1920, 1921
92. Willimott and Wokes, 1926
93. Harden and Robison, 1920
94. Goss, 1925
95. Priston, 1926
96. Hess and Unger, 1918, 2
97. Willimott and Wokes, 1927
98. Miller, 1926
99. Kohman, Eddy, Carlsson and Halliday, 1926
100. Kansas Agricultural Experimental Station, 1926–28
101. Eckman, 1922
102. Craven and Kramer, 1927
103. Miller, 1925.
104. Dutcher and Outhouse, 1922–23
105. Georgia Agricultural Experimental Station, 1927
106. Kohman, Eddy and Halliday, 1928
107. Givens and McClugage, 1919, 1
108. House, Nelson and Haber, 1929
109. Wisconsin Agri. Exp. Station, 1929
110.   „   „   „   1927
111. Delf, 1924
112. Sherman, La Mer and Campbell, 1921, 1922
113. Morgan, Field and Nichols, 1931
114. Morgan and Field, 1929
115. Kramer, Eddy and Kohman, 1929
116. Perry and Zilva, 1932

Vegetables. Among *green-leaf vegetables* the cabbage [Delf, 1918] and watercress [Coward and Eggleton, 1928] are two of the richest sources of vitamin C. It is also present in sorrel, scurvy grass (*Cochlearia officinalis*), lettuce, spinach, turnip tops, and other leaves, and in grasses. The perennial rye-grass (*Lolium perenne*) is as good a source as cabbage [Brouwer, 1927], but the antiscorbutic potency to a large extent disappears when it is converted into hay or silage [see also Lepkovsky *et al.*, 1925]. Hay, as a rule, contains but little of the vitamin and has been used by American investigators as one of the components of a control diet on which guinea-pigs acquire scorbutic symptoms in 2–3 weeks [see Hess and Unger, 1918, 1]. Rossi [1918], however, found fresh hay to possess antiscorbutic properties.

Among *root vegetables* there are great differences, raw carrot juice (minimum dose about 20 c.c.) and raw beetroot juice (minimum dose more than 20 c.c.) proving comparatively feeble, while raw swede juice is placed in the front rank, the minimum protective daily dose for a guinea-pig being 2·5 c.c. [Chick and Rhodes, 1918].

Neither the carrot nor its expressed juice can be regarded as a good source of antiscorbutic, but accurate quantitative experiments with the cooked vegetable have not so far been made. Hess and Unger's results [1919] are summarized in Table XIII, but the minimum doses were not ascertained. Young carrots were found to be decidedly more potent than old. Using an extract of fresh carrot made with absolute alcohol the equivalent of 25–50 g. of fresh carrots was required daily for the protection of a guinea-pig [Zilva, 1920, 2].

The potato would appear to occupy a mean position. The most extended investigations of this vegetable are due to Givens and McClugage [1920], who examined it raw, cooked, and dried under different conditions, and to Scheunert [1930]. The latter found 3 g. of raw new white potatoes or 4 g. of the same baked, to be a protective dose, the presence or absence of the peel making no difference. Old potatoes which had been stored for a year were equally good. Drying in the air (35–80° C.) destroyed most of the vitamin, but a considerable proportion of it remained when the potatoes were first steamed for 4 minutes or baked in their skins for 45–55 minutes, and afterwards dried [Givens and McClugage, 1920].

It is interesting to note that the cabbage and swede are nearly allied species, and belong to the same natural order of plants, viz. the Cruciferae.　The old legend teaching that plants with a cruciform arrangement of the flower possess special virtue in the service of mankind thus receives scientific support at this late date.

Fresh fruit.　Many fruits have been examined for antiscorbutic potency and in a number of cases the minimum protective dose has been determined, but so far little systematic study has been carried out as to the variation of vitamin C content with degree of maturity, mode of cultivation, variety, &c.　Information of this nature is available only in the case of the apple, orange, and grape fruit.

Citrus fruits.　Many of the *Citrus* fruits—orange, lemon, grape fruit—are highly active, the minimum protective dose for a guinea-pig being 1 to 1·5 c.c. daily of the juice.

It is surprising to find that the juice of West India limes (*C. medica* var. *acida*) is distinctly inferior to that of oranges and lemons and of the sweet lime (*C. limetta*), but such it has proved to be (see p. 254).　The experiments on this point included tests with monkeys as well as guinea-pigs.　Ordinary preserved lime juice was found to be almost devoid of antiscorbutic properties [Chick, Hume and Skelton, 1918, 3], but preserved lemon juice appeared to be distinctly more satisfactory.　Orange juice retained its antiscorbutic potency well for 16 to 19 months when preserved at room temperature in presence of a small proportion of the oil of the rind, whereas at 37° C. in the same time it became practically inactive. Lemon juice behaved in much the same manner at these temperatures, and also retained its potency in presence of the rind oil at 0° C. Potassium metabisulphite ($K_2S_2O_5$) preserves the juice well against fermentation and mould growth, but at room temperature exerts a destructive action on the antiscorbutic potency, even 0·02 per cent. causing definite deterioration in $2\frac{1}{2}$ months [J. Williams and Corran, 1930] whereas at 0° C. as much as 0·06 to 0·1 per cent. has little effect on the potency [Davey, 1921].　Even in absence of all preservative comparatively little change occurs in expressed lemon juice kept at 0° C. for seven months.　Entire oranges and lemons can be kept at 2–5° C. for five or six months without detriment to the potency of their juice [Davey, 1921].　According to J. Williams and Corran [1930] the zone of optimal stability for lemon juice at ordinary temperatures lies in the neighbourhood of the natural acidity of the juice (pH 2·2) and natural juice can be kept without loss of potency for as long as fourteen months at room temperature without any addition.　It becomes, however, heavily infected with moulds and yeasts.　In general, conditions which preserve sterility tend to cause deterioration of antiscorbutic potency.

Tablets, prepared by evaporating lemon juice over H_2SO_4 at 13·5 to 15·5° C., and mixing the syrup with a mixture of 97 per cent. lactose and 3 per cent. gum tragacanth, contained a large proportion of the vitamin C of the original juice, and retained their antiscorbutic properties for over twelve months at low temperature.　Each tablet was the equivalent of half a fresh lemon [Bassett-Smith, 1920; 1921].

A systematic investigation has shown that the vitamin C content of the juice of the orange and grape fruit is remarkably constant whether the fruit be picked at the beginning or end of the season [Bracewell and Zilva, 1931]. The longer the fruit remains on the tree the smaller is the yield of juice, so that the total vitamin C content of the fruit diminishes. There is no correlation between the content of soluble solids or the pH of the juice and its antiscorbutic potency. As far as can be seen at present the conditions of cultivation of the orange, origin of stock, age of tree, or nature of soil do not affect the vitamin content of the fruit.

Apple. Observations on the apple have shown that different varieties vary greatly in antiscorbutic potency [Bracewell, Hoyle and Zilva, 1930, 1, 2; Bracewell, Kidd, West and Zilva, 1931; Bracewell, Wallace and Zilva, 1931]. Thus out of eight varieties grown in England, Bramley's Seedling was found to be much the most potent, the minimum daily protective dose for a guinea-pig being 3 g. of the flesh of the fruit, whilst 20 g. of Worcester Pearmain did not afford full protection. No indications were obtained that the character of the soil, the age of the tree, the season, or state of maturity of the fruit had any influence on its vitamin C content. Apples stored in air at 1° C., 3° C., or 10° C., for periods of three months, showed little loss of antiscorbutic potency. This loss was somewhat greater when the fruit was stored at 10° C., in a mixture of 10 per cent. carbon dioxide, 11 per cent. oxygen, and 79 per cent. nitrogen (gas storage) for three months. Bramley's Seedling apples, whether fresh or stored at a low temperature in air, or 'gas stored', lost only a very small fraction of their vitamin C content when baked in their skins, during which process the temperature of the interior of the apples rose to about 95° C. Bramley's Seedling apples frozen at $-20°$ C., and kept at this temperature for four months, did not lose any antiscorbutic potency. Young apples of this variety about 3·2 cm. in diameter and 23 g. in weight, gathered at the end of July, were not more active per g. of tissue than the apples of the same environment gathered in October; the total amount of vitamin in the apple therefore increases as it grows on the tree. The distribution of the vitamin throughout the fruit is by no means uniform. The concentration increases as the skin is approached from the core and is more than six times as great in the peel as in the flesh near the core, so that apple peel must be considered as one of the richest sources of vitamin C. There are indications that a low nitrogen content may be associated with a high vitamin C content in the apple.

Bramley's Seedling apple genetically considered is a triploid with 57 chromosomes, whereas the other varieties referred to above are diploids with 34 chromosomes. Two other triploid varieties, namely, Belle de Boskoop and Blenheim Orange, have so far been found to possess also a high vitamin C content. The former is as active as the Bramley's Seedling apple and the latter somewhat less active [Crane and Zilva, 1931]. Whether any correlation exists between the genetic constitution and the vitamin C content of the apple cannot at present be stated.

Scheunert [1930] has also observed a varying antiscorbutic potency in different varieties of apple grown in Germany. These observations explain the variable results which were obtained by earlier workers with random samples of apple or apple juice. [See Holst and Frölich, 1912; Robison, 1919; Chick, 1920; Givens, McClugage and Van Horne, 1922; Kohman, Eddy and Carlsson, 1924.]

The pear seems to be definitely inferior to the apple in vitamin C content [Scheunert, 1930; Craven and Kramer, 1927].

Tomato. The tomato is a rich source of vitamin C, often barely inferior to the *Citrus* fruits. In the canned form it is still highly potent, 3 c.c. of juice having been found sufficient as a daily dose to protect guinea-pigs [Sherman, La Mer and Campbell, 1921; see also Hess and Unger, 1918-19]. Tomatoes ripened in ethylene are no richer in vitamin C than those ripened in the air and are less rich than those which ripen on the plant [Clow and Marlatt, 1930; House, Nelson and Haber, 1929]. Tomatoes grown and examined in South Africa were found to be less potent than those grown in England, 3 to 5 c.c. of the raw juice being the minimum dose as against 1·5 c.c. for the English fruit (Delf and Pullinger, unpublished results).

Many of the common fruits are comparatively poor sources of the vitamin, grapes, cherries, plums, and peaches falling within this class. Many 'berries'—blackberries, strawberries, raspberries, currants, and gooseberries—are moderately good sources of vitamin C, about 5 g. being a protective dose for guinea-pigs [Scheunert, 1930].

Certain varieties of the mango (e.g. Alphonso) are even richer in vitamin C than the *Citrus* fruits [Perry and Zilva, 1932.]

Dried vegetables and fruits (see also p. 259). *Dried vegetables,* in confirmation of human experience and of Holst's experimental work, have been found of very little value [Delf and Skelton, 1918; Givens and Cohen, 1918]. *Fruit juices* on the other hand can as a rule be dried, and the dry material can be kept without any great loss of potency. Dried grape juice and raspberry juice have, however, been found to be almost devoid of vitamin C [Givens and Macy, 1921].

Meat. Meat with milk comes last in the order of merit [Chick and Hume, 1917, 1]. Twenty c.c. of raw beef juice daily offered only very slight protection to guinea-pigs; a larger ration was not tolerated. Watery extracts of as much as 20 g. of lean meat offered no protection to guinea-pigs. That fresh meat possesses definite antiscorbutic properties is, however, clearly evident from human experience (see p. 261).

Milk is a variable and by no means rich source of the antiscorbutic vitamin. As much as 100 c.c. of some samples of fresh raw cow's milk daily and more may be required if scurvy in guinea-pigs is to be prevented by its agency alone [Chick, Hume and Skelton, 1918, 1, 2], whilst as little as 20 c.c. of a summer pasture milk has been found to afford protection [Dutcher *et al.*, 1920-21] and 40 c.c. of milk were found sufficient by Schwartze, Murphy and Hann [1929-30].

The dependence of the vitamin C content of milk on the diet of the cow and the effect upon it of heating, drying, &c., are discussed later on in Chapter IX.

EFFECT OF HEATING, DRYING, AND PRESERVING ON THE
VITAMIN C CONTENT OF FOODSTUFFS.

The conditions of stability of vitamin C in lemon juice, &c., have
been already discussed (p. 199). The behaviour of foodstuffs towards
rise of temperature varies with different materials, owing to the
different conditions under which the vitamin exists in them. Oxidation usually plays an important part in the changes which are
produced.

Effect of Heating.

Following the experiments of Holst and Frölich [1912] upon the
effects of heat, a more complete series of experiments upon this
point was carried out by Delf [1918]. Working with raw cabbage
leaves, the minimum daily ration required to prevent scurvy in
guinea-pigs was determined to be less than 1·5 g. and greater than
0·5 g., i.e., about 1 g. When the cabbage was heated in water
at 60° C. for one hour, symptoms of severe scurvy were just prevented by a 5 g. ration. When the temperature was 70°, 80°, 90°,
or 100° C. for the same period, scurvy was not satisfactorily avoided.
If the time was reduced to twenty minutes, the same ration, 5 g.,
prevented scurvy when the temperature was 90° C. and just failed
to do so when the temperature was 100° C.

The conclusion drawn from these results is that when cooked for
one hour at temperatures ranging from 80° to 100° C., cabbage
leaves lose about 90 per cent. of the antiscorbutic value originally
possessed (antiscurvy value of 5 g. ration reduced by cooking to
the equivalent of about 0·5 g. raw cabbage). In a similar manner
the loss on heating in water either (a) for sixty minutes at 60° C.,
or (b) for twenty minutes at 90–100° C., was estimated at about 80
per cent. of the original (antiscurvy value of 5 g. reduced to the
equivalent of about 1 g. raw cabbage).

The destructive influence of heat on vitamin C is thus seen to be
enhanced to a comparatively slight degree with rise of temperature.
Upon the above estimates, the rate of destruction is accelerated only
about threefold (the time required for destruction of 80 per cent. of the
original value being reduced to one-third) when the temperature is
raised from 60° C. to boiling-point, i.e., by 40° C., so that the temperature coefficient would be about 1·3 for 10° C. rise of temperature.

These results confirm those of Holst and Frölich [1912] in showing
the great sensitiveness of the antiscurvy factor in cabbage to
temperatures of 100° C. and below. This instability of the antiscurvy factor is a matter of the greatest importance in estimating
the antiscorbutic value of cooked vegetables and the relative merits
of different methods of cooking, and will be referred to later under
that heading (p. 262)

Delf's work was subsequently [1920] extended to the juices of
cabbage, swedes, and oranges, and revealed the fact that cabbage
juice was much more affected by exposure to 100° C. for an hour
than either of the other two under similar conditions of exposure.
Her results are summed up in Table XIV, the minimum daily
doses being stated which were required before and after treatment
for protection of guinea-pigs.

TABLE XIV.

| | Minimum doses in c.c. | | | Percentage loss of potency. | |
| | Before treatment. | After heating for 1 hour at | | | |
		100°	130°	100°	130°
Cabbage juice	1	7.5	—	87	—
Swede juice	2.5	5	10	50	75
Orange juice	1.5	1.5	3	0	50

Sherman, La Mer and Campbell [1921; 1922; La Mer, 1922], who have investigated the effect of temperature and hydrogen ion concentration on the destruction of vitamin C in tomato juice, using the method described on p. 203, confirmed the comparative stability of the vitamin at 100° C. and also the relatively low temperature coefficient found by Delf for cabbage. Their results may be briefly summarized as follows.

TABLE XV.

pH.	Temp. °C.	Time—hours.	Percentage Destruction of Vitamin C in Tomato Juice.
4.3	60	1	25
,,		4	35
,,	80	1	40
,,		4	53
,,	100	1	50
,,		2	58
,,		4	68
5.1 — 4.9	100	1	58
11 — 9		1	65 (increasing to 90-95 on preservation for 24 hours at 10° C., in partially filled bottles)
	Temperature coefficient for 10° C. (60–80°) 1.23 (80–100°) 1.12		

These results suggest that the stability increases with the hydrogen ion concentration (acidity) of the vitamin solution. Holst had previously arrived at the same conclusion, his opinion being based mainly upon the fact that acid fruit juices retained their antiscorbutic properties much longer than vegetable juices. Harden and Zilva [1918, 6] have shown, as already mentioned, that the presence of alkalis, even when dilute (1/50 N sodium hydroxide) and at room temperature, has a rapidly destructive effect upon the antiscorbutic vitamin. These authors have called attention to the danger involved in the practice of adding sodium carbonate when boiling green vegetables.

It has been suggested that the loss in antiscorbutic value suffered by vegetables during cooking might be lessened if the water in which they are heated were made slightly acid with citric acid. The suggestion was originally made in respect of germinated lentils in order to preserve the antiscurvy value as far as possible where these may form the only source of antiscorbutic material in a diet [Greig,

1918]. It has, however, been shown experimentally by Delf [1918] that, when 0·5 per cent. citric acid is added to the water in which germinated lentils are boiled, the loss in antiscurvy properties is, if anything, greater than when no addition of acid is made.

It follows, therefore, that in cooking vegetables there should be no addition either of acid or alkali to the water in which they are boiled.

The commercial process of canning vegetables also leads to a considerable degree of destruction of the vitamin C in vegetables like cabbage and runner beans, whereas in tomatoes very little destruction occurs unless there is exposure to air. Cabbage heated with water in hermetically sealed tins for 1 hour at 90–100° C. lost about 70 per cent. of its potency; runner beans exposed to 100° C. under the same conditions on two successive days for a total of two hours and twenty minutes lost about 75–90 per cent. [Campbell and Chick, 1919]. Tomato when converted into a purée and canned, during which process it was exposed at 80–100° C. for 100 minutes in an open vessel and concentrated to half its bulk, lost 85 per cent. of its antiscorbutic potency [Delf, 1920].

Actual investigation of products canned commercially has shown that in many cases vitamin C is still present, although a certain amount of loss has usually taken place. This holds for many fruits and vegetables (see Tables XIII and XXI).

Peaches, plums, and apricots, all fruits of comparatively low vitamin C content, lose their vitamin C entirely when dehydrated or sun-dried, but if they are dipped in alkali and then exposed to sulphur dioxide before being dried, they retain it satisfactorily. This effect is probably due to the reducing effect of the sulphur dioxide during the process of drying [Morgan and Field, 1929 ; Morgan, Field and Nichols, 1931].

Raisins prepared by the hot or cold 'dip' process contain no vitamin C [Zilva, unpublished results].

Effect of Drying and Preservation.

The absence of the antiscorbutic principle from many dried food-stuffs, and its disappearance from some of the most powerful anti-scorbutics when these are reduced to the dry condition, is sufficient proof of the sensitiveness of vitamin C to drying, and in this respect the contrast between the antiberi-beri and the antiscurvy factors is very marked.

Holst and Frölich [1912] devoted much attention to the question of the effect of drying on the antiscorbutic principle of cabbage with the object of finding some method of preserving vegetables without destroying their antiscorbutic properties. It was soon found that at least three factors required consideration. (1) The effect of the actual process of drying ; (2) the effect of preservation of the dried material ; to which was added (3) the effect of cooking the dried material.

These investigators did not determine the minimum dose of fresh cabbage required for the protection of a guinea-pig, but worked on a basis of 30 g. of fresh cabbage or its equivalent in dried cabbage. This is now known to be twenty to thirty times the requisite minimum dose of fresh cabbage. It was found that after drying in the air at 37° C. for 8 days this dose of cabbage was still sufficient to protect from scurvy, and retained this power even after being boiled for half an hour in 0·5 per cent. NaCl or acetic acid solution. On preservation for 5 weeks of the dried cabbage this dose retained its efficiency when the material was kept dry, but lost it when it was exposed to water vapour. Further experiments confirmed the importance of water vapour in this respect [Holst and Frölich, 1920]. Cabbage dried as above preserved its antiscorbutic properties (in doses equivalent to 30 g. fresh cabbage) for 18 to 26 months when kept at 37° C. over phosphorus pentoxide, but lost them over calcium chloride, a less efficient drying agent. Partial loss resulted from preservation of the dried cabbage at 4° C. in closed vessels, without any desiccating agent; over calcium chloride the loss was less at lower temperatures. More definite results with regard to the loss in the actual process of drying were obtained by Delf and Skelton [1918], who found a loss of more than 93 per cent. of the antiscorbutic potency, when the cabbage was dried at 37° C. and stored at air temperature in a closed bottle for 2–3 weeks. When the cabbage was plunged into boiling water before being dried, to inactivate the enzymes, drying took place much more rapidly and the loss of potency was somewhat less, but still very considerable. Even when dried at 65° C. in an atmosphere of nitrogen [Ellis, Steenbock and Hart, 1921] a loss of the same order was observed.

Fruit juices on the other hand may be dried without serious loss of antiscorbutic potency by evaporation *in vacuo* [Harden and Robison, 1919, 1920; Robison, 1919], or after admixture with corn syrup by the 'spray process' [Givens and McClugage, 1919, 2]. The dry residue obtained from orange juice by Harden and Robison when kept over sulphuric acid for 2 years at air temperature protected guinea-pigs from scurvy in doses of 0·5 g. (equal to 4·5 c.c. fresh juice), whilst another sample, kept in a sealed vessel at 29° C. for 14 months, lost more than 85 per cent. of its power [1921]. The material dried by the 'spray process' was still effective after 14–20 months [Givens and McClugage, 1920-21]. These authors also found that commercially dried lemon juice (raw and neutralized), tomato juice, grape fruit juice, and orange juice were all active after 14–20 months, whereas grape juice and raspberry juice were inactive. Dried tomato was found to be active in doses of 1 g.

When dried in the sun (in India) carrots, egg plant, spinach, turnips, and turnip tops lose nearly all their antiscorbutic power, whilst tomatoes, potatoes, and cabbage retain a certain proportion, which is, however, still further diminished by cooking [Shorten and Ray, 1919; 1921]. In this case what was actually determined was that 50 g. of the fresh vegetable protected guinea-pigs from scurvy for about 3 months, and that after drying the equivalent of 50 g. either did or did not protect. No minimum doses were determined either before or after drying. Commercial mixed dried vegetables were found to be inactive in the same dose. Dried tamarinds, amchur (dried mango), and cocum, three Indian fruits, were found to possess a low antiscorbutic potency [Chick Hume and Skelton, 1919].

CHAPTER IX

SOME NUTRITIONAL ASPECTS OF COW'S MILK WITH SPECIAL REFERENCE TO VITAMINS.

THE nutritional value of milk as a corrective to deficiencies of various types in the diet is now generally accepted. It is valuable to the adult and probably indispensable to the child and its increased consumption in this country should be advocated. In many diets it is the chief source of fat-soluble vitamins, of protein of good quality, and of calcium salts. Its importance is well illustrated in the experiments of Mann [1926] who compared the effects of several different additions to the dietary of boys in an Institution under well-controlled conditions. His results are summarized graphically in Fig. 32. The diet of these boys was considered adequate, although they were below the normal standard in height and weight. Mann found that an increase of growth, as measured by both height and weight, was promoted by the addition of one pint of whole milk per diem. The milk used was pasteurized. No effect on the height was produced by addition of caseinogen in amount equivalent to that contained in the milk or of margarine in amount equivalent to the extra calories. An improvement was, however, noticeable with New Zealand butter.

Whatever may be the interpretation of these observations, the results are important. They suggest that among the missing factors supplied by the milk addition were the fat-soluble vitamins, though the possibility cannot be entirely excluded that the extra calcium given may also have influenced the results. As mentioned later (p. 242) a similar result was obtained when additions of whole and separated milk respectively were made to the diets of school-children in different towns in Scotland [Orr, 1928; Leighton and Clark, 1929; Clark, 1929].

Untreated Cow's Milk.

Cow's milk in one form or another is the almost invariable substitute for human milk in cases where breast-feeding has for any reason to be abandoned. Though a discussion of the means to be employed for adapting cow's milk for this purpose lies outside the scope of this report, it is necessary to consider the matter, so that attention to the vitamin issue alone may not give a wrong impression. Some infants may be reared from a very early age upon unmodified cow's milk, but for others some modifications are required to render it more like human milk. The most usual difficulty arises from the excess of caseinogen in cow's milk. Dilution of the milk, a method often employed, while ensuring the right percentage of protein, lowers in similar proportion all the other constituents including fat, carbohydrate, salts, and vitamins. A child therefore fed upon milk diluted with water alone is partially starved of a large number of essential dietary constituents. This important fact must never be forgotten, and in the modification of cow's milk for infant-feeding dilution should always be made with milk products.

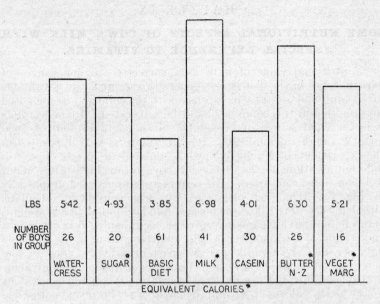

Fig. 32 a. Average gain in weight per boy in one year.

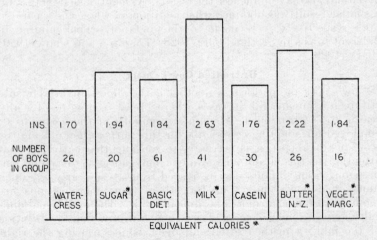

Fig. 32 b. Average increase in height per boy in one year.
(From Corry Mann (1926) Sp. Rep. Ser. Med. Res. Counc., London, No. 105)

The ideal diluent is the whey left when the casein is removed. If the milk is stirred during the formation of the curd, some of the fat passes into the whey. This method may be too difficult for ordinary use, but it must be remembered that vegetable oils cannot replace cream, and sugar solutions cannot replace whey (see Fig. 33).

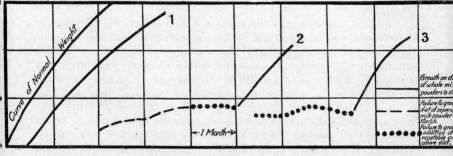

FIG. 33. These curves illustrate the inefficiency of vegetable oils such as linseed and olive oil to replace the fat of milk for promoting growth. Curve 1 represents the growth of a young rat fed upon a food paste composed of whole cream dried milk, and starch. The growth is not quite up to the normal standard, but it is evident that there is no serious deficiency of either vitamin A, D or B. The curve marked (---) shows the failure of young rats to grow on a similar paste composed of dried skimmed milk powder and starch. This failure is due to the absence of an adequate amount of the fat-soluble vitamins, and is not made good by the addition to the ration of linseed oil (curve 2 . . .) or olive oil (curve 3 . . .) in an amount equivalent to the deficiency of milk fat. Addition of butter fat, however, at once renders growth possible again (curves 2 and 3 ——).

Conditions determining the Vitamin Value of Cow's Milk.

The vitamin value of raw cow's milk varies greatly according to the diet and management of the cow. There is an extensive literature on the subject, to which only brief reference is here possible. Luce [1924, 1, 2] made an important investigation on the influence of sunlight and diet on the antirachitic and growth-promoting properties of the milk of a cow, and her work was carried still further by Chick and Roscoe [1926, 2]. The cow was in successive periods kept in the light and in the dark and was fed on fresh green grass and on a dry winter feed. It was found that the vitamin A content of the milk was much greater when the cow was receiving fresh green food than when the diet was one of cereals and roots. The vitamin D content was found to depend principally on the degree of insolation of the cow, but there was some indication that insolation accompanied by a diet of fresh green food, i.e., when the cow was on pasture in summer, was more effective than a similar degree of insolation combined with a diet composed only of cereals and roots.

A comparison of the value of human and cow's milk [Outhouse et al., 1927; 1928] when the cows were fed on dry fodder, which, however, included ensilage and alfalfa hay, showed that the vitamin A value of cow's milk was about the same as that of human milk; for B-vitamins the value of cow's milk was slightly better and for antirachitic value also distinctly better, although the cows had little exposure to sunshine. The values found for vitamin D did not approach those found in the investigation of Chick and Roscoe. Outhouse *et al.* [1928] give a summary of the literature pointing out the differing results of various workers according to the diet and environmental conditions of the cow on which the work was done. It may, however, be accepted that the value of the cow's milk in fat-soluble vitamins is at its maximum when the cow is on pasture in summer.

It has been shown that the vitamin A and vitamin D contents of winter milk can be enhanced by feeding the cow with cod-liver oil [Golding, Soames and Zilva, 1926], and the vitamin D content by administering irradiated yeast [Steenbock, Hart, Hanning and Humphrey, 1930; Wachtel, 1929]. Difference of opinion exists as to the effect on the antirachitic potency of the milk of irradiating a cow with ultra-violet rays from an artificial source. The inference from all that has been said is, however, that the application of ultra-violet rays to the skin of the cow would be expected to result in increasing the vitamin D value of the milk. Such a result has been obtained by many workers, but Steenbock, Hart, Riising *et al.* [1930, where the literature is set out and discussed], although finding that the milk of goats could be so affected, were unable to demonstrate an increased antirachitic value in cow's milk by artificial irradiation of the animal. In one of their experiments the milk of cows exposed to sun without change of diet from May 26 to June 16 showed no improvement as the result of insolation, but the milk of the same cows at the end of a summer on pasture was markedly superior.

The vitamin B and vitamin C contents of cow's milk appear also to vary with the diet of the animal. Kennedy and Dutcher [1922] found that 10 c.c. of milk from a cow on an adequate ration would supply an adequate daily provision of B-vitamins for a rat, while 15 c.c. from a cow on an inadequate diet would not. The anti-scorbutic value was found to vary more widely; in experiments with guinea-pigs, 20 c.c. of summer milk were found superior in nutritive value and in antiscorbutic potency to 60 c.c. of winter milk [Dutcher *et al.*, 1920–21]. A similar difference was found by Hess, Unger and Supplee [1920–21].

It must be recognized that cow's milk is a variable foodstuff, of which the vitamin value in any given instance cannot be assumed. Its use in infant-feeding must be specially safeguarded, not only by the use of milk products for the purpose of modification, but by the addition to the child's diet of the same supplements as are recommended for the breast-fed infant (p. 274).

Treated Cow's Milk (Irradiated, Heated, Dried, or Condensed).

IRRADIATED COW'S MILK.

The vitamin D value of cow's milk, whether raw or dried, can be much enhanced by ultra-violet irradiation; such milk may be of service prophylactically, in protecting children from rickets, but in the present state of knowledge it would be unwise to rely on it to the exclusion of cod-liver oil.

Cowell [1925; see also Daniels, Pyle and Brooks, 1925–26] showed that children could rapidly be cured of rickets by giving them every day a pint of milk which had been irradiated for 20 minutes. So long an irradiation in presence of oxygen is liable to impart to the milk an unpleasant flavour, which has been ascribed to the oxidation of proteins [Schultz, 1929], and may also damage the vitamin A it contains [Scheer, 1928]. Types of apparatus have now been devised in which the irradiation of milk can be accomplished in the absence of air or in an atmosphere of carbon dioxide [see Scheer, 1928]. Milk irradiated in this way has been shown to be a reliable prophylactic or curative agent for rickets and to be free from any objectionable taste or smell.

Coward [1929, 2], as the result of numerous tests, has found great variation in the antirachitic value of fresh cow's milk after irradiation for periods up to 30 seconds. Such a variation is not surprising and is to be expected, since the ergosterol (provitamin) content of milk is subject to considerable variations [Hentschel and Fischer, 1930]. The antirachitic value of milk thus irradiated was found to have been increased 5–50 times, and it was calculated that when irradiation was effective about 3 pints were equal in antirachitic value to one teaspoonful of a good cod-liver oil. So short an irradiation would not have the drawbacks alluded to above.

HEATED COW'S MILK.

A question of great moment is the influence of heat upon the nutritive value of cow's milk, and in certain respects the evidence on this question is conflicting. The matter was discussed at some length by Lane-Claypon [1916] in whose book are many references to authorities who consider that there is no proof of any inferiority of heated or pasteurized, as compared with raw, milk. Since then more information upon the effect of heat upon the vitamins and other constituents of milk has accumulated.

The evidence as to any deleterious effect of *careful* pasteurization on the nutritive properties of cow's milk is not decisive. It is in any case at present advisable to pasteurize the ordinary milk supply to prevent the spread of milk-borne diseases.

Owing to the variability of the vitamin content of milk, whether heated or raw, it is wise in all cases to supplement a diet of milk with vitamin additions. Of the vitamins present in milk, vitamin C is the most sensitive to the combined effects of heat and oxidation and evidence of the connexion between the use of pasteurized or heated milk and the incidence of infantile scurvy is presented on p. 264.

Effect of Heating on the Vitamin C of Milk.

Pasteurizing. Direct comparison, by a modified form of the comparative method of Sherman, La Mer and Campbell (p. 203), of fresh milk with the same milk after aerobic pasteurization at 60° C. for 30 minutes [Schwartze, Murphy and Cox, 1931–32] showed that the degree of diminution of the vitamin C content varied with the metal with which the milk came in contact during the process, being 20–40 per cent. (i.e. hardly perceptible) with aluminium, slightly greater with tinned copper, and 80–90 per cent. with copper.

Boiling. It was found by Barnes and Hume [1919, 1, 2] that when milk was scalded i.e. quickly heated to boiling in an enamelled pan and then allowed to cool in the air, it suffered comparatively little loss—not more than 25 per cent.—of its antiscorbutic power. A similar result was obtained by Schwartze, Murphy and Hann [1929–30] for milk boiled in glass or aluminium vessels.

Sterilizing. As regards the effect of higher degrees of heat, i.e. temperatures above 100° C., it would appear that these cause a rapid destruction of the antiscorbutic vitamin. Milk heated to 120° C., for ten minutes to one hour, has been examined by several investigators [Chick, Hume and Skelton, 1918, 1, 2; Hart, Steenbock and Smith, 1919]. No accurate estimate of its antiscorbutic power has been made, but after having been heated at 120° C. for one hour it can be used with impunity as a constituent of the basal diet of guinea-pigs for experiments with antiscorbutics (p. 202).

Effect of Heating on the Calcium of Milk.

Evidence has been forthcoming that the calcium supply in cow's milk is affected by heating. Daniels and Loughlin [1920] studied the problem on rats and found that the animals grew less well on pasteurized milk than on milk just brought to the boil, and that this was due to an insufficiency of calcium in the pasteurized milk. The calcium was found to be thrown out of solution by the more prolonged heating and the precipitate thus formed was mechanically lost.

When milk was brought to a temperature of 145–50° F., maintained at it for 30 minutes and tested 5 hours later, the loss in diffusible calcium was computed to be about 2 per cent.; at higher temperatures, up to 209° F., the loss rose to 2.5–3.6 per cent. [Mattick and Hallett, 1929].

From the Rowett Institute also comes evidence that when milk is heated there is a reduction in the diffusible calcium [Magee and Harvey, 1926, 1]. Young pigs on a diet of cereals and milk showed a lower retention of calcium, phosphorus, and nitrogen when the milk was heated than when fresh or sour [Magee and Harvey, 1926, 2]. When groups of calves were fed respectively on fresh milk, on pasteurized milk, and on pasteurized milk to which calcium lactate had been added, it was found that the increase in weight in the group on pasteurized milk, without any addition, was distinctly inferior to that in the other two groups. In one experiment the calves in the group receiving pasteurized milk actually contracted rickets [Orr *et al.*, 1926].

It was also found that heat caused the disappearance by volatilization of 20 per cent. or more, according to the severity of the heating, of the total iodine of separated milk [Magee and Glennie, 1928].

Although it cannot be disputed that the calcium supply in milk is damaged by heating, yet it might well be argued that in comparison with human milk, cow's milk contains so much calcium (38 mg. of CaO per 100 g. in human milk to 175 mg. in cow's milk [Schall and Heisler, 1927]) that a heavy loss might occur before the human infant fed on it would suffer any deprivation. If, however, it be assumed that for this reason young infants would not suffer from diminution of available calcium in pasteurized milk, it must be remembered that milk is also one of the most important sources of calcium for children older than those who are wholly milk-fed, and any impoverishment of the calcium supply in diets which may already contain insufficient of this element is much to be deprecated.

Evidence, however, exists that heating cow's milk may render the available calcium insufficient even for babies wholly fed on it. Daniels and Stearns [1924] found that a series of infants maintained on pasteurized milk to which antiscorbutic had been added failed to grow, and in some cases actually showed a negative calcium balance, while those which received milk that had simply been brought to the boil grew better, and, except in one case, remained in positive calcium balance, though not apparently retaining the optimal amount of calcium. The faecal calcium in the periods during which pasteurized milk was given was greater than in the periods in which boiled milk was given, suggesting that the calcium was not merely lost mechanically but that a portion of it was in a form in which it was incapable of utilization. These experimental results are so important that they demand confirmation and extension.

This matter is a very important one in view of the ever increasing spread of milk pasteurization in the large cities, and cannot be lightly dismissed. The evidence indicates that heating may be detrimental to the mineral content of milk and that the duration of the heating is more important than the temperature, if this does not exceed the boiling point. There is, however, little doubt that regular addition of vitamin D as cod-liver oil would, to a large extent, correct any calcium deficiency by securing the optimum utilization of the calcium presented to the organism. Raw, sterile milk is of course the ideal to be aimed at, but as such milk is at present unobtainable, there seem to be two alternatives, either to use pasteurized milk or to bring raw milk to the boil shortly before drinking. In the latter case the heating should not be prolonged.

Dried Cow's Milk.

On general grounds, it would appear likely that much that has been said about heated milk would be applicable also to dried milk, in so far as the processes used in drying involve heating. The majority of dried milks are prepared by one or other of two processes, which may be termed respectively the drum and the 'spray' processes [Rep. L. G. Board, 1918]. The drum process involves an exposure of the milk upon a revolving drum heated internally by steam at 140° C. The exposure is, however, very short and is probably insufficient to cause any significant destruction of the vitamins. In the spray process the milk is sprayed into a chamber through which a current of dry air at a temperature of 115° C. is passing. The dried powder falls to the bottom of this chamber and is, therefore, exposed to a temperature above 100° C. until it is removed for packing. It is probable that some destruction of the vitamins might occur if the dried powder remained in the chamber for longer than an hour. Certain special advantages are claimed for a spray process in which the milk is atomized cold and is smoothly distributed into a large stream of air, heated only to a very moderate extent. The contact with the hot air stream is brief and the dry powder is continuously removed from the influence of heat by settling into hoppers, outside the hot air stream. Any partial or general exposure of the milk to a raised temperature is thus minimized as far as possible.

The water-soluble B-vitamins do not appear to suffer damage in drying by the spray process [Johnson, 1921; Johnson and Hooper, 1921]. It is, however, probable that slow oxidation will gradually diminish the amount of the fat-soluble vitamins if the dried milks are kept for long periods before being used [see Hume, 1923, p. 140].

Investigation of the antiscorbutic value of dried milk has given conflicting results, due, doubtless, to the variation in value of the original milks before drying, to the exact methods used in drying and to the length of time the dried milk has been kept. Johnson and Hooper [1922] state that the antiscorbutic value of fresh milk is not very great and is injured by the process of drying. Barnes and Hume [1919, 1, 2], working at a time of year when the antiscorbutic potency of fresh milk was low, found that a sample of dried milk prepared at the same time, though not from the raw milk tested, was lower than the raw milk in antiscorbutic potency. They were unable to protect guinea-pigs from scurvy with any amount of dried milk which these animals were able to consume, but a monkey, which had developed scurvy on dried milk, was cured by the administration of the same amount of fresh milk, just scalded. Barnes and Hume concluded that the dried milk had about one-half the antiscorbutic value of fresh milk. They obtained indications that the vitamin C value of both fresh and dried cow's milk improved after the cows from which it was derived went out to pasture.

Hart, Steenbock and Ellis [1921] examined various milk powders and found that a considerable destruction of antiscorbutic vitamin occurred during drying, that various samples differed considerably from one another, and that less damage was suffered in the drum than in the spray process. Hess [1920], on the other hand, found that infants could sometimes be cured of scurvy by the use of dried milk. Jephcott and Bacharach [1921] found that guinea-pigs could be protected from scurvy by winter or summer milk specially dried by the drum process, but they did not compare the same milks before and after drying. A sample of milk dried by the spray process and of unknown age conferred no protection from scurvy upon guinea-pigs. Cavanaugh, Dutcher and Hall [1924], on the other hand, used milk dried by a form of the spray process in which special precautions were taken, and compared the milk thus dried with the same sample before drying. They claim that no damage was done to the antiscorbutic vitamin by this process.

It has been shown already that fresh milk is very variable in its vitamin content, and as the process of drying brings in fresh sources of variation, it can be taken for granted that the vitamin content of a dried milk is less than that of the same milk in the raw condition.

It is at once apparent that half cream and separated milks when dried will be deficient in the fat-soluble accessory factors, nor can such fats as olive oil or lard be used to make the deficiency good.

The antirachitic power of dried milk, like that of fresh milk (p. 220), is increased by ultra-violet irradiation [Hess and Weinstock, 1925, 1; Mackay and Shaw, 1925; Eddy, 1927; György, 1925; Supplee and Dow, 1927].

Condensed Milks.

The usual process employed for the preparation of the various types of sweetened condensed milks involves a preliminary ' pasteurization', or rather heating, at 80–90° C., followed by concentration at 50° C. under reduced pressure for two or three hours. It is probable that such treatment would not effect any serious destruction of the water-soluble or the fat-soluble vitamins.

An examination of sweetened condensed milk for antiscorbutic potency was carried out by Hume [1921], who, working with monkeys, found that the protective dose was almost identical with that of its equivalent of fresh milk (150 c.c.). Hess also found that this material retained most of the antiscorbutic potency of fresh milk [1921].

Unsweetened condensed milk, on the other hand, which is subject to more drastic heating in order to ensure its preservation (preheating at 82·5–98·5° C. for 1–20 minutes; condensing at 55·7° C., and sterilizing at 107–115·5° C. for 1–20 minutes), loses more than 40 per cent. of its antiscorbutic power [Hart, Steenbock and Smith, 1919].

Condensed milks are classified as full-cream milks or machine-skimmed milks. The former are often, and the latter almost invariably, sweetened by the addition of sucrose (cane sugar). Any form of machine-skimmed milk, whether condensed or not, is unsuitable for the nutrition of the infant, owing to its low content of fat, which is further diminished when the milk is diluted before use. The dilutions necessary to reduce the effect of the added sucrose in sweetened condensed milks are so great as to result in the production of a foodstuff very deficient in fat, vitamins and salts.

CHAPTER X

VITAMINS AND HUMAN DIETS.

Introduction.

THE known chemical characteristics and the biological actions of the recognized vitamins have been considered in the earlier chapters of this work. It is now proposed to review the general problem in relation to human nutrition. Many of the facts have already been discussed in some detail, but primarily in relation to experimental work rather than from their human interest.

In the last decade our knowledge of vitamins has advanced so greatly that the possibilities of its practical application to human diets have much increased. Eight years ago it was necessary to say 'it is therefore a matter for regret that our limited knowledge of the accessory substances should restrict to some extent the consideration of practical issues' [Med. Res. Coun. 1924]. Meanwhile knowledge has grown and, though still very incomplete, the limiting factor in practical application is often one of finance rather than of ignorance.

A large proportion of the facts discovered about vitamins has resulted from animal experiments and although it is certain that many of them are of the greatest importance in human nutrition, it is equally clear that their significance in some cases is either not known or imperfectly understood as far as man is concerned. Laboratory work is, in fact, a long way ahead of clinical investigation in this field at the present time.

Nutrition in man, in relation to vitamins, may be considered from two general aspects:

(1) The production and maintenance of perfect health and optimal growth;

(2) The prevention or cure of specific deficiency diseases.

One reason for this suggested differentiation is the fact that a deficient vitamin intake may not immediately result in actual disease, but may bring about abnormal development of specific structures which makes disease of these parts ultimately almost inevitable. Striking instances of this are given in Chapter IV, where evidence is adduced to show that a deficient intake of vitamin D in infancy may bring about defective formation of teeth, and subsequent increased susceptibility to dental decay, while deficient vitamin A intake may cause malformation of the gum epithelium, and may lead to subsequent development of periodontal disease, including pyorrhoea alveolaris. Undoubtedly there are many other instances where a deficient intake of vitamins is related to disease in this indirect way.

So far as Western civilization is concerned, it is no doubt true that the rareness of the occurrence of frank deficiency diseases, such as scurvy, xerophthalmia, and beri-beri indicates that an absolute deficiency of vitamins scarcely ever exists in the individual diet. On the other hand, it is now becoming generally recognized that much subnormal health and development, and even incidence of disease, are associated with a partial deficiency of one or more of these accessory substances. The influence of such partial deficiencies, even when relatively slight, may be extremely serious when they occur in very early life, and, if we may judge from the results of experiments on animals, an adequate supply of these indispensable dietary components later in life may fail to make good the damage caused by a deficiency in youth. There is also danger that the effects of such a partial or latent deficiency may persist as a chronic condition throughout adult life. It is difficult to provide convincing evidence of this, since the well-known symptoms which characterize the disease may not be present, and the only method of clinching the diagnosis would be to make widespread therapeutic trials with the vitamin or vitamins suspected to be deficient and to observe whether general improvement in health took place. Green and Mellanby [1930] have pointed out how wide is the margin between the doses of vitamin A which will just maintain a rat in life, if it is not attacked by infection, and the dose which will wholly prevent those infections. The latter dose is about four times as great as the former. Animals receiving doses between these maximum and minimum amounts, while showing no overt symptoms of vitamin A deficiency, yet suffer from a partial or latent deficiency and are proportionately liable to infection in consequence. This example serves to show that a *latent deficiency disease* is a real thing and not an imaginary concept.

The optimal intake of vitamins depends greatly on many conditions influencing the human organism. These include the age, the rate of growth, the climate, the degree of exposure to infection, the composition of the diet as a whole, and the degree of sunshine to which the body is exposed.

It is probable that the adult, at any rate relative to his size, has smaller requirements for vitamins than the growing child, but we have little knowledge of the absolute requirements of either for any given vitamin. The diet of the adult is so varied, and different samples of the same foodstuff vary so greatly, that it would be difficult to assess the vitamin value of any particular diet. The diet of infants is simpler and it is possible to express their vitamin needs roughly in terms of cow's milk. About 500–1,000 c.c. (1–2 pints) of raw cow's milk provides enough or nearly enough of the vitamins A and C and of the B-vitamins of the yeast complex, but not enough of vitamin D. Cow's milk, however, is so variable in composition that this statement may need qualifying, and does not provide more than a slender basis for calculation.

There are certain times when special demands are made on the metabolism, as, for instance, during hard physical work. Thus it has been observed that both beri-beri and scurvy are more rapidly contracted by men engaged in hard manual exercise than by others receiving the same diets who are not so engaged. This should be borne in mind when dietaries or rations are being planned for those engaged in severe manual work, such as soldiers and labourers. Pregnancy and lactation in women and growth in children also call for larger supplies of the vitamins.

The fact that outspoken deficiency diseases are almost unknown in this country has occasioned much scepticism in the minds of some

Vitamin Deficiencies and Disease.

VITAMIN A.

It is noteworthy that milk, cream, butter, and, in particular, cod-liver oil (all rich sources of vitamin A or of vitamin D or of both) have long been included in the treatment of diseases of malnutrition and of tuberculosis. In this fact there is an illustration of the results of scientific investigation justifying the selections based on long practical experience.

Although the value of animal fats as sources of vitamin A is so well established, it would not appear that 'vitamin A' from plant sources is at all inferior in value from the dietetic point of view. It is probable that all over the world, except perhaps in very high latitudes, the poorer sections of the community rely chiefly upon carotene-containing vegetables as their main source of vitamin A. Such vegetable products are very widely distributed and it therefore comes about that no community is completely devoid of them except in times of drought and famine. A florid development in adults of the symptoms of absolute deprivation of vitamin A is therefore rare. Such florid symptoms as do occur in the human being are those of xerophthalmia, hemeralopia, and presumably of different infections, following upon hypoplasia and cornification of the mucous tract, as seen in the rat.

The length of time during which man can be deprived of vitamin A before developing symptoms of xerophthalmia is uncertain and by analogy with the rat must vary greatly in different individuals. It will depend upon the degree of deficiency of the diet and the extent of the reserves of vitamin A which the individual has stored up, chiefly in the liver. These reserves will be determined by the individual's previous dietary history.

Vitamin A in Food.

The provision of an adequate supply of vitamin A in the diet does not, except in certain circumstances, present such a difficult economic problem as does that of certain of the other vitamins. Animal sources of vitamin A, such as milk-fat, eggs, mammalian liver, and cod-liver oil, are expensive, but when it is remembered that this vitamin is supplied by all green vegetables and others which contain the yellow colouring matter carotene, the problem can be cheaply solved wherever vegetables can be grown. For example, green spinach and green cabbage (but not white [Coward and Drummond, 1921]) are weight for weight as good as the best New Zealand butter [Hume and Smith, 1930]; carrot also is excellent [Moore, 1929, 2]; yellow maize [Steenbock and Boutwell, 1920, 1], yellow peas [Steenbock, Sell and Boutwell [1921] are all good sources while similar articles of food, without the yellow pigment, are valueless in this particular. Red palm-oil is very rich, being equivalent to a cod-liver oil of more than ordinary strength, and if it can be made palatable may prove an excellent source of vitamin A. Some margarines can now be obtained in this country, at a very small increased cost, which have been fortified with vitamins to make them equal in this respect to butter.

Both vitamin A and carotene, as contained in natural foodstuffs, keep well unless exposed to conditions which favour oxidation; light encourages oxidation but ordinary cooking does little damage. Even after air has been bubbled through cod-liver oil for four hours at 100° C., the oil still retains considerable activity in the cure of xerophthalmia, although similar treatment for 12 hours completely inactivates it [McCollum, Simmonds, Becker and Shipley, 1922]. Storage and transport do not therefore constitute a problem in maintaining a supply of this vitamin. Under some conditions oxidation seems to be promoted during the drying of the vegetables; thus, alfalfa hay which had been allowed to lie in the field for ten days exposed to sun and every kind of weather was found to be inferior to alfalfa hay cured in the dark [Steenbock, Nelson and Black, 1924–25]. It would not therefore be wise to rely blindly on dried vegetables as a source of vitamin A, although some such preparations are rich in this respect.

Xerophthalmia and Hemeralopia.

Xerophthalmia in young children. The xerophthalmia of rats fed on diets deficient in vitamin A was examined carefully by Knapp [1908], who appeared to appreciate the relationship it bore to certain forms of conjunctivitis in children, usually ascribed to faulty nutrition. He was, of course, unaware of the existence of the then undiscovered fat-soluble vitamins, but a study of the rations which he employed shows that they were deficient in that respect.

M. Mori [1904] described a form of external eye disease prevalent among infants in Japan, the symptoms of which bear close resemblance to those shown by rats deprived of the fat-soluble factors. In his work, also carried on prior to the discovery of vitamin A, he approached very near to the correct explanation when he attributed the condition to a deficiency of fat. He states that cod-liver oil was a useful prophylactic, whilst olive oil and sesame oil were useless.

More recently, Bloch [1917, 1, 2, 3; 1918; 1921; 1924] and also Monrad [1917] have described a form of external eye disease in young children in Denmark, which they associate with a deficiency of fat. Bloch gives a detailed account of sixty-four cases in babies treated at the State hospital, Copenhagen, in 1912–16. All the patients had been artificially fed, and the most severe and characteristic cases occurred in children about twelve months old who had been fed on separated milk. The eye disease showed every stage of severity from xerosis of the conjunctiva, in the slighter cases, to hardening of the cornea, leading to ulceration, necrosis, and ultimate blindness, in the more severe ones. Treatment of the eye condition in the ophthalmic department of the hospital gave little relief and no permanent improvement. On further study the children proved to be weak, anaemic, ill developed, apathetic and with poor appetite. In some cases, especially those of younger children, the eye lesion was associated with a state of general atrophy. In the older children the general condition was not usually so severe, although the eye condition was frequently worse; there was often distinct swelling, with oedema of the subcutaneous tissues, but no tenderness.

Hemeralopia, keratomalacia, and xerophthalmia in adults. In older children and adults receiving defective diet, hemeralopia or night-blindness has often been observed in endemic form and this appears to be an expression of a mild deficiency of vitamin A. The different symptoms exhibited in the varying degrees of severity of this disorder are described by Pillat [1929, 2]. It is suggested that the night-blindness is caused by a failure in the regeneration of the visual purple, after its bleaching by strong light. Fridericia and Holm [1925] were able to demonstrate this for rats starved of vitamin A. Exposure to a strong light, by accelerating the bleaching of the visual purple, should therefore precipitate an attack of night-blindness. Aykroyd [1930, 2, see below] narrates several cases where this seems certainly to have been the case.

In adults suffering from night-blindness there are often only slight physical alterations to be seen in the affected eyes, few showing typical xerosis of the conjunctiva [Meissner, 1919]. In the case of a family of undernourished children observed at the University Kinderklinik, Vienna, in May–June 1921, night-blindness was accompanied by marked xerosis of the conjunctiva in a boy and girl aged 8 and 9 years respectively (Wagner, unpublished observation).

This form of night-blindness, which has been termed deficiency-hemeralopia (Ausfallshemeralopie, Zak), was common during the late war among Austrian prisoners of war in Russia and was studied by various Austrian physicians, themselves prisoners [Zak, 1917; Meissner, 1919; Hift, 1918]. They found the disorder to be a frequent one among Russian peasants in peace time, especially in the period of religious fasting before Easter. During this period all animal foods were forbidden, including fish, eggs, milk, and butter; the diet enjoined was strictly vegetarian and included fats and oils of vegetable origin only. The curve of incidence of the disease showed a sharp peak in spring. Lightly cooked liver or cod-liver oil were the popular remedies for the disease, and their striking effect was confirmed by the Austrian observers. Hift [1920] found that the night-blindness could be cured within two or three days by administration of cod-liver oil, Zak [1920] by one or two meals each consisting of 150 g. of liver, by 3 eggs given daily for four days, or by 400 c.c. expressed juice of carrots taken daily for five or six days.

In case of prisoners of war, hemeralopia was frequently found to accompany scurvy, but many cases, on the other hand, showed no symptoms at all suggestive of the latter disease, and consideration of the type of foodstuffs found to act as specific cures, points definitely to a deficiency of vitamin A as the cause of the disease.

Night-blindness is common in certain districts of Japan, especially among coolies working in rice-fields in summer time, and among Japanese soldiers when undertaking heavy forced marches in summer. From the fact that cod-liver oil has not here proved invariably to be curative (S. Mori, private communication, 1923) it may be doubted whether in these cases the disease is always dietetic in origin. A clearer example is afforded by the small epidemics occurring since the European War among Japanese railway work-

men in Manchuria ; these have usually been localized and associated
with some particular boarding-house. The incidence reaches its
height in the months of February and March, and S. Mori, who has
investigated these outbreaks, considers the scarcity and high price
of fish in the winter months to be the direct cause. In the month of
April fish at once becomes cheaper and more plentiful and the outbreaks of night-blindness promptly disappear. Cures have been
observed to take place within 12–24 hours after administration of
cod-liver oil. [S. Mori, private communication.]

The occurrence of night-blindness together with keratomalacia
among soldiers in a military camp north of Peiping, in China, is
described by Pillat [1929, 1]. Ninety-one cases of eye disease, due to
deficiency of vitamin A, were seen ; of these 12 had keratomalacia,
9 in both eyes and 3 in one eye only. The three cases with keratomalacia in one eye were night-blind in the other eye. The diet was
adequate in calories and none of the sick soldiers was emaciated,
but they had pasty, puffy faces, dry skin, and scanty hair. No
mention is made that they were subject to an increased incidence
of infections of the mucous membrane, although the degree of
deficiency must have been severe. The soldiers' diet was rice, corn,
millet, very little flour, a small quantity of meat once a month and
no green vegetables at all. In the case of two of the soldiers, it is
mentioned that their eyes became much better after they had par-
taken of three meals of green vegetables. Pillat considers that severe
cold and heavy physical labour were factors contributing to produce
the state of deficiency (see p. 227).

Wille [1922] noted the frequent occurrence of xerophthalmia
among inmates of institutions in the Dutch East Indies, where
coco-nut oil was the chief source of fat in the dietary. He found
that the giving of 100 g. of ox liver three times a week to such individuals effectively prevented the disease.

An interesting case is described from Guatemala [Macphail, 1929]
where the lack of opportunity to eat bananas seems to have been
the factor which differentiated a group of workers developing night-
blindness from those who did not. The sufferers were members of
railway gangs whose food was corn cakes, beans, rice, coffee and
sugar, with meat once a week. The disease only occurred among
men working on those parts of the line which did not pass through
banana country. Milk was used as the cure.

Night-blindness is not unknown in England at the present time.
In the ophthalmological department of an infirmary in the north of
England seventeen cases of xerophthalmia and night-blindness were
seen in the course of one year among a total of about 4,000 patients.
Treatment with adequate doses of cod-liver oil, butter, and milk was
uniformly successful. This observation [Spence 1931] may indicate
a latent deficiency of vitamin A among our population which is more
widespread than is usually recognized.

Aykroyd [1930, 2] has described conditions in Newfoundland in
which night-blindness is developed with considerable frequency,
while xerophthalmia and keratomalacia are apparently unknown,
so that the deficiency is either too short in duration, or insufficiently
severe in degree, to produce these symptoms. In Newfoundland,

those who become night-blind are generally men pursuing the summer fishing, but the condition can occur at other times of the year and sometimes also among pregnant women. The diet of the inhabitants of Newfoundland and Labrador seems to border on deficiency in more than one particular, since beri-beri, scurvy, and night-blindness have all been observed. The diet of fishermen when they are living on board ship or in huts far from their homes is even more restricted than that of the other inhabitants. The ship's stores usually consist of white flour, ship's biscuit, salt beef and pork, molasses, margarine, potatoes, beans, and peas. Very few carry fresh vegetables, eggs, or milk. The only sources of vitamin A therefore are the beans or peas, of which the carotene content may vary considerably.

In several of the cases which Aykroyd saw and treated, the onset of the disease was immediately preceded by an exposure to strong sunlight; the ascription of the cause of night-blindness to the failure in regeneration of the visual purple is thus supported. One patient was an old sufferer who protected himself by wearing dark glasses, but developed an attack of night-blindness after being temporarily deprived of them. Another was a boy of eighteen who connected the onset of the trouble with a day of exposure to bright sunshine. The Newfoundlanders have learnt to treat the condition themselves with fresh cod's liver or with cod-liver oil. The rapidity of the improvement is astonishing as was also noticed by Pillat; vision became normal in 12–24 hours after the beginning of treatment, and a single dose of 1–2 oz. of cod-liver oil was found sufficient to bring about a cure. The Newfoundlanders regard the liver of a gull or puffin as even more potent than that of a cod. Aykroyd discusses the antiquity of the treatment by liver. For the treatment of night-blindness Hippocrates recommended that the patient should eat, once or twice, as large an ox liver as possible, raw, and dipped in honey.

Other Pathological Conditions referred to a Deficiency in Vitamin A.

Infections of the mucous membrane. Although experimental work on animals shows that lowered immunity to infection of the mucous membrane, and possibly anaemia, are associated with a partial deficiency of vitamin A, there is little positive evidence to link up these conditions with deficiency in the human subject. Both in Newfoundland and in China the circumstances described are such that a number of individuals must be existing in a state of latent deficiency. By analogy with the rat, mucous membrane infections should be prevalent and both Aykroyd and Pillat should have noticed them. Pillat only mentions that six out of the twelve keratomalacia cases had raised temperatures and Aykroyd (verbal communication) states that such infections were not noticeably frequent. In Newfoundland liability to encounter infection might, however, not be great, owing to the sparsity of the rural population.

The official figures of the Medical Officer of Health for Bombay City in the period 1920–29 show that respiratory infections provide by far the commonest cause of death in a population where cases of xerophthalmia occur [Wills and Talpade, 1930], and where the conditions are presumably very favourable to infection. No large-scale human tests have, however, as yet been described, in which the possible preventive action of vitamin A against respiratory infection has been tried out under properly controlled conditions. The preliminary results obtained by Green, Pindar, Davies and Mellanby in giving massive doses of vitamins A and D as a prophylactic against puerperal sepsis are described elsewhere (see p. 270).

Stone in kidney and bladder. There is no doubt that in rats stones in the kidney and bladder are produced on diets low in vitamin A but not absolutely devoid of it [Osborne and Mendel, 1917, 4; Fujimaki, 1926; McCarrison, 1926–27; 1927–28; 1929–30, 2]. An infection of the mucous membrane is, however, probably a necessary preliminary. At present there is no evidence to connect the aetiology of urinary calculi in rats with that of stone in human beings. Newcomb and Ranganathan [1929–30, 1, 2] have collected urinary calculi from patients in India, together with a medical and dietary history of each case. They have analysed the calculi and compared their composition with those of calculi from rats and find the compositions to be different in the two series. In human stones uric acid and urates are very common, the content of CaO is high and the content of MgO low, and there is much oxalate and little carbonate. In stones from rats there is no uric acid or urate, the content of MgO is high, and of CaO low, there is much carbonate and little oxalate and more P_2O_5 than in the human specimens. Unfortunately the case histories have not yet been analysed, but McCarrison [1929–30, 1] mentions that stone is commoner among wheat eaters than among rice eaters in India, and he also finds whole wheat flour much more productive of stone in rats than rice. Butter and milk [1929–30, 2; 1927–28] he finds preventive, doubtless due to their vitamin A content.

Anaemia. Mention of the possible part played by a vitamin A deficiency in promoting anaemia should not be omitted. Keefer and Yang [1929] discuss the relationship of vitamins to the production of anaemia in human beings and point out that 'all of the so-called deficiency diseases may exist without anaemia'. They emphasize the point that a diet which is sufficiently lacking in one factor to produce a deficiency disease is also liable to be lacking in other factors and the combination may be liable to promote anaemia. Berglund, Keefer and Yang [1928–29] speak of cases of anaemia in China, coupled with diarrhoea, where the diarrhoea responded dramatically to treatment with cod-liver oil. Less severe cases of a similar anaemia in pregnant women responded quickly to a generous well-balanced diet. The giving of cod-liver oil to patients with other forms of secondary anaemia had no effect on the course of the disease.

Evidence suggesting a causal relation between vitamin B deficiency and certain forms of anaemia is discussed on p. 252.

VITAMIN D.

Inter-relation of Light and Diet as Sources of Vitamin D.

Vitamin D is richly present in cod- and other fish-liver oils; it is also present in the fat of egg yolk, butter fat and, to some extent, in other animal fats and vegetable oils (for margarine enriched with vitamins, see p. 230), but not in lard. Milk is not a very rich source, even when the cows have been much exposed to sunshine. Most foodstuffs have their content of vitamin D much increased if exposed to ultra-violet irradiation.

Vitamin D, like vitamin A, in so far as it occurs in foodstuffs, is possessed of great stability during storage and transport, but is more resistant to oxidation than vitamin A (see p. 24). Oxidation is favoured by light and high temperature. The very low content of vitamin D in most natural foodstuffs has raised a doubt as to whether we depend at all on our food for our supply of this vitamin, or whether it is not exclusively obtained by the action of sunshine. The outbreak of osteomalacia (see pp. 48, 240), which occurred in Vienna as a sequel of the War shows clearly, however, that in winter we do depend on our diet for our provision of this vitamin. It is quite certain that famine was the cause of the disease in Vienna. It was truly called hunger-osteomalacia, but it was equally truly cured by summer sunlight and could also have been cured by ultra-violet irradiation from an artificial source. The immediate causative factor in this outbreak, however, was deterioration in the diet and not any reduction in the supply of sunshine.

It may also be deduced from the experience of the Vienna outbreak that the sunlight enjoyed in the summer under the ordinary conditions of life in temperate latitudes is not enough to ensure protection during the subsequent winter and that for this purpose reliance must be placed on diet. Although it is difficult to discriminate between the relative importance of light and diet as sources of vitamin D, it is often possible to decide which deficiency was the cause of any given outbreak, though the patients could be cured by a supply of vitamin D from either source. Thus, while failure in diet conditioned the outbreak in Vienna, the custom of purdah is the factor which determines the development of osteomalacia in India, since in that country men who eat the same diet but do not keep purdah are not affected. On the other hand it should be remembered that the occurrence of osteomalacia might be prevented in India by dietary alterations as well as by the abolition of the purdah. It would, however, probably be necessary to include something as potent as cod-liver oil in the diet to protect people as severely starved of ultra-violet irradiation as women living under conditions of purdah in India.

Light and diet should be regarded as factors which supplement one another in the supply of vitamin D. Where the ultra-violet irradiation is optimal less support is needed from the diet, but further North, as the sunlight becomes progressively less intense and the body more completely clothed, more and more does the function of protection pass from the light to the diet. Where adaptation is complete the diet adequately fulfils its function, as, for example, among the Eskimo who on their natural diet of meat, fish and oil are healthy and have good teeth, while their breast-fed babies have no rickets. When they change to a 'civilized' diet, while still living in the same latitudes, they are no longer adapted, the health deteriorates, the teeth decay, and the babies get rickets.

Kloster [1931] has published an interesting study of the incidence of rickets in a collection of villages and hamlets on the Varanger Fiord in Norway, situated within the Arctic circle. The population, which subsists on the fishing industry, belongs to three different races, Lapps, Norwegians, and Quains (Finlanders). Signs of rickets were present in 163 (43·4 per cent.) out of 376 children under 7 years of age and in 60 (13·3 per cent.) out of 451 attending school. The villages inhabited by Lapps showed generally the lowest incidence of rickets, in spite of greater poverty and a lower standard of housing, cleanliness and general hygiene. This is attributed partly to the habit of using reindeer skin as clothing, which enables the Lapp women and the elder children to spend more time outdoors in the cold weather, but chiefly to the fact that the Lapps received a larger supply of vitamin D in their diet. This is supplied by the very large quantities consumed of fresh fish (cod, haddock, and coal fish, up to 1 kg. per head daily) served with the liver oil (up to 70 g. per head daily) and fresh liver. The incidence of rickets was highest (present in 73 per cent. of children below school age) in a relatively well-to-do village (Skallelv) inhabited by Finlanders who enjoyed a 'better' diet including meat and milk (average amount ca. 500 g. daily) and consequently a better supply of calcium salts and of vitamin A, but much less fresh fish, fish-liver, and liver oil.

A study of ancient skeletons suggests that osteomalacia, which through the deformities caused in the pelvis has a crippling effect on reproduction, was the cause of the extinction, about the end of the fifteenth century, of the Norse colony founded in A.D. 985 by Eric the Red at Herjolfsnes in Greenland. If this interpretation is correct, the disappearance of this colony affords a clear case of extermination through failure to adapt the diet in such a manner as to supplement the lack of ultra-violet rays from the sun in those high latitudes [Maxwell, 1930].

In Britain, at the present day, the adaptation of diet to climate is incomplete; osteomalacia is very rare, but bad teeth are almost universal and rickets is a common disease.

A full account of the aetiology of rickets is given elsewhere (see Chapter III), together with a description of the animal experiments which played so large a part in elucidating the problem.

Osteomalacia.

The dietary experiments unfortunately provided by the late war, together with excellent surveys in India and China, have placed it beyond doubt that osteomalacia in the adult is analogous to rickets in the child. Both represent states in which there is a breakdown of calcium metabolism due to an insufficient supply of vitamin D derived either from food or from the action of light; both are curable when vitamin D is supplied in either of these ways.

The essential feature of the disease in adults is a loss of calcium from the bones, which leads to their softening and consequent deformity. McCrudden [1910] found that the total ash of a bone from a case of osteomalacia was much reduced, and the calcium was reduced to a greater extent than the phosphorus. He determined the calcium balance in a series of eight cases and in each instance found that calcium was being lost to the body. Miles and Feng [1925] found that the calcium content of the serum was below normal in osteomalacia and in most cases which they investigated there was a constant loss of calcium from the body.

The most striking clinical feature of this crippling, painful, and even dangerous disease is a progressive deformity of the skeleton. The disease is particularly liable to appear during pregnancy, but it often also occurs in girls at the age of puberty; males are more rarely affected. The geographical distribution of the disease differs from that of rickets. It is not common in temperate climates, and is met with most frequently in India and China; numerous cases have been reported, however, from the Balkan States. Its sociological distribution throws some light on its aetiology. In India and China it is commoner among the relatively well-to-do than among the very poor; in India it affects chiefly Mohammedan and high-caste Hindu women who practise the system of seclusion known as purdah. In the Balkans it is confined almost entirely to the Mohammedan population.

In 1919–20 hunger osteomalacia, or, as it was then called, 'Knochenerweichung' or bone-softening, broke out among adults of the poorest class in Vienna [Dalyell and Chick, 1921]. The disease chiefly affected the middle-aged and old people of either sex; it was not observed in pregnant women, possibly because they were provided with better food. All the sufferers were extremely poor, though sometimes belonging to the middle class. The symptoms were pain on movement, which produced a waddling gait with special difficulty in mounting stairs, severe pain in the sacral region on pressure or movement and pain in the ribs on compression of the thorax; tetany was frequently present. Observations on dietetic therapy showed that little improvement took place on addition of sugar or cereals to the diet, even in cases where it had previously been very low in calories. Cod-liver oil was by far the most efficient therapeutic agent.

The seasonal incidence of the disorder was very striking [Hume and Nirenstein, 1921]. The disease was first noted in the late autumn of 1918 and the number of fresh cases increased steadily during the winter, reaching a maximum in April 1919. On the approach of summer there was a rapid decline to a low level which continued throughout the autumn; in January 1920, fresh cases began to appear and a maximum was again reached in April. In the late autumn of 1920, coinciding with great improvement in the food supplies of the city, the disease disappeared almost entirely. Though it was not fully realized at the time when the observations were made, it is now quite clear that the seasonal incidence of the disease was due to the seasonal variation in the amount of ultra-violet radiation from the sun.

In India and in China the conditions in which osteomalacia occurs are different from those which obtained in Vienna. In Vienna the epidemic was the result of a dietary emergency which did not recur; in India and China the disease is caused by social customs or conditions which tend to be only very slowly remedied, and consequently is endemic. In both these countries the sufferers are chiefly women and very largely pregnant women, pregnancy supplying the extra strain on the calcium metabolism needed to precipitate the disease. In the Kangra Valley in India, however, men and boys are also affected [Wilson and Surie, 1929–30].

In India osteomalacia is associated with the custom of purdah, [Stapleton, 1925; Vaughan, 1926; 1928], which confines women to the house and prevents their exposure to ultra-violet radiation from the sun. At the same time, the diet, rich in cereals, poor in meat and genuine milk fat, and quite devoid of liver oils, is not adapted for a life without sunshine [Scott, 1916–17; Green-Armytage, 1928]. The disease is cured by administration of cod-liver oil or by exposure to sunlight [Vaughan, 1926, 1928; Green-Armytage, 1928]. Vaughan mentions the interesting point that in Kashmir there are three indigenous cures for 'trouble in the bones'—a special clay called Baramulla earth, which contains 16·2 per cent. of calcium phosphate; pills made of fish-liver; rubbing the body with mustard oil and exposing it to sunlight. In the cases from the Kangra Valley it is claimed that the sufferers were not deprived of sunshine and that the deficiency must be a dietetic one; possibly there is an insufficiency of calcium or phosphorus, since addition of fresh fruit and vegetables to the diet hastened the cures when vitamin D was given *per os* [D. C. Wilson, 1930–31, 1].

In Northern and Western China the disease is also endemic among women. The diet is very poor, consisting almost entirely of cereals, chiefly millet, a limited amount of vegetables and no milk, meat, or eggs [Miles and Feng, 1925; Maxwell and Miles, 1925]. Maxwell [1930] correlates the increase of osteomalacia in the province of Shansi, where it is most frequent, with an enormous increase in the growth of the poppy and in the use of opium, which keeps its users indoors. Binding of the feet, the customs of the people, and the extremely disturbed condition of the country also play a part in keeping the women indoors, while the disturbed political conditions also operate to diminish the live stock and in general to deteriorate the food supply. A deficiency of calcium in the diet is probably here also contributory. The disease yields to the various forms of vitamin D therapy.

It now seems probable that the rare cases of the osteomalacia of pregnancy described in England, N. Germany, and the United States, of which the aetiology was previously obscure, are a sporadic expression of the same disease. Starlinger [1927] describes the dramatic cure of a woman who had suffered for fourteen years from osteomalacia which became progressively worse after repeated pregnancies till she was almost entirely bedridden. Treated at last with vitamin D, as irradiated ergosterol, she showed marked improvement after twelve days and got rapidly better. There is nothing in the case history to show why this woman should have fallen a victim to osteomalacia, but it is easy to imagine that a woman, who combined little liking for outdoor exercise with a distaste for animal fats, might during pregnancy fall below the margin of safety. Many women tend to remain indoors during pregnancy and to enjoy little exposure to sunlight, so that with the added drain of the foetus, it is more than probable that they are in negative calcium balance. According to the old wives' saying : ' A tooth is lost for every child which is born.' Pregnant women should therefore take special steps to combåt this tendency by securing for themselves an increased supply of vitamin D, either in their diet or through sunlight or other forms of irradiation.

In some of the districts (e.g. India [D. C. Wilson, 1930-31, 2]) where osteomalacia is frequent, girls of 10–17 years are liable to develop a mild form of the disease which appears to be identical with the condition known as late rickets sometimes encountered in this country. There appears in fact to be no definite separation of the two conditions, late rickets sometimes merging into severe osteomalacia.

The conditions of puberty, pregnancy, and lactation seem to demand an increased supply of all essential factors including vitamin D, and serious disturbances in the mineral metabolism of the body may result if the necessary minimum quantity is not provided.

Vitamin D and the Supply of Calcium.

A dietary factor which cannot be omitted in considering vitamin D is the element calcium. Vitamin D is concerned with the metabolism of calcium and operates to secure the most economical use of the supply of this element in the diet. From an analysis of a number of typical American dietaries, Sherman [1920, 2] concluded that the calcium intake of one person in six fell below the calculated requirement. Mann [1926] in studying the effect of various additions to the dietary of boys living in an Institution found that growth was best promoted by the addition of one pint of whole milk a day (see p. 217). Similar results were obtained by Orr [1928], Leighton and Clark [1929], and Clark [1929], when additions of whole and of separated milk respectively were made to the diets of children attending the elementary day-schools in different towns in Scotland. The fact that the separated milk proved as beneficial as the whole milk suggests that the effect might be referred to the mineral content of the milk rather than to the vitamin D content, which in any case would be small. The extra supply of calcium salts would, however, enhance the value of any vitamin D present in the diet.

In a survey of the diets in certain Scottish towns [Orr and Clark, 1930], it was found that in 24·5 per cent. of the families the supply of calcium fell below the generally accepted standard of requirements for adults. For Dundee the values were recalculated on a higher scale, which takes account of the growth requirements of the children in the family. On this standard the necessary intake of calcium for optimum growth was only attained by nine out of thirty-seven families. It is recommended that more milk and green vegetables should be consumed in order to make up this deficiency. Sherman [1920, 2] also recommends that more milk should be consumed, and at the same time suggests that calcium carbonate or phosphate should be habitually added to human food, either separately or in the table salt. The addition of calcium is also beneficial because it increases the calcifying action of butter and antagonizes the anticalcifying action of cereals [E. Mellanby, 1921, 1925]. Addition of vitamin D at the same time would secure the more economical utilization of any added calcium, but sunshine is the only cheap form in which vitamin D can be obtained. Oranges are particularly rich in calcium though they contain no vitamin D, and possess the advantage that they are eaten raw, whereas green vegetables boiled in water always suffer impoverishment through diffusion of the salts into the surrounding water.

VITAMIN B₁ (ANTINEURITIC).

The problems of the aetiology of beri-beri are more fully discussed elsewhere (p. 122) and it suffices here to discuss human diets on which beri-beri in the recognized sense has developed and the measures which have been found satisfactory for its prevention.

Beri-beri as the Result of a Diet consisting too exclusively of an Over-milled Cereal.

Rice is the staple diet of a great part of the poorer population of southern and eastern Asia, and it is in Japan, the Malay States, Java, and the Philippines that classical outbreaks of this disease have occurred. The researches of the investigators mentioned on p. 123 have succeeded in correlating the disease with the consumption of steam-milled, white, polished rice. Where the rice is merely husked and the outer skin and germ are retained, or where the rice is milled in domestic or native mills, so that the separation of these constituents is much less complete, beri-beri does not occur. Further, in localities where it is epidemic, beri-beri has been both prevented and cured by substituting whole rice or rice prepared in the native manner, for the fine white polished rice.

Eijkman [1897, 2] quotes an observation of Vorderman, which points forcibly to the connexion between beri-beri and highly milled rice. This worker made a survey of the prisons of Java and Madura, noting the type of rice consumed and the incidence of beri-beri. His observations extended over a population of more than 279,000 persons. The results summarized in Table XVII show how closely the incidence of beri-beri is correlated with the degree of milling which the rice has undergone.

TABLE XVII.

Relation between the incidence of beri-beri in Javanese prisons and the type of rice consumed (Vorderman).

Type of rice consumed.	No. of prisons examined.	No. in which beri-beri occurred.	Per cent.	Proportion of cases of beri-beri among total no. of inmates.
1. 'Half polished'; $\frac{3}{4}$ of the 'silver-skin' adherent.	37	1	2·7	1 in 10,000
2. $\frac{1}{2}$ of the 'silver-skin' adherent.	13	6	46	1 in 416
3. 'Polished;' less than $\frac{1}{4}$ of the 'silver-skin' adherent.	51	36	71	1 in 39

Apart from these general observations, there have been a few definite human experiments, which may be cited here. Strong and Crowell [1912] obtained volunteers from the prisoners in a jail in the Philippine Islands, and these were divided into four groups placed upon strictly controlled diets. All received a certain amount of fish, bacon, lard, bananas, potatoes, and sugar, but rice was the staple article of diet and was provided in three different forms for the four groups of prisoners. The results were as follows:

TABLE XVIII.

Type of rice.	No. of men.	Cases of beri-beri.
Group 1. White polished rice and extract of rice polishings (bran).	8	2
Groups 2 and 4. White polished rice.	17	13
Group 3. Red rice, i.e., whole unmilled rice. . .	7	1 (very slight)

This experiment suggests that when the diet consists mainly of cereal food, beri-beri can generally be prevented if a whole unmilled cereal is employed, but that there is not a great margin of safety. It will be noticed that the other subsidiary articles of diet were poor in content of antiberi-beri vitamin.

In conflict with the smoothness of the foregoing experience, McCarrison [1924] points out that a century ago, long before the introduction of machine milling of rice, beri-beri was endemic in India, as it still is to-day, in the north-east coast division of the Madras Presidency (Northern Circars). He also shows that in India at the present time the incidence of beri-beri does not exactly correspond to the type of milling in vogue. He believes that the supplemental foods in a diet are most important in determining whether beri-beri will develop or not, whatever may be the kind of rice consumed. It is probable that even a diet of whole untouched rice does not provide enough vitamin B_1 for a man, though it may suffice for a bird. If this be true, it is obvious that beri-beri may occur where the diet consists almost entirely of whole rice, unsupplemented, and may not occur where the diet consists largely of highly polished rice, well supplemented with other foods, rich in vitamin B_1. This argument does not, however, upset the thesis that, since polished rice is poorer in vitamin B_1 than is whole rice, given the same but inadequate supplements, beri-beri is more likely to occur on the diet containing polished rice than on that containing whole rice. It does, however, rather shake the belief that to abolish milling would abolish beri-beri.

Experiments on pigeons [McCarrison, 1924] showed that a series of Indian rices ranged themselves in order of value for 'vitamin B' according to the accepted ideas. Raw milled unpolished rice was highest, then parboiled milled unpolished rice, and parboiled milled highly polished rice, and finally, very much lower, raw milled polished rice. In this system of grading the term 'milled' is used to include the whole process of husking and removing the germ and pericarp.

Any washing of the rice was found to deteriorate its value in vitamin B_1. The vitamin is water-soluble and evidently diffuses easily out of the cells, when they are plunged in water, particularly when the cells have first been killed by parboiling.

The process of parboiling in the preparation of the rice affects the vitamin content in an interesting manner in two directly opposite ways. After parboiling, the whole grain may not be as rich in vitamin B_1 as before, since some of the vitamin may have diffused from the outermost layers of the grain into the surrounding water. Rice which has been parboiled and subsequently milled, compared with the same sample of grain submitted to the same degree of milling without first parboiling, is however, found to be greatly superior in antineuritic value [Aykroyd, 1932]. Presumably therefore during the process some of the vitamin from the peripheral layers of the grain diffuses inwards, into the endosperm. When parboiled and polished rice is soaked in water the vitamin diffuses out again and can be recovered from the surrounding water [Aykroyd, 1932].

In British Guiana milled parboiled rice is used, and to this fact the absence of beri-beri is attributed.

Outbreaks of beri-beri among wheat-eating populations are not common. The peoples who are accustomed to consume white wheaten bread belong to the more highly civilized and richer countries, where the diet is varied and a sufficiency of the antiberi-beri vitamin B_1 is obtained from other constituents. There are, however, a few instructive instances among which the following four cases may be mentioned.

(1) In Newfoundland and Labrador the population subsists largely on bread during the winter and spring. Formerly, when the bread was baked from ' brown ' flour, beri-beri was unknown. At the present time, with the advance of civilization, the bread is made from pure white wheaten flour, and beri-beri is frequent. Little [1912] relates the following interesting occurrence. In 1910 a ship ran ashore laden with a cargo of wholemeal wheaten flour, and, in order to lighten her, a considerable portion of her load was removed and was subsequently consumed by the population in the adjacent districts. The result was that no case of beri-beri was reported in that region for a period of one year following this event.

The conditions in Labrador and Newfoundland have been reinvestigated by Aykroyd [1930, 2]. Beri-beri still occurs and a certain number of the cases show a minor degree of oedema. In winter, in the absence of meat and fresh vegetables, the diet tends to resolve itself into one of white bread and tea. The peak of incidence of the disease comes in May. Aykroyd gives an interesting analysis of the winter stores of those families in which beri-beri occurred, and of a similar set of families, a little better off, in which the disease did not occur. Both consumed an equal amount per head of white wheaten flour, but the non-beri-beri families had in addition more meat, more potatoes, and other vegetables, and on the average twice as much peas and beans added to the diet. In a few cases ignorance seemed to be the cause of the restricted diet, but in most it was sheer poverty.

(2) Beri-beri was a rare disease on Norwegian ships before the year 1894. In that year an alteration was made in the sailors' diet, in response to a popular agitation to ameliorate the hard conditions of their life at sea. The sailors had previously lived on biscuit baked from rye flour (in the milling of which there is no separation of the germ); after this date masters of ships were compelled to supply bread baked from white wheaten flour or from a mixture of wheat and rye flour, and beri-beri became a frequent disease in the Norwegian mercantile marine [Holst, 1911–12].

There is an amusing story of one old sea captain who disapproved of the new-fangled reforms and insisted upon a supply of rye flour being taken on board for his own personal consumption. He was rewarded for his independence with the satisfaction of effecting cures among his men, who, when stricken with beri-beri, were supplied with biscuit from the captain's private supplies. As, however, these gradually showed signs of depletion, he was finally compelled to husband them in order to preserve his own health.

(3) The deficiency in white wheaten bread is under ordinary conditions made good by the varied diet enjoyed by Europeans. If, however, the 'mixed' diet is derived from canned and preserved foods the case is otherwise, and beri-beri may be expected to appear. This was no doubt the cause of the beri-beri which was reported among our troops in the late war in the Dardanelles and in Mesopotamia [Wilcox, 1916, 1, 2]. In the latter campaign it is illuminating to note that the disease was confined to the British troops and was not reported among the Indian soldiers. This immunity was to be expected, for in addition to atta, a coarsely ground whole wheat flour, the native soldier received a generous daily ration of dhal or dry pulses of various kinds, which are rich in antiberi-beri vitamin (see Table XI, p. 162).

(4) The difference between the types of cereal ration issued respectively to the British and Indian troops was the basis of an unconscious 'experiment', which took place during the siege of Kut-el-Amara (Dec. 1915–April 1916). In his account of the medical arrangements during the siege, Hehir [1917] writes: 'In an early stage of the siege, a recrudescence of beri-beri among British troops gave rise to some apprehension, but it then disappeared whilst in Indian troops and followers during the latter half of the siege scurvy caused anxiety.'

At another place in this diary we learn that the British troops were receiving white wheaten flour until Feb. 5, 1916, after which date they were compelled to take part of their flour ration in the form either of barley flour or of atta. It is very significant that beri-beri should have occurred while the British troops were enjoying white wheaten bread and should have cleared up when they were compelled to share the coarsely milled, germ-containing flour of their Indian comrades. The incidence of scurvy during this siege showed an entirely opposite distribution; the British soldiers were protected by the large ration of meat, including horse flesh, which they consumed, while the Indian soldiers, largely vegetarian in habit, suffered terribly from this disease (see also below, p. 249).

The lesson to be learned from the above experience is that, for the prevention of beri-beri, it is important that the germ and bran of wheat should be included in the manufacture of bread or biscuit for any population living on a restricted diet. This is specially desirable in the case of soldiers on active service where the rest of the rations may consist largely of canned foods, which in many cases may be regarded as devoid of the less heat-stable vitamins (B_1 and C), owing to conditions under which they have been sterilized and preserved. Many people, however, will not eat brown bread when white bread is available, but in the case of soldiers such a regulation could be enforced.

Non-cereal Foods in Relation to Beri-beri.

In this connexion attention may be drawn to two articles of diet, especially rich in the vitamin B_1, and also specially suited to the needs of armies on active service, viz. yeast extract and preserved eggs.

Yeast is one of the most valuable sources of the antineuritic factor, and, in the form of an extract, gives the savoury taste to many of the soup cubes at present on the market. One commercial extract (marmite) has been found on examination to retain a considerable part of the original value of the yeast from which it has been prepared (see Table XI, p. 162). The addition of such an item to the soldier's ration affords a useful and agreeable method of increasing the supply of antiberi-beri vitamin in his diet, but no exact data are available as to the amount required for a man.

A very interesting case in which yeast functioned as the one supplementary food which stood between a community and beri-beri is afforded by the experience of the inhabitants of the island of Nauru in the Pacific Ocean [Bray, 1928–29]. The diet did not contain rice as a staple, but consisted originally of fish and coco-nut products, including a fermented drink, 'toddy', made from the flower spathe of the coco-nut palm. The island has been governed since the Peace, under mandate, by the Commonwealth of Australia, and the making of toddy was prohibited. To make up for its loss, the natives tended to use more of the imported foods, refined sugar, white flour, and canned meats. The infantile mortality was extremely high and one of the more important factors contributing to it was finally diagnosed as infantile beri-beri, which had become prevalent since the prohibition of toddy-drinking. Toddy yeast was actually used to cure the babies. Such an example suggests the question how far other native races may depend on their home-brewed fermented drinks for protection against beri-beri and pellagra as well as scurvy (p. 258).

Dried eggs. Dried eggs have been found experimentally to retain the valuable antiberi-beri properties of the fresh article. They are probably much too expensive an article to be included in the ordinary soldier's ration, but there can be no question of their suitability for inclusion in hospital stores. A large proportion of the medical casualties on foreign service is due to intestinal diseases, and both during the acute stage and the subsequent convalescence the diet is largely restricted to bread, condensed or canned milk, and invalid foods, all of which may be regarded as either free from vitamin B_1 or very poor in it. It was noted by Willcox [1916, 1] that among twenty-six cases of beri-beri diagnosed in the autumn of 1915, eighteen had previously suffered from diseases of the digestive and alimentary system. It is not improbable that the restricted diet necessitated by these disorders may have been the predisposing cause of the beri-beri which occurred subsequently. The addition of eggs would have materially enriched these invalid diets in respect of antiberi-beri properties, and in the form of dried eggs the addition could be made with the greatest convenience.

Before leaving this subject it may prove useful to give as an illustration the details of certain diets which have been found to occasion beri-beri, and to compare them with certain others, which under similar circumstances of climate, locality, &c., were found to be satisfactory.[1]

TABLE XIX.

Showing relative amounts of foodstuffs deficient and rich respectively in antineuritic vitamin present in satisfactory diets and in those found to occasion beri-beri; the amounts are expressed as oz. per week.

Foodstuff.	Nos. expressing approximate value in preventing beri-beri. Wheat germ = 100.	Diet A. (Beri-beri producing) A 1	A 2	Diet B (Satisfactory).	Diet C (Satisfactory.)
Foods deficient in vitamin B_1					
Rice	. . .	28		21	28
Bread (white flour) . . .	. . .	224	224	112	168
Jam	. . .	.	.	7	7
Sugar	. . .	14	14	7	
Cheese	. . .	14	14	14	
Dry fruit	. . .	.	.	14	
Salt fish	. . .	.	.	20	
Margarine or butter or oil .	. . .	14	14	7	3.5
X = Total no. of oz. weekly of foods deficient in antiberi-beri factor	. . .	294	266	202	206
Foods richer in vitamin B_1					
Oatmeal	10	.	.	14	14
Fresh meat or bacon . . .	10	42	42	30	42
Peas, beans, lentils . . .	50		28	14	21
Potatoes (or fresh vegetables)	5	14	14	42	28
V = Total no. of oz. weekly of foods containing antiberi-beri factor	. . .	56	84	100	105
Ratio V/X	. . .	0.2	0.3	0.5	0.5

Diets A 1 and A 2, given in Table XIX, were issued during the late European War to a camp in a Mediterranean area in which beri-beri occurred. Although in many ways similar these diets differed greatly as regards the protection afforded against beri-beri. Both, however, were inferior to Diets B and C, which were issued to similar neighbouring communities, in which no beri-beri was

---

[1] Permission to publish the details of this investigation was originally granted by Major L. Braddon, R.A.M.C., and the Director-General of the Army Medical Service.

reported.   After the diagnosis of beri-beri had been substantiated for certain men receiving Diets A 1 and A 2, a careful search among the healthy men of the same community revealed a widespread abnormality in knee-jerks and other nervous reflexes.   This is an important observation, as it shows definitely that the normal health may be undermined by a deficiency in diet before any symptoms are apparent to the casual observer or to the individual himself.

In Table XIX an arrangement is adopted by which foodstuffs deficient in the antiberi-beri factor are collected in one group and those more valuable in this respect in a second.   The points to be noticed are, firstly, the large preponderance of cereal food (see p. 131) in the diets A 1 (252 oz. weekly) and A 2 (224 oz.) compared with B (133 oz.) and C (196 oz.) ;   and, secondly, the smaller proportion of vitamin-containing foodstuffs.   A 1, 56 oz. weekly ; A 2, 84 oz. ; B, 100 oz. ; C, 105 oz.

If the ratio—no. of oz. vitamin-containing food / no. of oz. vitamin-deficient food—be calculated for the four diets, we get a series of values rising from 0·2 for diet A1 to 0·5 for diets B and C.   It would seem that this ratio might provide a useful indication of the value of a diet for the prevention of beri-beri.

In an ordinary mixed diet the necessary amount of vitamin B_1 is supplied chiefly in the eggs, vegetables, fruit, milk, and meat consumed, although of these only eggs and green-leaf vegetables can be considered as *rich* sources of the vitamin.

Elaborate preventive experiments on pigeons have been carried out by Jansen in Batavia [1923] with a number of foodstuffs, many of them indigenous.   The express object was to ascertain which of them were suitable to supply the antineuritic vitamin B_1 to a diet of polished rice, a matter of great importance in the East.   Such were found to be : eggs, meat, bran, and in general the germ and pericarp of cereals, katjang-idjo (*Phaseolus radiatus*) pea-nuts and their press cake, peté beans (*Parkia roxburghii* Don), kanari kernels (*Canarium commune* L.), and djawa nut (*Pennisetum macrochaeton* Jacq.).   All these can be safely used with twice their dry weight of polished rice.   The following on the other hand should be substituted for polished rice or taken with not more than an equal weight of it : maize, unmilled cereals, milk, boiled potatoes, boiled sweet potatoes, soy beans, tempe kedele (a preparation from soy beans).   The remaining foodstuffs examined did not afford protection : white bread, maize meal, banana, coco-nut press cake, cassava root (gaplek) (*Manihot utilissima* Pohl.), or cassava meal, sago, dried shrimps, telor terubuk (salted dried roe of the Indian shad (*Clupea* (*Alosa*) *macrura* Blkr.), dried melindjo (fruits of *Gnetum gnemon* L.), dried fish, terassi (decayed shrimps, used as a flavouring for rice), tao-tjo (a preparation from soy beans), durian (fruit of *Durio zebethinus* Murr.), spinach (dried), French beans (dried), kangkong leaves dried (*Ipomoea aquatica*), nangka fruits (*Artocarpus integrifolia* L.), used as an ingredient of a sauce for rice dishes, kemiri nuts (*Aleurites triloba*, Forsk).

The effects of exposure to heat and of cooking on vitamin B_1 are fully described on p. 143.

Period of Development of Beri-beri.

The period of development of beri-beri has been determined with some care by Fraser and Stanton [1909] who found that the disease occurred among Japanese coolies after a period of 80–90 days upon a diet consisting mainly of polished rice. In Strong and Crowell's experiments (p. 244) the members of the groups receiving whole polished rice showed symptoms of beri-beri after 61–75 days.

Intestinal Stasis.

It has been claimed that a relatively deficient supply of the vitamin B complex is a common cause of constipation or intestinal stasis, and that this latter condition is in turn responsible for many chronic diseases and disabilities. Such claims are usually based on the contention that in experimental animals deprived of vitamin B the food progresses through the alimentary tract more slowly than in those receiving a complete diet. There is, however, evidence that any observed delay in the progress of food along the intestine is not caused simply by vitamin B deficiency. The severer grades of this deficiency may be associated with an atonic condition of the stomach which possibly explains the lack of appetite almost invariably accompanying vitamin B deficiency. No convincing clinical evidence is available to show that the vitamin B complex determines the normal functioning of the human bowel, and until such is forthcoming it is unnecessary to assume that vitamin B deficiency is concerned in the production of the constipation so commonly met with among Western peoples.

Vitamin B₁ in the Diet of Infants.

A good deal of discussion has taken place concerning the value of extra supplies of vitamin B_1 to infants who are being fed either at the breast or on cow's milk. Hoobler [1928] has claimed that a characteristic group of symptoms can be recognized in American infants as the result of a deficient supply of vitamin B_1. These include anorexia, loss of weight, fretfulness, pallor, and stiffness of the limbs and neck. The symptoms are said to respond rapidly to the administration of a rich source of vitamin B_1. Bloxsom [1929] found that a suspension of dried yeast caused an increased rate of growth, both in normal and under-nourished infants. It seems possible that a deficiency of this factor may be associated with at least minor nutritional disturbances in temperate climates where infantile beri-beri is unknown, and in view of the ease with which such a deficiency may be remedied it seems worth while bearing it in mind as a possible cause of poor development in infancy.

VITAMIN B₂ (ANTIDERMATITIS).

Diet in Relation to Pellagra.

Since the publication of the former Monograph [Med. Res. Coun. 1924] pellagra has been definitely recognized as a deficiency disease, but its exact aetiology and relation to the consumption of maize as a staple are still not understood. These points are discussed elsewhere (see Chapter VII), and it suffices here, as in dealing with beri-

beri, to indicate the type of diet on which the disease has been
known to develop and those foodstuffs which have been found
efficacious in its cure and prevention.

The most careful dietary investigations on pellagra have been
made in Egypt by W. H. Wilson and in the United States by
Goldberger and his colleagues. Wilson as already explained (p. 179)
believes that the disease is caused by a dietary in which the ' biological value' of the total protein, calculated on Thomas's figures
[1921], falls below a certain figure. He analysed many diets from
this point of view and showed how they fell into line with his hypothesis. The diet on which any deficiency disease is liable to occur
is, however, generally a poor one and, because it is possible to
demonstrate low biological value of the protein as a common
factor, it does not necessarily follow that this is the causative
factor. From Wilson's analysis of diets, it is difficult to attach a
special antipellagrous value to any particular article, but experience
has shown that meat, milk, and eggs, whose proteins all have a
biological value of a high order, are valuable both protectively
and curatively. Later [1929] Wilson slightly modified his view to
include a vitamin factor in the aetiology of pellagra. He still considers, however, that, for persons living on the border-line of
sufficiency in respect of their intake of that vitamin, the value of
the protein intake would be the determining factor in the
incidence of pellagra.

Goldberger and his colleagues attribute pellagra to a deficiency
of a dietary factor contained in the yeast vitamin complex. In the
United States the diet on which pellagra is liable to occur in the
mill villages is a very restricted one, owing to poverty and to
the small amount of ground available for cultivation, either as
vegetable gardens or farms. When, for any cause, the economic
conditions deteriorate, as for instance in the great Mississippi floods
of 1927, the incidence of pellagra rises [Goldberger and Sydenstricker, 1927]. In that area the diet is said to consist of the
three 'M's'—meat, meal, and molasses; the meat is salt pork,
chiefly fat with very little lean, and the meal is maize meal.
According to the people's means, this dietary is supplemented with
vegetables and butter, poultry, and eggs, but only to a very small
extent. A typical dietary is described as consisting of corn (maize)
meal (corn bread, boiled hominy or mush), wheat flour (biscuit),
white rice, dried beans, white meat (salt pork), cane molasses, and
greens. It is believed that this diet will lead to the development
of pellagra within three to six or eight months in fully 40-50 per
cent. of those partaking of it, the time depending on the nutritional
status of the individual when the diet is begun. When it is
adequately supplemented with pellagra-preventing foods, such as
milk, lean meat and vegetables, pellagra does not develop. With
such a basic diet as is described above there would be needed daily
for full prevention in the adult, of lean beef about (not over) one
half pound, or of dried cowpeas fully one half pound, or of butter
milk about one quart, or of canned tomatoes about one quart, or of
dried pure yeast about one oz. [Goldberger and Sydenstricker,
1927]. Owing to its cheapness and usefulness canned salmon was

specially tested [Goldberger and Wheeler, 1929], and it was found that the protective amount, on the same basis of estimation, was 6 oz. daily or possibly less. Amounts as large as 1 lb. daily of cooked carrots or rutabaga (swede turnips) were found insufficient [Goldberger and Wheeler, 1927, 1].

In selecting the food or foods to be used in treating the sick, Goldberger and Sydenstricker [1927] summarize thus: 'The physician must of necessity choose such as will most satisfactorily fit the tastes and digestive capacity of the patient. Such considerations and actual experience indicate that milk, fresh meat, eggs, and dried yeast are the foods of first choice.' Thus it is seen that Goldberger and his colleagues arrive at the same conclusion as Wilson with regard to the most suitable curative substances, except as regards the addition of dried yeast to the list. Yeast was found valuable in the cure of pellagra in the Ukraine by Tcherkes (see p. 181).

That a deficiency of vitamin A plays a part in the aetiology of pellagra is maintained by Leitch [1930] who considers cod-liver oil as important as yeast for treating the disease. He has found marked improvement to follow the subcutaneous injection of vitamin A concentrates, and draws attention to a disease somewhat resembling pellagra which occurs in Sierra Leone and which was attributed by E. J. Wright [1926] to a combined A and B avitaminosis. The main features of this disease are ulcerative lesions of the skin and mucous membranes, especially at muco-cutaneous junctions, and nervous symptoms including paraesthesia, paresis, deafness, and impairment of vision. It is stated that the disease may be cured by adding cod-liver oil and yeast to the diet. In this connexion it may be mentioned that subacute combined degeneration of the spinal cord in dogs, a condition analogous to that found in human pellagra, has been shown to be associated with vitamin A deficiency (p. 31).

Although the aetiology of pellagra is not yet fully understood, it is apparent from the sketch here given that sufficient information has accumulated to make the extinction of pellagra a problem of finance rather than of exact knowledge.

Anaemia.

A severe type of macrocytic anaemia prevalent in the tropics, especially among pregnant women, with a blood picture resembling that of ordinary pernicious anaemia, has been studied by Wills [1931]. This investigator observed dramatic improvement and cure when such cases were treated with a yeast extract (marmite) rich in vitamins B_1 and B_2; the doses given were large, viz. 1 drachm (4 g.) 2–4 times a day. The condition of the patients was often complicated with oedema which also yielded rapidly to the above treatment. Similar cures were obtained with therapeutic water-soluble preparations of liver extract. Some observers have found such liver extracts tested on rats to be even richer than yeast in vitamin B_2, while relatively poor in vitamin B_1 [Guha, 1931, 2; Chick, unpublished results, quoted by Wills, 1931], a result, doubtless, due to the fact that at one stage in preparation the portion soluble in strong alcohol is removed [Cohn *et al.*, 1927]. Gilroy [1931], on the other hand, using rather larger doses, found both B-vitamins present in 9 out of 11 specimens of liver extract.

Further observations are needed to decide which constituent or constituents of the B-vitamin complex were acting as curative agent in the cures with yeast extract by Wills described above. The fact that none of the cases showed symptoms resembling beri-beri supports the suggestion that a deficiency of vitamin B_2 may be a factor in the aetiology of this form of anaemia. This suggestion is the more likely seeing that most Indian diets are markedly deficient in foodstuffs rich in animal proteins, which are also the richest sources in nature of vitamin B_2.

Yeast and other sources of B-vitamins have been found without therapeutic value in ordinary pernicious anaemia [Cohn *et al.*, 1928; Davidson, 1931].

Vitamin C.

Scurvy has a longer clear history than the other deficiency diseases, and long before the age of vitamins it was realized that scurvy was caused by the lack of something in the diet, something elusive and incorporeal, connected with the property of freshness which disappeared from food which had once possessed it, as it became stale. It was well known that the disease could be cured by introducing fresh food into the diet.

An examination of the literature shows that before any experimental work had been done with guinea-pigs to evaluate foodstuffs for vitamin C, ordinary human experience had attached to many items a relative set of values, which subsequent experiment only confirmed. In point of fact a table of relative values, constructed upon the sifted evidence of the past, would contain the principal foodstuffs, ranged in an order not differing markedly from that constructed upon the results of experimental work as set out in Table XIII (p. 205) and described on pp. 209–212.

It is therefore useful to consider the descriptions of some notable outbreaks of scurvy under the heading of the foodstuffs which were chiefly concerned.

Fruit. The great value of fresh vegetables and fruit in the prevention and cure of human scurvy has so often been emphasized that its reiteration is a commonplace. This experience is confirmed by the figures given for the relative antiscorbutic values of foodstuffs in Table XIII. The juice of fresh citrous fruits has for centuries been regarded as antiscorbutic material *par excellence*. The 'experiment' made by Dr. Lind [1757] in 1747, quoted above, p. 187, is one of the most carefully recorded instances, but others are to be found in abundance.

Curran [1847] mentions two 'hopeless' scurvy patients who received ½ oz. lemon juice with sugar and water thrice daily, and relates that the patients sat up and took food with cheerfulness in the course of two days. He also records that in the case of a gentleman affected with scurvy of a very severe description, the eating of a single rhubarb tart produced a most decided amelioration, equally sensible to the patient and his friends'.

Lind [1757] recounts the tragic history of four ships which sailed from England to Bombay in April 1600, carrying 480 men on board, including merchants and other officials, in order to establish the East India Company. The Commodore upon his own ship had arranged for a regular issue of lemon juice, three table-spoonsful daily, to all hands, and four months later, when the flotilla reached the Cape, his men were all in good health. On the other three ships, however, the seamen were so severely attacked by scurvy that the passengers had to work as common seamen. In all, 105 men died from scurvy during the voyage, and when Bombay was finally reached after a voyage of four months, the entire work of unloading had to be performed by the crew of the Commodore's ship.

Budd [1840] relates how the voyage of the *Suffolk* to Madras in 1794, which occupied nearly six months, during which no land was touched, was accomplished with almost entire freedom from scurvy. A regular ration of 2/3 oz. lemon juice was served out daily.[1] Scorbutic symptoms were noticed in a few men, but these disappeared on increasing the lemon-juice ration. Perhaps the most impressive instance of all is to be found in the history of the Navy itself, between the latter part of the eighteenth century, when thousands of cases of scurvy were reported annually, and the early years of the nineteenth century when, after the regular issue of lemon juice had been made compulsory in 1804, scurvy became a comparatively rare disease in the Navy.

Lime juice. The results of experimental work recorded in Table XIII (p. 205) showing the inferiority of the juice of West Indian limes (*Citrus medica*, var. *acida*), both in the fresh and preserved state, compared with that of lemons (*Citrus medica*, var. *Limonum*), are difficult to reconcile with the popular esteem in which the former has generally been held as a preventive of scurvy. It is not, however, generally known that when ' lime juice ' earned its laurels in the field of medicine, the term was used to signify the juice of lemons from the Mediterranean. Such was the case until the middle of the nineteenth century, when owing to political reasons and to favourable reports upon the acidity of the product, in which quality the antiscorbutic virtue was held to reside, the supply of West Indian lime juice was gradually substituted. By the date 1870 very little, if any, lemon juice was issued officially.

This point has been investigated from an historical standpoint by A. Henderson Smith [1918, 1919], and the results of her inquiry afford an important confirmation of the experimental findings given above. She was unable to find any recorded instances in which scurvy had been prevented or cured by preserved lime juice, in absence of other antiscorbutic agents. On the contrary, a careful comparison of certain Arctic expeditions in the fifties of last century equipped with *lemon* juice, with those of later date supplied with preserved *lime* juice demonstrated the inferiority of the latter. The most impressive case quoted is that of the Relief Expeditions sent in search of Sir John Franklin, 1847–59, where

---

[1] In 1840 the navy ration was 1 oz. lemon juice daily with $1\frac{1}{2}$ oz. sugar, served after two weeks at sea [Budd, 1840].

those ships which were supplied with lemon juice of good quality
enjoyed remarkable immunity from scurvy for long periods of
time. One instance, that of the *Investigator* under Captain
McClure, was specially noteworthy, for, in this case, there was no
scurvy for twenty-seven months after leaving England, notwithstanding great privations. The event was otherwise in the *Alert*
and the *Discovery*, two ships which left England in 1875 under
Captain Nares, in an attempt to find the North Pole. These ships
were equipped with all the improvements that the advance of
twenty years had discovered and plentifully supplied with lime
juice of the best quality. Notwithstanding these advantages
serious scurvy broke out at the end of the first winter spent in the
Arctic regions. A commission of inquiry was held by the Admiralty
on the return of these ships in 1876, but no satisfactory cause was
found to explain the unexpected disaster. The commission took
no notice of the fact that the 'lime juice' provided in 1875 was
the juice of the West Indian lime, whereas in the fifties it had
been the juice of the Mediterranean lemon, but there is little doubt
that in this difference lies the explanation of the different experience in the two expeditions.

Following this period a general distrust of 'lime juice' as a
preventive of scurvy may be traced in the writings of those who
had given careful attention to the history of later Arctic discovery,
and the theory previously alluded to (p. 186) that scurvy is due
to chronic ptomaine poisoning, by tainted and salted meat, found
ready acceptance. For example, the experience of the Jackson-
Harmsworth Expedition to Franz Josef Land in 1894–97 was
accepted as being in accord with this theory [Jackson and Harley,
1900, 1, 2] on the basis of the following facts.

The land sledging party was for three years without any lime juice
and without any scurvy, but large quantities of fresh bear meat were
consumed. The ship party, on the *Windward*, took their daily 1 oz. of
lime juice with regularity, and were well supplied with canned and
salted meat, but after one winter the whole crew developed scurvy
and there were three deaths. There is no record that the meat was
tainted or putrid when consumed, but it was afterwards assumed that
it must have been so. In earlier days 'lime juice' had for so long
been regarded as the equivalent in diet of fresh vegetables and
fruit, that the supporters of the 'tainted' meat theory maintained
further that fresh vegetables also were not concerned in the
prevention or cure of scurvy, but that the disease was connected
only with the quality of the meat eaten.

Polar expeditions to-day are as liable to scurvy as ever unless
proper precautions are taken. The germination of peas or beans
might be resorted to on the ship, but on sledging parties a concentrate of lemon juice should be regarded as indispensable. Zilva
(personal communication) has prepared concentrated lemon juice
for such expeditions in the following manner. The lemon juice
was concentrated in a copper vessel, tinned on the inside, heated by
a steam coil at a pressure of 23–26 in. and a temperature of 140° F.
A batch of about 60 litres was thus reduced to about one-third of
its volume in three-quarters of an hour. At the end of this time

the concentrated juice was quickly cooled by means of an internal cooling coil. Sterilized bottles of about one litre capacity were filled with carbon dioxide and the concentrate was fed into them through a flamed nozzle from the bottom of the vat. The bottles were sealed with paraffin. It is desirable to test this concentrate for its antiscorbutic potency before issuing it, as in some instances this was found to be damaged by the manipulation. When undamaged, the potency was retained for four years when the juice was kept at $0°$ C. In the course of preparation, the essential oil is lost, but it can be replaced at the time of bottling, and the flavour restored. The daily dose recommended per man is an amount of the concentrate equivalent to 70 c.c. of the original juice. This may be more than is necessary, but the whole method of preparation is planned to give a margin of safety.

Lemon juice concentrated about $4\frac{1}{2}$ times by the above method was used by the members of the British Arctic Air Route Expedition to Greenland in 1930–31 led by H. G. Watkins. The antiscorbutic potency of this preparation was particularly well demonstrated in the case of one member, Augustine Courtauld (age 26, weight about 10 stone). From July 20 to October 26, 1930, Courtauld's main source of vitamin C was seal and bird meat. On the latter date he set out from the base to the Central Station where he remained until May 5, 1931. Apart from a little strawberry jam, marmalade, a handful of raisins, prunes and dates, and two-fifths of a frozen ptarmigan, all consumed before December 6, Courtauld existed until May 5, 1931, on a dietetically well-balanced, but vitamin C-free, sledging ration, consisting of the following:

Pemmican	4·0 oz.
Margarine	4·0 oz.
Plasmon oats	1·4 oz.
Sugar	2·3 oz.
Chocolate	1·7 oz.
Plasmon powder	1·1 oz.
Pea flour	1·1 oz.
Cocoa	0·6 oz.

and occasionally a teaspoonful of condensed milk

Total 16·2 oz. = about 2,500 calories.

He also took daily one dessertspoonful of the concentrated lemon juice, one spoonful of cod-liver oil (every second day), about one gram of a salt mixture and about one gram of dried yeast. He gradually reduced his sledging ration to 9 oz. per day. From March 22 to May 5 he was snowed up in his hut, and during the last fortnight was without light or heat. He felt no craving for any particular article of food. He watched carefully for symptoms of scurvy, but none supervened and he felt normal in every way. His teeth and gums remained in good condition and he could throughout bite hard uncooked food without discomfort. He was able, when relieved, to ski about one mile unaided to the relief camp. Samples of the same batch of concentrated lemon juice tested by Zilva in London in February 1931 were found to have lost little of their antiscorbutic potency after a year's storage at $0°–1°$ C.

Vegetables. Among the vegetables investigated experimentally the cabbage was found to be pre-eminent, and, even after cooking, the minimum preventive ration for guinea-pigs remained small in comparison with root and other vegetables.

The following incident, related to Holst and Frölich [1912] by a political refugee from Russia, bears testimony to the value of cabbage for the prevention of human scurvy, even when taken in the form of soup, after prolonged stewing. In a Russian prison, in which the narrator had been confined with 1,400 other prisoners, the diet consisted of tea, coarse bread, and cabbage soup. The preparation of the soup was so unclean that twenty of the inmates, including himself, who were of gentle birth and upbringing, could not endure to take it. After about six months these twenty prisoners showed symptoms of scurvy, while no case occurred among those who had consumed the soup regularly.

Among herbs and ' cresses' esteemed in the past for antiscorbutic virtues it is interesting to note that those belonging to the natural order Cruciferae occupied a high place. This natural order includes also the cabbage and the swede, which were found to be the most valuable of the vegetables investigated experimentally. 'Scurvy grass' (*Cochlearia officinalis*), a small plant frequently found growing near the sea-shore, figures largely in old records of scurvy cures among mariners. Thus Bachstrom in 1734 tells the following story :

' A sailor in the Greenland ships was so over-run and disabled with scurvy, that his companions put him into a boat, and sent him on shore, leaving him there to perish without the least expectation of recovery. The poor wretch had quite lost the use of his limbs; he could only crawl about the ground. This he found covered with a plant which he, continually grazing like a beast of the field, plucked up with his teeth. In a short time he was by this means perfectly recovered, and, upon his returning home, it was found to be the herb "scurvy grass".' (Rendering given by Lind [1757, p. 395].)

Potatoes. Among roots and tubers the potato easily takes the first place in practical importance, not so much because of its intrinsic value, but because, owing to its abundance, cheapness, and general acceptability, large quantities are regularly consumed. Its consumption in fact exceeds that of all other vegetables combined [Hess, 1920].

Although a classic remedy for scurvy, the potato has only a comparatively low antiscorbutic power compared weight for weight with some other vegetables [Chick and Rhodes, 1918; Givens and Cohen, 1918; Givens and McClugage, 1920; Scheunert 1930]. Nevertheless, there is no doubt that in northern climates the potato is of the utmost value in preventing scurvy during the winter and spring, epidemics of scurvy having repeatedly followed failure of the potato harvest, e.g., in Ireland in 1847 and in Norway in 1914. The outbreaks of scurvy reported in Glasgow [1917], Manchester [Report 1917], and Newcastle [Harlan, 1917] in the spring of 1917 are doubtless to be attributed to the great scarcity of potatoes at that period.

Onions take a position between the more and the less potent vegetables. They possess a special importance, however, owing to the ease with which they can be transported, and they are much appreciated, whether raw or cooked, by reason of their flavour. For these reasons they should always be included in rations for soldiers, sailors, or other communities of people at the end of long lines of communication cut off from fresh supplies.

Germinated pulses and cereals. There is so far little direct evidence of the antiscorbutic value of germinated pulses in human diets. The custom of eating germinated cereals and pulses obtains in some parts of China and in the Malay States and the Dutch Indies, where germinated beans, 'towgay', are a common article of native diets. There is, however, no evidence that the antiscorbutic value of these foods has been recognized.

One instance, however, in which germinated beans were found to be of great value for the cure of scurvy is recorded by Wiltshire [1918], and yields complete confirmation of the experimental work described on p. 189. This observer succeeded in curing 27 cases of mild scurvy among Serbian soldiers (selected at random from a total of 57) by the sole measure of including in their daily dietary 4 oz. (dry wt.) of germinated haricot beans. Although this ration was not very acceptable the progress made was, if anything, better than that of the remaining 30 patients who received instead a daily ration of 4 oz. fresh lemon juice. The beans were consumed after boiling for ten minutes only. Germinated peas were also found to be a satisfactory curative agent for scurvy by Stevenson in Archangel [1920].

The use of germinated pulses as an article of diet certainly deserves a prolonged trial in circumstances in which fresh food is scarce or unobtainable. Dry peas, beans, or lentils contain less than 15 per cent. of moisture, are admirably adapted for transport, and can be germinated on the spot if and when required. Pulses of various sorts, as 'dhall', form a staple article of the native Indian diet, and had this knowledge of their value after germination been applied in Mesopotamia in 1915 it is possible that the terrible wastage from scurvy in that campaign [Mesopotamia Commission Report, 1917] might have been prevented (see p. 262).

Beer and malt. Captain Cook was a great believer in the antiscorbutic virtues of a fresh infusion of malt (sweet-wort). His second voyage, 1772-75, was accomplished with an amazing record of good health among his crew, there being only four deaths during the period, of which one only was from sickness. He 'took a large quantity of "malt", of which was made sweet-wort; to such of the men as showed the least symptoms of scurvy this was given, from one to two or three pints a day each man, or in such proportion as the surgeon found necessary. This was, without doubt, one of the best antiscorbutic sea medicines then discovered, when used in time' [Captain Cook, p. 227]. According to Sir John Pringle, writing in 1776, quas, 'a small brisk acidulous liquor,' made from ground salt and rye meal, was regularly served out in Russian prisons as an antiscorbutic [1776].

Certain fermented liquors made from other germinated seeds have also been held in high esteem for the prevention of scurvy. Kafir beer, 'leting' or 'joala', is an instance of this. It is the product of rapid fermentation of partly germinated Kafir corn (*Sorghum vulgare*) and maize, and is consumed quickly after preparation. The Kafirs are in the habit of taking large quantities when living in their own kraals in South Africa, and it is believed to be a valuable antiscorbutic. It has been the custom of the mining companies on the Rand to arrange for the brewing of this beer in the compounds of the native labourers, and large quantities are consumed. Outbreaks of scurvy were reported by Dyke (1918) among companies of Kafir labourers in France in cases where this 'joala' was replaced by a second type of beer, 'mahew', a fermented drink also made from millet and maize, but in the preparation of which *the grain is not previously germinated.*

Kafir beer has been examined by Delf [1921] who found, using monkeys as experimental animals, that fresh Kafir beer contains about as much vitamin C as fresh English dairy milk. A monkey on an average daily ration of 85 c.c. was attacked with scurvy on the 114th day, and behaved very much as a monkey in a previous experiment in England with a ration of 125 c.c. fresh milk. The individual idiosyncrasies of monkeys are, however, so great that this conclusion can only be regarded as provisional. This beer was made from Kafir corn malt and maize meal and was fermented only for a very short time. A considerable quantity (30 lb.) of the malt was added per barrel of 45 gallons just before fermentation, which only lasted 2–4 days, after which the beer was only coarsely strained and used. 'It is drunk as a very thin watery gruel full of yeast and bubbling with carbonic acid.' As the germinated Kafir corn, from which the malt was prepared by drying, has been found by Delf to contain a certain small amount of antiscorbutic (p. 205), it seems possible that the antiscorbutic property of the beer is due to the suspended malt. Modern English beer, which is prepared from kilned malt and drunk clear, has been found to be free from demonstrable antiscorbutic properties [Harden and Zilva, 1918, 5]. Green malt contains some vitamin C, but loses it during the kilning process.

Dried vegetables. Dried vegetables have repeatedly been tried and found useless for preventing human scurvy, and in this respect the results of the experimental work find abundant confirmation in the records of failure which have been preserved. Owing to the convenience with which they can be transported, dried herbs and vegetables have been repeatedly adopted for the supply of armies and other large bodies of men separated from supplies of fresh food—and with disastrous results.

As long ago as 1720, Kramer, chief surgeon with the Austrian army in Hungary, was confronted with a serious outbreak of scurvy among the troops, and in his perplexity he wrote to Vienna for help and advice. The College of Physicians in that city arranged for a large and varied supply of dried antiscorbutic herbs to be dispatched to his aid. The consignments arrived and were given a prolonged trial, but the result was that thousands perished from scurvy. Kramer epitomized the knowledge gained by his tragic experience in the oft-quoted paragraph in his *Medicina Castrensis*,1720:

'The scurvy is the most loathsome disease in nature : for which
no cure is to be found in your medicine chest, no, not in the best
furnished apothecary's shop. Pharmacy gives no relief, surgery as
little. Beware of bleeding : shun mercury as a poison : you may
rub the gums, you may grease the rigid tendons in the knee, to
little purpose. But if you can get green vegetables ; if you can
prepare a sufficient quantity of fresh, noble antiscorbutic juices, if
you have oranges, lemons, or citrons ; or their pulp and juice
preserved with whey in cask, so that you can make a lemonade, or
rather give to the quantity of 3 or 4 oz. of their juice in whey, you
will, without other assistance, cure this dreadful evil.' [Translation
given by Lind, 1757.]

Dried vegetables were repeatedly tried in the Navy with similar
results, and by the middle and end of the eighteenth century all
persons who were well informed upon this subject were convinced
of their uselessness for the prevention of scurvy. The following is
a sample of what appears constantly in the correspondence of the
Medical Board of the Admiralty at this period: *Digests of 'In'
Letters*, 4806, 37. 1, August 22, 1773, Ref. M. Report from
Commissioners for Sick and Hurt :

'On reference of a letter from Earl Suffolk sending a box
containing specimens of a plant and herbs prepared and dried for
the purpose of curing the scurvy at sea. Acquaint Lord Suffolk
they cannot recommend its introduction.'

And in 1757 Lind, in describing methods suggested for preventing scurvy at sea, writes :

'The latest proposal to the Lords of the Admiralty was a
magazine of dried spinach prepared in the manner of hay. This was
to be moistened and boiled in their food. To which it was objected by
a very ingenious physician (Dr. Cockburn), that no moisture whatever could replace the natural juices of the plant lost by evaporation,
and, as he imagined, altered by a fermentation which they under-
went in drying.' [Lind, 1757, p. 148.]

When scurvy ceased to be a permanent menace this knowledge
was soon forgotten, and Kramer's experience was repeated again in
the American Civil War. In that campaign, large rations of dried
vegetables, including dried potatoes, were issued to the men, but
proved powerless to prevent scurvy, of which there were many
outbreaks [Medical History, 1888]. At the present day it again
needs to be emphasized that *vegetables which have been dried have
lost almost the whole of their antiscorbutic properties.* During the
period of the late war the public were often energetically advised
in the daily press to dry and preserve vegetables for dispatch to
prisoners of war in Germany or to provide 'fresh' vegetables for
our fleet when at sea (e.g., *Daily Chronicle*, October 19, 1917).

Dried fruits have been shown to have a distinct, though feeble,
antiscurvy value in experimental trials. This result also coincides
with human experience. The dried tamarind, cocum, and mango
('amchur') mentioned in Table XIII all possess a reputation in India
as antiscorbutic materials. It is related that when scurvy broke
out among our troops in 1833–34 at Nassirabad in Rajputana, great
benefit was obtained by eating *anola*, the strongly acid dried

fruits of *Phyllanthus emblica*, which is commonly sold in the bazaars [McNab, 1837]. This difference between vegetables and acid fruits, in respect of the degree to which antiscurvy properties are preserved in the dry condition, may be due to the influence of an acid medium in checking the process of destruction which the antiscorbutic factor slowly undergoes after the cells of the plant have been disorganized by drying.

Meat. Many careful observers in the past have noted that the antiscurvy value of fresh meat, though significant, was much inferior to that of vegetables or fruit. Curran [1847] mentions three patients with scurvy at the Swift Hospital in Dublin in the epidemic of 1847, who had consumed $\frac{3}{4}$ lb. of meat on five days in the week while developing the disease.

Sir Gilbert Blayne relates an incident of the Fleet at Barbados in 1781, where a party of soldiers serving as marines were affected with scurvy and were sent to an army hospital where no fresh animal food was allowed. These men recovered much more quickly on the vegetable diet provided than the seamen on the ships who were deprived of vegetables but were fed on fresh meat.

There is no doubt, however, that scurvy can be prevented by the use of fresh meat alone if the ration is large. The history of Arctic experience is full of such cases. Dr. Rae, surgeon to the Hudson Bay Company, in his evidence to the Scurvy Commissioners of 1876, stated that among the inhabitants of that district scurvy was almost unknown. The people subsisted almost entirely on meat, but the amount consumed was upon the following scale, 8 lb. fresh venison daily per man, 4 lb. per woman, 2 lb. per child.

Nansen and Johansen, after leaving the *Fram*, spent nine months, including the winter of 1895–6, on Frederick Jackson Island in a rudely constructed hut. They remained in good health and free from scurvy, although obtaining no lemon juice and no fresh vegetables, and subsisting mainly on fresh walrus and bear meat preserved by cold.

Jackson and Harley [1900, 1, 2] describe an interesting incident at Kharborova, Yugor Straits, where six Russian priests arrived in the autumn, attended by a small Russian boy. The priests by their religious vows were prevented from eating the fresh meat available: they subsisted on salt fish and there were no vegetables. In the following May the little boy was found to be the only surviving member of the party, and had buried all his late masters in the snow. He suffered from no religious disability and had fed largely on reindeer meat through the winter. A further instance is provided in the experience of Scott's first expedition (Voyage of the *Discovery*) where an outbreak of scurvy was cured by the inclusion in the dietary of his party of large quantities of fresh seal meat. The case of the Jackson-Harmsworth Expedition, referred to above in the discussion of lime juice, is another instance of similar experience. The interpretation of these facts made by the leaders of the expedition induced them to support the theory that scurvy was a disease due to chronic poisoning by the toxins developing in canned meat.

From Hehir's report on the medical history of the siege of Kut-el-Amara [Hehir, 1917] it is clear that in this case also, when no fresh vegetables were available, British soldiers were protected from scurvy by their regular ration of meat or horseflesh, but the amounts they consumed were considerable, 8 to 20 oz. daily. The Indian troops in Kut, on the other hand, who were vegetarian and refused meat on principle, suffered severely from scurvy.

Canned and preserved meats can be dismissed in a word as offering no possible protection from scurvy. Meat in its fresh condition contains the antiscurvy factor in comparatively low concentration, and after exposure to the temperature necessary for sterilization it is impossible that any significant antiscorbutic properties should be retained.

The value of frozen meat is probably intermediate between that of fresh meat and canned meat and is likely to be low, if it has been for a long period in the frozen condition. Wiltshire [1918], describing outbreaks of scurvy among Serbian soldiers, states that out of 132 cases occurring in 1917 all had received a ration of frozen meat nearly every day.

Stefansson [1918] met with several cases of scurvy among the members of his expedition to Melville Island in 1916–17. These were due to abstinence from fresh meat and were cured by inclusion of meat in the diet, much being eaten raw.

The comparative effect of a number of antiscorbutic materials on adult scurvy was tested by Stevenson [1920] on Russian prisoners at Archangel among whom scurvy had broken out. Germinated peas and beans (8 oz. daily), fresh meat (10 oz.), canned fruit (8 oz.), lactic acid milk (2 pints), and fresh lemon juice (4 oz.), all produced a favourable effect and ultimate cure. Lemon juice and lactic acid milk proved to be the best remedies, canned fruit and fresh meat the least effective. Germinated beans were not found as suitable as germinated peas and tended to cause digestive troubles.

Influence of Cooking upon the Antiscorbutic Value of Foods.

Seeing that the antiscorbutic accessory food factor is sensitive to high temperatures, it is clear that the value of fresh vegetables and fruit must of necessity be greatly impaired by cooking. When there is scarcity of fresh food, either by actual deficiency or by difficulty in transport or distribution, it is well to realize that raw fruit and salads have a value, weight for weight, far exceeding that of cooked fruit or cooked vegetables, and that a smaller ration will suffice to afford protection from scurvy. It is unfortunate that most fresh fruit and all salads are perishable articles of food and inconvenient for distribution. They are not available at all periods of the year nor are they universally acceptable, and the fact remains that the bulk of the population in this country takes its antiscorbutic food in the cooked condition. This being so, the method adopted for cooking becomes of great importance.

It is clear from the experimental results obtained by Delf [1918] (p. 213) that in ordinary cooking processes variation in the temperature employed has a comparatively small influence upon the rate of destruction of the antiscorbutic vitamin. For example, if in cooking cabbage the temperature is lowered from 100° C. (boiling-point) to 80° C. the rate of destruction of the antiscorbutic factor is decreased only to about one-half: in other words the loss in anti-scurvy value caused by boiling for half an hour would be equalled by stewing for about one hour at 80° C. This time would, however, need to be greatly increased, with a consequent greater loss in anti-scurvy value, if the cabbage were to be rendered palatable. Cooking for a short period of time at a higher temperature is, therefore, much to be preferred to cooking for the much longer time necessary at a lower temperature.

In experiments made on this point by Eddy, Shelow and Pease [1921–22] it was found that the antiscorbutic potency was diminished to less than 10 per cent. of that of raw cabbage, whether the vegetable was cooked for 45–90 minutes in an open kettle at 100° C. or for about 15 minutes in a pressure boiler in absence of air at 121° C. No practical advantage is, therefore, to be gained by adopting temperatures above 100° C.

For the preparation of food in large quantities methods of slow cooking are the more convenient, and hence arises the great popularity of the stew in camps and other situations where the arrangements for cooking are perforce of a temporary character. Methods of slow cooking at temperatures below boiling-point are also economical of fuel, and it is for this reason that the hay-box and other forms of 'self cookers' were at one time widely recommended. Direct experiments have shown that the necessary long continued exposure to a comparatively low temperature is equivalent in its effect to exposure to 100° C for about three times as long as would be required for cooking in the ordinary way.

The conclusion to be drawn from these considerations is that for those articles of food upon which dependence is placed for protection from scurvy, all forms of slow cooking should if possible be avoided. In case of fresh meat of inferior quality it is often necessary to resort to slow stewing in order to provide an appetizing meal, but in such cases efforts should always be made to cook the vegetables separately and for as short a time as possible.

In this connexion it is instructive to place on record two outbreaks of scurvy in recent times which have been attributed to neglect of this principle. Scurvy broke out in a camp in Scotland in the spring of 1917 and 82 men were affected. At the time potatoes were scarce, but the ration contained a fair proportion of fresh meat and 2 oz. of swedes were available daily. These, as will be seen from Table XIII, are among the most potent antiscorbutic vegetables we possess, and, if cooked satisfactorily, should have afforded considerable protection. The cause of the outbreak was investigated by Hill, who discovered that the meat was always served as a stew, the vegetables being added and the whole cooked for about 5 hours. This circumstance was considered by Hill to be a sufficient explanation of the outbreak.

A second example is afforded by an outbreak of scurvy during the late war between May and July 1918 in a Kafir labour battalion in France in which 142 cases of pronounced scurvy were diagnosed. The daily ration contained 8 oz. of fresh vegetables, but these were

cooked with the meat and boiled for a period of at least 3 hours.
In the opinion of the medical officer by whom the circumstances of
the outbreak were thoroughly investigated this fact was an
important contributory cause [Dyke, 1918]. An outbreak of scurvy
among children in a tuberculosis sanatorium in Vienna, investigated
by Chick and Dalyell [1920], was also attributed to the method of
cooking employed.

Vitamin C and Infantile Scurvy.

Experimental work has shown [Frölich, 1912; Chick, Hume and
Skelton, 1918, 1] that if scurvy is to be prevented by the agency of
milk alone, a quantity must be consumed which practically amounts
to a complete milk diet. This result is in accord with the physiological rôle played in nature by mammalian milk, as a food specially
adapted for the complete nourishment of the young during the
early period of life. Owing to the paucity of vitamin C in milk and
the ease with which it is destroyed by heat, it would be expected
that reference to the literature should bring to light accounts of
outbreaks of scurvy where infants have been fed on heated milk, and
this is in fact the case. Neumann [1902] attributed the many cases
of infantile scurvy encountered in his private practice in 1901–2 to
the practice of pasteurizing milk for infant feeding then recently
introduced as a safeguard against transmission of bacterial infections. He found on inquiry that most of these infants had been
receiving milk from one dairy in which it was the custom to
' pasteurize ' the milk at 90–95° C. before delivery, and that in their
homes the milk, as an extra precaution, had been heated for a
second time in a Soxhlet or other apparatus at or near 100° C. for
10–15 minutes. Heubner [1903] has published similar experiences,
and, in common with Neumann, has expressed the opinion that the
marked increase of infantile scurvy which he noticed in Berlin about
the same period must be attributed to the practice of pasteurizing
milk before giving it to infants, which had been recently introduced
and enthusiastically adopted, even to the extent of repeating the
operation more than once.

The best studied instance to be found in the literature is probably
that recorded by Hess and Fish [1914]. These investigators described an outbreak of mild and subacute infantile scurvy in the
Hebrew Infant Asylum, New York, among infants who had been
fed for several months upon a diet of cow's milk previously
heated to 60° C. (145° F.) for thirty minutes. It had always been
the custom in this Institution to give orange juice as an extra antiscorbutic to the babies fed upon pasteurized cow's milk, but it had
been discontinued as a result of the pronouncement of the American
Medical Milk Commission (1912) that, for purposes of infant feeding, heated milk might be considered the equivalent of raw milk.
The result was that an outbreak of mild scurvy occurred two to
four months later. The babies were not very ill, they were fretful,
anaemic, had no appetite, and ceased to gain weight or grow. They
were all over six months old, and it would have been reasonable
to attribute the condition to teething troubles. The scorbutic nature
of the illness was proved, however, by the ease and rapidity with

which the symptoms cleared up when orange juice or other anti-scorbutic was restored to the diet, or when raw milk was substituted for the pasteurized milk. These conclusions of Hess and Fish have received confirmation in very similar observations made by D. J. M. Miller [1917].

In Vienna for a few years after the late war scurvy was comparatively common in infants, and this has been attributed not only to the actual shortage of milk but also to the breakdown in the milk transport, with the result that the milk supply on many occasions had been repeatedly 'pasteurized' before delivery. In a large foundling institution, children fed on such repeatedly heated milk were found to be in a state of latent scurvy, similar to that described by Hess and Fish [Chick and Dalyell, 1921]. In certain children of 1–3 years old this condition continued for many months, with occasional attacks of overt scurvy. If left untreated the children became extremely dwarfed, inert, and backward. The effect of vitamin therapy in restoring such children to a normal condition is well seen in the contrast between two children, boy and girl twins, shown in Fig. 34, both of whom had suffered from attacks of severe scurvy in the first year of life. At the time of the photograph they were 28 months old. Ida P. (left) had for six months previously received treatment with vitamin C (raw swede juice, orange or lemon juice) and vitamins A and D (butter and cod-liver oil), while Johann P. (right) had, during this period, remained in a ward in which no extra vitamin therapy was given.

The above evidence indicates that an antiscorbutic supplement is absolutely indispensable for infants fed on heated milk. As regards the most suitable antiscorbutic material to be adopted, orange juice is easily the best from many points of view ; it is very potent, is convenient, needs no preparation and is acceptable to the vast majority of infants. Under normal conditions oranges are cheap and plenti-ful in winter and spring. The fresh juice of raw swede turnips is an excellent substitute for orange juice, if for any reason this is not available; its antiscorbutic value was found by Chick and Rhodes [1918] to be about 60 per cent. of that of an equal volume of orange juice and far in excess of that of the other root vegetables examined. Swede turnips have also the merit of being abundant and cheap. The preparation of the juice is exceedingly simple. The clean cut surface of the raw swede is grated on an ordinary kitchen grater and the pulp folded in a small piece of muslin and squeezed with the fingers, when the juice readily runs out. Its slightly sweetish taste is not disliked by infants. It was used successfully in Vienna in 1919–22 when oranges were unobtainable, and it has been recom-mended in some infant welfare centres. The juice of fresh tomatoes is an excellent and cheap antiscorbutic for infants during summer and autumn. Canned tomatoes have also been found satisfactory by Hess and Unger [1918–19], and these are always available. Where the presence of starch is not a drawback, cooked potato is also recom-mended by some workers [Barlow, 1894 ; Hess and Fish, 1914]. The cooked potato is shaken up in water and the resulting fluid used as a diluent of cow's milk in the same manner as barley water.

For curative purposes, potato cream, orange juice, or grape juice is usually employed, although neither the potato nor the grape is of high antiscorbutic potency. It has been shown, however [Harden, Zilva and Still, 1919; Zilva, 1923, 2], that lemon juice, from which the free citric acid has been removed by treatment with calcium carbonate and alcohol, is a valuable remedy, inasmuch as, owing to the absence of acid, a very large amount can be administered without causing digestive disturbance. This preparation can readily be concentrated, and in this form a highly potent antiscorbutic material can be administered without inconvenience. It is also possible to effect the cure of scurvy by intravenous injection of neutralized orange or lemon juice. Orenstein [1925] states that this is the most effective method of treatment in acute cases.

Incidence of Scurvy.

It might be thought that under ordinary conditions of life, adult scurvy would be extinct to-day. This is, however, unfortunately not so. In Western Europe at the present time cases are occasionally met with, chiefly among men or women in very poor circumstances who are living alone and do not bother to provide for themselves out of their very small incomes any kind of fresh vegetables, meat, or milk. A series of such cases was recently collected in Copenhagen by Meulengracht [1927]; most of the patients were unemployed bachelors or widowers living by themselves in a single room and preparing their own food.

A survey of cases of scurvy diagnosed at the Boston City Hospital and at the Massachusetts General Hospital [Shattuck, 1928] also shows that scurvy among adults under normal conditions of life is by no means extinct. In the five years 1923–27, 22 adult cases were diagnosed, in all of which restriction of the diet from some cause or other could be demonstrated. There is no doubt that scurvy is a disease to which the food crank is liable.

Aykroyd [1930, 2] in his survey of deficiency disease in Newfoundland and Labrador, found that cases of scurvy still occurred, and considered that the population was probably only protected from the disease during the long hard winter by the store of cranberries (20–40 lb. per head) which are collected in the summer and eaten raw or lightly cooked during the winter.

Frank cases of scurvy are usually easy to recognize and satisfactory to treat. Whether minor degrees of vitamin C deficiency are at all a common cause of disability or predisposition to disease in man is difficult to determine with certainty. Many observers working in warm climates where cereals form the staple article of the diet of the natives are of opinion that this is the case, even though definite scurvy may be rare. They therefore recommend that the consumption of leafy vegetables and fruit should be strongly encouraged. The diets in such instances, however, are apt to be deficient in other essential factors besides vitamin C, so that it is not a simple matter to prove how far a relative deficiency of vitamin C alone is an important contributory factor in the production of vague ill-health or of diseases other than scurvy.

Göthlin [1931] has employed a modification of the capillary

resistance test for diagnosing a possible deficiency of vitamin C. The test consists in applying a compression band above the elbow of the subject and ascertaining the number of petechiae which appear in 15 minutes in a circular area 60 mm. in diameter in the bend of the elbow, using pressures of 35, 50, and 65 mm. of mercury. The number of these petechiae increases with the deficiency of vitamin C. In this way he has shown that in Sweden many school-children in April–May are subject to a partial deficiency of vitamin C which in some cases disappears during the summer months.

Period of Development of Scurvy.

The period of development of scurvy is probably four to eight months. Scurvy is rarely seen in infants less than six months old, and according to Barlow [1883, 1884] is most common about the eighth month of life.

In the old days, when fresh food was scarce or absent during the winter, and scurvy was a common disease, it was usually in the following spring, after several months of deprivation, that symptoms occurred. Hehir has stated that four months is the minimum time in which he has observed scurvy to develop among Indian troops on active service [Hehir, 1917, p. 71]. Stevenson [1920] made similar observations on Russian prisoners at Archangel, among whom scurvy supervened usually in 4–7 months after the date of their capture (200 cases). The prison diet was low in calories and almost entirely deficient in antiscorbutic vitamin, although $\frac{1}{2}$–1 oz. of preserved lime juice was administered daily. These persons before capture had all enjoyed an ample diet including fresh milk, meat, potatoes, and vegetables. Holst and Frölich [1912] quote two cases in which the period of development was observed to be longer. One is the case of a fanatical vegetarian in Christiania who wished to prove to the world that existence could be maintained on bread and water alone. During the period of his self-imposed trial he was guilty of backsliding on two occasions only, once for a pound of sugar and once for a bottle of beer. The bread was presumably rye bread and afforded adequate protection from beri-beri, but definite symptoms of scurvy in the form of haemorrhages in the legs were noticed after seven and a half months. This period of development is not very different from that in the narrative of the Russian refugee (see above, p. 257) in the Russian convict prison, where scurvy developed after six months upon a similar diet.

There is a certain amount of evidence showing that these periods of development may be shortened in case of men performing hard manual work or exposed to damp or cold climatic conditions. In both cases metabolism would be stimulated, and it would be reasonable to suppose that any reserve of accessory factors would be the sooner exhausted (see p. 227). The following are instances.

It was commonly observed that scurvy was specially prevalent among sailors exposed to cold, damp, or very rough weather. Lind [1757] places this circumstance before diet in his dissertation on the 'Causes of the scurvy'. He gives instances of beleaguered cities where the garrison on hard duty succumbed to the malady before the inhabitants.

In the expedition of the *Alert* and the *Discovery* to seek the North Pole in 1875 the men wintered on the ships within the Arctic circle. There was no definite scurvy diagnosed during this period, although the diet was defective from the point of view of antiscorbutic substances, notably by the substitution of lime juice for lemon juice. In the spring of 1876 the sledging parties set out, and with the performance of hard manual labour scurvy at once made its appearance, the first case occurring within ten days of departure. At first the officers escaped, but, as the men fell sick and the labour of dragging the sledges devolved more and more upon the officers, they also fell victims to the disease. In due course scurvy also broke out among the crews left behind upon the ships during the spring and summer of 1876, but its onset was distinctly later [A. H. Smith, 1918, 1919].

A second instructive example is found in the outbreak of scurvy in the Scottish camp referred to on p. 263. In this instance the first cases to develop, and a large majority of those showing severe symptoms, were among a small section of the population who were engaged in hard manual work for a few hours daily.

CHAPTER XI

VITAMINS IN RELATION TO THE DIET OF THE MOTHER AND THE INFANT.

EXPERIMENTAL evidence and modern clinical experience are in accord in teaching that an optimal intake of vitamins is of special importance in early life and during other periods of growth. During pregnancy and lactation the problem is two-fold—the maintenance of health of the mother and of optimal conditions for the development of the foetus and infant. The diet of the mother in relation to vitamins will first be considered.

Diet of the Mother in Pregnancy.

The duty of the maternal organism during pregnancy is to supply all the substances necessary for the growth of the foetus. These substances the mother either gets ready-made in her food, or herself synthesizes from it, or supplies by depletion of her own body tissues. If the maternal diet is deficient in the special substances essential for the existence and growth of the foetus, then the necessary withdrawal from her own stores may result in varying degrees of ill-health of the mother herself and ultimately of the foetus. Ill-health of the pregnant mother, sometimes of a gross nature, is not uncommon, while disturbances of a slighter nature arising from the same cause are probably so common as to be regarded as almost normal.

Some of the commoner defects of the maternal diet during pregnancy in this country are deficiency of vitamin D, vitamin A, calcium, iron and iodine.

DEFICIENCY OF VITAMIN D AND CALCIUM.

An abundance of both vitamin D and calcium is essential for the proper development of the bony skeleton and teeth of the embryo. The maternal stores of vitamin D are small, but the bones of the mother constitute a large depot for calcium. These essentials she transfers to the developing foetus from her own tissues. If her diet is deficient the drain on her bone calcium may be so great as to result in osteomalacia (see p. 239). A more common evidence of this sacrifice is probably the increased incidence of dental caries to which pregnant women are subject (p. 242), indicating a loss of resistance in the teeth due to withdrawal of calcium.

The problem of the intake of vitamin D and calcium in pregnant women has been investigated by K. U. and G. Toverud [1929, 1, 2; 1930, 1, 2; 1931]. Among 16 women living in a home for expectant mothers and receiving an ordinary Norwegian diet they found that towards the end of pregnancy all were in negative calcium balance and 11 in negative phosphorus balance. These negative balances could be made positive either by increasing the calcium intake to 1·6–2 g., and the phosphorus to 1·8–2 g. daily, or in some cases by increasing the vitamin D intake by giving cod-liver oil or eggs. The addition of vitamin D was not effective, however, when the calcium and phosphorus intake was very low. A similar state of negative balance was often found in lactating women also. These investigators also found that diets deficient in calcium and vitamin D predisposed the offspring to rickets and dental caries.

Deficiency of Vitamin A.

The maternal liver and the foetal liver should contain large stores of vitamin A. The exact significance of a deficient intake of vitamin A by the mother is not yet definitely known, but there is evidence that part of the great susceptibility to sepsis after parturition is related to this dietetic defect. Green, Pindar, Davies and Mellanby [1931] found that, if rats became pregnant and their diet was then made deficient in vitamin A, chronic sepsis very often developed after parturition in the uterus and fallopian tubes. The same workers made an extensive investigation on the relation of diet to puerperal sepsis. Five hundred and fifty women attending an out-patient department were divided into two groups. In one group each member received a preparation containing vitamins A and D to be taken daily during the last month of pregnancy. The second group received no such addition and acted as controls. Neither group received additional vitamins during the puerperium, and, after parturition, examination of the case sheets showed the results briefly summarized in Table XX.

In the control group the incidence of sepsis (4·7 per cent.), as defined by the B.M.A. standard of morbidity, was more than four times that occurring in the group which had received the vitamin A supplement (1·1 per cent.), while the incidence of puerperal pyrexia was 50 per cent. greater in the control group.

Table XX.

Effect of giving Vitamins A and D during Pregnancy on Incidence of Puerperal Sepsis.

	Group receiving extra vitamins A and D		Controls
No. of cases	275	. . . . . .	275
Primiparae	147 (53·4 %)	. . . . . .	145 (52·7 %)
	Cases Morbid (B.M.A. standard).		
Cystitis (*B. coli*)	1 (0·33 %)	Cystitis—*B. coli* .	4 (1·4 %)
Following manual rotation .	2 (0·7 %)	,, —Staph. .	1 (0·35 %)
		Bacilluria—Strep. .	1 (0·35 %)
		Acute Mastitis . .	2 (0·7 %)
		Septic Endometritis	2 (0·7 %)
		Acute Bronchitis .	1 (0·35 %)
		Septicaemia . . .	1 (0·35 %)
Total	3 (1·09 %)	Total	13 (4·7 %)
Puerperal Pyrexia . . .	53 (19·2 %)	. . . . . .	85 (30·9 %)
Maternal Mortality	0	. . . . . .	1 (0·35 %)

The results of this test indicate a certain degree of prophylaxis against puerperal sepsis, due to the addition of fat-soluble vitamins to the diet.

It is probable that other ills of pregnancy may be due to defects in diet, but the subject has been so little investigated that very few positive statements can be made. For instance, the anaemias of pregnancy and the puerperium may indicate a deficient iron intake, but there is evidence that vitamins A and B may also be implicated (p. 252).

Although, therefore, the part played by vitamins in pregnancy is not fully understood, women would be well advised to ensure that their diet at this period is rich in these substances, and especially in the fat-soluble vitamins. The inclusion, for instance, of a pint of milk, an egg (or its yolk), and a serving of green vegetables daily is to be recommended. If poverty precludes the purchase of these foods, a teaspoonful of cod-liver oil and 1 gram (15 grains) of tricalcium phosphate (bone ash) should be taken daily.

Diet of the Mother in Lactation.

Lactation, like pregnancy, involves special demands on the maternal metabolism and the indications that the maternal diet must be specially rich in vitamins apply equally to this period. A mother animal cannot put into her milk constituents which her body cannot make and which are not present in her food. On the other hand, a mother suffering from dietary deficiency may take any incoming vitamins for herself so that they are not passed on to the milk and do not reach the infant. Such a case is described in the Report on Studies of Rickets in Vienna [Med. Res. Coun., 1923] (see p. 273). The conventional views of the perfection of mother's milk and of the sacrifice of the mother's body to the growing foetus can no longer be upheld without modification. It is true that, when produced on a proper diet, the milk of a species is the ideal food for the infant of that species, and that the milks of different species are differently constituted, according to the rate of growth and special needs of the young. Doubtless there is an ideal standard composition and an ideal vitamin content for both woman's and cow's milk, when the woman or the cow is living under natural conditions to which she is fully adapted. In civilization and domestication, however, such conditions rarely occur, and, depending on the very different conditions of life or diet in which the mother is placed, the milk may vary widely in its composition and vitamin content [McCollum, Simmonds and Pitz, 1916; Kennedy and Dutcher, 1922].

Vitamin Deficiencies in Human Milk.

That breast milk may be grossly deficient in one or other of the vitamins is shown by the occurrence of diseases among breast-fed infants due to vitamin deficiency. Some instances of this are given below.

Vitamin A. There is no record of xerophthalmia amongst breast-fed babies, but since the disease has usually been diagnosed in the final stage by the occurrence of corneal ulcers, the deficiency would have to be severe and prolonged to produce such marked symptoms.

Vitamin D. Rickets is common among breast-fed children, as for example in the United States, where Eliot [1925], working in New Haven, Conn., found a very slight degree of rickets almost universal. In a survey of 300 infants, 75-80 per cent. of which were breast-fed, those without rickets, past or present, numbered only about 10 per cent. Eliot states: ' If any two groups of infants show the need of early antirachitic treatment more than others, they are the large, rapidly growing, breast-fed infants and the premature babies. Our investigations have shown that a slight degree of early rickets is wellnigh universal in our climate and in our state of society.'

Hess and Weinstock [1927] state that in the month of March, in New York, all the bottle-fed, and from one-half to one-third of the breast-fed, babies show signs of rickets.

Antineuritic vitamin B_1. Infantile beri-beri occurs among breast-fed babies in the Philippines [McLaughlin and Andrews, 1910] and in the island of Nauru in the Pacific (see p. 247).

Pellagra. In the case of pellagra, it would appear [Harris, 1919] that children of pellagrous parents are often born in a very poor nutritive condition, not capable of diagnosis as infantile pellagra but very probably referable to that disease. Simonini [1905] states that the pellagrous mother should not nurse her child, but an extensive survey of pellagra among infants in Italy, quoted by Harris [1919], did not reveal a single case of pellagra in a nursing child.

Vitamin C. Scurvy occurs in breast-fed babies, but appears to be rare; instances were observed in Central Europe during and after the late war [Chick and Dalyell, 1919], but they must be regarded as isolated cases. Hess [1920] dismisses most of the cases of scurvy in breast-fed babies described in the literature as not really scurvy or not really developed on an adequate supply of breast milk.

EXPERIMENTAL INVESTIGATIONS ON THE VITAMIN CONTENT OF HUMAN MILK.

In addition to the above observations more complete studies have been made of the vitamin content of human milk. In America human milk has been tested by means of experiments on rats for its value in vitamin A by Macy *et al.* [1927; 1927, 1], vitamin B [1927, 2] and vitamin D [Outhouse *et al.* 1928]. The milk was obtained from the Detroit Wet Nursing Bureau; it was the pooled milk of 10–16 women receiving ordinary dietaries not specially controlled, but in no case receiving cod-liver oil. Such milk was found to provide enough vitamin A for a rat in a daily dose of 3 0 c.c. or less and is therefore described as a good source of vitamin A. Much larger daily doses of the same milk, as much as 20 c.c., were needed to supply rats with a sufficiency of the B-vitamins. The daily amount needed to prevent rickets in rats, on a rickets-producing diet, could not be determined, as the maximum amount given, 40 c.c. daily, exercised no antirachitic action whatever. Hess and Weinstock [1927] were, however, able to detect antirachitic potency for rats in a daily dose of 25–30 c.c. of human milk.

It is therefore clear that human milk from such women as attend the Detroit Wet Nursing Bureau satisfies the needs of rats for vitamin A easily, for one or both of the B-vitamins with difficulty, and for vitamin D not at all. It must not be assumed that the needs of the human infant for these three vitamins bear the same quantitative relation to one another as do those of the rat, but these results give an indication that human milk may easily be poor in vitamin D and in the B-vitamins. In point of fact there is good evidence that infants at the breast may in some cases suffer from lack of these vitamins.

Prophylactic Treatment of the Mother by Vitamin Supplements during Lactation.

Allowing that human milk is not always perfect in its vitamin content, the question arises how best to make good any possible deficiencies. Vitamin supplements may be given to the mother or to the child, but there is no doubt that it is the best policy to give them to both.

A poor woman living in Vienna at the time of food shortage in 1922 (see p. 240), whose breast-fed baby had craniotabes, was medicated with cod-liver oil, cod-liver paste, and other foods, but her milk, tested regularly by observations on the growth of rats, showed no improvement over a period of three months, neither did the baby's craniotabes improve. The mother, however, who was in a very poor nutritive condition at the beginning of treatment, increased 40 lb. in weight before the end of the period. In the course of the same observations, the milk of another woman, who was young, healthy, and well nourished, was tested on rats before and after her treatment with cod-liver oil. In this case the improvement in the nutritive value of the milk after treatment was startling.

Macy et al. [1930] found that when 15 g. of cod-liver oil and 10 g. of yeast were added to the daily diet of three lactating women, they derived much benefit, and their calcium and phosphorus retention was improved. One of the women was previously in negative calcium balance and another in negative phosphorus balance, but in each case the negative was converted into a positive balance as the result of treatment. The effect on the babies was not recorded.

Hess, Weinstock and Sherman [1927] mention a case in which milk from a woman was found to have antirachitic potency after she had been irradiated with a mercury vapour quartz lamp, although none could be detected before treatment.

The cases quoted above show that nursing mothers may derive great benefit from treatment with supplementary vitamins, which should therefore on no account be withheld from them. The children also may be benefited in some instances, but in others the supplements administered to the mother may never reach them and it is therefore desirable that they too should be treated directly. Nursing mothers should be encouraged to eat a diet rich in the various accessory factors; reference to the table of foodstuffs (Appendix I) will indicate which these are. The diet chosen should also be well provided with salts, particularly with those of calcium, in which, as has already been shown, diets in this country are liable to be deficient (see p. 242). The mother should expose herself as much as possible, and without the intervention of glass, to the action of sunshine, taking due precautions against excessive exposure. If but little sunshine is available she should take cod-liver oil or a concentrate of vitamins A and D, since, unless she is able to afford an expensive diet, the supply of vitamin D is unlikely to be sufficient without the help of sunshine.

The B-vitamins may be given in her diet in the form of eggs, green vegetables, liver or marmite, which last is, however, of variable potency. Dried yeast may be taken but is unpalatable; some commercial products, however, are valuable and not at all disagreeable. It must be borne in mind that according to Sure [1928, 2] the lactating mother dissipates at least 60 per cent. of the daily vitamin B intake in the metabolism of transfer to the milk.

The inclusion of suitable fresh fruit and green vegetables will provide a supply of vitamin C.

Vitamins in Infancy.

It is clear from what has been previously written that an adequate supply of vitamins in the food is of greater import in infancy, childhood, and adolescence than at any other time of life. On the whole, it is probable that the younger the age the greater is the importance of an adequate supply of these substances.

Most of the deficiency diseases of infants, so far as they are at present known, have been dealt with in the different chapters. These include rickets and infantile tetany (Chap. III), defective teeth (Chap. IV), scurvy and xerophthalmia (Chap. X). It only remains now to consider briefly how an abundant supply of vitamins can be guaranteed to the normal child.

Every infant should if possible be breast-fed for 8 or 9 months. If the mother's diet is good and is rich in dairy and vegetable products, accessory supplies of vitamins to the infant at this stage are probably of minor importance. Even under these conditions, however, additional supplies of fat-soluble vitamins to the infant in the form of one or two teaspoonsful daily of cod-liver oil and of antiscorbutic vitamin in the form of a teaspoonful or more of orange juice are advisable.

Supplementary additions of vitamins are even more essential (1) when the infant is partially or entirely artificially fed and (2) at the time of and following weaning. The importance of vitamins is then very great, partly because their addition helps to avoid or overcome many of the difficulties of feeding at these times, and partly because some of the foods given, as for instance cereals, make a special demand on the vitamin supply. Only too often, even in the early months of life, is some form of prepared cereal included in the diet. So long as the young infant is putting on weight and thriving on cow's milk the addition of cereals or proprietary foods containing cereal products is unjustifiable. A time comes, however, often at the age of 8 or 9 months, when increase in weight ceases and development on cow's milk is less satisfactory. At this time the addition of extra carbohydrate either as sugar or more frequently as cereal brings about rapid improvement and growth. Especially under these circumstances is it imperative to give cod-liver oil or some rich form of vitamins A and D. Even without the addition of cod-liver oil the infant on the cereal-containing diet puts on weight rapidly and the mother is encouraged to increase the cereal food. This increase in growth is, however, often misleading, and, unless additional fat-soluble vitamins are given, the child may develop rickets and become catarrhal and susceptible to broncho-pneumonia. Even when florid rickets is avoided, it does not mean that calcification of the developing bones and teeth is perfect, for, as seen in Chapter IV, although a large proportion of children avoid this disease, there are relatively few whose teeth are properly calcified. It is probably at the weaning period, when the cusps of the molar teeth are joining up, that the risk of defective calcification of the teeth is greatest, so that it is specially important at this time to give vitamin D. The necessity for the increase of vitamin A in the diet, when artificial feeding is resorted to, is less understood, but there is reason to believe that an abundant store of this vitamin in the liver of a child is a form of insurance against certain infective conditions such as chronic catarrh and broncho-pneumonia. The mere fact that the liver stores such large quantities of vitamin A when the food is rich in this substance is an indication of its importance in the animal economy.

Egg yolk is a valuable source of both vitamins A and D and should take its place in the dietary of all artificially-fed infants, after the age of about three months. Other valuable sources of vitamin A, that should be given to infants under these conditions, include purées of vegetables such as spinach and carrots. Potato purée, although not rich in any known vitamins, is often useful for young children, especially as it enables the cereal intake to be cut down.

All children, and especially artificially-fed children, should receive a supplement of vitamin C. As this has now become a common practice, scurvy is a rare condition in infants, but it may be that a subnormal state of health due to a partial deficiency of this vitamin is more common (see pp. 103, 267). A few teaspoonsful of orange juice daily are much appreciated by the average infant and eliminate all possibility of any abnormality due to a deficiency of the antiscorbutic vitamin.

As regards the vitamin B complex, but little is known of the normal infant's requirements. Some authorities consider it useful to give infants a small amount of yeast extract such as marmite in order to provide for any possible deficiency in this respect.

To sum up, it is good to provide all infants with abundant supplies of vitamins, and this object can be best attained according to present knowledge in the following ways :

(1) By breast feeding of the infant for 8 or 9 months.

(2) By supplying the following foods to infants when partially or entirely artificially fed.

(a) Cow's milk to form the bulk of the diet up to 8 or 9 months and the basis of the diet for a year afterwards. At no time in the first year after weaning ought an infant to receive less than 1 to 2 pints daily, and after this not less than a pint.

(b) Cod-liver oil, to supply vitamins A and D (and iodine) in the following quantities: infants 3 months—a teaspoonful daily, infants of 5 months and older—two teaspoonsful daily.

(c) Egg yolk, to supply vitamins D, A and B—$\frac{1}{2}$ to 1 egg daily.

(d) Orange juice or tomato juice for vitamin C—two or more. teaspoonsful daily.

(e) Marmite for vitamin B complex—a small quantity daily.

(f) Purées of vegetables, e. g. spinach, carrot and turnip, cabbage, potato may also be added from about 6 months of age.

It is important that infants should not be kept for too long exclusively on a milk diet, since both human and cow's milk are low in iron; the liver of the newly-born infant contains a reserve of iron, but this tends to become depleted and the baby becomes anaemic. Some supplement rich in iron should therefore be given as early as possible, hence stress is laid on the early addition to an infant's diet of meat gravy, spinach, egg yolk, cereals, &c. The subject is discussed by Mackay [1931], who gives a table of the value of various foodstuffs for iron and recommends the administration of an iron salt to the child. Iron ammonium citrate was found satisfactory and is particularly favourable, since it may contain traces of copper and manganese, whose action is also beneficial. With dried milk this salt may be included in the milk before drying in an amount which will give $31\frac{1}{2}$ grains of the salt to 1 lb. of the dried milk.

Supplementary feeding with vitamin-containing foods is particularly useful for marasmic infants and for those whose progress is retarded. To what extent marasmus is dependent upon abnormal nutrition is not known, but there is reason to believe that defective maternal feeding plays an important part in its aetiology. It is certainly true that such infants often make good improvement when fed along the lines indicated. Sometimes marasmic infants respond well to exposure to ultra-violet radiations even when they have failed to do so to cod-liver oil. A possible explanation of this may be that these infants fail to absorb the vitamin content of the oil, but can utilize the vitamin D produced in the skin by the irradiation.

Proprietary Infants' Foods.

Apart from the foods prepared from cow's milk, proprietary infants' foods (Rep. L. G. Board, 1914) usually consist largely of cereals, frequently to some extent malted. The majority of these foods, when prepared for use according to the directions given, are seriously deficient in fat, and consequently deficient in fat-soluble vitamins. It is probable that many are also inadequate with respect to the water-soluble vitamins; all are certainly deficient in the antiscorbutic vitamin and many in mineral constituents. Addition of milk to such foods will, of course, increase the amount of these factors, but the resulting preparations will still be inferior to whole milk. Clinical experience shows that both scurvy and rickets have frequently occurred in children reared on these preparations.

Numerous observers have reported a type of malnutrition in infants fed upon food mixtures rich in carbohydrate and poor in fat [Cheadle, 1906; Still, 1900; 1905]. Such infants are frequently plump and well supplied with body-fat, and at first give the impression that they are well nourished, but they are usually flabby and show a lowered resistance to infective diseases and are particularly prone to rickets. There can now be little doubt that the ill effects of a diet deficient in fat are less a result of the insufficient supply of fat itself than of the indispensable accessory factors associated with the fat, but this must not be taken to imply that fat itself is not an important article of diet.

REFERENCES.

AALSMEER, W. C., and WENCKEBACH, K. F. (1929). *Wien. Arch. inn. Med.*, **16**, 193.
ABDERHALDEN, E. (1920¹). *Pfluegers Arch.*, **178**, 260.
—— (1920²). *Ibid.*, **182**, 133.
—— (1921¹). *Ibid.*, **187**, 80.
—— (1921²). *Ibid.*, **191**, 278.
—— (1921³). *Ibid.*, **192**, 163.
—— (1922¹). *Ibid.*, **193**, 329.
—— (1922²). *Ibid.*, 355.
—— (1922³). *Hoppe-Seyl. Z.*, **119**, 117.
—— (1922⁴). *Klin. Wschr.*, **1**, 160.
—— (1922⁵). *Pfluegers Arch.*, **195**, 199.
—— (1922⁶). *Ibid.*, 432.
—— (1922⁷). *Ibid.*, **197**, 89.
—— (1922⁸). *Ibid.*, 97.
—— (1222⁹). *Ibid.*, 105.
—— (1922¹⁰). *Ibid.*, 121.
—— (1923). *Ibid.*, **198**, 571.
ABDERHALDEN, E., and BRAMMERTZ, W. (1921). *Ibid.*, **186**, 265.
ABDERHALDEN, E., and LAMPE, A. E. (1913). *Z. ges. exp. Med.*, 1, 296.
ABDERHALDEN, E., and SCHAUMANN, H. (1918). *Pfluegers Arch.*, **172**, 1.
ABDERHALDEN, E., and SCHMIDT, L. (1920). *Ibid.*, **185**, 141.
ABDERHALDEN, E., and VLASSOPOULOS, V. (1930). *Ibid.*, **226**, 808.
ABDERHALDEN, E., and WERTHEIMER, E. (1921¹). *Ibid.*, **191**, 258.
—— (!921²). *Ibid.*, **192**, 174.
—— (1922¹). *Ibid.*, **194**, 647.
—— (1922²). *Ibid.*, **195**, 460.
—— (1922³). *Ibid.*, 480.
AGDUHR, E. (1926¹). *Acta paediat.*, **5**, 319.
—— (1926²). *Ibid.*, **6**, 165.
—— (1928¹). *Ibid.*, **7**, 289.
—— (1928²). *Ibid.*, **8**, 364.
—— (1928³). *Ibid.*, 489.
—— (1928⁴). *Brit. Med. J.*, i, 639.
—— (1929). *Acta paediat.*, **9**, 170.
AHMAD, B. (1930). *Biochem. J.*, **24**, 860.
ALLEN, E. (1919). *Anat. Rec.*, **16**, 93.
ANDEREGG, L. T. (1924). *J. Biol. Chem.*, **59**, 587.
ANDEREGG, L. T., and NELSON, V. E. (1925). *Ind. Eng. Chem.*, **17**, 451.
—— (1926). *Ibid.*, **18**, 620.
ANDERSON, R. J., and KULP, W. L. (1922). *J. Biol. Chem.*, **52**, 69.
ANGUS, T., ASKEW, F. A., BOURDILLON, R. B., BRUCE, H. M., CALLOW, R. K.,
    FISCHMANN, C., PHILPOT, J. ST. L., and WEBSTER, T. A. (1931). *Proc. Roy.
    Soc.*, B. **103**, 340.
ANREP, G. V., and DRUMMOND, J. C. (1920–21). *J. Physiol.*, **54**, 348.
APPLETON, V. B. (1921). *J. Home Econ.*, **13**, 604.
ASCHOFF, L. (1905). *Über die Wirkungen des Sonnenlichts auf den Menschen*,
    Freiburg.
ASKEW, F. A., BOURDILLON, R. B., BRUCE, H. M., CALLOW, R. K., PHILPOT, J. St. L.,
    and WEBSTER, T. A. (1932). *Proc. Roy. Soc.*, B. **109**, 488.
ASKEW, F. A., BOURDILLON, R. B., BRUCE, H. M., JENKINS, R. G. C., and WEBSTER,
    T. A. (1930¹). *Ibid.*, B. **107**, 76.
—— (1930²). *Ibid.*, 91.
ASKEW, F. A., BRUCE, H. M., CALLOW, R. K., PHILPOT, J. St. L., and WEBSTER T. A.
    (1931) *Nature*, Lond., **128**, 758.
AUB, J. C. (1928–29). Harvey Lectures, Harvey Soc., N.Y., **24**, 151.
AYKROYD, W. R. (1930¹). *Biochem. J.*, **24**, 1479.
—— (1930²). *J. Hyg.* Camb., **30**, 357.
—— (1932). *Ibid.*, **32**, 184.
AYKROYD, W. R., and ROSCOE, M. H. (1929). *Ibid.*, **23**, 483.
BACHARACH, A. L., and ALLCHORNE, E. (1928). *Ibid.*, **22**, 313.
BACHMANN, F. M. (1919). *J. Biol. Chem.*, **39**, 235.
BACOT, A., and HARDEN, A. (1922). *Biochem. J.*, **16**, 148.
BAMBERGER, P. (1929). *Deuts. med. Wschr.*, **55**, 339.

BAMBERGER, P., and SPRANGER (1928). *Deuts. med. Wschr.*, **54**, 1116.
BARGER, G. (1914). *The Simpler Natural Bases*, p. 112. Longmans, Green & Co.
BARLOW, O. W. (1930). *Amer. J. Physiol.*, **93**, 161.
BARLOW, T. (1883). *Med.-Chir. Trans.*, Lond., **66**, 100.
—— (1894). *Brit. Med. J.*, ii, 1029.
BARNES, D. J., BRADY, M. J., and JAMES, E. M. (1930). *Amer. J. Dis. Child.*, **39**, 45.
BARNES, R. E., and HUME, E. M. (1919[1]). *Lancet*, Lond., ii, 323.
—— (1919[2]). *Biochem. J.*, **13**, 306.
BASSETT-SMITH, P. W. (1920). *Lancet*, Lond. i, 1102 ; ii, 997.
—— (1921). *Ibid.*, ii, 321.
BAUMANN, L., and HOWARD, C. P. (1917). *Amer. J. Med. Sci.*, **153**, 650.
BAUMGARTNER, L., KING, E. J., and PAGE, I. H. (1929). *Biochem. Z.*, **213**, 170.
BEARD, H. H. (1925–26[1]). *Amer. J. Physiol.*, **75**, 668.
—— (1925–26[2]). *Ibid.*, 682.
—— (1926). *Ibid.*, **76**, 206.
BECHDEL, S.I., ECKLES, C. H., and PALMER, L. S. (1926). *J. Dairy Sci.*, **9**, 409.
BECHDEL, S. I., HONEYWELL, H. E., DUTCHER, R. A., and KNUTSEN, M. H. (1928). *J. Biol. Chem.*, **80**, 231.
BEDSON, S. (1921). *Brit. Med. J.*, ii, 792.
BEDSON, S. P., and ZILVA, S. S. (1923). *Brit. J. Exp. Path.*, **4**, 5.
BELL, M., and MENDEL, L. B. (1921–22). *Proc. Soc. Exp. Biol.*, N.Y., **19**, 395.
—— (1922). *Amer. J. Physiol.*, **62**, 145.
BERGLUND, H., KEEFER, C. S., and YANG, C. S. (1928–29). *Proc. Soc. Exp. Biol.*, N.Y., **26**, 418.
BERTRAND, G., and SEIDELL, A. (1923). *Bull. Soc. chim. biol.*, **5**, 794.
BETHKE, R. M., KENNARD, D. C., and SASSAMAN, H. L. (1927). *J. Biol. Chem.*, **72**, 695.
v. BEZNÁK, A. (1923). *Biochem. Z.*, **141**, 1.
BEZSSONOFF, N. (1921[1]). *C. R. Acad. Sci.*, Paris, **173**, 417.
—— (1921[2]). *Ibid.*, 466.
—— (1922[1]). *Ibid.*, **175**, 846.
—— (1922[2]). *Bull. Soc. chim. biol.*, Paris, 4, 83.
—— (1923). *Biochem. J.*, **17**, 420.
—— (1924[1]). *C. R. Acad. Sci.*, Paris, **179**, 572.
—— (1924[2]). *Bull. Soc. chim. biol.*, **6**, 35.
—— (1925). *C. R. Acad. Sci.*, Paris, **180**, 970.
—— (1926[1]). *Ibid.*, **183**, 921.
—— (1926[2]). *Ibid.*, 1309.
—— (1927). *Bull. Soc. chim. biol.*, Paris, **9**, 568.
BILLARD, G. (1922). *J. Physiol. Path. gén.*, **20**, 182.
BILLS, C. E. (1927). *J. Biol. Chem.*, **72**, 751.
BILLS, C. E., and BRICKWEDDE, F. G. (1928). *Nature*, Lond., **121**, 452.
BILLS, C. E., HONEYWELL, E. M., and COX, W. M. jr. (1928). *J. Biol. Chem.*, **80**, 557
BILLS, C. E., HONEYWELL, E. M., and MACNAIR, W. A. (1928). *Ibid.*, **76**, 256.
BILLS, C. E., and MCDONALD, F. G. (1926). *Ibid.*, **68**, 821.
BILLS, C. E., and WIRICK, A. M. (1930). *Ibid.*, **86**, 117.
BING, F. C., and MENDEL, L. B. (1929). *J. Nutrition*, **2**, 49.
BLACKBERG, S. N. (1928–29). *Proc. Soc. Exp. Biol.*, N.Y., **26**, 254.
BLAND-SUTTON, J. (1889). *J. Comp. Med. Surg.*, **10**, 1.
BLEGVAD, O. (1923). *Dissertation*, Copenhagen.
BLOCH, C. E. (1917[1]). *Ugeskr. Læg.*, **79**, 282.
—— (1917[2]). *Ibid.*, 309.
—— (1917[3]). *Ibid.*, 349.
—— (1918). *Rigshospitalets Börneafdeling Meddelelser*, **2**, 1, 17 ; **3**, 57.
—— (1921). *J. Hyg.*, Camb., **19**, 283.
—— (1924[1]). *J. Dairy Sci.*, **7**, 1.
—— (1924[2]). *Amer. J. Dis. Child.*, **27**, 139.
BLOXSOM, A. P. (1929). *Ibid.*, **37**, 1161.
BOAS, M. A. (1924[1]). *Biochem. J.*, **18**, 422.
—— (1924[2]). *Ibid.*, 1322.
—— (1926). *Ibid.*, **20**, 153.
—— (1927). *Ibid.*, **21**, 712.
BOAS-FIXSEN, M. A. (1931). *Ibid.*, **25**, 596.
BOOCK, E., and TREVAN, J. (1922). *Ibid.*, **16**, 780.
BOURDILLON, R. B., BRUCE, H. M., FISCHMANN, C., and WEBSTER, T. A. (1931). *Sp. Rep. Ser. Med. Res. Coun.*, Lond., No. 158.

BOURDILLON, R. B., FISCHMANN, C., JENKINS, R. G. C., and WEBSTER, T. A. (1929). *Proc. Roy. Soc.*, B. **104**, 561.

BOURDILLON, R. B., JENKINS, R. G. C., and WEBSTER, T. A. (1930). *Nature*, Lond., **125**, 635.

BOYD, J. D., and DRAIN, C. L. (1928). *J. Amer. Med. Ass.*, **90**, 1867.

BOYD, J. D., DRAIN, C. L., and NELSON, M. V. (1929). *Amer. J. Dis. Child.*, **38**, 721.

BOYD, F. D., and LELEAN, P. S. (1919). *R.A.M.C. Jl.*, **33**, 426.

BRACEWELL, M. F., HOYLE, E., and ZILVA, S. S. (1930[1]). *Biochem. J.*, **24**, 82.

—— (1930[2]). *Sp. Rep. Ser. Med. Res. Coun.*, Lond., No. 146.

BRACEWELL, M. F., KIDD, F., WEST, C., and ZILVA, S. S. (1931). *Biochem. J.*, **25**, 138.

BRACEWELL, M. F., WALLACE, T., and ZILVA, S. S. (1931). *Ibid.*, 144.

BRACEWELL, M. F., and ZILVA, S. S. (1931). *Ibid.*, 1081.

BRADDON, W. L. (1905). *Rpt. H.M. Sec. of State for Colonies* (F.M.S. Govt. Printing Office, Kuala Lumpur).

—— (1907). *Causes and Prevention of Beri-beri*, Lond.

BRADDON, W. L., and COOPER, E. A. (1914). *J. Hyg.*, Camb., **14**, 331.

BRAY, G. W. (1928–29). *Trans. Soc. Trop. Med. Hyg.*, Lond., **22**, 9.

BRÉAUDAT, L., and DENIER (1911). *Ann. Inst. Pasteur*, **25**, 167.

BROUWER, E. (1927). *Biochem. Z.*, **187**, 183.

BRUINS, H. R., OVERHOFF, J., and WOLFF, L. K. (1931). *Biochem. J.*, **25**, 430.

BUDD, G. (1840). *Tweedie's System of Practical Medicine*, Lond., Article 'Scurvy'.

BULL, L. B. (1918). *J. Comp. Path. Therap.*, **31**, 193.

Bull. Wisc. Expt. Sta. (1927). **396**, 45.

—— (1929). **405**, 48.

BUNTING, R. W. (1925). *Dental Cosmos*, **67**, 771.

BUNTING, R. W., HADLEY, F. P., JAY, P., and HARD, D. G. (1930). *Amer. J. Dis. Child.*, **40**, 536.

BURTON, G. W. (1928). *J. Home Econ.*, **20**, 35.

CAJORI, F. A. (1920). *J. Biol. Chem.*, **43**, 583.

CALLOW, R. K. (1931). *Meeting of Section B, Brit. Ass.*, Sept. 25th.

CALLOW, R. K., and FISCHMANN, C. F. (1931). *Biochem. J.*, **25**, 1464.

CAMPBELL, M. E. D., and CHICK, H. (1919). *Lancet*, Lond., ii, 320.

CAPPER, N. S. (1930[1]). *Biochem. J.*, **24**, 453.

—— (1930[2]). *Ibid.*, 980.

CARD, L. E. (1929). *Poultry Sci.*, **8**, No. 6.

CARD, L. E., MITCHELL, H. H., and HAMILTON, T. S. (1930). *Poultry Sci. Proc.*

CARLEY, P. S. (1930). *New Orleans Med. Surg. J.*, **82**, 740.

CARR, F. H., and PRICE, E. A. (1926). *Biochem. J.*, **20**, 497.

CARRICK, C. W., and HAUGE, S. M. (1925). *J. Biol. Chem.*, **63**, 115.

CARTER, C. W., and DRURY, A. N. (1929). *Proc. Physiol. Soc. J. Physiol.*, **68**, i.

CARTER, C. W., KINNERSLEY, H. W., and PETERS, R. A. (1930[1]). *Biochem. J.*, **24**, 832.

—— (1930[2]). *Ibid.*, 1844.

CAVANAUGH, G. W., DUTCHER, R. A., and HALL, J. S. (1924). *Ind. Eng. Chem.*, **16**, 1070.

CHAMBERLAIN, W. B., BLOOMBERG, H. D., and KILBOURNE, E. D. (1911). *Philipp. J. Sci.* (B) **6**, 177.

CHAMBERLAIN, W. P., and VEDDER, E. B. (1911[1]). *Ibid.*, 251.

—— (1911[2]). *Ibid.*, 395.

CHEADLE, W. B. (1906). *Artificial Feeding and Food Disorders in Infants* (Lond.) 6th ed.

CHICK, H. (1920). *Brit. Med. J.*, ii, 147.

—— (1929). *Biochem. J.*, **23**, 514.

CHICK, H., and others (1923). *Sp. Rep. Ser. Med. Res. Coun.*, Lond., No. 77.

CHICK, H., and COPPING, A. M. (1930[1]). *Ibid.*, **24**, 932.

—— (1930[2]). *Ibid.*, 1744.

—— (1930[3]). *Ibid.*, 1764.

CHICK, H., COPPING, A. M., and ROSCOE, M. H. (1930). *Ibid.*, 1748.

CHICK, H., and DALYELL, E. J. (1919). *Wien. klin. Wschr.*, **32**, 1219.

—— (1920). *Brit. Med. J.*, ii, 546.

—— (1921). *Ibid.*, ii, 1061.

CHICK, H., DALYELL, E. J., HUME, E. M., MACKAY, H. M. M., SMITH, H. H., and WIMBERGER, H. (1922). *Lancet*, Lond., ii, 7.

CHICK, H., and DELF, E. M. (1919). *Biochem. J.*, **13**, 199.

CHICK, H., and HUME, E. M. (1917[1]). *Trans. Soc. Trop. Med. Hyg.*, Lond., **10**, 141.

—— (1917[2]). *R.A.M.C. Jl.*, **29**, 121.

CHICK, H., and HUME, E. M. (1917–19[1]). *Proc. Roy. Soc.*, B. **90**, 44.
—— (1917–19[2]). *Ibid.*, 60.
CHICK, H., HUME, E. M., and SKELTON, R. F. (1918[1]). *Biochem. J.*, **12**, 131.
—— (1918[2]). *Lancet*, Lond., i, 1.
—— (1918[3]). *Ibid.*, ii, 735.
—— (1919). *Ibid.*, 322.
CHICK, H., KORENCHEVSKY, V., and ROSCOE, M. H. (1926). *Biochem. J.*, **20**, 622.
CHICK, H., and RHODES, M. (1918). *Lancet*, Lond., ii, 774.
CHICK, H., and ROSCOE, M. H., (1926[1]). *Biochem. J.*, **20**, 137.
—— (1926[2]). *Ibid.*, 632.
—— (1927). *Ibid.*, **21**, 698.
—— (1928). *Ibid.*, **22**, 790.
—— (1929[1]). *Ibid.*, **23**, 498.
—— (1929[2]). *Ibid.*, 504.
—— (1930). *Ibid.*, **24**, 105.
CHICK, H., and TAZELAAR, M. (1924). *Ibid.*, **18**, 1346.
CHITTENDEN, R. H., and UNDERHILL, F. P. (1917). *Amer. J. Physiol.*, **44**, 13.
CLARK, M. L. (1929). *Lancet*, Lond., i, 1270.
CLAYTON, M. M. (1929). *J. Nutrition*, **2**, 491.
CLOW, B., and MARLATT, A. L. (1930). *J. Agric. Res.*, **40**, 767.
COHEN, B. (1917–18). *Proc. Soc. Exp. Biol.*, N.Y., **15**, 102.
COHEN, B., and MENDEL, L. B. (1918). *J. Biol. Chem.*, **35**, 425.
COHN, E. J., MINOT, G. R., FULTON, J. F., ULRICHS, H. V., SARGENT, F. C., WEARE, J. H., and MURPHY, W. P. (1927). *Ibid.*, **74**, lxix.
COHN, E. J., MINOT, G. R., ALLES, G. A., and SALTER, W. T. (1928). *Ibid.*, **77**, 326.
COLLAZO, J. A. (1923). *Biochem. Z.*, **136**, 278.
—— (1924). *Ibid.*, **140**, 256.
COLLAZO, J. A., RUBINO, P., and VARELA, B. (1929). *Wien. Arch. inn. Med.*, **19**, 137.
COLLIP, J. B. (1925). *J. Biol. Chem.*, **63**, 395.
—— (1926). *Medicine*, **5**, 1.
COLLISON, D. L., HUME, E. M., SMEDLEY-MACLEAN, I., and SMITH, H. H. (1929). *Biochem. J.*, **23**, 634.
CONNELL, S. J. B., and ZILVA, S. S. (1924[1]). *Ibid.*, **18**, 638.
—— (1924[2]). *Ibid.*, 641.
COOK (CAPT.). *Voyages* (Everyman Edition. Dent, Lond.).
COOPER, E. A. (1912). *J. Hyg.*, Camb., **12**, 436.
—— (1913). *Biochem J.*, **7**, 268.
—— (1914[1]). *J. Hyg.*, Camb., **14**, 12.
—— (1914[2]). *Biochem. J.*, **8**, 250.
—— (1914[3]). *Ibid.*, 347.
COOPER, E. A., and BRADDON, W. L. (1914). *J. Hyg.*, Camb., **14**, 331.
COOPER, E. A., and FUNK, C. (1911). *Lancet*, Lond., ii, 1266.
COPLANS, M. (1904). *Trans. Epidem. Soc.*, Lond., **23**, 1.
COPPING, A. M. (1929). *Biochem. J.*, **23**, 1050.
COWARD, K. H. (1923). *Ibid.*, **17**, 145.
—— (1929[1]). *J. Physiol.*, **67**, 26.
—— (1929[2]). *Lancet*, Lond., ii. 1090.
COWARD, K. H., and DRUMMOND, J. C. (1920). *Biochem. J.*, **14**, 665.
—— (1921). *Ibid.*, **15**, 530.
COWARD, K. H., DYER, F. J., MORTON, R. A., and GADDUM, J. H. (1931). *Ibid.*, **25**, 1102.
COWARD, K. H., and EGGLETON, P. (1928). *Lancet*, Lond., i, 97.
COWARD, K. H., KEY, K. M., DYER, F. J., and MORGAN, B. G. E. (1930). *Biochem. J.*, **24**, 1952.
—— (1931). *Ibid.*, **25**, 551.
COWARD, K. H., MORGAN, B. G. E., and DYER, F. G. (1930). *J. Physiol.*, **69**, 349.
COWELL, S. J. (1925). *Brit. Med. J.*, i, 594.
COWGILL, G. R., DEUEL, H. J. jr., PLUMMER, N., and MESSER, F. C. (1926). *Amer. J. Physiol.*, **77**, 389.
COWGILL, G. R., DEUEL, H. J. jr., and SMITH, A. H. (1925). *Ibid.*, **73**, 106.
COWGILL, G. R., and MENDEL, L. B. (1921). *Ibid.*, **58**, 131.
COWGILL, G. R., ROSENBERG, H. S., and ROGOFF, J. (1930). *Ibid.*, **93**, 641.
COWGILL, G. R., SMITH, A. H., and BEARD, H. H. (1925). *J. Biol. Chem.*, **63**, xxiii.
CRAMER, W. (1923). *Lancet*, Lond., i, 1046.
—— (1924). *Ibid.*, i, 633.
CRAMER, W., DREW, A. H., and MOTTRAM, J. C. (1921). *Ibid.*, ii, 1202.
—— (1922). *Proc. Roy. Soc.*, B. **93**, 449.

CRAMER, W., DREW, A. H., and MOTTRAM, J. C. (1923). *Brit. J. Exp. Path.*, **4**, 37.
CRAMER, W., and KINGSBURY, A. N. (1924). *Ibid.*, **5**, 300.
CRANE, M. B., and ZILVA, S. S. (1931). *J. Pomology*, **9**, 228.
CRAVEN, V., and KRAMER, M. M. (1927). *J. Agric. Res.*, **34**, 385.
CRAWFORD, M. E. F., GOLDING, J., PERRY, E. O. V., and ZILVA, S. S. (1930). *Biochem. J.*, **24**, 682.
CRIST, J. W., and DYE, M. (1929). *J. Biol. Chem.*, **81**, 525.
CROHN, B. B., and ROSENBERG, H. (1924). *J. Amer. Med. Ass.*, **83**, 326.
CRUZ-COKE, E. (1930). *C. R. Soc. Biol.*, Paris, **105**, 238.
CUMMINGS, M. J., and MATTILL, H. A. (1931). *J. Nutrition*, **3**, 421.
CURRAN, J. O. (1847). *Dublin J. Med. Sci.*, **7**, 83.
DALLDORF, G., and ZALL, C. (1930). *J. Exp. Med.*, **52**, 57.
DALYELL, E. J., and CHICK, H. (1921). *Lancet*, Lond., ii, 842.
DAMON, S. R. (1921). *J. Biol. Chem.*, **48**, 379.
—— (1923). *Amer. J. Hyg.*, **3**, 247.
—— (1924). *J. Path. Bact.*, **27**, 163.
DANIELS, A. L., and BROOKS, L. (1927–28). *Proc. Soc. Exp. Biol.*, N.Y., **25**, 161.
DANIELS, A. L., and HUTTON, M. K. (1925–26). *Ibid.*, **23**, 225.
DANIELS, A. L., and LOUGHLIN, R. (1918). *J. Biol. Chem.*, **33**, 295.
—— (1920). *Ibid.*, **44**, 381.
DANIELS, A. L., PYLE, S. I., and BROOKS, L. (1925–26). *Proc. Soc. Exp. Biol.*, N.Y., **23**, 821.
DANIELS, A. L., and STEARNS, G. (1924). *J. Biol. Chem.*, **61**, 225.
DANYSZ-MICHEL, and KOSKOWSKI, W. (1922). *C. R. Acad. Sci.*, Paris, **175**, 54.
DAUBNEY, C. G., and ZILVA, S. S. (1926). *Biochem. J.*, **20**, 1055.
DAVEY, A. J. (1921). *Ibid.*, **15**, 83.
DAVIDSOHN, H. (1924). *Biochem. Z.*, **150**, 304.
DAVIDSON (1931). *Lancet*, Lond., ii, 1395.
DEAS, J. (1924). *J. Biol. Chem.*, **61**, 5.
DELF, E. M. (1918). *Biochem. J.*, **12**, 416.
—— (1920). *Ibid.*, **14**, 211.
—— (1921). *Pub. S. Afr. Inst. Med. Res.*, No. XIV.
—— (1924). *Biochem. J.*, **18**, 674.
—— (1925). *Ibid.*, **19**, 141.
DELF, E. M., and SKELTON, R. F. (1918). *Ibid.*, **12**, 448.
DE SANCTIS, A. G., and CRAIG, J. D. (1930). *J. Amer. Med. Ass.*, **94**, 1285.
DIELS, O. (1929). *Z. angew. Chem.*, **42**, 911.
DIXON, W. E., and HOYLE, J. C. (1928). *Brit. Med. J.*, ii, 832.
DONALDSON, S. and TASKER, J. (1930). *Proc. Transv. Mine Med. Off. Ass.*, Feb. and Mch.
DOUGHERTY, J. E. (1926). *Amer. J. Physiol.*, **76**, 265.
DRUMMOND, J. C. (1917). *Biochem. J.*, **11**, 255.
—— (1918[1]). *Ibid.*, **12**, 25.
—— (1918[2]). *J. Physiol.*, **52**, 95.
—— (1919[1]). *Biochem. J.*, **13**, 77.
—— (1919[2]). *Ibid.*, **13**, 81.
—— (1919[3]). *Ibid.*, 95.
DRUMMOND, J. C., AHMAD, B., and MORTON, R. A. (1930). *J. Soc. Chem. Ind.*, Lond., **49**, 291 T.
DRUMMOND, J. C. and BAKER, L. C. (1929). *Biochem. J.*, **23**, 274.
DRUMMOND, J. C., CHANNON, H. J., and COWARD, K. H. (1925). *Ibid.*, **19**, 1047.
DRUMMOND, J. C. and COWARD, K. H. (1920). *Ibid.*, **14**, 734.
—— (1921). *Lancet*, Lond., ii, 698.
—— (1922). *J. Soc. Chem. Ind.*, Lond., **41**, 561 R.
—— (1924). *Ibid.*, **43**, 544.
DRUMMOND, J. C., COWARD, K. H., and HANDY, J. (1925). *Biochem. J.*, **19**, 1068.
DRUMMOND, J. C., CROWDEN, G. P., and HILL, E. L. G. (1922). *J. Physiol.*, **56**, 413.
DRUMMOND, J. C., and FUNK, C. (1914). *Biochem. J.*, **8**, 598.
DRUMMOND, J. C., and HILDITCH, T. P. (1930). *Empire Marketing Bd. Rep.*, No. 35.
DRUMMOND, J. C., and MARRIAN, G. F. (1926). *Biochem. J.*, **20**, 1229.
DRUMMOND, J. C., and MORTON, R. A. (1929). *Ibid.*, **23**, 785.
DRUMMOND, J. C., and WATSON, A. F. (1922). *Analyst*, **47**, 341.
DRUMMOND, J. C., ZILVA, S. S., and COWARD, K. H. (1922). *Biochem. J.*, **16**, 518.
DRURY, A. N., HARRIS, L. J., and MAUDSLEY, C. (1930). *Ibid.*, **24**, 1632.
DUBIN, H. E., and FUNK, C. (1923). *J. Metab. Res.*, **4**, 467.
DUGUID, J. B. (1930). *J. Path. Bact.*, **33**, 697.
DUGUID, J. B., DUGGAN, M. M., and GOUGH, J. (1930). *Ibid.*, 353.
DULIÈRE, W., MORTON, R. A., and DRUMMOND, J. C. (1929). *J. Soc. Chem. Ind.*, Lond., **48**, 316 T.

DUTCHER, R. A. (1918[1]). *J. Biol. Chem.*, **36**, 63.
—— (1918[2]). *Ibid.*, 551.
DUTCHER, R. A., ECKLES, C. H., DAHLE, C. D., MEAD, S. W., and SCHAEFER, O. G. (1920–21). *Ibid.*, **45**, 119.
DUTCHER, R. A., HARSHAW, H. M., and HALL, J. S. (1921). *Ibid.*, **47**, 483.
DUTCHER R. A., and OUTHOUSE, J. (1922–23). *Proc. Soc. Exp. Biol.*, N.Y., **20**, 450.
DUTCHER, R. A., PIERSON, E. M., and BIESTER, A. (1920). *J. Biol. Chem.*, **42**, 301.
DUTCHER, R. A., and WILKINS, S. D. (1921). *Amer. J. Physiol.*, **57**, 437.
DYE, M., MEDLOCK, O. C., and CRIST, J. W. (1927). *J. Biol. Chem.*, **74**, 95.
DYER, F. J. (1931). *Quart. J. Pharm. Pharmacol.*, **4**, 503.
DYKE, H. W. (1918). *Lancet*, Lond., ii, 513.
EASTCOTT, E. V. (1924). *Trans. Roy. Soc.*, Canada, III, **18**, 117.
—— (1928). *J. Phys. Chem.*, **32**, 1094.
ECKMAN, P. F. (1922). *J. Amer. Med. Ass.*, **78**, 635.
EDDY, W. R. (1916). *J. Biol. Chem.*, **27**, 113.
—— (1927). *Arch. Pediat.*, **44**, 320.
—— (1929). *Amer. J. Publ. Hlth.*, **19**, 1309.
EDDY, W. H., GURIN, S., and KERESZTESY, J. (1930). *J. Biol. Chem.*, **87**, 729.
EDDY, W. H., HEFT, H. L., STEVENSON, H. C., and JOHNSON, R. (1921). *Ibid.*, **47**, 249.
EDDY, W. H., and KELLOG, M. (1927). *Amer. J. Publ. Hlth.*, **17**, 27.
EDDY, W. H., KERR, R. W., and WILLIAMS, R. R. (1923–24). *Proc. Soc. Exp. Biol.*, N.Y., **21**, 307.
—— (1924). *J. Amer. Chem. Soc.*, **46**, 2846.
EDDY, W. H., and KOHMAN, E. F. (1924). *Ind. Eng. Chem.*, **16**, 52.
EDDY, W. H., KOHMAN, E. F., and CARLSSON, V. (1925). *Ibid.*, **17**, 69.
—— (1926). *Ibid.*, **18**, 85.
EDDY, W. H., SHELOW, E., and PEASE, R. A. (1921–22). *Proc. Soc. Exp. Biol.*, N.Y., **19**, 155.
EDDY, W. H., and STEVENSON, H. C. (1919–20[1]). *Ibid.*, **17**, 52.
—— (1919–20[2]). *Ibid.*, 122.
—— (1919–20[3]). *Ibid.*, 218.
—— (1920). *J. Biol. Chem.*, **43**, 295.
EDELSTEIN, E., and SCHMAL, S. (1926). *Z. Kinderheilk.*, **41**, 30.
EDIE, E. S., EVANS, W. H., MOORE, B., SIMPSON, G., and WEBSTER, T. A. (1912). *Biochem. J.*, **6**, 234.
EDIE, E. S., and SIMPSON, G. C. E. (1911). *Brit. Med. J.*, i, 1421.
EGGLETON, P., and GROSS, L. (1925). *Ibid.*, **19**, 633.
EICHHOLZ, W., and KREITMAIR, H. (1928). *Münch. med. Wschr.*, **75**, 79.
EIJKMAN, C. (1890). *Geneesk. Tijdschr. Ned.-Ind.*, **30**, 295.
—— (1896). *Ibid.*, **36**, 214.
—— (1897[1]). *Virchows Arch.*, **148**, 523.
—— (1897[2]). *Ibid.*, **149**, 187.
—— (1897[3]). *Arch. Schiffs- u. Tropen-Hyg.*, **1**, 268.
—— (1906). *Arch. Hyg.*, **58**, 150.
—— (1927). *Verslag. Kon. Akad. Wetensch.*, Amsterdam, **36**, 221.
—— (1929). *Nobel Lecture.*
EIJKMAN, C., and HOOGENHUIJZE, C. J. C. van (1916). *Proc. Kon. Akad. Wetensch.*, Amsterdam, **18**, 1467.
EIJKMAN, C., HOOGENHUIJZE, C. J. C. van, and DERKS, T. J. G. (1922). *J. Biol. Chem.*, **50**, 311.
ELIOT, M. M. (1925). *J. Amer. Med. Ass.*, **85**, 656.
ELLIOT, W. E., CRICHTON, A., and ORR, J. B. (1922). *Brit. J. Exp. Path.*, **3**, 10.
ELLIS, N. R., STEENBOCK, H., and HART, E. B. (1921). *J. Biol. Chem.*, **46**, 367.
EMBREY, H. (1923). *Philipp. J. Sci.*, **22**, 77.
EMMETT, A. D. (1920). *Science*, **52**, 157.
EMMETT, A. D., and ALLEN, F. P. (1919). *J. Biol. Chem.*, **38**, 325.
EMMETT, A. D., and LUROS, G. O. (1920). *Ibid.*, **43**, 265.
EMMETT, A. D., and McKIM, L. H. (1917). *Ibid.*, **32**, 409.
EMMETT, A. D., and STOCKHOLM, M. (1920). *Ibid.*, **43**, 287.
ERDHEIM, J. (1914). *Rachitis und Epithel-Körperchen* (Wien).
ESCHER, H. H. (1909). *Dissertation*, Zürich.
EULER, B. v., EULER, H. v., and HELLSTRÖM, H. (1928). *Biochem. Z.*, **203**, 370,
EULER, B. v., EULER, H. v., and KARRER, P. (1928). *Helv. chim. Acta.*, **12**, 278. .
EULER, H. v., DEMOLE, V., KARRER, P., and WALKER, O. (1930). *Ibid.*, **13**, 1078.
EULER, H. v., and KARRER, P. (1931). *Ibid.*, **14**, 1040.
EULER, H. v., and MYRBÄCK, K. (1925). *Hoppe-Seyl. Z.*, **148**, 180.
EULER, H. v., MYRBÄCK, K., and KARLSSON, S. (1926). *Ibid.*, **157**, 263.

EVANS, H. M. (1924[1]). *Science*, **60**, 20.
—— (1924[2]). *Anat. Rec.*, **27**, 204.
—— (1925). *Proc. Nat. Acad. Sci.*, Wash., **11**, 373.
—— (1928[1]). *Amer. J. Physiol.*, **85**, 149.
—— (1928[2]). *J. Nutrition*, **1**, 23.
—— (1928[3]). *J. Biol. Chem.*, **77**, 651.
EVANS, H. M., and BISHOP, K. S. (1922[1]). *Anat. Rec.*, **23**, 17.
—— (1922[2]). *J. Metab. Res.*, **1**, 335.
—— (1923[1]). *J. Amer. Med. Ass.*, **81**, 889.
—— (1923[2]). *J. Metab. Res.*, **3**, 202.
—— (1923[3]). *Amer. J. Physiol.*, **63**, 396.
—— (1924). *Anat. Rec.*, **27**, 203.
EVANS, H. M., and BURR, G. O. (1924). *Ibid.*
—— (1925[1]). *Ibid.*, **29**, 356.
—— (1925[2]). *Proc. Nat. Acad. Sci.*, Wash., **11**, 334.
—— (1927[1]). *Memoirs Univ. California*, 8.
—— (1927[2]). *J. Amer. Med. Ass.*, **88**, 1462.
—— (1927[3]). *Ibid.*, **89**, 1587.
—— (1928[1]). *J. Biol. Chem.*, **76**, 263.
—— (1928[2]). *Ibid.*, 273.
—— (1928[3]). *Ibid.*, **77**, 231.
EVANS, H. M., and HOAGLAND, D. R. (1927), *Amer. J. Physiol.*, **80**, 702.
EVANS, H. M., and LEPKOVSKY, S. (1929). *J. Biol. Chem.*, **83**, 269.
—— (1931). *J. Nutrition*, **3**, 353.
EVANS, H. M., and SCOTT, K. J. (1922). *Science*, **56**, 650.
FABER, H. K. (1920). *J. Biol. Chem.*, **43**, 113.
FALCONER, E. H. (1926). *Amer. J. Physiol.*, **76**, 145.
FALKENHEIM, C. (1928). *Jahrb. Kinderhlk.*, Beiheft 3, Heft 19.
FARMER, C. J., and REDENBAUGH, H. E. (1925–26[1]). *Amer. J. Physiol.*, **75**, 27.
—— (1925–26[2]). *Ibid.*, 45.
FEARON, W. R. (1925). *Biochem. J.*, **19**, 888.
FERGUSSON, M., and FINDLAY, L. (1918). *Sp. Rep. Ser. Med. Res. Coun.*, Lond., No. 20.
FILDES, P. (1921). *Brit. J. Exp. Path.*, **2**, 16.
FINDLAY, G. M. (1921[1]). *J. Path. Bact.*, **24**, 175.
—— (1921[2]). *Ibid.*, 446.
—— (1921[3]). *Ibid.*, 454.
—— (1921[4]). *J. Amer. Med. Ass.*, **77**, 1604.
—— (1923[1]). *Biochem. J.*, **17**, 887.
—— (1923[2]). *J. Path. Bact.*, **26**, 1.
—— (1925). *Brit. J. Exp. Path.*, **6**, 16.
—— (1928). *J. Path. Bact.*, **31**, 353.
FINDLAY, G. M., and MACKENZIE, R. (1922). *Biochem. J.*, **16**, 574.
FINDLAY, G. M., and MACLEAN, I. (1925). *Ibid.*, **19**, 63.
FINDLAY, L. (1908). *Brit. Med. J.*, ii, 13.
—— (1922). *Lancet*, Lond., i, 825.
FISHER, R. B. (1931). *Biochem. J.*, **25**, 1410.
FORBES and KEITH (1914). *Ohio Agri. Sta. Tech. Ser. Bull.* No. 5.
FRÄNKEL, S., and SCHARF, A. (1921). *Biochem. Z.*, **126**, 265.
FRASER, H., and STANTON, A. T. (1909). *Lancet*, Lond., i, 451.
—— (1911). *The Etiology of Beriberi : Stud. Inst. Med. Res.* F.M.S. No. 12.
FRIDERICIA, L. S. (1924). *J. Biol. Chem.*, **62**, 471.
FRIDERICIA, L. S., FREUDENTHAL, P., GUDJONNSSON, S., JOHANSEN, G., and SCHOUBYE, N. (1927). *J. Hyg.*, Camb., **27**, 70.
FRIDERICIA, L. S., and HOLM, E. (1925). *Amer. J. Physiol.*, **73**, 63.
FRÖLICH, TH. (1912). *Z. Hyg. InfektKr.*, **72**, 155.
FÜRST, V. (1912). *Ibid.*, 121.
FUJIMAKI, Y. (1926). *Progress of the Science of Nutrition in Japan.* Tadasu Saiki. League of Nations Hlth. Organisation, Geneva.
FULMER, E. I., DUECKER, W. W., and NELSON, V. E. (1924). *J. Amer. Chem. Soc.*, **46**, 723.
FULMER, E. I., and NELSON, V. E. (1924). *Chem. Abst.*, **18**, 846.
FULMER, E. I., NELSON, V. E., and WHITE, A. (1923). *J. Biol. Chem.*, **57**, 397.
FUNK, C. (1911). *J. Physiol.*, **43**, 395.
—— (1912). *J. State Med.*, **20**, 341.
—— (1912–13[1]). *J. Physiol.*, **45**, 75.
—— (1912–13[2]). *Ibid.*, 489.
—— (1913[1]). *Ibid.*, **46**, 173.

FUNK, C. (1913²). *J. Trop. Med.*, **6**, 166.
—— (1914¹). *J. Physiol.*, **47**, xxv.
—— (1914²). *Hoppe-Seyl. Z.*, **89**, 378.
—— (1922). *The Vitamines.* (Williams & Wilkins Co., Baltimore).
FUNK, C., and COLLAZO, J. A. (1925). *Chem. Zell-Gewebe*, **12**, 195.
FUNK, C., and DOUGLAS, M. (1914). *J. Physiol.*, **47**, 475.
FUNK, C., and DUBIN, H. E. (1920). *J. Biol. Chem.*, **44**, 487.
—— (1921). *Ibid.*, **48**, 437.
FUNK, C., and FREEDMAN, L. (1923). *Ibid.*, **56**, 85.
FUNK, C., HARROW, B., and PATON, J. B. (1923). *Ibid.*, **57**, 153.
FUNK, C., and MACALLUM, A. B. (1913). *Biochem. J.*, **7**, 356.
—— (1915). *J. Biol. Chem.*, **23**, 413.
—— (1916). *Ibid.*, **27**, 63.
FUNK, C., and PATON, J. B. (1922). *J. Metab. Res.*, **1**, 737.
FUNK, C., and SCHÖNBORN, E. v. (1914). *J. Physiol.*, **48**, 328.
GAGLIO, (1919). *Policlinico* (sez. prat.) **26**, 1381.
GALVAO, P. E., and CARDOSO, D. M. (1930). *Arch. Inst. Biol.*, **3**, 219.
GAMBLE, J. L., ROSS, G. S., and TISDALL, F. F. (1923). *Amer. J. Dis. Child.*, **25**, 455, 470.
GAVRILESCU, N., and PETERS, R. A. (1931). *Biochem. J.*, **25**, 1397.
Georgia Agric. Exp. Sta. (1927). *Ann. Rep.*, **40**, 28.
GERSTENBERGER, H. J. (1921). *Amer. J. Dis. Child.*, **21**, 315.
GERSTENBERGER, H. J., and NOURSE, J. D. (1926). *J. Amer. Med. Ass.*, **87**, 1108.
GIBSON, R. B., and CONCEPCION, I. (1916). *Philipp. J. Sci.*, **11**, 119.
GILLAM, A. E., and MORTON, R. A. (1927). *J. Soc. Chem. Ind.*, **46**, 415 T.
—— (1931). *Biochem. J.*, **25**, 1346.
GILROY, E. (1931). *Lancet.*, Lond., ii, 1093.
GIVENS, M. H., and COHEN, B. (1918). *J. Biol. Chem.*, **36**, 127.
GIVENS, M. H., and McCLUGAGE, H. B. (1919¹). *Ibid.*, **37**, 253.
—— (1919²). *Amer. J. Dis. Child.*, **18**, 30.
—— (1920). *J. Biol. Chem.*, **42**, 491.
—— (1920–21). *Proc. Soc. Exp. Biol.*, N.Y., **18**, 164.
GIVENS, M. H., McCLUGAGE, H. B., and VAN HORNE, E. G. (1922). *Amer. J. Dis. Child.*, **23**, 210.
GIVENS, M. H., and MACY, I. G. (1921). *J. Biol. Chem.*, **46**, xi.
Glasgow (1917). *Rep. Glasgow Hlth. Ctte.*, quoted in *Brit. Med. J.*, (1917) ii, 28.
GLITSCHER and HASSELBACH (1926). *Brit. J. Actinotherapy*, **1**, Sept.
GÖTHLIN, G. F. (1931). *Skand. Arch. Physiol.*, **61**, 225.
GOETTSCH, M. (1928). *Quart. J. Pharm.*, **1**, 168.
GOLDBERGER, J. (1914). *Publ. Hlth. Rep.*, Wash., **29**, 1683.
—— (1916). *Ibid.*, **31**, 3159.
—— (1922). *J. Amer. Med. Ass.*, **78**, 1676.
GOLDBERGER, J., and LILLIE, R. D. (1926). *Publ. Hlth. Rep.*, Wash., **41**, 1025.
GOLDBERGER, J., and SYDENSTRICKER, E. (1927). *Ibid.*, **42**, 2706.
GOLDBERGER, J., and TANNER, W. F. (1924). *Ibid.*, **39**, 87.
—— (1925). *Ibid.*, **40**, 54.
GOLDBERGER, J., WARING, C. H., and WILLETS, D. G. (1915). *Ibid.*, **30**, 3117.
GOLDBERGER, J., and WHEELER, G. A. (1927¹). *Ibid.*, **42**, 1299.
—— (1927²). *Ibid.*, 2383.
—— (1929). *Ibid.*, **44**, 2769.
GOLDBERGER, J., WHEELER, G. A., LILLIE, R. D., and ROGERS, L. M. (1926). *Ibid.*, **41**, 297.
—— (1928¹). *Ibid.*, **43**, 657.
—— (1928²). *Ibid.*, 1385.
GOLDBERGER, J., WHEELER, G. A., ROGERS, L. M., and SEBRELL, W. H. (1930). *Ibid.*, **45**, 1297.
GOLDBERGER, J., WHEELER, G. A., and SULLIVAN, M. X. (1915). *Bull. U. S. Hyg. Lab.*, No. 120.
GOLDBERGER, J., WHEELER, G. A., and SYDENSTRICKER, E. (1920). *Publ. Hlth. Rep.*, Wash., **35**, 648.
GOLDBERGER, J., WHEELER, G. A., and TANNER, W. F. (1925). *Ibid.*, **40**, 927.
GOLDBLATT, H. (1923). *Biochem. J.*, **17**, 298.
GOLDBLATT, H., and BENISCHEK, M. (1927). *J. Exp. Med.*, **46**, 699.
GOLDBLATT, H., and SOAMES, K. M. (1922). *Lancet*, Lond., ii, 1321.
—— (1923¹). *Biochem. J.*, **17**, 294.
—— (1923²). *Ibid.*, 446.
GOLDBLATT, H., and ZILVA, S. S. (1923). *Lancet*, Lond., ii, 647.
GOLDING, J., SOAMES, K. M., and ZILVA, S. S. (1926). *Biochem. J.*, **20**, 1306.

GOLDING, J., and ZILVA, S. S. (1928). *Biochem. J.*, **22**, 173.

GOODALL, A., and SLATER, J. K. (1931). *Brit. Med. J.*, i, 789.

GOSS, H. (1925). *Hilgardia*, **1**, 15.

GRANT, A. H., and GOETTSCH, M. (1926). *Amer. J. Hyg.*, **6**, 211, 228.

GRANT, A. H., SUYENAGA, B., and STEGEMAN, D. E. (1927[1]). *Amer. Rev. Tuberc.*, **16**, 628.

—— (1927[2]). *Ibid.*, 642.

GRAYZEL, D. M., and MILLER, E. G. (1928). *J. Biol. Chem.*, **76**, 423.

GREEN, H. N., and MELLANBY, E. (1928[1]). *Biochem. J.*, **22**, 102.

—— (1928[2]). *Brit. Med. J.*, ii, 691.

—— (1930). *Brit. J. Exp. Path.*, **11**, 81.

GREEN, H. N., PINDAR, D., DAVIS, G., and MELLANBY, E. (1931). *Brit. Med. J.*, ii, 595.

GREEN-ARMYTAGE, V. B. (1928). *Ind. Med. Gaz.*, **63**, 357.

GREENWALD, I., and GROSS, J. (1925). *J. Biol. Chem.*, **66**, 185, 217.

—— (1926). *Ibid.*, **68**, 325.

GREIG, W. D. W. *Private communication*, quoted by Delf (1918).

GRETTIE, D. P., and KING, C. G. (1929). *J. Biol. Chem.*, **84**, 771.

GRIJNS, G. (1901). *Geneesk. Tijdschr. Ned.-Ind.*, **41**, 3.

—— (1909). *Ibid.*, **49**, 216.

GROSS, L. (1923). *Biochem. J.*, **17**, 569.

—— (1924). *J. Path. Bact.*, **27**, 27.

GUEST, A. E., NELSON, V. E., PARKS, T. B., and FULMER, E. I. (1926). *Amer. J. Physiol.*, **76**, 339.

GUHA, B. C. (1931[1]). *Biochem. J.*, **25**, 931.

—— (1931[2]). *Ibid.*, 945.

—— (1931[3]). *Ibid.*, 960.

GUHA, B. C., and DRUMMOND, J. C. (1929). *Ibid.*, **23**, 880.

GULICK, A. (1922). *Amer. J. Physiol.*, **59**, 483.

—— (1924). *Ibid.*, **68**, 131.

GULLAND, J. M., and PETERS, R. A. (1929). *Biochem. J.*, **23**, 1122.

—— (1930). *Ibid.*, **24**, 91.

GYÖRGY, P. (1925). *Klin. Wschr.*, **4**, 1118.

—— (1929). *Ibid.*, **8**, 684.

HANKE, M. T. (1929). *J. Amer. Dent. Ass.*, **16**, 2263.

—— (1930). *Ibid.*, **17**, 957.

HANSEMANN (1906). *Berl. klin. Wschr.*, **43**, 201.

HAPP, W. M. (1922). *Johns Hopk. Hosp. Bull.*, **33**, 163.

HARA, S. (1923). *Biochem. Z.*, **142**, 79.

HARDEN, A., and ROBISON, R. (1919). *R.A.M.C. Jl.*, **32**, 48.

—— (1920). *Biochem. J.*, **14**, 171.

—— (1921). *Ibid.*, **15**, 521.

HARDEN, A., and ZILVA, S. S. (1917). *Ibid.*, **11**, 172.

—— (1918[1]). *Ibid.*, **12**, 93.

—— (1918[2]). *Ibid.*, 259.

—— (1918[3]). *Ibid.*, 270.

—— (1918[4]). *Ibid.*, 408.

—— (1918[5]). *J. Inst. Brew.*, Lond., **24**, 197.

—— (1918[6]). *Lancet*, Lond., ii, 320.

—— (1919). *J. Path. Bact.*, **22**, 246.

—— (1920[1]). *Biochem. J.*, **14**, 131.

—— (1920[2]). *Ibid.*, 263.

—— (1921). *Ibid.*, **15**, 438.

—— (1924). *Ibid.*, **18**, 1129.

HARDEN, A., ZILVA, S. S., and STILL, G. F. (1919). *Lancet*, Lond., i. 17.

HARLAN, G. P. (1917). *Brit. Med. J.*, ii, 46.

HARRIS, H. F. (1919). *Pellagra*, Macmillan & Co., New York.

HARRIS, K. D., and SMITH, E. A. (1928). *Amer. J. Physiol.*, **84**, 599.

HARRIS, L. J. (1930). *Lancet*, Lond., i, 236.

HARRIS, L. J., and INNES, J. R. M. (1931). *Biochem. J.*, **25**, 367.

HARRIS, L. J., and MOORE, T. (1928). *Ibid.*, **22**, 1461.

—— (1929[1]). *Ibid.*, **23**, 261.

—— (1929[2]). *Ibid.*, 1114.

HARRIS, L. J., and STEWART, C. P. (1929). *Ibid.*, 206.

HARRISON, R. D., SHORR, E., McCLELLAN, W. S., and DU BOIS, E. F. (1930). *J. Clin. Invest.*, **8**, 215.

HART, E. B., and McCOLLUM, E. V. (1914). *J. Biol. Chem.*, **19**, 373.

HART, E. B., MILLER, W. S., and McCOLLUM, E. V. (1916), *Ibid.*, **25**, 239.

HART, E. B., STEENBOCK, H., and ELLIS, N. R. (1921). *J. Biol. Chem.*, **46**, 309.
HART, E. B., STEENBOCK, H., KLINE, O. L., and HUMPHREY, G. C. (1930). *Ibid.* **86**, 145.
HART, E. B., STEENBOCK, H., and LEPKOVSKY, S. (1922). *Ibid.*, **52**, 241.
HART, E. B., STEENBOCK, H., LEPKOVSKY, S., and HALPIN, J. G. (1925). *Ibid.*, **66**, 813.
HART, E. B., STEENBOCK, H., LEPKOVSKY, S., KLETZIEN, S. W., and JOHNSON, O. N. (1925). *Ibid.*, **65**, 579.
HART, E. B., STEENBOCK, H., SCOTT, H., and HUMPHREY, G. C. (1927). *Ibid.*, **73**, 59.
HART, E. B., STEENBOCK, H., and SMITH, D. W. (1919). *Ibid.*, **38**, 305.
HARTWELL, G. A. (1922). *Biochem. J.*, **16**, 78.
—— (1928). *Ibid.*, **22**, 1212.
—— (1930). *Ibid.*, **24**, 967.
HASSAN, A., and DRUMMOND, J. C. (1927). *Ibid.*, **21**, 653.
HAUGE, S. M. (1930). *J. Biol. Chem.*, **86**, 161.
HAUGE, S. M., and CARRICK, C. W. (1926[1]). *Ibid.*, **69**, 403.
—— (1926[2]). *Poult. Sci.*, **5**, 166.
HAUGE, S. M., and TROST, J. F. (1928). *J. Biol. Chem.*, **80**, 107.
—— (1930). *Ibid.*, **86**, 167.
HAWKING, F. (1927). *Biochem. J.*, **21**, 728.
HAYASAKA, E. (1929–30). *Tohoku J. Exp. Med.*, **14**, 85.
HAYASAKA, E., and INAWASHIRO, R. (1929–30). *Ibid.*, 53.
HEATON, T. B. (1922). *Biochem. J.*, **16**, 800.
HEHIR, Col. (1917). *Mesopotamia Commission Report*, Appendix III.
HEILBRON, I. M., GILLAM, A. E., and MORTON, R. A. (1931). *Biochem. J.*, **25**, 1352.
HEILBRON, I. M., HESLOP, R. N., MORTON, R. A., DRUMMOND, J. C., and REA, J. L. (1932). *Chem. Ind.* **51**, 164.
HEILBRON, I. M., KAMM, E. D., and MORTON, R. A. (1926). *Chem. Ind.*, Lond., **45**, 932.
—— (1927). *Biochem. J.*, **21**, 78.
HEILBRON, I. M., and MORTON, R. A. (1931). *J. Soc. Chem. Ind.*, **50**, 183 T.
HELLER, V. G. (1923). *J. Biol. Chem.*, **55**, 385.
HELLER, V. G., McELROY, C. H., and GARLOCK, B. (1925). *Ibid.*, **65**, 255.
HENTSCHEL, H., and FISCHER, W. (1930). *Klin. Wschr.*, **9**, 1761.
HENTSCHEL, H., and SCHINDEL, L. (1930). *Ibid.*, 262.
HERZENBERG, H. (1929). *Beitr. path. Anat.*, **82**, 27.
HERZOG, F. (1921). *Frankfurt. Z. Pathol.*, **26**, 50.
HESS, A. F. (1920). *Scurvy, Past and Present.* J. B. Lippincott & Co., Philadelphia.
—— (1921). *J. Amer. Med. Ass.*, **76**, 693.
—— (1930). *Rickets*, p. 211. Henry Kimpton, Lond.
HESS, A. F., and FISH, M. (1914). *Amer. J. Dis. Child.*, **8**, 385.
HESS, A. F., and KILLIAN, J. (1918–19). *Proc. Soc. Exp. Biol.*, N.Y., **16**, 43.
HESS, A. F., and LEWIS, J. M. (1928). *J. Amer. Med. Ass.*, **91**, 783.
HESS, A. F., LEWIS, J. M., and RIVKIN, H., (1929). *Ibid.*, **93**, 661.
HESS, A. F., PONCHER, H. G., DALE, M. L., and KLEIN, R. I. (1930). *Ibid.*, **95**, 316.
HESS, A. F., and UNGER, L. J. (1917). *Ibid.*, **69**, 1583.
—— (1918[1]). *J. Biol. Chem.*, **35**, 479.
—— (1918[2]). *Ibid.*, 487.
—— (1918–19). *Proc. Soc. Exp. Biol.*, N.Y., **16**, 1.
—— (1919). *J. Biol. Chem.*, **38**, 293.
—— (1920–21). *Proc. Soc. Exp. Biol.*, N.Y., **18**, 143.
—— (1921[1]). *J. Amer. Med. Ass.*, **77**, 39.
—— (1921[2]). *Amer. J. Dis. Child.*, **22**, 186.
—— (1922). *J. Amer. Med. Ass.*, **78**, 1596.
HESS, A. F., UNGER, L. J., and PAPPENHEIMER, A. W. (1921–22[1]). *J. Biol. Chem.*, **50**, 77.
—— (1921–22[2]). *Proc. Soc. Exp. Biol.*, N.Y. **19**, 8.
—— (1921–22[3]). *J. Exp. Med.*, **36**, 427.
—— (1921–22[4]). *Proc. Soc. Exp. Biol.*, N.Y. **19**, 238.
HESS, A. F., UNGER, L. J., and SUPPLEE, G. C. (1920–21). *J. Biol. Chem.*, **45**, 229.
HESS, A. F., and WEINSTOCK, M. (1924[1]). *Amer. J. Dis. Child.*, **27**, 1.
—— (1924[2]). *J. Biol. Chem.*, **62**, 301.
—— (1924–25). *Proc. Soc. Exp. Biol.*, N.Y. **22**, 5, 6.
—— (1925[1]). *J. Biol. Chem.*, **63**, 297.
—— (1925[2]). *Ibid.*, **64**, 181.
—— (1925[3]). *Ibid.*, 193.
—— (1925–26). *Proc. Soc. Exp. Biol.*, N.Y., **23**, 407.

HESS, A. F., and WEINSTOCK, M. (1926–27). *Proc. Soc. Exp. Biol.*, N.Y., **24**, 759.

—— (1927). *Amer. J. Dis. Child.*, **34**, 845.

HESS, A. F., WEINSTOCK, M., and HELMAN, F. D. (1925). *J. Biol. Chem.*, **63**, 305.

HESS, A. F., WEINSTOCK, M., and RIVKIN, H., (1928–29). *Proc. Soc. Exp. Biol.*, N.Y., **26**, 255.

—— (1929–30). *Ibid.*, **27**, 298.

HESS, A. F., WEINSTOCK, M., RIVKIN, H., and GROSS, J. (1930). *J. Biol. Chem.*, **87**, 37.

HESS, A. F., WEINSTOCK, M., and SHERMAN, E. (1927). *J. Amer. Med. Ass.*, **88**, 24.

HESS, A. F., and WINDAUS, A. (1926–27). *Proc. Soc. Exp. Biol.*, N.Y., **24**, 171.

HESS, W. R. (1921). *Hoppe-Seyl. Z.*, **117**, 284.

HESS, W. R., and MESSERLE, N. (1921). *Ibid.*, **119**, 176.

HETLER, R. A., MEYER, C. R., and HUSSEMANN, D. (1931). *Bull. Illinois Agric. Expt. Sta.*, 369.

HEUBNER, O. (1903). *Berl. klin. Wschr.*, **40**, 285.

HIFT, R. (1918). *Wien. klin. Wschr.*, **31**, 939.

—— (1920). *Wien. med. Wschr.*, **70**, 601.

HOAGLAND, R. (1923). *Bull. U. S. Dept. Agric.*, 1138.

HOAGLAND, R., and SNIDER, G. G. (1930). *J. Agric. Res.*, **41**, 205.

HÖJER, J. A. (1924). *Studies in Scurvy.* Upsala. (*Acta Paediat.*, III Suppl.)

—— (1926). *Brit. J. Exp. Path.*, **7**, 356.

HÖJER, J. A., and WESTIN, G. (1925). *Dent. Cosmos*, **67**, 1.

HOET, J., (1922). *Arch. int. Physiol.*, **19**, 129.

HOET, J., LECLEF, G., and DELARUE, G. (1924). *Ibid.*, **23**, 284.

HOFMEISTER, F. (1920). *Biochem. Z.*, **103**, 218.

—— (1922). *Ibid.*, **129**, 477.

HOGAN, A. G., and HARSHAW, H. M. (1926). *Bull. Miss. Agric. Expt. Sta.*, 94.

HOGAN, A. G., and HUNTER, J. E. (1928). *J. Biol. Chem.*, **78**, 433.

HOLM, E. (1925). *Amer. J. Physiol.*, **73**, 79.

HOLST, A. (1907) *J. Hyg.*, Camb., **7**, 619.

—— (1911–12). *Trans. Soc. Trop. Med. Hyg.*, Lond., **5**, 76.

HOLST, A. and FRÖLICH, T. (1907). *J. Hyg.*, Camb., **7**, 634.

—— (1912). *Z. Hyg. InfektKr.*, **72**, 1.

—— (1920). *J. Trop. Med.*, **23**, 261.

HOLST, P. M. (1927). *J. Hyg.*, Camb., **26**, 437.

HOLTZ, F., and SCHREIBER, E. (1930). *Hoppe-Seyl. Z.*, **191**, 1.

HOOBLER, B. R. (1928). *J. Amer. Med. Ass.*, **91**, 307.

HOPKINS, F. G. (1906). *Analyst*, **31**, 395.

—— (1912). *J. Physiol.*, **44**, 425.

—— (1920). *Biochem. J.*, **14**, 725.

HOPKINS, F. G., and NEVILLE, A. (1913). *Ibid.*, **7**, 97.

HORBACZEWSKI, J. (1910). *Öst. Sanitätsw.*, **31**.

—— (1912). *Ibid.*, **21**.

HOSOYA, S., and KUROYA, M. (1923[1]). *Sci. Reps. Govt. Inst. Inf. Dis.*, Tokyo, **2**, 233.

—— (1923[2]). *Ibid.*, **2**, 265.

HOTTINGER, A. (1927[1]). *Z. Kinderhlk.*, **44**, 282.

—— (1927[2]). *Klin. Wschr.*, **6**, 1793.

HOU, H. C. (1928). *Chinese J. Physiol.*, **2**, 345.

—— (1929). *Ibid.*, **3**, 171.

HOUSE, M. C., NELSON, P. M., and HABER, E. S. (1929). *J. Biol. Chem.*, **81**, 495.

HOWE, P. R. (1919). *J. Amer. Dent. Ass.*, **6**, 413.

—— (1921). *Dent. Cosmos*, **63**.

—— (1923). *J. Amer. Dent. Ass.*, **10**, 755.

HOYLE, E. (1929). *Biochem. J.*, **23**, 54.

HOYLE, E., and ZILVA, S. S. (1927). *Ibid.*, **21**, 1121.

HOYLE, J. C. (1930[1]). *J. Pharmacol.*, **38**, 271.

—— (1930[2]). *Ibid.*, **40**, 351.

HOYLE, J. C., and BUCKLAND, H. (1929). *Biochem. J.*, **23**, 558.

HUCKEL, R., and WENZEL, H. (1929[1]). *Z. Kreislaufforsch.*, **21**, 409.

—— (1929[2]). *Arch. exp. Path. Pharmak.*, **141**, 292.

HUGHES, J. S., AUBEL, C. E., and LIENHARDT, H. F. (1928). *Bull. Kans. Agric. Expt. Sta.*, **23**, 48.

HUGHES, J. S., LIENHARDT, H. F., and AUBEL, C. E. (1929). *J. Nutrition*, **2**, 183.

HUGHES, J. S., NITCHER, C., and TITUS, R. W. (1925). *J. Biol. Chem.*, **63**, 205.

HULDSCHINSKY, K. (1919). *Deuts. med. Wschr.*, **45**, 712.

—— (1920). *Z. orthop. Chir.*, **89**, 426.

—— (1926). *Klin. Wschr.*, **5**, 1927.

HUME, E. M. (1921). *Biochem. J.*, **15**, 163.

HUME, E. M. (1922). *Lancet*, Lond., ii, 1318.

—— (1923). *Sp. Rep. Ser. Med. Res. Coun.*, Lond., No. 77.

HUME, E. M., LUCAS, N. S., and SMITH, H. H. (1927). *Biochem. J.*, **21**, 362.

HUME, E. M., and NIRENSTEIN, E. (1921). *Lancet*, Lond., ii, 849.

HUME, E. M., and SMEDLEY-MACLEAN, I. (1930). *Ibid.*, i, 290.

HUME, E. M., and SMITH, H. H. (1923). *Biochem. J.*, **17**, 364.

—— (1924). *Ibid.*, **18**, 1334.

—— (1930). *Lancet*, Lond., ii, 1362.

HUMPHREYS, F. E., and ZILVA, S. S. (1931). *Biochem. J.*, **25**, 579.

HUNT, C. H. (1928[1]). *J. Biol. Chem.*, **78**, 83.

—— (1928[2]). *Ibid.*, **79**, 723.

HUNT, C. H., and KRAUS, W. E. (1928). *Ibid.*, 733.

HUNT, C. H., and WINTER, A. R. (1922). *Science*, **56**, 114.

HUNTER, D. (1931). *Quart. J. Med.*, **24**, 393.

HUSTON, R. C., LIGHTBODY, H. D., and BALL, C. D. jr. (1928). *J. Biol. Chem.*, **79**, 507.

HUTCHINSON, R. (1911). *Food and the Principles of Dietetics*, Lond., p. 434.

HUTCHISON, H. S., and SHAH, S. J. (1922). *Quart. J. Med.*, **15**, 167.

IDE, M. (1906). *Zbl. Bakt.*, Abt. II, **18**, 193.

IGARASHI, E., and TAGAYA, T. (1929). *J. Biochem.*, Tokyo, **11**, 239.

INAWASHIRO, R., and HAYASAKA, E. (1928). *Tohoku J. Exp. Med.*, **12**, 1.

JACKSON, F. G., and HARLEY, V. (1900[1]). *Proc. Roy. Soc.*, **66**, 250.

—— (1900[2]). *Lancet*, Lond., i, 1184.

JACKSON, L., and MOODY, A. M. (1916). *J. Infect. Dis.*, **19**, 511.

JAMESON, H. L., DRUMMOND, J. C., and COWARD, K. H. (1922). *Biochem. J.*, **16**, 482.

JANSEN, B. C. P. (1923). *Rep. Dutch-Indian Med. Civil Service*, Part I.

JANSEN, B. C. P., and DONATH, W. F. (1925). *Mededeel. Dienst Volksgezondheid Ned.-Ind.*, Part III, 225.

—— (1926[1]). *Proc. Kon. Akad. Wetensch.*, Amsterdam, **29**, 1390.

—— (1926[2]). *Verslag. Kon. Akad. Wetensch.*, Amsterdam, **35**, 923.

—— (1927). *Geneesk. Tijdschr. Ned.-Ind.*, **66**, 810.

JANSEN, B. C. P., KINNERSLEY, H. W., PETERS, R. A., and READER, V., (1930). *Biochem. J.*, **24**, 1824.

JAPHA, A. (1905). *Arch. Kinderhlk.*, **42**, 66.

JARUSSOWA, N. (1928). *Biochem. Z.*, **198**, 128.

JAVILLIER, M., BAUDE, P., and LÉVY-LAJEUNESSE, S. (1925). *Bull. Soc. chim. biol.*, Paris, **7**, 39.

JENDRASSIK, A. (1923). *J. Biol. Chem.*, **57**, 129.

JENDRASSIK, A., and KEMENYFFI, A. G. (1927). *Biochem. Z.*, **189**, 180.

—— (1928). *Ibid.*, **201**, 269.

—— (1929). *Ibid.*, **216**, 238.

JEPHCOTT, H. and BACHARACH, A. L. (1921). *Biochem. J.*, **15**, 129.

—— (1926). *Ibid.*, **20**, 1351.

—— (1928). *Ibid.*, **22**, 60.

JOHNS, C. O., FINKS, A. J., and PAUL, M. S., (1919). *J. Biol. Chem.*, **37**, 497.

JOHNSON, J. M. (1921). *Publ. Hlth. Rep.* Wash., **36**, 2044.

JOHNSON, J. M., and HOOPER, C. W. (1921). *Ibid.*, 2037.

—— (1922). *Ibid.*, **37**, 989.

JONES, D. B. and MURPHY, J. C. (1924). *J. Biol. Chem.*, **59**, 243.

JONES D. B., MURPHY, J. C., and NELSON, E. M. (1928). *Ind. Eng. Chem.*, **20**, 205.

JONES, D. B., NELSON, E. M., and MURPHY, J. C. (1928). *Ibid.*, 648.

JONES, J. H. (1927). *J. Biol. Chem.*, **75**, 139.

JONES, M. R., JAMES, L., and SMITH, C. E. (1923–24). *Proc. Soc. Exp. Biol.*, N.Y., **21**, 199.

JUHASZ-SCHÄFFER, A. (1931). *Virchows Arch.*, **281**, 3.

Kansas Agr. Expt. Sta. Rep. (1926–28) 123.

KARR, W. G. (1920). *J. Biol. Chem.*, **44**, 255, 277.

KARRER, P., EULER, H. v., HELLSTRÖM, H., and RYDBOM, M. (1931). *Svenska Chem. Tidskr.*, **43**, 105.

KARRER, P. and MORF, R. (1931). *Helv. chim. Acta*, **14**, 1033.

KARRER, P., MORF, R., and SCHÖPP, K. (1931[1]). *Ibid.*, 1036.

—— (1931[2]). *Ibid.*, 1431.

KAY, H. D., and ZILVA, S. S. (1923). *Biochem. J.*, **17**, 872.

KEEFER, C. S., and YANG, C. S. (1929). *Nat. Med. J. China*, **15**, 419.

KELLAWAY, C. H. (1921). *Proc. Roy. Soc.*, B. **92**, 6.

KENNEDY, C., and DUTCHER, R. A. (1922). *J. Biol. Chem.*, **50**, 339.

KENNEDY, C., and PALMER, L. S. (1922). *Ibid.*, **54**, 217.

—— (1926). *Amer. J. Physiol.*, **76**, 316.

KENNEDY, C., and PALMER, L. S. (1928). *J. Biol. Chem.*, **76**, 607.
—— (1929). *Ibid.*, **83**, 493.
KENNEDY, W. P. (1926). *Quart. J. Exp. Physiol.*, **16**, 281.
KENNY, C. L. (1926). *Dissertation*, Columbia Univ., New York, quoted by SHERMAN and SMITH (1931).
KERR, R. W. (1927–28). *Proc. Soc. Exp. Biol.*, N.Y., **25**, 344.
KERR, R. W., EDDY, W. H., and WILLIAMS, R. R. (1925–26). *Ibid.*, **23**, 416.
KEY, K. M., and ELPHICK, G. K. (1931). *Biochem. J.*, **25**, 888.
KEY, K. M., and MORGAN, B. G. E. (1932). *Ibid.*, **26**, 196.
KIEFERLE, F., and ZEILE, K. (1926). *Fortschr. Landw.*, **1**, 83.
KIFER, H. B., and MUNSELL, H. E. (1929). *J. Agric. Res.*, **39**, 355.
KINNERSLEY, H. W., and PETERS, R. A. (1925). *Biochem. J.*, **19**, 820.
—— (1927). *Ibid.*, **21**, 777.
—— (1928). *Ibid.*, **22**, 419.
—— (1929). *Ibid.*, **23**, 1126.
—— (1930[1]). *Ibid.*, **24**, 711.
—— (1930[2]). *Ibid.*, 1856.
KINNERSLEY, H. W., PETERS, R. A., and READER, V. (1928). *Ibid.*, **22**, 276.
—— (1930). *Ibid.*, **24**, 1820.
KLAUDER, T. V., and WINKELMAN, N. W. (1928). *J. Amer. Med. Ass.*, **90**, 364.
KLAUSNER-CRONHEIM, I. (1930). *Deuts. med. Wschr.*, **56**, 1566.
KLEIN, I. J. (1929). *J. Amer. Med. Ass.*, **92**, 621.
KLOSTER, J. (1931). *Acta Paediat.*, **12**, Suppl. III.
KNAPP, P. (1908). *Z. exp. Path. Ther.*, **5**, 147.
KNUDSON, A., and MOORE, C. N. (1928). *J. Biol. Chem.*, **78**, xix.
—— (1929). *Ibid.*, **81**, 49.
KNUDSON, A., and RANDLES, F. S. (1925). *Ibid.*, **63**, xxxi.
KOCH, E. M., and CAHAN, M. M. (1927). *Amer. J. Dis. Child.*, **34**, 187.
KOCH, E., KOCH, F. C., and LEMON, H. B. (1929). *J. Biol. Chem.*, **85**, 159.
KOCH, E., and RAGINS, I. K. (1929). *Ibid.*, 141.
KOCH, J. (1912). *Z. Hyg. InfektKr.*, **72**, 321.
KOHL (1902). *Untersuch. über das Carotin*, Leipzig.
KOHMAN, E. F. (1920). *Amer. J. Physiol.*, **51**, 378.
KOHMAN, E. F., EDDY, W. H., and CARLSSON, V. (1924). *Ind. Eng. Chem.*, **16**, 1261.
KOHMAN, E. F., EDDY, W. H., CARLSSON, V., and HALLIDAY, N. (1926). *Ibid.*, **18**, 302.
KOHMAN, E. F., EDDY, W. H., and HALLIDAY, N. (1928). *Ibid.*, **20**, 202.
KOLLATH, W. (1929). *Klin. Wschr.*, **8**, 444.
—— (1930). *Arch. exp. Path. Pharmak.*, **142**, 86.
KON, S. K. (1927[1]). *Biochem. J.*, **21**, 834.
—— (1927[2]). *Ibid.*, **21**, 837.
—— (1929). *J. Nutrition*, **1**, 467.
—— (1931). *Biochem. J.*, **25**, 482
KON, S., DANIELS, F., and STEENBOCK, H. (1928). *J. Amer. Chem. Soc.*, **50**, 2573.
KON, S. K., and DRUMMOND, J. C. (1927). *Biochem. J.*, **21**, 632.
KON, S. K., and WATCHORN, E. (1928). *J. Hyg.*, Camb., **27**, 321.
KOPP, J. H. (1836[1]). *J. prakt. Heilk.*, **82** (IV), 115.
—— (1836[2]). *Denkwürdigkeiten der ärztlichen Praxis*, Frankf. a. M., **3**, 398.
KORENCHEVSKY, V. (1922). *Sp. Rep. Ser. Med. Res. Coun.*, Lond., No. 71.
—— (1923). *J. Path. Bact.*, **26**, 382.
KOSSEL, A., and KUTSCHER, F. (1900). *Hoppe-Seyl. Z.*, **31**, 165.
KRAMER, M. M., EDDY, W. H., and KOHMAN, E. F. (1929). *Ind. Eng. Chem.*, **21**, 859.
KREITMAIR, H., and HINTZELMANN, U. (1928). *Arch. exp. Path. Pharmak.*, **137**, 203.
KREITMAIR, H., and MOLL, TH. (1928). *Münch. med. Wschr.*, **75**, 637.
KRUSE, H. D., and McCOLLUM, E. V., (1929). *Physiol. Rev.*, **9**, 126.
KUHN, R., and BROCKMANN, H. (1931[1]). *Ber. deuts. chem. Ges.*, **64**, 1859.
—— (1931[2]). *Hoppe-Seyl. Z.*, **200**, 255.
KUHN, R., and LEDERER, E. (1931[1]). *Naturwissenschaften*, **19**, 306.
—— (1931[2]). *Ber. deuts. chem. Ges.*, **64**, 1349.
KUMER, L. (1931). *Wien. klin. Wschr.*, **44**, 849.
KUROYA, M., and HOSOYA, S. (1923). *Sci. Reps. Govt. Inst. Inf. Dis.*, Tokyo, **2**, 287.
LALAND, P. (1932). *Hoppe-Seyl. Z.*, **204**, 112.
LAMB, G. (1902). *Lancet*, Lond., i, 10.
LA MER, V. K. (1922). *Dissertation*, New York.
LANE-CLAYPON, J. E. (1916). *Milk and its Hygienic Relations*, Lond.
LASSEN, H. C. A. (1930). *J. Hyg.*, Camb., **30**, 300.
LATASTE, F. (1884). Quoted by BLAND-SUTTON, *Trans. Path. Soc.*, p. 472.
LEADER, V. R. (1930). *Biochem. J.*, **24**, 1172.

LECOQ, R. (1931). *J. Biol. Chem.*, **91**, 671.
LEICHTENTRITT, B., and ZIELASKOWSKI, M. (1922). *Biochem. Z.*, **131**, 499, 513.
LEIGH-CLARE, J. L. (1927[1]). *Biochem. J.*, **21**, 368.
—— (1927[2]). *Ibid.*, 725.
LEIGHTON, G., and CLARK, M. L. (1929). *Lancet*, Lond., i, 40.
LEITCH, J. N. (1930). *Dietetics in Warm Climates* (Harrison & Sons, Lond.).
LEPKOVSKY, S., HART, E. B., HASTINGS, E. G., and FRAZIER, W. C. (1925). *J. Biol. Chem.*, **66**, 49.
LEPKOVSKY, S., and NELSON, M. T. (1924). *Ibid.*, **59**, 91.
LEPKOVSKY, S., WOOD, C., and EVANS, H. M. (1930). *Ibid.*, **87**, 239.
LEPPER, E. H., and ZILVA, S. S. (1925). *Biochem. J.*, **19**, 581.
LEVENE, P. A. (1928). *J. Biol. Chem.*, **79**, 465.
LEVENE, P. A., and VAN DER HOEVEN, B. J. C. (1924). *Ibid.*, **61**, 429.
—— (1925). *Ibid.*, **65**, 483.
—— (1926). *J. Pharmacol.*, **29**, 227.
LEVINE, V. E. (1924–25). *J. Biol. Chem.*, **62**, 157.
LEVINE, V. E., McCOLLUM, E. V., and SIMMONDS, N. (1922). *Ibid.*, **53**, 7.
LIFSCHÜTZ, I. (1913). *Biochem. Z.*, **48**, 373.
LIND, J. (1757). *A Treatise on the Scurvy*, Lond., 2nd ed.
LINSERT, O. (1931). Quoted by WINDAUS, A., LÜTTRINGHAUS, A., and DEPPE (1931) *Liebigs Ann.*, **489**, 252.
LITTLE, J. M. (1912). *J. Amer. Med. Ass.*, **58**, 2029.
LOPEZ-LOMBA, J., and RANDOIN, L. (1923[1]). *C. R. Acad. Sci.*, Paris, **176**, 1003.
—— (1923[2]). *Ibid.*, 1573.
LUCAS, G. H. W. (1924). *J. Phys. Chem.*, **28**, 1180.
LUCAS, N. S. (1931). *Biochem. J.*, **25**, 57.
LUCE, E. M. (1924[1]). *Ibid.*, **18**, 716.
—— (1924[2]). *Ibid.*, 1279.
—— (1926). *J. Biol. Chem.*, **71**, 187.
LUCKIESH, M. (1930). *Artificial Sunlight*, p. 34 (Crosby, Lockwood & Son., Lond.).
LUNSGAARD, E. (1930). *Biochem. Z.*, **217**, 162.
LUNIN, N. (1881). *Hoppe-Seyl. Z.*, **5**, 31.
MacCALLUM, W. G., and VOEGTLIN, C. (1909). *J. Exp. Med.*, **11**, 118.
McCARRISON, R. (1919). *Ind. J. Med. Res.*, **6**, 275, 550, 557.
—— (1921). *Studies in Deficiency Disease*, Lond.
—— (1924). *Brit. Med. J.*, i, 414.
—— (1926–27). *Ind. J. Med. Res.*, **14**, 895.
—— (1927–28). *Ibid.*, **15**, 485.
—— (1928). *Beri-Beri Columbarum*, *Ind. Med. Res. Mem.*, No. 10.
—— (1929–30[1]). *Ind. J. Med. Res.*, **17**, 1103.
—— (1929–30[2]). *Ibid.*, 1115.
McCARRISON, R., and NORRIS, R. V. (1924). *Ind. Med. Res. Mem.*, No. 2.
McCLENDON, J. F., and COLE, W. C. C. (1919). *Amer. J. Physiol.*, **49**, 145.
McCLENDON, J. F., COLE, W. C. C., ENGSTRAND, O., and MIDDLEKAUFF, J. E. (1919). *J. Biol. Chem.*, **40**, 243.
McCOLLUM, E. V. (1911). *Amer. J. Physiol.*, **29**, 210.
—— (1917). *J. Amer. Med. Ass.*, **68**, 1379.
—— (1918). *Ibid.*, **71**, 937.
McCOLLUM, E. V., and DAVIS, M. (1913). *J. Biol. Chem.*, **15**, 167.
—— (1913–14). *Proc. Soc. Exp. Biol.*, N.Y., **11**, 101.
—— (1914). *J. Biol. Chem.*, **19**, 245.
—— (1915[1]). *Ibid.*, **21**, 179.
—— (1915[2]). *Ibid.*, **23**, 181.
—— (1915[3]). *Ibid.*, 231.
McCOLLUM, E. V., and KENNEDY, C. (1916). *Ibid.*, **24**, 491.
McCOLLUM, E. V., and PARSONS, H. T. (1920). *Ibid.*, **44**, 603.
McCOLLUM, E. V., and PITZ, W. (1917). *Ibid.*, **31**, 229.
McCOLLUM, E. V., and SIMMONDS, N. (1917). *Ibid.* **32**, 181.
—— (1918). *Ibid.*, **33**, 55.
—— (1928). *The Newer Knowledge of Nutrition.* Macmillan & Co., New York.
McCOLLUM, E. V., SIMMONDS, N., and BECKER, J. E. (1922). *Ibid.*, **53**, 313.
—— (1925). *Ibid.*, **63**, 547.
—— (1926–27). *Proc. Soc. Exp. Biol.*, N.Y., **24**, 952.
McCOLLUM, E. V., SIMMONDS, N., BECKER, J. E., and SHIPLEY, P. G. (1922). *J. Biol. Chem.*, **53**, 293.
McCOLLUM, E. V., SIMMONDS, N., KINNEY, E. M., and GRIEVES, C. J. (1922). *Johns Hopk. Hosp. Bull.*, **33**, 202.

McCollum, E. V., Simmonds, N., and Parsons, H. T. (1921). *J. Biol. Chem.*, **47**, 111, 139, 175, 207, 235.

McCollum, E. V., Simmonds, N., Parsons, H. T., Shipley, P. G., and Park, E. A. (1921). *Ibid.*, **45**, 333.

McCollum, E. V., Simmonds, N., and Pitz, W. (1916). *Ibid.*, **27**, 33.

—— (1917[1]). *Ibid.*, **29**, 341.

—— (1917[2]). *Ibid.*, 521.

McCollum, E. V., Simmonds, N., Shipley, P. G., and Park, E. A. (1922). *Ibid.*, **51**, 41.

McCosh, S. S., Macy, I. G., and Hunscher, H. A. (1931). *Ibid.*, **90**, 1.

McCrudden, F. H. (1910). *Arch. Int. Med.*, **5**, 596.

MacDonald, M. B. (1922). *J. Biol. Chem.*, **54**, 243.

—— (1923). *Ibid.*, **56**, 489.

MacDonald, M. B., and McCollum, E. V. (1920–21). *Ibid.*, **45**, 307.

Mackay, H. M. M. (1931). *Sp. Rep. Ser. Med. Res. Coun.*, Lond., No. 157.

Mackay. H. M. M., and Shaw, H. F. (1925). *Brit. Med. J.*, ii, 344.

McLaughlin, A. J., and Andrews, V. L. (1910). *Philipp. J. Sci.* (B), **5**, 149.

MacLeod, F. L. (1927). *J. Amer. Med. Ass.*, **88**, 1947.

McNab (1837). *Quart. J. Cal. Med. Phys. Soc.*, **1**, 306.

Macphail, N. P. (1929). *United Fruit Co., Med. Dept., 18th Ann. Rep.*, 172.

Macy, I. G., Hunscher, H. A., McCosh, S. S., and Nims, B. (1930). *J. Biol. Chem.*, **86**, 59.

Macy, I. G., and Outhouse, J. (1929). *Amer. J. Dis. Child.*, **37**, 379.

Macy, I. G., Outhouse, J., Graham, A., and Long, M. L. (1927[1]). *J. Biol. Chem.*, **73**, 175.

—— (1927[2]). *Ibid.*, 189.

Macy, I. G., Outhouse, J., Long, M. L., and Graham, A. (1927). *Ibid.*, 153.

Magee, H. E., and Glennie, A. E. (1928). *Biochem. J.*, **22**, 11.

Magee, H. E., and Harvey, D. (1926[1]). *Ibid.*, **20**, 873.

—— (1926[2]). *Ibid.*, 885.

Mandl, F. (1926). *Zbl. Chir.*, **53**, 260.

—— (1929). *Ibid.*, **56**, 1739.

Mann, H. C. Corry (1926). *Sp. Rep. Ser. Med. Res. Coun.*, Lond., No. 105.

Marcus, J. K. (1928). *J. Biol. Chem.*, **80**, 9.

Marfan, A. B. (1911). *Le rachitisme et sa pathogénie* (Paris).

Marrian, G. F. (1928). *Biochem. J.*, **22**, 836.

Marrian, G. F., Baker, L. C., Drummond, J. C., and Woollard, H. (1927). *Biochem. J.*, **21**, 1336.

Marrian, G. F., and Parkes, A. S. (1928). *Proc. R. Micr. Soc.*, **48**, 257.

Marshall, J. A. (1922). *J. Amer. Dent. Ass.*

Martin, C. J., and Robison, R. R. (1922). *Biochem. J.*, **16**, 407.

Mason, K. E. (1925). *Proc. Nat. Acad. Sci.*, Wash., **11**, 377.

—— (1926). *J. Exp. Zool.*, **45**, 159.

—— (1929). *J. Nutrition*, **1**, 311.

Mattick, E. C. V., and Hallett, H. S. (1929). *J. Agric. Res.*, **19**, 452.

Mattill, H. A. (1922). *J. Biol. Chem.*, **50**, xii.

—— (1926–27). *Amer. J. Physiol.*, **79**, 305.

—— (1927). *J. Amer. Med. Ass.*, **89**, 1505.

Mattill, H. A., and Carman, J. S. (1922–23). *Proc. Soc. Exp. Biol.*, N.Y., **20**, 420.

Mattill, H. A., Carman, J. S., and Clayton, M. M. (1924). *J. Biol. Chem.*, **61**, 729.

Mattill, H. A., and Clayton, M. M. (1925). *Ibid.*, **63**, xxvii.

—— (1926). *Ibid.*, **68**, 665.

Mattill, H. A., and Congdon, C. C. (1924). *Ibid.*, **59**, xii.

Mattill, H. A., and Conklin, R. E. (1920). *Ibid.*, **44**, 137.

Mattill, H. A., and Pratt, A. D. (1928–29). *Proc. Soc. Exp. Biol.*, N.Y., **26**, 82.

Mattill, H. A., and Stone, N. C. (1923). *J. Biol. Chem.*, **55**, 443.

Maxwell, J. P. (1930). *Proc. R. Soc. Med.*, **23**, 639.

Maxwell, J. P. and Miles, L. M. (1925). *J. Obstet. Gynaec.*, **32**, No. 3.

Mazé, M. P. (1925). *C. R. Acad. Sci.*, Paris, **180**, 1683.

Medes, G. (1926). *J. Lab. Clin. Med.*, **11**, 871.

Medical History of the War of Rebellion (1888). Washington, vol. iii.

Medical Research Council (1923). *Studies of rickets in Vienna. Sp. Rep. Ser. Med. Res. Coun.*, Lond., No. 77.

—— (1924). *Report on the present state of knowledge of Accessory Food Factors (Vitamins). Sp. Rep. Ser. Med. Res. Coun.*, Lond., No. 38 (revised).

—— (1930). *A standard for the antirachitic Vitamin D. Brit. Med. J., Lancet*, Lond., and *Pharmaceutical J.*, Aug. 30.

MEESEMAECKER, R. (1930). *C. R. Acad. Sci.*, Paris, **190**, 216.

MEISSNER, M., (1919). *Wien. klin. Rdsch.*, **33**, 15.

MELLANBY, E. (1918–19[1]). *J. Physiol.*, **52**, xi (Jan. 1918).

—— (1918–19[2]). *Ibid.*, **52**, liii (Dec. 1918).

—— (1919). *Lancet*, Lond., i, 407.

—— (1920). *Ibid.*, i, 856.

—— (1921). *Sp. Rep. Ser. Med. Res. Coun.*, Lond., No. 61.

—— (1922). *Brit. Med. J.*, ii, 490.

—— (1924). *Ibid.*, i, 895.

—— (1925). *Sp. Rep. Ser. Med. Res. Coun.*, Lond., No. 93.

—— (1926[1]). *J. Physiol.*, **61**, xxiv.

—— (1926[2]). *Brit. Med. J.*, i, 515.

—— (1930[1]). *Ibid.*, i, 677.

—— (1930[2]). *Rep. Publ. Hlth. Cong. and Exhibition*, p. 86.

—— (1931[1]). *J. Amer. Med. Ass.*, **96**, 325.

—— (1931[2]). *Brain.*, **54**, 247.

—— (1931[3]). *Brit. Med. J.*, i, 85 (suppl.).

MELLANBY, E., and GREEN, H. N. (1929). *Ibid.*, i, 984.

MELLANBY, E., SURIE, E. M., and HARRISON, D. C. (1929). *Biochem. J.*, **23**, 710.

MELLANBY, M. (1918). *Lancet*, Lond., ii, 767.

—— (1920). *Dent. Rec.*, **40**, 63.

—— (1921). *Brit. J. Dent. Sci.*, **64**, 80.

—— (1923[1]). *Brit. Dent. J.*, **44**, 1.

—— (1923[2]). *Ibid.*, 1031.

—— (1923[3]). *Proc. R. Soc. Med.*, **16**, 74 (Sect. Odont.)

—— (1924). *Brit. Dent. J.*, **45**, 545.

—— (1927[1]). *Ibid.*, **48**, 737.

—— (1927[2]). *Ibid.*, 1481.

—— (1928). *Ibid.*, **49**, 769.

—— (1929). *Sp. Rep. Ser. Med. Res. Coun.*, Lond., No. 140.

—— (1930[1]). *Proc. R. Soc. Med.*, **23** (Sect. Odont. 41).

—— (1930[2]). *Sp. Rep. Ser. Med. Res. Coun.*, Lond., No. 153.

MELLANBY, M., and KILLICK, E. M. (1926). *Biochem. J.*, **20**, 902.

MELLANBY, M., and PATTISON, C. L. (1926). *Brit. Dent. J.*, **47**, 1045.

—— (1928). *Brit. Med. J.*, ii, 1079.

—— (1932). *Ibid.*, i, 507.

MELLANBY, M., PATTISON, C. L., and PROUD, J. W. (1924). *Brit. Med. J.*, ii, 354.

MENDEL, L. B., and VICKERY, H. B. (1928–29). *Proc. Soc. Exp. Biol.*, N.Y., **26**, 552.

Mesopotamia Commission Report (1917).

MEULENGRACHT, E. (1927). *Acta. med. Scand.*, **67**, 43.

MEYER, A. W., and McCORMICK, L. M. (1927–28). *Stanford Univ. Pub. Univ. Ser. Med. Sci.*, **2**, pp. 107

MEYER, L. F., and NASSAU, E. (1924). *Klin. Wschr.*, **3**, 2132.

—— (1925). *Ibid.*, **4**. 2380.

MILES, L. M., and FENG, C. T. (1925). *J. Exp. Med.*, **41**, 137.

MILLER, C. D. (1925). *J. Home Econ.*, **17**, 377.

—— (1926). *Biochem. J.*, **20**, 515.

—— (1927). *B. P. Bishop Museum*, Bull. No. 37.

—— (1929). *Ibid.*, Bull. No. 64.

MILLER, D. J. M. (1917). *Cleveland Med. J.*, **16**, 541.

MILLER, E. W. (1920). *J. Biol. Chem.*, **44**, 159.

MILLER, H. G. (1926–27). *Amer. J. Physiol.*, **79**, 255.

MILLER, H. G., and YATES, W. W. (1924). *J. Biol. Chem.*, **62**, 259.

MILLER, W. L. (1924). *Science*, **59**, 197.

MINOT, G. R., and MURPHY, W. P. (1926). *J. Amer. Med. Ass.*, **87**, 470.

MITCHELL, H. H. (1919). *J. Biol. Chem.*, **40**, 399.

—— (1924). *Ibid.*, **58**, 905.

MIYADERA, K. (1921). *Biochem. Z.*, **124**, 244.

MONRAD, S. (1917). *Ugeskr. Læg.*, **79**, 1177.

MOORE, (1914). *Canada Dept. Agri. Rep. Exp. Farm Brit. Columbia*, 21.

MOORE, T. (1929[1]). *Lancet*, Lond., i, 499.

—— (1929[2]). *Biochem. J.*, **23**. 803.

—— (1929[3]). *Lancet*, Lond., ii, 380.

—— (1930). *Biochem. J.*, **24**, 692.

—— (1931). *Ibid.*, **25**, 275.

MORGAN, A. F. (1923). *Amer. J. Physiol.*, **64**, 522.

—— (1924). *Ibid.*, **69**, 634.

MORGAN, A. F., and FIELD, A. (1929). *J. Biol. Chem.*, **82**, 579.

MORGAN, A. F., FIELD, A., and NICHOLS, P. F. (1931). *J. Agric. Res.*, **42**, 35.
MORGAN, A. F., and FRANCIS, L. D. (1924). *Amer. J. Physiol.*, **69**, 67.
MORGAN, A. F., and SMITH, L. L. W. (1928–29). *Proc. Soc. Exp. Biol.*, N.Y., **26**, 44.
MORGAN, A. F., and STEPHENSON, H. D. (1923). *Amer. J. Physiol.*, **65**, 491.
MORI, M. (1904). *Jahrb. Kinderhlk.*, **59**, 175.
MORI, S. (1922[1]). *J. Amer. Med. Ass.*, **79**, 197.
—— (1922[2]). *Johns Hopk. Hosp. Bull.*, **33**, 357.
—— (1923). *Amer. J. Hyg.*, **3**, 99.
MORO, E. (1926). *Klin. Wschr.*, **5**, 925.
MORPURGO, B. (1902). *Zbl. allg. Path. path. Anat.*, **13**, 113.
—— (1907). *Verh. deuts. path. Ges.*, 282.
MORRISON, R. R., PEACOCK, P. R., and WRIGHT, S. (1928). *Biochem. J.*, **22**, 1138.
MORTON, R. A., and HEILBRON, I. M. (1928). *Ibid.*, 987.
MORTON, R. A., HEILBRON, I. M., and KAMM, E. D. (1927). *Ibid.*, **21**, 1279.
MOTT, F. W., and HALIBURTON, W. D. (1899). *Brit. Med. J.*, ii, 5.
MOUREU, C., and DUFRAISSE, C. (1928). *J. Soc. Chem. Ind.*, Lond., **47**, 819 T, 848 T.
MOURIQUAND, G., MICHEL, P., and BERNHEIM, (1924[1]). *C. R. Acad. Sci.*, Paris, **178**, 1098.
—— (1924[2]). *Ibid.*, **179**, 541.
MUCKENFUSS, A. M. (1918). *J. Amer. Chem. Soc.*, **40**, 1606.
—— (1919). *Arch. Paediat.*, **36**, 80.
MUNSELL, H. E. and KIFER, H. B. (1929). *J. Home Econ.*, **21**, 514.
MYERS, C. N., and VOEGTLIN, C. (1920). *J. Biol. Chem.*, **42**, 199.
NAGAYAMA, T., MACHIDA, H., and TAKEDA, Y. (1928). *J. Biochem.*, Tokyo, **10**, 17.
NAGAYAMA, T., and MUNEHISA, T. (1929). *Ibid.*, **11**, 191.
NAGAYAMA, T., and SATO, N. (1928). *Ibid.*, **10**, 27.
NAGAYAMA, T., and TAGAYA, T. (1929). *Ibid.*, **11**, 225.
NARAYANAN, B. T. (1930). *Biochem. J.*, **24**, 6.
NARAYANAN, B. T., and DRUMMOND, J. C. (1930). *Ibid.*, 19.
NELSON, E. M., and STEENBOCK, H. (1924–25). *J. Biol. Chem.*, **62**, 575.
—— (1925[1]). *Ibid.*, **64**, 299.
—— (1925[2]). *Amer. J. Physiol.*, **73**, 341.
NELSON, V. E., FULMER, E. I., and CESSNA, R. (1921). *J. Biol. Chem.*, **46**, 77.
NELSON, V. E., HELLER, V. G., and FULMER, E. I. (1923). *Ibid.*, **57**, 415.
—— (1925). *Ind. Eng. Chem.*, **17**, 199.
NELSON, V. E., JONES, R. L., ADAMS, G., and ANDEREGG, L. T. (1927). *Ibid.*, **19**, 841.
NELSON, V. E., JONES, R. L., HELLER, V. G., PARKS, T. B., and FULMER, E. I. (1926). *Amer. J. Physiol.*, **76**, 325.
NEUMANN, H. (1902). *Deuts. med. Wschr.*, **28**, 647.
NEWCOMB, C. (1930). *Ind. J. Med. Res.*, **17**, 721.
NEWCOMB, C., and RANGANATHAN (1929–30[1]). *Ibid.*, 1037.
—— (1929–30[2]). *Ibid.*, 1055.
NEWTON, C. L. (1928). *J. Home Econ.*, **20**, 760.
NORRIS, E. R., and CHURCH, A. E. (1930[1]). *J. Biol. Chem.*, **85**, 477.
—— (1930[2]). *Ibid,*, **87**, 139.
—— (1930[3]). *Ibid.*, **89**, 437.
—— (1930[4]). *Ibid.*, 589.
NORTHROP, J. H. (1917). *Ibid.*, **30**, 181.
NOVARO, P. (1920). *Pathologica*, **12**, 87, 133.
OHLER, W. R. (1914). *J. Med. Res.*, **31**, 239.
OLCOTT, H. S., and McCANN, D. C. (1931). *J. Biol. Chem.*, **94**, 185.
OLCOTT, H. S., and MATTILL, H. A. (1931[1]). *Ibid.*, **93**, 59.
—— (1931[2]). *Ibid.*, 65.
OLCOVICH, H. S., and MATTILL, H. A. (1931). *Ibid.*, **92**, xxxi.
ORBAN, B. (1927). *J. Amer. Dent. Ass.*, **14**, 1619.
ORENSTEIN, A. J. (1925). *Personal Communication.*
ORR, J. B. (1928). *Lancet*, Lond., i, 202.
ORR, J. B., and CLARK, M. L. (1930). *Ibid.*, ii, 594.
ORR, J. B., CRICHTON, A., HALDANE, E., and MIDDLETON, W. (1926). *Scot. J. Agric.*, **9**, 377.
ORR-EWING, J., and READER, V. (1928). *Biochem. J.*, **22**, 440, 443.
ORTON, C. R., McCOLLUM, E. V., and SIMMONDS, N. (1922). *J. Biol. Chem.*, **43**, 1.
OSBORNE, T. B., and HARRIS, I. F. (1905). *J. Amer. Chem. Soc.*, **25**, 853.
OSBORNE, T. B., and LEAVENWORTH, C. S. (1920–21). *J. Biol. Chem.*, **45**, 423.
OSBORNE, T. B., and MENDEL, L. B. (1911). *Feeding experiments with isolated food substances. Pub. Carnegie Instn.* No. 156, Parts I and II.
—— (1912). *J. Biol. Chem.*, **13**, 233.
—— (1913[1]). *Ibid.*, **15**, 311.

OSBORNE, T. B., and MENDEL, L. B. (1913[2]). *J. Biol. Chem.*, **16**, 423.
—— (1914). *Ibid.*; **17**, 401.
—— (1915). *Ibid.*, **20**, 379.
—— (1917[1]). *Ibid.*, **29**, 289.
—— (1917[2]). *Ibid.*, **31**, 149.
—— (1917[3]). *Ibid.*, **32**, 309.
—— (1917[4]). *J. Amer. Med. Ass.*, **69**, 32.
—— (1918). *J. Biol. Chem.*, **34**, 17.
—— (1919[1]). *Ibid.*, **37**, 187.
—— (1919[2]). *Ibid.*, 557.
—— (1919[3]). *Ibid.*, **39**, 29.
—— (1920[1]). *Ibid.*, **41**, 549.
—— (1920[2]). *Ibid.*, **42**, 465.
—— (1921). *J. Amer. Med. Ass.*, **76**, 905.
—— (1922[1]). *J. Biol. Chem.*, **54**, 739.
—— (1922[2]). *J. Amer. Med. Ass.*, **78**, 1121.
—— (1923). *J. Biol. Chem.*, **58**, 363.
—— (1924). *Amer. J. Physiol.*, **69**, 543.
—— (1925). *J. Biol. Chem.*, **63**, 233.
OSBORNE, T. B., and WAKEMAN, A. J. (1919). *Ibid.*, **40**, 383.
OUTHOUSE, J., MACY, I. G., and BREKKE, V. (1928). *Ibid.*, **78**, 129.
OUTHOUSE, J., MACY, I. G., BREKKE, V., and GRAHAM, A. (1927). *Ibid.*, **73**, 203.
PALLADIN, A. (1924). *Biochem. Z.*, **152**, 228.
PALLADIN, A., and EPELBAUM, S. (1929). *Ibid.*, **204**, 140.
PALLADIN, A., and KUDRJAWZEWA, A. (1924). *Ibid.*, **152**, 373.
PALLADIN, A., and NORMARK, P. (1924). *Ibid.*, 420.
PALLADIN, A., and SSAWRON, E. (1924). *Ibid.*, **153**, 86.
PALM, T. A. (1890). *Practitioner*, **45**, 271, 321.
PALMER, L. S. (1915). *J. Biol. Chem.*, **23**, 261.
PALMER, L. S., and ECKLES, C. H. (1914[1]). *Ibid.*, **17**, 191.
—— (1914[2]). *Ibid.*, 211.
—— (1914[3]). *Ibid.*, 223.
—— (1914[4]). *Ibid.*, 237.
—— (1914[5]). *Ibid.*, 245.
PALMER, L. S., and HOFFMAN, C. T. (1922–23). *Proc. Soc. Exp. Biol.*, N.Y., **20**, 118.
PALMER, L. S., and KEMPSTER, H. L. (1919[1]). *J. Biol. Chem.*, **39**, 299.
—— (1919[2]). *Ibid.*, 313.
—— (1919[3]). *Ibid.*, 331.
PALMER, L. S., and KENNEDY, C. (1921). *Ibid.*, **46**, 559.
—— (1922–23). *Proc. Soc. Exp. Biol.*, N.Y., **20**, 506.
—— (1927[1]). *J. Biol. Chem.*, **74**, 591.
—— (1927[2]). *Ibid.*, **75**, 619.
PAPPENHEIMER, A. M. (1930). *J. Exp. Med.*, **52**, 805.
PARKES, A. S. (1928). *Quart. J. Exp. Physiol.*, **18**, 397.
PARKES, A. S., and DRUMMOND, J. C. (1925). *Proc. Roy. Soc.* B **98**, 147.
—— (1926). *Brit. J. Exp. Biol.*, **3**, 251.
PARSONS, H. T. (1920). *J. Biol. Chem.*, **44**, 587.
PARSONS, H. T., and HUTTON, M. K. (1924). *Ibid.*, **59**, 97.
PARSONS, L. G. (1927). *Arch. Dis. Child.*, **2**, 1928.
PATON, N. (1920). *Proc. R. Soc. Med.*, **13** (Sect. Dis. Child.), 77.
PEACOCK, P. R. (1926). *Lancet*, Lond., ii, 328.
PECK, E. C. (1924). *China Med. J.*, **38**, 135.
PEIPER, H. (1922). *Klin. Wschr.*, **1**, 1263.
PEKELHARING, C. A. (1905). *Ned. Tijdschr. Geneesk.*, **70**, 111.
PERRY, E. O. V., and ZILVA, S. S. (1932). (Unpublished results.)
PESKETT, G. L. (1927). *Biochem. J.*, **21**, 1102.
—— (1927–28). *Proc. Soc. Exp. Biol.*, N.Y., **25**, 340.
PESKETT, G. L., and O'BRIEN, J. R. P. (1930). *Chem. Ind.*, **49**, 516.
PETERS, R. A. (1924). *Biochem. J.*, **18**, 858.
—— (1930[1]). *J. State Med.*, **37**, No. 12 (Harben Lectures).
—— (1930[2]). *Ibid.*, **38**, Nos. 1 and 2 (Harben Lectures).
PETERS, R. A., KINNERSLEY, H. W., ORR-EWING, J., and READER, V. (1928). *Biochem. J.*, **22**, 445.
PFANNENSTIEL, W. (1927). *Med. Klinik*, **23**, 1913.
—— (1928). *Münch. med. Wschr.*, **75**, 1113.
Pharmacopoeia Commission (1931). *Reps. of Sub-Committees* 3, *General Medical Council*, Lond.
PIERSON, E. (1926). *S. Dak. Agric. Expt. Sta. Ann. Rep.*, 1925–26, 23.

PIERSON, E. M., and DUTCHER, R. A. (1920). *Science*, **51**, 70.

PILCHER, J. D., and SOLLMAN, T. (1925). *J. Pharmacol.*, **26**, 203.

PILLAT, A. (1929[1]). *Nat. Med. J. China*, **15**, 585.

—— (1929[2]). *Ibid.*, 614.

PITZ, W. (1918). *J. Biol. Chem.*, **33**, 471.

PLIMMER, R. H. A. (1920). *Biochem. J.*, **14**, 570.

PLIMMER, R. H. A., and ROSEDALE, J. L. (1926). *J. State Med.*, **34**, 117.

PLIMMER, R. H. A., ROSEDALE, J. L., and RAYMOND, W. H. (1927). *Biochem. J.*, **21**, 913.

PLIMMER, R. H. A., ROSEDALE, J. L., RAYMOND, W. H., and LOWNDES, J. (1927). *Ibid.*, 1141.

POHL, R. (1926). *Nachr. Ges. Wiss. Göttingen*, 142.

—— (1927). *Ibid.*, Math.-physik. Klasse, 2, 185.

POULSSON, E. (1929). *Strahlentherapie*, **34**, 648.

POULSSON, E., and LÖVENSKIOLD, H. (1928). *Biochem. J.*, **22**, 135.

POWERS, G. F., PARK, E. A., SHIPLEY, P. G., McCOLLUM, E. V., and SIMMONDS, N. (1922). *J. Amer. Med. Ass.*, **78**, 159.

PRINGLE, J. (1776). *Discourse Roy. Soc.* ' Upon some late improvements for preserving the health of marines.'

PRINGSHEIM, H. H. (1906). *Zbl. Bakt.*, Abt. II, **16**, 111.

PRISTON, J. L. (1926). *J. R. Nav. Med. Serv.*, **12**, 1.

PUTSCHER, W. (1929). *Z. Kinderhlk.*, **48**, 269.

QUINN, E. J., BURTIS, M. P., and MILNER, E. W. (1927). *J. Biol. Chem.*, **72**, 557.

RABL, C. R. H. (1929). *Deuts. med. Wschr.*, **55**, 63.

RAMOINO, P. (1916). *Pathologica*, **15**, 1.

RANDOIN, L. (1923). *C. R. Acad. Sci.*, Paris, **177**, 498.

RANDOIN, L., and LECOQ, R. (1926[1]). *Ibid.*, **182**, 1408.

—— (1926[2]). *Ibid.*, 1564.

—— (1927[1]). *C. R. Soc. Biol.* Paris, **96**, 671.

—— (1927[2]). *Bull. Soc. Chim. biol.*, **9**, 49.

RANDOIN, L., and SIMONNET, H., (1924). *Ibid.*, **6**, 601.

READER, V. (1927). *Biochem. J.*, **21**, 901.

—— (1928). *Ibid.*, **22**, 434.

—— (1929[1]). *Ibid.*, **23**, 61.

—— (1929[2]). *Ibid.*, 689.

—— (1930[1]). *Ibid.*, **24**, 77.

—— (1930[2]). *Ibid.*, 1827.

READER, V., and DRUMMOND, J. C. (1926). *Ibid.*, **20**, 1256.

REDMAN, T. (1928). *Ibid.*, **22**, 14.

—— (1929). *Ibid.*, **23**, 256.

REERINK, E. H., and van WIJK, A. (1929). *Ibid.*, 1294.

—— (1931). *Ibid.*, **25**, 1001.

REINDEL, F., WALTER, E., and RAUCH, H. (1927). *Liebigs Ann.*, **452**, 34.

REMY, E. (1928). *Z. Untersuch. Lebensmitt.*, **55**, 385.

Rep. Loc. Gvt. Bd. (1914). Food Rep. No. 20. ' On the use of proprietary infants' foods for infant feeding.'

—— (1918). Food Rep. No. 24. ' Upon an inquiry as to dried milks with special reference to their use in infant feeding.'

Rep. on the Health of the City of Manchester (1917), 49.

ROBB, E. F., MEDES, G., McCLENDON, J. F., GRAHAM, and MURPHY (1921). *J. Dent. Res.*, **3**, 1.

ROBERTS, W. M. (1930). *Quart. J. Med.*

ROBISON, R. (1919). *R.A.M.C. Jl.*, **32**, 53.

ROCHE, J. (1921). *Arch. int. Physiol.*, **24**, 413.

—— (1925). *C. R. Acad. Sci.*, Paris, **180**, 467.

—— (1931). *Bull. Soc. Chim. biol.*, Paris, **13**, 202.

ROSCOE, M. H. (1927[1]). *Biochem. J.*, **21**, 211.

—— (1927[2]). *J. Hyg.*, Camb., **27**, 103.

—— (1930). *Biochem. J.*, **24**, 1754.

—— (1931[1]). *Ibid.*, **25**, 1205.

—— (1931[2]). *Ibid.*, 2050.

—— (1931[3]). *Ibid.*, 2056.

ROSE, M. S., and MACLEOD, G. (1921–22). *Proc. Soc. Exp. Biol.*, N.Y., **19**, 391.

ROSE, W. B., STUCKY, C. J., and COWGILL, G. R. (1930). *Amer. J. Physiol.*, **92**, 83.

ROSE, W. B., STUCKY, C. J., and MENDEL, L. B. (1929–30). *Ibid.*, **91**, 520.

ROSEDALE, J. L. (1927). *Biochem. J.*, **21**, 1266.

—— (1929). *Ind. J. Med. Res.*, **17**, 217.

ROSEDALE, J. L., and OLIVEIRO, C. J. (1928). *Biochem. J.*, **22**, 1362.

ROSENHEIM, O. (1927). *Biochem. J.*, **21**, 387.
ROSENHEIM, O., and DRUMMOND, J. C. (1920). *Lancet*, Lond., i, 862.
—— (1925). *Biochem. J.*, **19**, 753.
ROSENHEIM, O., and SCHUSTER, E. (1927). *Ibid.*, **21**, 1329.
ROSENHEIM, O. and STARLING, W. W. (1931). *Chem. Ind.*, **50**, 443.
ROSENHEIM, O., and WEBSTER, T. A. (1925). *Lancet*, Lond., i, 1025.
—— (1926[1]). *Biochem. J.*, **20**, 537.
—— (1926[2]). *Ibid.*, 1340.
—— (1926[3]). *Ibid.*, 1342.
—— (1926[4]). *Lancet*, Lond., ii, 806.
—— (1926[5]). *Chem. Ind.*, **45**, 932.
—— (1927[1]). *Biochem. J.*, **21**, 111.
—— (1927[2]). *Ibid.*, 127.
—— (1927[3]). *Ibid.*, 389.
—— (1927[4]). *Lancet*, Lond., i, 306.
—— (1927[5]). *Ibid.*, ii, 622.
—— (1927[6]). *Nature*, Lond., **120**, 440.
ROSSI, G. (1918). *Arch. Fisiol.*, **16**, 125.
ROTHLIN, E. (1922). *Hoppe-Seyl. Z.*, **121**, 300.
ROUSSEL, T. (1845). *La Pellagra*, Paris.
—— (1866). *Traité de la pellagra et des pseudopellagras*, Paris.
RUBINO, P., and COLLAZO, J. A. (1923). *Biochem. Z.*, **140**, 258.
RUSSELL, H. L., and MORRISON, F. B. (1922). *Bull. Wisc. Agric. Expt. Sta.*, **330**, 123.
RUSSELL, H. L., MORRISON, F. B., and EBLING, W. H. (1926). *Ibid.*, **388**, 125.
RUSSELL, W. C. (1930). *J. Nutrition*, **2**, 265.
RYGH, O. (1931). *Avh. Norske Vid.-Akad.* Oslo I, Mat. Naturw. Klasse No. 8.
RYGH, O., and RYGH, A. (1932). *Hoppe-Seyl. Z.*, **204**, 114.
RYGH, O., RYGH, A., and LALAND, P. (1932). *Ibid.*, 105.
SAHASHI, Y. (1926[1]). *Sci. Papers Inst. Phys. Chem. Res.*, Tokyo, **4**, 207.
—— (1926[2]). *Ibid.*, **5**, 191.
—— (1927). *Biochem. Z.*, **189**, 208.
—— (1928). *Bull. Inst. Phys. Chem. Res.*, Tokyo, **7**, 1191.
SALMON, W. D. (1925). *J. Biol. Chem.*, **65**, 457.
—— (1927). *Ibid.*, **73**, 483.
SALMON, W. D., GUERRANT, N. B., and HAYS, I. M. (1928[1]). *Ibid.*, **76**, 487.
—— (1928[2]). *Ibid.*, **80**, 91.
SALMON, W. D., HAYS, I. M., and GUERRANT, N. B. (1928). *J. Infect. Dis.*, **43**, 426.
SAMBON, L. W. (1913). *Brit. Med. J.*, ii, 119, 297.
SANDWITH, F. N. (1898). *Ibid.*, 881.
SANTOS, F. O. (1922). *Amer. J. Physiol.*, **59**, 310.
SCHALL, H., and HEISLER, A. (1927). *Nahrungsmittel-Tabelle* (Curt Kabitzsch, Leipzig).
SCHAUMANN, H. (1908). *Arch. Schiffs- u. Tropen-Hyg.*, **12**, Beihft. 5, 37.
—— (1910). *Ibid.*, **14**, Beihft. 8, 11.
—— (1911). *Trans. Soc. Trop. Med. Hyg.*, Lond., **5**, 59.
SCHEER, K. (1928). *Münch. med. Wschr.*, **75**, 642.
SCHEUNERT, A. (1927). *Züchtungskunde*, **2**, 264.
—— (1930). *Der Vitamingehalt der deutschen Nahrungsmittel* (Julius Springer, Berlin).
SCHEUNERT, A., and RESCHKE, J. (1931). *Deuts. med. Wschr.*, **57**, 349.
SCHEUNERT, A., and SCHIEBLICH, M. (1923). *Biochem. Z.*, **139**, 57.
SCHICK, B., and WAGNER, R. (1923). *Z. Kinderhlk.*, **35**, 264.
SCHLUTZ, F. W., and MORSE, M. (1925). *Amer. J. Dis. Child*, **30**, 199.
SCHLUTZ, F. W., and ZIEGLER, M. R. (1926). *J. Biol. Chem.*, **69**, 415.
SCHMIDTMANN, M. (1928). *Zbl. allg. Path. path. Anat.*, **43**, 8.
SCHMIDT-NIELSEN, S. and S. (1931). *Kon. Norsk. Vid. Sels. Forhand.*, **3**, 177.
SCHULTZ (1929). *Z. Kinderheilk.*, **47**, 449.
SCHULZ, O. (1929). *Arch. wiss. prakt. Tierhlk.*, **6**, 259.
SCHWARTZE, E. W., MURPHY, F. J., and COX, G. J. (1931–32). *J. Nutrition*, **4**, 211.
SCHWARTZE, E. W., MURPHY, F. J., and HANN, R. M. (1929–30). *Ibid.*, **2**, 325.
SCOTT, A. C. (1916–17). *Ind. J. Med. Res.*, **4**, 140.
SCOTTI-FOGLIENI, L. (1926[1]). *Boll. Soc. Biol. Sper.*, **1**, 627.
—— (1926[2]). *Boll. Soc. med. chir.*, Pavia, 2 s. **1**, Fasc. 1, 89.
—— (1927). *Boll. Soc. Biol. Sper.*, **2**, 152
—— (1928). *Arch. Fisiol.*, **26**, 83.
SEEL, H. (1931). *Arch. exp. Path. Pharmak.*, **159**, 93.
SEEL, H., and DANNMEYER (1930). *Ibid.*, **157**, 86.
—— (1931). *Strahlentherapie*, **39**, 449.

Seidell, A. (1916). *Pub. Hlth. Rep.* Wash., **31**, 364.
—— (1917). *J. Biol. Chem.*, **29**, 145.
—— (1921¹). *Publ. Hlth. Rep.*, Wash., **36**, 665.
—— (1921²). *Ind. Eng. Chem.*, **13**, 1111.
—— (1922¹). *Pub. Hlth. Rep.*, Wash., **37**, 801.
—— (1922²). *J. Amer. Chem. Soc.*, **44**, 2042.
—— (1922³). *Pub. Hlth. Rep.*, Wash., **41**, 297.
—— (1924¹). *Ibid.*, **39**, 294.
—— (1924²). *Bull. Soc. chim. biol.*, **6**, 503.
—— (1925). *Science*, **62**, 138.
—— (1926). *J. Biol. Chem.*, **67**, 593.
Sexton, W. A. (1928). *Biochem. J.*, **22**, 1133.
Shattuck, G. C. (1928). *J. Amer. Med. Ass.*, **90**, 1861.
Shear, M. J. (1925–26). *Proc. Soc. Exp. Biol.*, N.Y., **23**, 546.
Sheppard, W. S. (1912). *Brit. Med. J.*, ii, 1773.
Sherman, H. C. (1920¹). *Food Products.* Macmillan & Co., New York.
—— (1920²). *J. Biol. Chem.*, **44**, 21.
—— (1926). *Chemistry of Food and Nutrition.* New York, p. 408.
Sherman, H. C., and Axtmayer, J. H. (1927). *J. Biol. Chem.*, **75**, 207.
Sherman, H. C., and Boynton, L. C. (1925). *J. Amer. Chem. Soc.*, **47**, 1646.
Sherman, H. C., and Burton, G. W. (1926). *J. Biol. Chem.*, **70**, 639.
Sherman, H. C., and Cammack, M. L. (1926). *Ibid.*, **68**, 69.
Sherman, H. C., and Grose, M. R. (1923–24). *Proc. Soc. Exp. Biol.*, N.Y., **21**, 11.
Sherman, H. C., and Kramer, M. M. (1924). *J. Amer. Chem. Soc.*, **46**, 1055.
Sherman, H. C., La Mer, V. K., and Campbell, H. L. (1921). *Proc. Nat. Acad. Sci.*, Wash., **7**, 279.
—— (1922). *J. Amer. Chem. Soc.*, **44**, 165.
Sherman, H. C., and MacArthur, E. H. (1927). *J. Biol. Chem.*, **74**, 107.
Sherman, H. C., and Macleod, F. L. (1925). *J. Amer. Chem. Soc.*, **47**, 1658.
Sherman, H. C., and Munsell, H. E. (1925). *Ibid.*, 1639.
Sherman, H. C., and Pappenheimer, A. M. (1920–21). *Proc. Soc. Exp. Biol.*, N.Y., **18**, 193.
—— (1921). *J. Exp. Med.*, **34**, 189.
Sherman, H. C., and Sandels, M. R. (1928–29). *Proc. Soc. Exp. Biol.*, N.Y., **26**, 536.
—— (1931). *J. Nutrition*, **3**, 395.
Sherman, H. C., and Smith, S. L. (1931). *The Vitamins.* (The Chemical Catalog Co., New York.)
Sherman, H. C., and Storms, L. B. (1925). *J. Amer. Chem. Soc.*, **47**, 1653.
Shiga, K., and Kusama, S. H. (1911). *Arch. Schiffs- u. Tropen-Hyg.*, **15**, Beihft. 3, 57.
Shipley, P. G., Park, E. A., McCollum, E. V., and Simmonds, N. (1922). *Amer. J. Dis. Child.*, **23**, 91.
Shipley, P. G., Park, E. A., Powers, G. F., McCollum, E. V., and Simmonds, N. (1921–22). *Proc. Soc. Exp. Biol.*, N.Y., **19**, 43.
Shipp, H. L., and Zilva, S. S. (1928¹). *Biochem. J.*, **22**, 408.
—— (1928²). *Ibid.*, 1449.
Shohl, A. T., Bennett, H. B., and Weed, K. L. (1928). *Ibid.*, **78**, 181.
Shorten, J. A., and Ray, C. B. (1919). *Ind. J. Med. Res.*, Spec. Ind. Sci. Congress No. 60.
—— (1921). *Biochem. J.*, **15**, 274.
Siler, J. F., Garrison, P. E., and MacNeal, W. J. (1913). *Rep. of Thompson, McFadden Pellagra Commission of the New York Post-graduate Medical School and Hospital.*
Simmonds, N., Becker, J. E., and McCollum, E. V. (1927¹). *J. Biol. Chem.*, **74**, lxviii–lxix.
—— (1927²). *J. Amer. Med. Ass.*, **88**, 1047.
—— (1928). *J. Nutrition*, **1**, 39.
Simonini (1905). *La Pellagra nell'infanza.* Vicenza.
Simonnet, H. (1920). *C. R. Soc. Biol.*, Paris, **83**, 1508.
—— (1921). *Bull. Soc. chim. biol.*, **3**, 583.
Simpson, G. C. E., and Edie, E. S. (1911). *Ann. Trop. Med. Parasit.*, **5**, 313.
Sims (1924). *Trans. Roy. Soc. Canada*, III, **18**, 116.
Sipple, H. L., and King, C. G. (1930). *J. Amer. Chem. Soc.*, **52**, 420.
Smith, A. H. (1918). *Lancet.*, Lond., ii, 813.
—— (1919). *R.A.M.C. Jl.*, **32**, 93, 188.
Smith, A. H., Cowgill, G. R., and Croll, H. M. (1925). *J. Biol. Chem.*, **66**, 15.
Smith, E. L., and Hazley, V. (1930). *Biochem. J.*, **24**, 1942.
Smith, G. H., and Wason, I. M. (1923). *J. Immunol.*, **8**, 195.

SMITH, H. H., and CHICK, H. (1926). *Biochem. J.*, **20**, 131.

SMITH, J. H. C. (1931). *J. Biol. Chem.*, **90**, 597.

SMITH, M. E. (1930). *Pub. Hlth. Rep.*, Wash., **45**, 116.

SMITH, M. E., and HENDRICK, E. G. (1926). *Ibid.*, **41**, 201.

SMITH, S., and ZILVA, S. S. (1932). *Chem. Ind.* **51**, 166.

SOAMES, K. M., and LEIGH-CLARE, J. C. (1928). *Biochem. J.*, **22**, 522.

SOCIN, C. A. (1891). *Hoppe-Seyl. Z.*, **15**, 93.

S. Dak. Agric. Expt. Sta. (1927). *Ann. Rep. 1926–27*, 14.

SOUTHGATE, H. W. (1924[1]). *Biochem. J.*, **18**, 769.

—— (1924[2]). *Ibid.*, 1248.

SOUZA, G. de P., and McCOLLUM, E. V. (1920). *J. Biol. Chem.*, **44**, 113.

SPENCE (1931). *Arch. Dis. Child.*, **6**, 17.

Sp. Rep. Ser. Med. Res. Coun., Lond. (1924). No. 38 (revised).

SPIES, T. D., and GLOVER, E. C. (1930). *Amer. J. Path.*, **6**, 485.

STAMMERS, A. D. (1924[1]). *Lancet*, Lond., ii, 598.

—— (1924[2]). *Biochem. J.*, **18**, 9.

STANLEY, A. (1903). *Brit. Med. J.*, ii, 1636.

STANNUS, H. S. (1911–12). *Trans. Soc. Trop. Med. Hyg.*, Lond., **5**, 112.

—— (1913–14). *Ibid.*, **7**, 32.

STAPLETON, G. (1925). *Lancet*, Lond., i, 1119.

STARLINGER, W. (1927). *Deuts. med. Wschr.*, **53**, 1553.

STEENBOCK, H. (1919). *Science*, **50**, 352.

STEENBOCK, H., and BLACK, A. (1924). *J. Biol. Chem.*, **61**, 405.

—— (1925). *Ibid.*, **64**, 263.

STEENBOCK, H., and BOUTWELL, P. W. (1920[1]). *Ibid.*, **41**, 81.

—— (1920[2]). *Ibid.*, 163.

—— (1920[3]). *Ibid.*, **42**, 131.

STEENBOCK, H., BOUTWELL, P. W., and KENT, H. E. (1918). *Ibid.*, **35**, 517.

—— (1919). *Ibid.*, **41**, xii–xiii.

STEENBOCK, H., and COWARD, K. H. (1927). *Ibid.*, **72**, 765.

STEENBOCK, H., and DANIELS, A. L. (1925). *J. Amer. Med. Ass.*, **84**, 1093, 1097.

STEENBOCK, H., and GROSS, E. G. (1919). *J. Biol. Chem.*, **40**, 501.

—— (1920). *Ibid.*, **41**, 149.

STEENBOCK, H., HART, E. B., HANNING, F., and HUMPHREY, G. C. (1930). *Ibid.*, **88**, 197.

STEENBOCK, H., HART, E. B., HOPPERT, C. A., and BLACK, A. (1925). *Ibid.*, **66**, 441.

STEENBOCK, H., HART, E. B., RIISING, B. M., HOPPERT, C. A., BASHEROV, S., and HUMPHREY, G. C. (1930). *Ibid.*, **87**, 103.

STEENBOCK, H., HART, E. B., RIISING, B. M., KLETZIEN, S. W. F., and SCOTT, H. T. (1930). *Ibid.*, 127.

STEENBOCK, H., KENT, H. E., and GROSS, E. G. (1918). *Ibid.*, **35**, 61.

STEENBOCK, H., and NELSON, E. M. (1923). *Ibid.*, **56**, 355.

STEENBOCK, H., NELSON, E. M., and HART, E. B. (1921). *Amer. J. Physiol.*, **58**, 14.

STEENBOCK, H., and NELSON, M. T. (1924–25). *J. Biol. Chem.*, **62**, 209.

STEENBOCK, H., NELSON, M. T., and BLACK, A. (1924–25). *Ibid.*, 275.

STEENBOCK, H., SELL, M. T., and BOUTWELL, P. W. (1921). *Ibid.*, **47**, 303.

STEENBOCK, H., SELL, M. T., and BUELL, M. V. (1921). *Ibid.*, 89.

STEENBOCK, H., SELL, M. T., and JONES, J. H. (1923). *Ibid.*, **55**, 411.

STEENBOCK, H., SELL, M. T., and NELSON, E. M. (1923). *Ibid.*, 399.

STEENBOCK, H., SELL, M. T., NELSON, E. M., and BUELL, M. V. (1921). *Ibid.*, **46**, xxxii–xxxiii.

STEFANSSON, V. (1918). *J. Amer. Med. Ass.*, **71**, 1715.

STEIDLE, H. (1924). *Biochem. Z.*, **151**, 181.

STEIGMANN, A. (1928). *Kolloidzschr.*, **45**, 165.

STEPHENSON, M. (1920). *Biochem. J.*, **14**, 715.

STEPHENSON, M., and CLARK, A. B. (1920). *Ibid.*, 502.

STEPP, W. (1909). *Biochem. Z.*, **22**, 452.

—— (1911). *Z. Biol.*, **57**, 135.

—— (1912). *Ibid.*, **59**, 366.

STERN, R. O., and FINDLAY, G. M. (1929). *J. Path. Bact.*, **32**, 63.

STEVENSON, A. G. (1920). *R.A.M.C. Jl.*, **35**, 218.

STILL, G. F. (1900). *Practitioner*, **64**, 611.

—— (1905). *Ibid.*, **75**, 462.

STOELTZNER, W. (1928). *Münch. med. Wschr.*, **75**, 1584.

STRONG, R. P., and CROWELL, B. C. (1912). *Philipp. J. Sci.*. (B) **7**, 271.

STRUDWICK, F. *Private Communication.*

STUCKY, C. J., and ROSE, W. B. (1929). *Amer. J. Physiol.*, **89**, 1.

SUMI, M. (1929). *Bull. Inst. Phys. Chem. Res.*, Tokyo, **8**, 640.

SUNDERLIN, G., and WERKMAN, C. H. (1928). *J. Path. Bact.*, **16**, 17.
SUPPLEE, G. C., and DOW, O. D. (1925). *J. Biol. Chem.*, **63**, 103.
—— (1926). *Amer. J. Dis. Child.*, **31**, 41.
—— (1927). *Ibid.*, **34**, 364.
SURE, B. (1923¹). *J. Biol. Chem.*, **58**, 681.
—— (1923²). *Ibid.*, 693.
—— (1924–25). *Ibid.*, **62**, 371.
—— (1925). *Ibid.*, **63**, 211.
—— (1926¹). *Ibid.*, **69**, 29.
—— (1926²). *Ibid.*, 41.
—— (1926³). *Ibid.*, 53.
—— (1927¹). *Ibid.*, **74**, 37.
—— (1927²). *Ibid.*, 45.
—— (1927³). *Ibid.*, 55.
—— (1927⁴). *Ibid.*, 71.
—— (1928¹). *Ibid.*, **76**, 659.
—— (1928²). *Ibid.*, 685.
—— (1928³). *Ibid.*, **80**, 297.
—— (1928⁴). *J. Agric. Res.*, **37**, 87.
—— (1929). *J. Biol. Chem.*, **82**, 287.
—— (1929–30). *Proc. Soc. Exp. Biol.*, N.Y., **27**, 148.
—— (1930). *Bull. Arkans. Agric. Expt. Sta.*, 250.
SURE, B., KIK, M. C., and WALKER, D. J. (1929). *J. Biol. Chem.*, **83**, 387.
SURE, B., and SMITH, M. E. (1929). *Ibid.*, **84**, 727.
—— (1930–31). *Proc. Soc. Exp. Biol.*, N.Y., **28**, 442.
SUZUKI, U., SHIMAMURA, T., and ODAKE, S. (1912). *Biochem. Z.*, **43**, 89.
SWEETMAN, M. D., and PALMER, L. S. (1928). *J. Biol. Chem.*, **77**, 33.
SWEITZER (1928). *Minnesota Medicine*, **11**, 719.
SWOBODA, F. K. (1920). *J. Biol. Chem.*, **44**, 531.
TAKAHASHI, K. (1922). *J. Chem. Soc. Japan.*, **43**, 828. Quoted from *Physiol. Abst.* (1923) **8**, No. 1877.
TAKAHASHI, K., and KAWAKAMI, K. (1923). *J. Chem. Soc.*, Japan, **44**, 590.
TAKAHASHI, K., NAKAMIYA, Z., KAWAKAMI, K., and KITASATO, T. (1925). *Sci. Pap. Inst. Phys. Chem. Res.*, Tokyo, **3**, 81.
TAKAKI, K. (1885). *Sei-i-K-wai*, August 1885 and April 1886, **5**, 41.
—— (1887). *Lancet*, Lond., ii, 189.
——(1906). *Ibid.*, i, 1369, 1451, 1520.
TANNER, F. W. (1925). *Chem. Reviews*, **1**, 397.
TANSLEY, K. (1931). *J. Physiol.*, **71**, 44 2.
TAYLOR, J., and THANT, U. (1928). *Ind. J. Med. Res.*, **16**, 747.
TAYLOR, N. B., WELD, C. B., BRANION, H. D., and KAY, H. D. (1931¹). *Canad. Med. Ass. J.*, **24**, 763.
—— (1931²). *Ibid.*, **25**, 20.
TCHERKES, W. (1929). *Research on Pellagra. Dept. Nutritional Res.*, Ukraine.
THJÖTTA, T., and AVERY, O. T. (1921). *J. Exp. Med.*, **34**, 97.
THOMAS, C. (1909). *Arch. Anat. Physiol.*, 219.
THURSTON, L. M., ECKLES, C. H., and PALMER, L. S. (1926). *J. Dairy. Sci.*, **9**, 37.
THURSTON, L. M., PALMER, L. S., and ECKLES, C. H. (1929). *Ibid.*, **12**, 394.
TIGER, R., and SIMONNET, H. (1121). *Bull. Soc. chim. biol.*, **3**, 580.
TILLMANS, J., HIRSCH, P., and HIRSCH, W. (1932). *Z. Unters. Lebensm.*, **63**, 1.
TILLMANS, J., HIRSCH, P., and SIEBERT, F. (1932). *Ibid.* 21.
TOPLEY, W. W. C., GREENWOOD, M., and WILSON, J. (1931). *J. Path. Bact.*, **34**, 163.
TOVERUD, G. (1923). *J. Biol. Chem.*, **58**, 583.
—— (1926). Suppl. to ' *Den Norske Tandlæge-Forenings Tidende* '.
—— (1931). *Acta Paediat.*, **12**, Suppl. 2.
TOVERUD, K. U., and TOVERUD, G. (1929¹). *Skand. Arch. Physiol.*, **55**, 281.
—— (1929²). *Norsk. Mag. Lægevidensk.*, **90**, 1245.
—— (1930¹). *Ibid.*, **91**, 53.
—— (1930²). *Ibid.*, 286.
—— (1931). *Acta Paediat.*, **12**, Suppl. 2.
TOZER, F. M. (1918). *Biochem. J.*, **12**, 445.
—— (1921¹). *Ibid.*, **15**, 28.
—— (1921²). *J. Path. Bact.* **24**, 306.
TSCHECHE, R. (1932). *Chem. Ztg.* **56**, 166.
TSCHERKES, L. A. (1926). *Biochem. Z.*, **167**, 203.
TSUKIYE, S. (1922). *Ibid.*, **131**, 124
TSUKIYE, S., and OKADA, T. (1922). *J. Biochem.*, Tokyo, **1**, 445.
UNDERHILL, F. P., and MENDEL, L. B. (1925). *Publ. Hlth. Rep.*, Wash., **40**, 1087.

UNDERHILL, F. P., and MENDEL, L. B. (1928).   *Amer. J. Physiol.*, **83**, 589.
UNGLEY, C. C., and SUZMAN, M. M. (1929).   *Brain*, **52**, 271.
VARELA, B., COLLAZO, J., MOREAU, J., and RUBINO, P. (1929).   *Arch. path. Anat.*, **274**, 270.
VAUGHAN, K. O. (1926).   *Brit. Med. J.*, i, 413.
—— (1928).   ' *The Purdah system and its effect on motherhood* ', Camb., W. Heffer & Sons.
VEDDER, E. B. (1912).   *Philipp. J. Sci.*, (B) **7**, 415.
—— (1913).   *Beri-beri*, Lond.
—— (1916).   *Arch. Intern. Med.*, **18**, 137.
—— (1918).   *J. Hyg.*, Camb., **17**, 1.
VEDDER, E. B., and CLARK, E. (1912).   *Philipp. J. Sci.*, (B) **7**, 423.
VEDDER, E. B., and WILLIAMS, R. R. (1913).   *Ibid.*, **8**, 175.
VERZÁR, F. (1931).   *Pfluegers Arch.*, **227**, 499.
VERZÁR, F., ÁRVAY, A. v., and KOKAS, E. v. (1931)   *Biochem. Z.*, **240**, 19.
VERZÁR, F., and KOKAS, E. v. (1931).   *Pfluegers Arch.*, **227**, 511.
VOEGTLIN, C, and MYERS, C. N. (1919).   *J. Pharmacol.*, **13**, 301.
VOEGTLIN, C., NEILL, M. H., and HUNTER, A. (1920).   *Bull. U. S. Hyg. Lab.*, No. 116.
VOEGTLIN, C., and WHITE, G. F. (1916–17).   *J. Pharmacol.*, **9**, 155.
VOGT-MØLLER, P. (1931).   *Lancet*, Lond., ii, 182.
VOGT-MØLLER, P., and BAY, F. (1931).   *Vet. J.*, **87**, 165.
WACHTEL, M. (1929).   *Münch. med. Wschr.*, **76**, 1513.
WADDELL, J., and STEENBOCK, H. (1928).   *J. Biol. Chem.*, **80**, 431.
—— (1931).   *J. Nutrition*, **4**, 79.
VAN DER WALLE, N., (1922).   *Biochem. J.*, **16**, 713.
WALSHE, F. M. R. (1917–18).   *Quart. J. Med.*, **11**, 320.
—— (1920).   *Med. Sci.*, **2**, 41.
WARREN, S., and NISSEN, H. A. (1931).   *New Eng. J. Med.*, **205**, 135.
WASON, I. M. (1921).   *J. Amer. Med. Ass.*, **76**, 908.
WEATHERBY, L. S., and WATERMAN, E. W. (1928).   *Ind. Eng. Chem.*, **20**, 968.
WEBSTER, T. A., and BOURDILLON, R. B. (1928[1]).   *Nature*, Lond., **121**, 502.
—— (1928[2]).   *Biochem. J.*, **22**, 1223.
WEBSTER, T. A., and HILL, L. (1924).   *Ibid.*, **18**, 340.
WEDGEWOOD, P. E., and FORD, F. L. (1924).   *Bull. Soc. Chim. Biol.*, **6**, 217.
WEECH, A. A. (1927).   *Johns Hopk. Hosp. Bull.*, **40**, 244.
WEICHARDT, W. (1920).   *Münch. med. Wschr.*, **67**, 1085.
WEILL, E., ARLOING, F., and DUFOURT, A. (1922).   *C. R. Soc. Biol.*, Paris, **86**, 1175.
WEILL, E., MOURIQUAND, G., and MICHEL, P. (1916).   *Ibid.*, **79**, 189.
WEILL, E., MOURIQUAND, G., and PÉRONNET (1918).   *Ibid.*, **81**, 607.
WELLS, A. H. (1921).   *Philipp. J. Sci.*, **19**, 67.
WERKMAN, C. H. (1923).   *J. Infect. Dis.*, **32**, 247, 255, 263.
WHEELER, G. A., GOLDBERGER, J., and BLACKSTOCK, M. R. (1922).   *Publ. Hlth. Rep.*, Wash., **37**, 1063.
WHIPPLE, B. K. (1920).   *J. Biol. Chem.*, **44**, 175.
WILDIERS, E. (1901).   *La Cellule*, **18**, 313.
WILLAMAN, J. J., and OLSEN, A. G. (1923).   *J. Biol. Chem.*, **55**, 815.
WILLCOCK, E. G., and HOPKINS, F. G. (1906).   *J. Physiol.*, **35**, 88.
WILLCOX, W. H. (1916[1]).   *R.A.M.C. Jl.*, **27**, 191.
—— (1916[2]).   *Lancet*, Lond., i, 553.
WILLE, W. A. (1922).   *Trans. Far East Ass. Trop. Med.*, i, 245.
WILLIAMS, J., and CORRAN, J. W. (1930).   *Biochem. J.*, **24**, 37.
WILLIAMS, R. J., (1919).   *J. Biol. Chem.*, **38**, 465.
—— (1920).   *Ibid.*, **42**, 259.
—— (1921).   *Ibid.*, **46**, 113.
WILLIAMS, R. J., and ROEHM, R. R. (1930).   *Ibid.*, **87**, 581.
WILLIAMS, R. J., WARNER, M. E., and ROEHM, R. R. (1929).   *J. Amer. Chem. Soc.*, **59**, 2764.
WILLIAMS, R. J., WILSON, J. L., and AHE, F. H. v. der (1927).   *Ibid.*, **49**, 227.
WILLIAMS, R. R. (1916).   *J. Biol. Chem.*, **25**, 437.
—— (1917).   *Ibid.*, **29**, 495.
—— (1921).   *Ind. Eng. Chem.*, **13**, 1107.
—— (1924).   *Science*, **60**, 499.
—— (1927).   *Biochem. J.*, **21**, 1349.
WILLIAMS, R. R., and CROWELL, B. C. (1915).   *Philipp. J. Sci.*, (B) **10**, 121.
WILLIAMS, R. R., and SALEEBY, N. M. (1915).   *Ibid.*, 99.
WILLIAMS, R. R., and SEIDELL, A. (1916).   *J. Biol. Chem.*, **26**, 431.
WILLIAMS, R. R., and WATERMAN, R. E. (1926).   *Ibid.*, **68**, 499.

WILLIAMS, R. R., and WATERMAN, R. E. (1927–28). *Proc. Soc. Exp. Biol.*, N.Y., **25**, 1.
—— (1928). *J. Biol. Chem.*, **78**, 311.
WILLIAMS, R. R., WATERMAN, R. E., and GURIN, S. (1929). *Ibid.*, **83**, 321.
—— (1930). *Ibid.*, **87**, 559.
WILLIMOTT, S. G. (1928). *Biochem. J.*, **22**, 67.
WILLIMOTT, S. G., and MOORE, T. (1926). *Ibid.*, **20**, 869.
—— (1927). *Ibid.*, **21**, 86.
WILLIMOTT, S. G., and WOKES, F. (1926). *Ibid.*, **20**, 1013.
—— (1927). *Pharm. J.*, **64**, 770.
WILLS, L. (1931). *Brit. Med. J.* i, 1059.
WILLS, L., and TALPADE, S. N. (1930–31[1]). *Ind. J. Med. Res.*, **18**, 283.
WILLSTÄTTER, R., and STOLL, A. (1913) *Untersuch. über das Chlorophyll*, Berl.
WILSON, D. C. (1930–31). *Ind. J. Med. Res.*, **18**, 951.
—— (1930–31[2]). *Ibid.*, 963.
WILSON, D. C., and SURIE, E. (1929–30). *Ibid.*, **17**, 889.
WILSON, M. G. (1926). *Amer. J. Dis. Child.*, **31**, 603.
WILSON, W. H. (1921). *J. Hyg.*, Camb., **20**, 1.
—— (1929). *Proc. Int. Cong. Med.*, Cairo, **2**, 461.
WILTSHIRE, H. W. (1918). *Lancet*, Lond., ii, 811.
WIMBERGER, H. (1922). *Sp. Rep. Ser. Med. Res. Coun.*, Lond., No. 77, p. 114.
WINDAUS, A. (1930[1]). *Nachr. Ges. Wiss. Göttingen*, 36.
—— (1930[2]). *Forschungen und Fortschritte*, June.
—— (1931). *Proc. Roy. Soc.*, B. **108**, 568.
WINDAUS, A., and AUHAGEN, E. (1929). *Liebigs Ann.*, **472**, 185.
—— (1931). *Hoppe-Seyl. Z.*, **196**, 108.
WINDAUS, A., AUHAGEN, E., BERGMANN, W., and BUTTE, H. (1930). *Liebigs Ann.*, **477**, 268.
WINDAUS, A., BORGEAUD, A., and BRUNKEN, J. (1927). *Nachr. Ges. Wiss. Göttingen*, 1.
WINDAUS, A., and BRUNKEN, J. (1928). *Liebigs Ann.*, **460**, 225.
WINDAUS, A., GAEDE, J., KÖSER, J., and STEIN, G. (1930). *Liebigs Ann.*, **483**, 17.
WINDAUS, A., and HESS, A. (1927). *Nachr. Ges. Wiss. Göttingen*, Math.-physik. Klasse 1926, **2**, 175.
WINDAUS, A., and LINSERT, O. (1928). *Liebigs Ann.*, **465**, 148.
WINDAUS, A., and LÜTTRINGHAUS, A. (1931). *Hoppe-Seyl. Z.*, **203**, 70.
WINDAUS, A., and RYGH, O. (1928). *Nachr. Ges. Wiss. Göttingen*, 202.
WINDAUS, A., TSCHESCHE, R., RUHKOPF, H., LAQUER, F., and SCHULTZ, F. (1931). *Nachr. Ges. Wiss. Göttingen*, III, 207.
Wisconsin Agricultural Experiment Station (1927). *Bull. Wisc. Agric. Expt. Sta.* **396**, 45.
—— (1929). *Ibid.*, **405**, 48.
WOHL, M. G. (1926). *J. Amer. Med. Ass.*, **87**, 901.
WOKES, F. (1928). *Biochem. J.*, **22**, 997.
WOLBACH, S. B., and HOWE, P. R. (1925). *J. Exp. Med.*, **42**, 753.
—— (1928). *Arch. Path. Lab. Med.*, **5**, 239.
WOOD, E. J. (1920). *Trans. Soc. Trop. Med. Hyg.*, Lond., **14**, 1.
WOODROW, J. W. (1928). *Phil. Mag.*, (vii) **5**, 944.
WOODS, E. (1925). *J. Biol. Chem.*, **66**, 57.
WOOLLARD, H. H. (1927). *J. Anat.*, **61**, 283.
WRIGHT, A. E. (1900). *Lancet*, Lond., ii, 565.
—— (1908). *Ibid.*, 725.
WRIGHT, E. J. (1926). *Sierra Leone Ann. Med. and San. Rep.*
WRIGHT, O. K. (1922). *Biochem. J.*, **16**, 137.
WRIGHT, H. (1905). *Review of Neurology and Psychiatry.*
YUDKIN, A. M., and LAMBERT, R. A. (1921–22[1]). *Proc. Soc. Exp. Biol.*, N.Y., **19**, 375.
—— (1921–22[2]). *Ibid.*, 376.
ZAJDEL, R., and FUNK, C. (1926). *Biochem. J.*, **20**, 26.
ZAK, E. (1917). *Wien. klin. Wschr.*, **30**, 592.
—— (1920). *Wien. med. Wschr.*, **70**, 600.
ZECHMEISTER, L., and CHOLNOKY, L. v. (1927). *Liebigs Ann.*, **455**, 70.
ZILVA, S. S. (1919[1]). *Biochem. J.*, **13**, 164.
—— (1919[2]). *Ibid.*, 172.
—— (1920[1]). *Ibid.*, **14**, 740.
—— (1920[2]). *Ibid.*, 494.
—— (1921). *Lancet*, Lond., i, 478.
—— (1922). *Biochem. J.*, **16**, 42.
—— (1923[1]). *Ibid.*, **17**, 410.

ZILVA, S. S. (1923²).   *Biochem. J.*, **17**, 416.
—— (1924¹).   *Ibid.*, **18**, 182.
—— (1924²).   *Ibid.*, 186.
—— (1924³).   *Ibid.*, 632.
—— (1925).   *Ibid.*, **19**, 589.
—— (1927¹).   *Ibid.*, **21**, 354.
—— (1927²).   *Ibid.*, 689.
—— (1928).   *Ibid.*, **22**, 779.
—— (1929).   *Ibid.*, **23**, 1199.
—— (1930).   *Ibid.*, **24**, 1687.
—— (1931).   *Ibid.*, **25**, 594.
ZILVA, S. S., and DRUMMOND, J. C. (1921).   *Lancet*, Lond., ii, 753.
—— (1922).   *Ibid.*, i, 1243.
ZILVA, S. S., DRUMMOND, J. C., and GRAHAM, M. (1924).   *Biochem. J.*, **18**, 178.
ZILVA, S. S., GOLDING, J., and DRUMMOND, J. C. (1924).   *Ibid.*, 872.
ZILVA, S. S., and MIURA, M. (1921¹).   *Ibid.*, **15**, 422.
—— (1921²).   *Ibid.*, 654.
—— (1921³),   *Lancet*, Lond., i, 323.
ZILVA, S. S., and WELLS, F. M. (1919).   *Proc. Roy. Soc.*, B. **90**, 505.
ZUCKER, T. F. (1922–23).   *Proc. Soc. Exp. Biol.*, N.Y., **20**, 136.
ZUCKER, T. F., JOHNSON, W. C., and BARNETT, M. (1922–23).   *Ibid.*, 20.
ZUCKER, T. F., and MATZNER, M. J. (1923–24).   *Ibid.*, **21**, 186.
ZUCKER, T. F., PAPPENHEIMER, A. M., and BARNETT, M. (1921–22)   *Ibid.*, **19**, 167.

APPENDIX 1

TABLE XXI.

Distribution of Vitamins in Foodstuffs, etc.

In this table o signifies that the vitamin has been tested for and not found, + that the material contains the vitamin, + + that it is a good source of the vitamin, and + + + that it is a rich source of the vitamin. The values entered under the heading vitamin B refer to the complex 'water-soluble B', entries being made under vitamins B_1 and B_2 when these have been separately estimated. References to the distribution of the vitamins will be found in the appropriate sections dealing with each vitamin separately.

Foodstuffs.	A	D	E	B_1	B_2	B	C
Oils and Fats.							
Almond oil . . .	o	. .	o				
Beef fat	+ +	+	. .	. .	. .	o	
,, ,, oil (oleo oil) .	+ to + +	. .	. .	. .	. .	o	o
,, ,, kidney fat . .	+ +						
Butter fat (pasture) .	+ +	+ +	+ +	. .	. .	. .	o
,, ,, (dry feed)	+	+	+	. .	. .	. .	o
Carrot oil	+ + +						
Cocoa butter . . .	o	o to +	o				
Coco-nut oil . . .	o to +	. .	+	. .	. .	o	o
Cotton-seed oil . .	o to +	+	+	. .	. .	o	o
,, ,, hardened	o	. .	+				
Cream	+ to + +	+	. .	. .	. .	+ +	o to +
Dog fat	+ +						
Fish-body oils.							
Coalfish	+						
Cod	+						
Eel	+ +						
Haddock	+						
Herring	+ +						
Salmon	+ to + +						
Sardine	o						
Fish-liver oils.							
Burbot	. .	+ + +					
Caplin (*Mallotus villosus*)	. .	+					
Cod	+ + +	+ + +	o to +				
Gadus Esmarkii . .	+ +						
Halibut	+ + +						
Herring	+ +						
Ling	+ +						
Plaice	+ +						
Pollock	+ +						
Puffer fish . . .	. .	+ + + (very high)					
Rat fish	+ +						
Raja clavata . . .	+ + +						
Salmon	+ + +	+ +					
Sardine							
Shark	+ +	+ + +					
Skate	+ +						
Ghee (Indian butter fat)	o to +						
Grape fruit-peel oil .	o						
Hemp-seed oil . .	. .	. .	+ +				
Horse fat . . .	+	. .	. .	. .	. .	o	o
Lampern, liver oil .	+	+ +					
Lamprey, sea, liver oil	+	+ +					
Lard	o to +	o	o	. .	. .	. .	o
Lemon-peel oil . .	o						

Foodstuffs.	A	D	E	B₁	B₂	B	C
Oils and Fats (*cont.*)							
Lettuce-seed oil	.	.	+ + +				
Linseed oil	o to +	o					
,, ,, hardened	o						
Maize, yellow, oil	+ to + +	+	+ + +	.	.	o	o
Margarine, animal	o to +	o to +		.	.	o	o
,, vegetable	o	.	.	.	.	o	o
,, enriched with vitamins	+ +	+ +	.	.	.	o	o
Mustard-seed oil	.	.	o	.	.	o	o
Mutton fat	+	.	+	.	.	o	o
Oat oil, whole oats	.	.	+ + +				
,, ,, husked	o						
Oleo stearin	+						
Olive oil	o to +	o to +	+	.	.	o	o
Orange-peel oil	+						
Palm oil	+ to + + +	o to +	+ +				
,, kernel oil	.	.	o				
Peach-kernel oil	.	.	+ +				
Pea-nut oil (*Arachis* oil)	o to +	o	+	.	.	o	o
Petrel, Australasian, stomach oil	.	+ +					
Petrel, fulmar, stomach oil	+ +	+ +					
Pig fat	+	.	+	.	.	o	o
,, kidney fat	+ +						
Poultry fat	+						
Rape oil	+						
Seagull (*Larus marinus*) liver oil	+ + +						
Seagull (*Larus marinus*) fat	+ +						
Sesame oil	o	o to +	o				
Soy-bean oil	o to +						
Walnut oil	.	.	+				
Whale oil	+ to + +						
Wheat oil	.	.	+ + +				
Wheat germ oil	+	.	+ + + (very rich)				
Yeast fat	o	.	o				
Cereals and Cereal Products.							
Barley, husked	.	.	.	+ +	.	.	o
,, sprouted	+	.	.	.	.	.	+
,, whole grain	+	.	.	+ +	.	+	o
Bread, rye	.	.	.	.	.	+ +	
,, wheaten, white, milk	+	.	.	.	.	.	o to +
Bread, wheaten, white, water	o	.	.	+	+	.	o
Bread, wheaten, wholemeal, milk	+	.	.	.	.	.	o to +
Bread, wheaten, wholemeal, water	+	.	.	+ +	+ +	.	o
Buckwheat	.	.	.	+			
Custard powders and egg substitutes	o	.	.	.	.	o	
Dari	.	.	.	+ +			
Hegari (Sorghum grain)	o						
Kafir corn, sprouted	.	.	.	.	.	.	+
Kaoliang, red	+	.	.	.	.	+ +	
,, white	+	.	.	.	.	+ +	
Maize, white, embryo	o	.	.	+ + +	+	.	o

Foodstuffs.	A	D	E	B₁	B₂	B	C
Cereals and Cereal Products (cont.)							
Maize, white, endosperm	o			o	o		o
" " wholegrain	o			+ +	+		o
" yellow, embryo	o to +		+ + +	+ + +	+		o
" " endosperm	+ +			o	o		o
" " gluten	+ +			o			o
" " whole grain	+ +	o to +	+	+ +	+		o
Maize, young cobs							+
Malt, extract, commercial				+		+	o
Malt, green	+						+ +
" kilned				+		+	o
Millet	+			+ +	+		o
Milo (Sorghum grain)	o						
Oats, husked							
" whole grain	o to +	o	+	+		+	o
" sprouted						+	+
Oatmeal	o to +						
Rice, bran				+ +			o
" embryo				+ + +			o
" parboiled, whole				+ +			
" " polished				+ +			
" polished	o		o to +	o	o		o
" polishings	+			+ + +			
" " ether extract			+ + +				
Rice, polishings, alcohol extract				+ + +	+		
Rice, starch				o	o		
" whole grain	+	o		+ +	+		
" wild	+					+ +	o
Rye, embryo	+ +	+					o
" whole grain	+			+ +			o
Wheat, bran	+			+ +	+ +		o
" embryo	+ +		+ + +	+ + +	+ +		o
" " extract (80 % alc.)				+ + +	o		
" endosperm	o			o	o		o
" flour, white	o			o	o		o
" " wholemeal	o to +			+	+		o
" middlings				+ +	+		o
" whole grain	+		+	+ +	+		o
Legumes.							
Beans, green, canned					o to +		doubtful
" haricot				+ +			o
" katjang idjo (*Phaseolus radiatus*)				+ + +			
Beans, kidney	+					+ +	
" mung	+					+ +	
" sprouted	+						+ +
" navy, canned	+						
" runner, green							+ to + +
" string, green	+ +					+	+ to + +
" velvet					+ +	+	
" " pod meal			+ +				
Cowpeas, dried (*Vignum sinense*)	+ +			+ +	+		
Cowpeas, sprouted							+ + +
Lentils	+			+ +		+ +	just +
" sprouted							+ +
Peas, dried	+			+ +	+ +		+
" green	+ +					+ +	+ + +

Foodstuffs.	A	D	E	B_1	B_2	B	C
Legumes (*cont.*)							
Peas, green, canned .	+ +	. .	. .	.	.	+ +	+ +
,, ,, sprouted	o to +	. .	. .	.	.	. .	+ +
,, yellow . . .	+ +	. .	. .	.	.	. .	.
Soy beans	+	. .	+	+	+	+	o
,, sprouted .	. .	. .	. .	. .	.	. .	doubtful
Nuts							
Almond	+	. .	. .	+	.	+	.
,, sprouted . .	. .	. .	. .	.	.	. .	+
Brazil-nut	+	. .	. .	.	.	+	.
Butter-nut . . .	+	. .	. .	.	.	+	.
Candle-nut . . .	low						
Chestnut	. .	. .	. .	+	.	+	.
Coco-nut	+	. .	.)	.	.	+	.
,, press-cake .	+	. .	+	.	.	o	.
Copra	o						
Filbert	. .	. .	. .	+ +	.	+	.
Hazel-nut	. .	. .	. .	+ +	.	+	.
Hickory-nut . . .	. .	. .	. .	. .	.	+ +	.
Litchi-nut . . .	o	. .	. .	.	.	o	.
Pea-nut (Arachis) .	+	. .	+	+ +	.	+	.
Pecan	+	. .	. .	.	.	+ +	.
Pine-nut	+	. .	. .	.	.	+ +	.
Walnut, black . .	. .	. .	. .	.	.	+	.
,, English . .	+	. .	+	.	.	+	.
Seeds.							
Babassu seed . . .	very low						
Cacao	very low						
Carrot seed . . .	+						
Citician ,, . . .	o						
Coffee bean . . .	. .	. .	. .	+			
Cohune seed . . .	o						
Cotton ,, . . .	+	. .	. .	.	.	+	.
,, ,, meal .	+						
Djave ,, . . .	o						
Fennel ,, . . .	o						
Kapok ,, . . .	low						
Lettuce ,, . . .	. .	. .	+ + +				
Linseed . . .	+ +	. .	. .	.	.	+	.
,, cake . . .	+						
Lucerne seed . . .	. .	. .	+ + +				
Rape ,, . . .	low						
Sesame ,, . . .	low						
Sunflower ,, . . .	low						
Vegetables.							
Artichoke, globe . .	+ +	. .	. .	.	.	+ +	.
Asparagus tips, bleached	+						
,, ,, green	+ +	. .	. .	.	.	+ +	+ + +
,, ,, boiled	. .	. .	. .	.	.	. .	very low
Bamboo shoots . .	. .	. .	. .	.	.	o	.
Beet, leaf and stem .	+ +	. .	. .	.	.	+	.
,, root	o to +	. .	. .	.	.	+	+
,, ,, juice . .	. .	. .	. .	.	.	+	+
,, ,, sugar . .	. .	. .	. .	.	.	o	.
Begonia leaf, fresh .	. .	. .	+ + +				
Bilimbi (*Averrhoa caramba*) . . .	. .	. .	. .	.	.	+	.
Brussels sprouts .	+ +	. .	. .	.	.	. .	.
Cabbage, canned . .	. .	. .	. .	.	.	. .	+ +
,, cooked . .	+	. .	. .	.	.	. .	+
,, etiolated . .	o to +	. .	. .	+ +	+	. .	.
,, green, fresh .	+ +	. .	+	+ +	+ +	. .	+ + +
,, ,, dried .	+	. .	. .	+ +	+ +	. .	+

Foodstuffs.	A	D	E	B_1	B_2	B	C
Vegetables (*cont.*)							
Cabbage, pickled . .							o
,, whole head	+						
Carrot, dried . . .				+ +	+		+
,, juice . . .							+
,, old, raw . .	+ +			+ +	+		+
,, ,, cooked .							+
,, young, canned							o
,, ,, cooked							+
,, ,, raw .	+			+ +	+		+ +
Cauliflower, cooked .						+	+ +
,, raw .	+					+	+ + +
Celery, leaf, green .	+ +						
,, ,, etiolated	+						
,, stalk . . .	o to +					+	+ +
Chard	+ +					+	
Chayote	+ +						
Clover	+ +					+ +	
Collards	+ +					+ +	+ +
Cucumber. . . .	o to +						+ +
Dandelion. . . .	+ +					+ +	+
Dasheen (*Caladium colocasia*) . . .	+					+	+
Duhat (*Eugenia jambolana*)						+	
Eggplant	+					+	+
Endive.	+						
Escarole	+ +						
Hay		+					o to +
Kale	+ +		+ +				
Kohl-rabi							+ (low)
Lettuce, etiolated .	+			+ +	+		+ + +
,, green . .	+ +		+ + +	+ +	+		+ + +
,, ,, dried .			+ + +	+ +	+		o
,, ,, ether extract	+		+ + +				
Lucerne (Alfalfa), dry	+ +		+ + +				
,, fresh . .			+ + +			+ +	
Mangold, leaf . .							+ + +
,, root . .	o to +						+
Mushroom, (*Agaricus campestris*) . . .		o				+	o
Mushroom, Morchel	o	+			o to +		
,, Pfifferling	+ +	+			o to +		
,, Steinpilz	o	+			o to +		
Okra						+	
Onion	o to +			+	+		+ to + +
Parsley						+ +	
Parsnip	o to +					+ +	
Pepper, green . .	+ +					+	+ + +
Pea seedlings, etiolated			+ + +				
,, ,, green .			+ + +				
Pollen				+ +			
Potato, cooked . .	+						+
,, raw . . .	+			+ +	+		+ + to + + +
,, peel . . .				+ +			
Pumpkin	+ +					+	+
Radish	o to +					+	+ +
Rape leaf . . .					+	+ +	
Rhubarb							+
Romaine	+ +					+ +	
Sauerkraut . . .	+	+				+	+ to + +
Straw		+					
Sorrel							+
Spinach, canned . .	+ +						+ to + +

Foodstuffs.	A	D	E	B_1	B_2	B	C
Vegetables (*cont.*)							
Spinach, cooked	+ +	. .	. .	+	+ +	.	+ to + +
„ dried	+ +	. .	. .	+	+ +		
„ raw	+ +	o to +	. .	+	+ +	.	+ + +
Squash, Hubbard	+ +						
Sugar cane	. .					. .	o
Swede	+					‡	
„ juice						. .	+ + +
Sweet potato	+ to + +					+	
„ „ juice						. .	+ +
„ „ leaf						+	
Tea infusion, black						o	o
„ „ green						. .	+ +
„ leaf, dried			+ +				
Timothy grass						+	
Turnip, leaf	+ +				+ +	+ +	+ +
„ root	o to +			+	+		+ +
Vegetable-marrow juice	. .				. .	. .	+ +
Velvet-bean leaf	. .			+	+ +		
Watercress, dried	+ +			+	+ +		
„ fresh	. .			+	+ +	.	+ + +
Yautia, white	+					+	
„ yellow	+ +					+ +	o to +
Fruits.							
Alligator pear	+ +					+	
Apple	+			+	+	+	+ to + +
„ canned	. .					. .	+ to + +
„ dried				+	+	. .	+
„ juice, conc.						. .	+ to + +
Apricot						. .	o to +
„ dried						. .	o
„ sulphured and dried						. .	+
Banana	+ to + +	low	+ +	+	+	. .	+ +
„ baked	. .					. .	+ to + +
„ dried				+	+	. .	o to +
Bilberry (*Vaccinium Myrtillus*)	. .					. .	o to +
Blackberry							+ +
Breadfruit	+ +					+	
Canteloup	+ +					+	+ +
Cashew apple	+						
Cherry	+ +					+	+ to + +
Chico (Sapodilla)	. .					. .	+ +
Cloudberry (*Rubus Chamaemorus*)	. .					. .	+
Cocum	. .						+
Cranberry juice	. .					. .	very low
Currant	. .					. .	+ +
„ dried	. .			o			
Custard apple	o						
Date	+			+			
Durian, white	o						
„ yellow	+						
Fig	+						
Grape	+					. .	very low
„ juice, conc.	+					+	o
Grape fruit	+					+	+ + +
„ juice	+					. .	+ + +
„ „ dried	. .					. .	+ +
Lemon	+					+	+ + +
„ juice	+					+	+ + +
„ „ dried	. .					. .	+ + +
„ „ preserved	. .					. .	o to +
„ „ tablets	. .					. .	+ +

Foodstuffs.	A	D	E	B_1	B_2	B	C
Fruits (*cont.*)							
Lemon peel . . .	+	. .	. .	. .	. .	. .	very low
Lime	o	. .	. .	. .	. .	. .	+ +
,, juice . . .	o	. .	. .	+	. .	. .	+ +
,, ,, concentrated	. .	. .	. .	. .	. .	. .	+
,, ,, preserved.	. .	. .	. .	. .	. .	o to +	o to +
Mango, dried . . .	. .	. .	. .	. .	. .	. .	low
,, ripe . . .	+ +	. .	. .	. .	. .	. .	+ + to + + +
,, unripe . .	+	. .	. .	. .	. .	. .	
Mangosteen . . .	o	. .	. .	. .	. .	. .	
Mulberry	. .	. .	. .	. .	. .	. .	+
Naartje (*Citrus nobilis Loureiro*) . . .	. .	. .	. .	. .	. .	. .	+ + +
Orange, pulp . . .	. .	. .	. .	+ +	+	+	
,, dried and minced	. .	. .	. .	. .	. .	. .	o to +
Orange juice . . .	+	. .	+	. .	. .	+	+ + +
,, ,, concentrated.	+	. .	. .	. .	. .	. .	+ + +
Orange juice, dried .	+	. .	. .	. .	. .	. .	+ + +
,, peel . . .	. .	. .	. .	. .	. .	. .	+ +
,, ,, dried .	. .	. .	. .	. .	. .	. .	+
,, ,, outer .	+ +	. .	. .	. .	. .	. .	+ +
Paw-paw (papaya) .	+ +	. .	. .	. .	. .	+	+ + +
Peach	+	. .	. .	. .	. .	+	+ to + +
,, canned. . .	+	. .	. .	. .	. .	. .	+ to + +
,, dried . . .	. .	. .	. .	. .	. .	. .	+
,, juice . . .	. .	. .	. .	. .	. .	. .	+ to + +
Pear	. .	. .	. .	. .	. .	+	+
,, canned . . .	. .	. .	. .	. .	. .	. .	+
Persimmon, Chinese	. .	. .	. .	. .	. .	. .	+
Pineapple . . .	+ +	. .	. .	. .	. .	. .	+ +
,, canned .	+ +	. .	. .	. .	. .	. .	+ +
,, juice . .	. .	. .	. .	. .	. .	. .	+ +
Plum	. .	. .	. .	. .	. .	. .	+ to + +
Prickly pear (*Opuntia decumana*) . . .	. .	. .	. .	. .	. .	. .	+ +
Prune	. .	. .	. .	. .	. .	. .	+
,, dried . . .	+ +	. .	. .	. .	. .	+	o
,, sulphured and dried	. .	. .	. .	. .	. .	. .	+
Raisin	o	. .	. .	. .	. .	+	o
Raspberry. . . .	. .	. .	. .	. .	. .	. .	+ +
,, juice dried.	. .	. .	. .	. .	. .	. .	o
Strawberry . . .	+	. .	. .	. .	. .	+	+ to + + +
,, canned .	+	. .	. .	. .	. .	. .	+ + to + + +
Tamarind, dried. .	. .	. .	. .	. .	. .	. .	+
Tomato, green . .	+	. .	. .	. .	. .	+ +	
,, ripe . .	+ +	. .	. .	+	+	+ +	+ + +
,, canned . .	+ +	. .	. .	. .	. .	+ +	+ + to + + +
,, dried . .	. .	. .	. .	. .	. .	+ +	+ +
Meat and Fish.							
Bacon	o to +						
Beef	. .	. .	+ +	+ +	+ +	. .	o to +
,, juice . . .	. .	. .	. .	. .	. .	+	o to +
Blood	. .	. .	. .	o	+		
,, meal . . .	o	o					
Chicken liver. . .	. .	+ +	. .	. .	. .	. .	+
Clams	+	+	. .	. .	. .	o	
Eels, dried . . .	+ +						
Fish, fat, muscle. .	+	+					

Foodstuffs.	A	D	E	B_1	B_2	B	C
Meat and Fish (*cont.*)							
Fish, white, muscle .	o to +	. .	. .	+			
,, liver . . .	+ + +	+ + +					
,, meal . . .	+ +	+ +					
,, roe	+ +	. .	. .	+			
Ham	o to +	. .	. .	+	+		
Liver extract, commercial	. .	. .	. .	+ +	+ + +		
Meat juice . . .	. .	. .	. .	. .	. .	+	very low
,, meal . . .	o	o					
Mutton	. .	. .	. .	+ +	+ +	. .	o to +
Ox brain . . .	+	. .	. .	+ +			
,, heart . . .	. .	. .	. .	+ +			
,, hypophysis . .	. .	. .	+ +				
,, kidney . . .	. .	. .	. .	. .	+ + +		
,, liver . . .	+ + +	. .	+ +	+ +	+ + +		
,, testes . . .	. .	. .	. .	+			
Oysters	+ +	+ +	. .	. .	. .	+ +	+
Pig brain . . .	+	. .	. .	. .	. .	+	
,, choroid . .	o						
,, heart . . .	. .	. .	+ +	. .	. .	+	
,, kidney . . .	. .	. .	. .	. .	. .	+	
,, liver . . .	+ + to + + +	+	+ +	. .	. .	+ +	+ +
,, muscle . . .	. .	. .	+ +				
,, pancreas . . .	. .	. .	+ +				
,, retina . . .	+ + +						
,, spleen . . .	. .	. .	+ +				
Placenta, human .	. .	. .	+ +				
Pork	o to +	. .	. .	+ +	+ +	. .	o to +
Poultry	o to +						
Rabbit liver . .	. .	. .	. .	. .	. .	. .	+ +
Rat heart . . .	. .	. .	+ +				
,, kidney . . .	+ +	. .	+ +				
,, liver . . .	+ + +	. .	+ +				
,, lung . . .	+ +						
,, muscle . . .	+	. .	+ +				
,, testes . . .	. .	. .	+ +				
,, blood . . .	+						
Salmon, canned . .	+						
Sheep brain . . .	. .	. .	. .	+ +			
,, liver . .	+ + +	o	. .	. .	. .	+ +	
Shrimps . . .	+						
Sweetbreads . . .	+	. .	. .	. .	. .	+ +	
Toheroa . . .	+ +						
Veal	o to +						
Whale meal . . .	o	o	. .	. .	. .	+	
Eggs.							
Duck, fresh . . .	+ +						
,, salted . . .	+ +	. .	. .	. .	. .	o	
Hen, fresh . . .	+ +	+ +	. .	+	+ to + +		
,, dried . . .	+ +	+	. .	. .	. .	. .	o
,, preserved . .	+ +						
,, yolk . . .	+ +	+ + +	+ +	+ +	+	. .	o
,, white . . .	o	o	. .	. .	. .	+ +	o
Milk and Milk Products.							
Buttermilk . . .	+	. .	. .	. .	. .	+	o to +
Caseinogen . . .	. .	. .	+	o	o		
Cheese, American cheddar . . .	+ +	. .	. .	o	+		
Cheese, skim milk .	+						
,, Limburger .	+ +						
,, Swiss . .	+ to + +						

Foodstuffs.	A	D	E	B_1	B_2	B	C
Milk and Milk Products (*cont.*)							
Cow's milk, whole, fresh	+ (varies)	o to + (varies)	+ (varies)	+	+ +	. .	+
Cow's milk, whole, condensed	+ + (varies)	. .	. .	+	. .	+	+
Cow's milk, whole, dried	+ + (varies)	o to + + (varies)	+ (varies)	. .	. .	+ +	o to +
Cow's milk, whole, pasteurized	+ (varies)	. .	. .	. .	. .	+	+
Cow's milk, whole, scalded	+ (varies)	. .	. .	. .	. .	+	+
Cow's milk, whole, sterilized	+ (varies)	. .	. .	. .	. .	+	o to +
Cow's milk, skim . .	o to +	. .	. .	. .	. .	. .	o to +
„ „ „ dried	o to +	. .	o	. .	. .	+	o to +
Goat's milk . . .	+	. .	. .	. .	. .	+	+
Human milk . . .	+	o to +	. .	+	+	. .	o to +
Lactic acid milk . .	. .	. .	. .	. .	. .	. .	+
Lactose, pure . . .	. .	. .	. .	. .	. .	o	o
Miscellaneous.	. .	. .	. .	. .	. .	o to +	o
Ale, pale	. .	. .	. .	. .	. .	. .	+
Beer, Kafir . . .	. .	. .	. .	. .	. .	. .	+
„ spruce . . .	. .	. .	. .	o	+	. .	+
„ stout . . .	o	o					
Cocoa	+	+ to + +					
Milk chocolate . .	(varies) + +	o					
Copepods							
Diatoms (*Nitzschia clōsterium*) . . .	+ + +	o + +					
Ergot of rye . . .	o	o		o	o		o
Honey	. .	. .	. .	. .	. .	. .	very low
Marmalade, orange .	o	. .	. .	. .	. .	+	
Molasses, beet . .	o	. .	. .	. .	. .	+ +	
„ cane . .	+ +						
Seaweed, *Cladophora* „ *Chondrus crispus*	o + +						
Seaweed, *Polysiphonia* „ *Ulva* . .	+ + o	. .	. .	. .	. .	o	o
Sugar, cane, pure .	o	. .	. .	. .	. .	o	o
„ glucose „ .	o to +	o	o to +	+ + +	+ + +	. .	o
Yeast, brewer's . . „ „ autoclaved	. .	. .	. .	o	+ +	. .	
„ „ autolysed	. .	. .	. .	+ + +			
Yeast, brewer's, dried „ „ extract (marmite) . . .	. .	. .	. .	+ + +	+ + +	. .	o

APPENDIX II

Official No. : C. H. 1055(1).
Geneva, 1931.

LEAGUE OF NATIONS.

HEALTH ORGANIZATION. PERMANENT COMMISSION ON BIOLOGICAL STANDARDIZATION.

CONTENTS.

REPORT OF THE CONFERENCE ON VITAMIN STANDARDS, HELD AT LONDON FROM JUNE 17th TO 20th, 1931.

LIST OF PARTICIPANTS.

Chairman :

Professor E. MELLANBY, Professor of Pharmacology, University of Sheffield, Sheffield.

Participants :

Professor J. C. DRUMMOND, Professor of Biochemistry, University College, University of London.

Professor H. VON EULER, Professor of Biochemistry, University of Stockholm, Stockholm.

Professor L. S. FRIDERICIA, Director, Institute of Hygiene of the University, Blegdamsvej 21, Copenhagen.

Professor B. C. P. JANSEN, Professor of Physiological Chemistry, University of Amsterdam, Amsterdam.

Professor E. V. McCOLLUM, Professor of Chemical Hygiene, School of Hygiene and Public Health, Johns Hopkins University, Baltimore.

Professor E. POULSSON, Director of the State Vitamin Institute, Skoyen-Oslo.

Mme G. L. RANDOIN, 'Directeur du Laboratoire de physiologie au Centre de recherches sur l'alimentation (Institut de recherches agronomiques), Directeur du laboratoire de physiologie de la nutrition a l'École des Hautes-Études', Paris.

Professor A. C. SCHEUNERT, 'Direktor des Tierphysiologischen Instituts der Universität', Leipzig.

Dr. A. SEIDELL, Chemist, National Institute of Health, United States Public Health Service, Washington, D.C.

Professor H. STEENBOCK, Professor of Agricultural Chemistry, University of Wisconsin, Madison, U.S.A.

Professor A. WINDAUS, 'Direktor, Allgemeines Chemisches Laboratorium der Universität Göttingen', Germany.

Technical Secretaries :

Dr. H. CHICK, Lister Institute of Preventive Medicine, London.

Dr. W. R. AYKROYD, Lister Institute of Preventive Medicine, London.

The following were also present :

Dr. C. E. BILLS, Director of Research, Mead, Johnson & Co., Evansville, Indiana, U.S.A.

Dr. R. BOURDILLON, National Institute for Medical Research, London.

Dr. KATHARINE-COWARD, Pharmaceutical Society's Laboratories, London.

Professor R. A. PETERS, School of Biochemistry, Oxford.

Dr. O. ROSENHEIM, National Institute for Medical Research, London.

Dr. S. S. ZILVA, Lister Institute of Preventive Medicine, London.

In the following recommendations, the question of standards and units for the four following vitamins only is considered:

     I. The fat soluble Vitamin A.

     II. The antirachitic Vitamin D.

     III. The antineuritic Vitamin B (also known as Vitamin B_1).

     IV. The antiscorbutic Vitamin C.

It is the general opinion that, in the present state of our knowledge, only these vitamins can be profitably discussed in this connexion.

I. THE FAT SOLUBLE VITAMIN A.

(a) *International Standard.*

The Conference recommends that carotene be accepted as an international provisional standard of reference for Vitamin A and that a selected sample of cod-liver oil be held in view as a possible secondary standard.

(b) *Mode of Preparation.*

It was decided that the information available does not yet justify the selection of one isomer of carotene as a standard. The similar biological activity of the two isomers that have recently been described is further justification for adopting as the provisional international standard a mixture prepared in an approved manner.

It was decided to employ a preparation of carotene made from carrots by Willstätter's method and purified by recrystallization by the method described in the memorandum issued by the Department of Biological Standards, National Institute for Medical Research, London (see Appendix II a, p. 319), until the melting-point determined is above 179° C. It was suggested that preparations should be made in various countries and dispatched immediately and with all necessary precautions against decomposition to the National Institute for Medical Research, London, where they will be mixed to form a uniform preparation by the most suitable method. The details of this final purification is to be left to the discretion of the authorities of the National Institute. It was suggested that original preparations of, say, 4 to 5 grammes might be made in the following institutions:

Department of Physiological Chemistry, University of Amsterdam.

'Laboratoire de physiologie de la nutrition, École des Hautes-Études', Paris.

'Tierphysiologisches Institut', Leipzig.

National Institute for Medical Research, Hampstead, London.

Department of Agricultural Chemistry, University of Wisconsin, U.S.A.

Biochemical Department, University of Stockholm, and 'Institut für organische Chemie der Universität', Zürich.

School of Hygiene and Public Health, Johns Hopkins University, Baltimore, U.S.A.

(c) *Place of Preparation.*

It was decided that the National Institute for Medical Research, London, acting for this purpose as the *central laboratory on behalf of the Health Organization of the League of Nations*, should be asked to undertake the final preparation of the sample of carotene to be used as the international standard for Vitamin A.

(d) *Mode of Distribution.*

It was considered desirable that, as far as possible, the standard preparation should be distributed to workers through the appropriate official institution in each country, preferably that now responsible for the distribution of similar biological standards. The material should be sent out in tubes of 10 mg. as described in Appendix IIa, p. 319.

(e) *Definition of Unit.*

The unit of Vitamin A recommended for adoption is the Vitamin A activity of 1 γ (0·001 mg.) of the international standard.

Note.—Daily doses of about 3γ to 5γ of the international standard, when administered to young rats suitably prepared on a Vitamin A-deficient diet, have been found adequate to restore growth and to cure xerophthalmia.

(f) *Permanence of the Standard.*

The Conference recommends that this international standard and unit be accepted provisionally for two years.

(g) *Subjects recommended for Future Investigations.*

It is highly desirable that, during the provisional period, further investigations of the standard should be made regarding the stability of the carotene preparation both when sealed in the original tubes and after it has been removed and dissolved for biological testing. In the latter connexion, emphasis is laid on the importance of minimizing contact with air or oxygen of the solutions used for animal feeding. It is recommended that they be always stored in an inert gas and at low temperature.

It will be of great value if investigators submit to the League of Nations Health Organization observations on the stability of the preparation, its behaviour in various solvents and under different conditions of storage, and any other information bearing on its use as a biological standard. The use of suitable 'antioxidants' ('*antioxygènes*' in French) should, in particular, be studied.

(h) *Biological Methods for Estimation of Vitamin A.*

It was decided not to recommend any one particular method of conducting the biological assay, but to invite members of the Conference to submit to the League of Nations Health Organization their observations on the value of the methods they have been using.

It is recommended that further attention be given to the methods based on the curative action of carotene for xerophthalmia and other lesions characteristic of Vitamin A deficiency, as well as to those based on increase in weight.

(i) *Selected Sample of Cod-Liver Oil for Use as a possible Secondary Standard.*

It is recommended that a supply of an approved sample of cod-liver oil be obtained with the object of making a series of comparative tests to determine its suitability as an alternative standard. The Conference is informed that the United States Department of Agriculture is making arrangements for such a standard substance to be available in the United States during the coming year.

It was decided to ask the United States Department of Agriculture to obtain sufficient supplies of the oil for distribution in order to enable investigators of other countries to assay this oil in terms of the international unit of standard carotene. It is hoped thus to obtain evidence regarding the stability of Vitamin A in cod-liver oil as affected by conditions and time of storage.

II. THE ANTIRACHITIC VITAMIN D.

(a) *International Standard to be adopted and Arrangements for Control.*

The Conference recommends that the standard solution of irradiated ergosterol at present issued from the National Institute of Medical Research, London, be adopted as international Vitamin D standard for the next two years.

If within this period it should become necessary, owing to threatened exhaustion of the present supply, to replace this solution by a fresh standard, the equivalence shall be determined by experts of different countries who have had the opportunity of comparing the proposed new standard with the one at present issued. It is suggested that the following Institutions, among others, be invited to co-operate in those tests:

'Allgemeines Chemisches Laboratorium', Göttingen.

'Tierphysiologisches Institut', Leipzig.

Food and Drugs Administration Laboratory, Department of Agriculture, Washington, D.C.

Biochemical Department, University of Stockholm.

Department of Agricultural Chemistry, University of Wisconsin.

School of Hygiene, Johns Hopkins University, Baltimore.

' Laboratoire de physiologie de la nutrition, École des Hautes-Études ', Paris.

Pharmaceutical Society, London.

(b) *Method of Preparation.*

1. It is recommended that, in the preparation of the solutions of irradiated ergosterol, used as standards of reference for Vitamin D (or as sub-standards), irradiation with ultraviolet light shall be done in ethereal solution in the absence of any appreciable traces of oxygen, and the solution should be kept in rapid motion. The conditions of exposure should be such as to transform between 30 per cent. and 80 per cent. of the ergosterol. The solution of the product and of further dilutions shall be made in a stable unsaturated natural vegetable oil, which has given a negative test for Vitamin D.

2. The standard solution of irradiated ergosterol at present issued from the National Institute for Medical Research, London (Standard Solution III), was, however, prepared as follows, in January 1929:

A 0·1 per cent. solution of the ergosterol in absolute alcohol was exposed for half an hour in a silica cell, 1 cm. thick, to the unfiltered radiation from a K.B.B. (Kelvin, Bottomley and Baird) mercury vapour lamp, taking 2·5 ampères and 125 volts at atmospheric pressure, at 15 cm. distance from cell to lamp. The resulting solution was mixed with a little olive oil, and then evaporated at 45° C. at a low pressure to remove the alcohol. The concentrated oily solution thus obtained was diluted with pure olive oil to give a concentration corresponding to 1 mg. of the original ergosterol in 10 c.c. of olive oil at 18° C. The olive oil used was tested for stability and gave a negative test for Vitamin D.

The additional larger quantity of standard (prepared January 1931), which is available for distribution later if required, was prepared with observance of the general conditions indicated under 1.

(c) *Mode of Distribution.*

The National Institute for Medical Research, London, *acting for this purpose as the central laboratory on behalf of the League of Nations Health Organization,* shall distribute to each country wishing to use the standard a sufficient quantity of the solution to enable the standard to be effectively applied according to the conditions in the particular country. Such quantity should be supplied only to a central institution nominated for the purpose by the country concerned, which will be responsible for the distribution either of the portion of international standard solution received or, wherever possible, of an equivalent sub-standard prepared by comparison therewith.

(d) *Stability of the International Standard.*

The stability of the standard solution at present issued from the National Institute for Medical Research, London, has proved satisfactory on the results of tests over a period of two years, when preserved at or below 0° C. with exclusion of air.

(e) *Definition of Unit.*

The unit of Vitamin D recommended for adoption is defined as the Vitamin D activity of 1 mg. of the international standard solution of irradiated ergosterol.

Note.—The international standard solution has been prepared to have such potency that approximately 1 mg. thereof given daily to a rachitic rat for eight successive days will produce a wide line of calcium deposits in the metaphysis of the proximal ends of the tibiae and of the distal ends of the radii.

(f) *Permanence of the Standard.*

The international standard at present recommended shall be regarded as provisional for the next two years, in the hope that a more stable crystalline substance may in the meantime become available.

(g) *Subjects recommended for Further Investigation.*

1. The influence of various oils as solvents upon the stability of solutions of irradiated ergosterol.

2. Further investigation of the crystalline antirachitic substances recently isolated from irradiated ergosterol. It was decided that Professor Windaus

and Dr. Bourdillon shall be asked to investigate the constancy of the physical properties of the crystalline products recently isolated by them respectively, in order to determine whether these may be regarded as pure substances. If so, the potency of these products should be accurately compared with that of the (present) international standard at intervals of three months during the next two years, in order to compare the stability in each case. If the results are satisfactory, it is hoped that one of these crystalline substances may eventually replace the solution of irradiated ergosterol as international Vitamin D standard.

3. The toxicity of the present standard and of the crystalline products should be investigated (see also p. 319).

(h) *Biological Methods for Estimation of Vitamin D.*

In using the international standard solution for the determination of the antirachitic potency of unknown preparations, it is recommended that not fewer than twenty rats (preferably more) be used for a determination, half of these to receive the standard and the remaining litter-mates the unknown substance. Provided this precaution is observed, it is considered permissible to use various biological methods of estimation, either prophylactic or therapeutic. For instance, the 'line' test, X-ray examination or determination of the bone ash, are all considered reliable methods.

III. The Antineuritic Vitamin B.

(a) *International Standard.*

The Conference recommends the adoption, as international standard, of the adsorption product of the antineuritic Vitamin B prepared in the Medical Laboratory, Batavia (Java), by the method of Seidell, as described by Jansen and Donath.

(b) *Terminology.*

The international standard preparation should be known as the 'standard adsorption product of the antineuritic Vitamin B'.

(c) *Method of Preparation.*

The international standard is prepared by extracting rice polishings with water, sufficient sulphuric acid being added to make the pH 4·5. Salicylic acid to a concentration of 0·2 per cent. and toluene are then added to prevent bacterial decomposition. The process of extraction is continued for two days, after which the solution is filtered. For each 100 kilogrammes of the original rice polishings, 3 kilogrammes of fuller's earth (specially selected for its adsorptive powers) are added to the solution, which is then stirred for twenty-four hours. Subsequently, the solution is filtered off and the fuller's earth, after being washed with water and alcohol, is dried; 3 kilogrammes of the fuller's earth adsorbate represents the antineuritic Vitamin B from 100 kilogrammes of rice polishings.

(d) *Place of Preparation.*

It is recommended that the Medical Laboratory, Batavia, Java, should be asked, through Professor Jansen, of Amsterdam, to prepare a batch of 25 kilogrammes of the standard preparation. This should provide an adequate supply for many years.

(e) *Place of Distribution.*

It is suggested that this batch of standard adsorption product of antineuritic Vitamin B should be kept at the National Institute for Medical Research, London, *acting for this purpose as central laboratory on behalf of the Health Organization of the League of Nations.*

One hundred grammes would be an amount suitable for distribution to individual laboratories. No special precautions are necessary in keeping this preparation, except that it should be stored in a dry place. In the presence of moisture, bacterial decomposition readily takes place.

(f) *Definition of Unit.*

The unit recommended for adoption is the antineuritic activity of 10 milli-grammes of the international standard adsorption product.

Note.—A daily dose of 10 to 20 mg. of this preparation is required to maintain normal growth in a young rat on a diet deficient in the antineuritic Vitamin B but complete in all other respects, including the antidermatitis Vitamin (B_2); the curative 'day dose' for a pigeon (300 grammes weight) suffering from polyneuritis on a diet of polished rice is about 20 to 30 mg. (method of Kinnersley and Peters).

(g) *Permanence of the International Standard Recommended.*

This standard adsorption product should serve as a provisional international standard for five years, or until advances in the knowledge of this vitamin make a revision desirable.

(h) *Recommendations for Further Investigations.*

1. The standard adsorption product should be investigated for its content of other B-vitamins.

2. Although there is no evidence that loss of potency is liable to occur in the standard adsorption product, the Conference suggests that the following laboratories be asked to undertake a further investigation of its stability :

Department of Physiological Chemistry, University of Amsterdam.
National Institute of Health, United States Public Health Service, Washington, D.C.
Institute of Hygiene, University of Copenhagen.
School of Biochemistry, University of Oxford.
'Tierphysiologisches Institut', Leipzig.
Biochemical Institute, University of Stockholm.
'Laboratoire de physiologie au Centre de recherches sur l'alimentation (Institut des recherches agronomiques)', Paris.
Lister Institute of Preventive Medicine, London.

(i) *Biological Methods for Estimation of the Antineuritic Vitamin B.*

The Conference expresses no opinion on the relative merits of current biological methods for estimation of the antineuritic Vitamin B (as recorded in the report on this vitamin, presented to this Conference and in the literature generally). It considers that good evidence is provided by that report that the different methods described, either prophylactic or curative in type, and employing either the rat or the pigeon as experimental animal, may yield equally valid results.

IV. THE ANTISCORBUTIC VITAMIN C.

(a) *International Standard.*

The Conference recommends the adoption as international standard of the fresh juice of the lemon, Citrus limonum.

(b) *Definition of Unit.*

The unit of the antiscorbutic Vitamin C recommended for adoption is the Vitamin C activity of 0·1 c.c. of fresh juice of the lemon, *Citrus limonum,*

Note.—This is about 1/10th of the daily dose necessary to prevent development of macroscopic scorbutic lesions in a young guinea-pig maintained on a scurvy-producing diet.

(c) *Method of Use.*

The fresh lemon juice used as standard may be decitrated as follows : to the expressed juice after filtration through muslin an excess of calcium carbonate is added until effervescence stops. After standing for one hour, the mixture is filtered through a Buchner funnel. The decitrated juice should have a reaction of *p*H about 6 and should be administered to the experimental animal within two hours of filtration.

(d) *Permanence of Standard.*

This international standard shall be regarded as provisional for the next two years.

* * *

NOTE ON THE TOXICITY OF IRRADIATED ERGOSTEROL.

In view of the toxic effects which have been reported after administration of certain specimens of irradiated ergosterol, this Conference suggests the advisability of testing all preparations of irradiated ergosterol, destined for medicinal use, for toxicity as well as for antirachitic potency.

APPENDIX II a.

MEMORANDUM ON CAROTENE SUPPLIED FOR TESTING ITS SUITABILITY AS A POSSIBLE STANDARD FOR VITAMIN 'A'.

Preparation.

The material provided has been prepared as follows : Commercial carotene (B.D.H.) was dissolved in benzene and filtered, and the clear solution poured into a large volume of warm absolute alcohol. The crystallization was allowed to proceed at 37° C., and the crystals filtered off at the same temperature. All these operations were carried out in an atmosphere of CO_2. The crystalline material was dried *in vacuo*. Melting point 179° to 180° C. (taken in electrically heated ' Berl block').

For distribution into tubes the material was dissolved in benzene at 37° C. to make a 2 per cent. solution ; 0·5 c.c. of this solution was run into each of the brown glass tubes in which the material is distributed, the whole process of solution and filling out being again carried out in an atmosphere of CO_2. The filled tubes were transferred to a desiccator containing paraffin shavings and $CaCl_2$. The desiccator was evacuated and left attached to a pump until the benzene had completely evaporated and the carotene had been deposited, mainly as a crystalline residue, at the bottom of each tube. When drying was complete, the desiccator and contained tubes were again filled with CO_2, evacuated, and refilled with CO_2. The tubes, before filling, had been drawn out into narrow constrictions to facilitate sealing, which was thus rapidly effected with minimal contamination of the CO_2 by air.

Suggestions for Use.

It is assumed that less than the whole contents of one tube (10 mg.) will be required for a test. The tube having been opened, the necessary quantity of carotene can be removed with the aid of a fine glass rod or narrow platinum spatula, and immediately dissolved in the chosen solvent. The partly used tube should be enclosed in a test tube of suitable size, which should then be drawn out in preparation for sealing. The test tube and contained specimen tube can then be refilled with CO_2 in the vacuum desiccator, as above described, removed, quickly sealed, and preserved in a cold, dark place until again required. The prepared solution, if it is to be used for several tests, should be preserved from light and oxygen by similar or equivalent precautions.

January 6th, 1931.

Department of Biological Standards,
National Institute for Medical Research, London.

INDEX

Adrenal glands, effect of vitamin B_1 deficiency on, 135.

Ale, pale, vitamin C in, 207.

—, —, vitamins in, 312.

Alfalfa seed, vitamin E in, 115.

— —,vitamins in, 307.

—, vitamin B_1 in, 163.

—, — B_2 in, 163.

—, vitamins in, 308.

Allantois, effect of vitamin E deficiency on, 108.

Alligator pear, vitamins B_1 and B_2 in, 163.

— —, vitamins in, 309.

Almond, vitamin A in, 45.

—, — B_1 in, 162.

—, — B_2 in, 162.

—, — C in, 207.

—, vitamins in, 307.

Almond oil, vitamin E in, 114.

— —, vitamins in, 304.

Amino-acid deficiency theory of aetiology of pellagra, 178.

Anaemia due to vitamin A deficiency, 237.

— — — — — B_2 deficiency, 252.

Antimony trichloride reaction for vitamin A, 37.

Antineuritic vitamin : see Vitamin B_1.

Antiscorbutic vitamin : see Vitamin C.

Apple, vitamin A in, 45.

—, — B_1 in, 163.

—, — B_2 in, 163.

—, — C in, 207, 211.

—, vitamins in, 309.

Apricot, vitamin C in, 207.

—, vitamins in, 309.

Arachis oil, vitamin A in, 45.

— —, — D produced in, by irradiation, 74.

— —, — E in, 114.

— —, vitamins in, 305.

Arsenic trichloride reaction for vitamin A, 37.

Artichoke, French, vitamin A in, 45.

—, vitamins B_1 and B_2 in, 163.

—, — in, 307.

Asparagus, vitamin B_1 in 163.

—, — B_2 in, 163.

—, — C in, 205.

—, vitamins in, 307.

Babassu seed, vitamins in, 307.

Bacon, vitamins in, 310.

Bacterial infections in mice and rats, effects of vitamin A on, 30.

— reproduction and growth factors, 172.

Bamboo shoots, vitamins B_1 and B_2 in, 163.

— —, — in, 307.

Banana, vitamin A in, 45.

—, vitamin B_1 in, 163.

—, — B_2 in, 163.

—, — C in, 207.

—, — E in, 116.

—, vitamins in, 309.

Barley, effect of, on structure of dog's teeth, 92.

— in production of rickets, 60.

—, vitamin B_1 in, 157, 162.

—, — B_2 in, 162.

—, — C in, 205.

—, vitamins in, 305.

Beans, vitamin B_1 in, 162.

—, — B_2 in, 162.

—, — C in, 206.

—, vitamins in, 306.

Beef fat, vitamins in, 304.

— muscle, vitamin B_1 in, 156.

—, vitamins in, 310.

Beer, Kafir, as antiscorbutic, 259.

—, —, vitamin C in, 207.

—, —, vitamins in, 312.

— and malt as antiscorbutics, 258.

—, spruce, vitamin C in, 207.

—, —, vitamins in, 312.

—, vitamin B_1 in, 164.

—, — B_2 in, 164.

—, — C in, 207.

Beet, vitamin A in, 45.

—, vitamin B_1 in, 163.

—, — B_2 in, 163.

—, — C in, 205, 209.

—, vitamins in, 307.

Begonia leaf, vitamin E in, 115.

— —, vitamins in, 307.

Beri-beri : aetiology : early conception, 10.

—: —: factors other than vitamin B_1, 126.

—: —: primarily due to deficiency of antineuritic vitamin, 127.

—: —: rice, milled and undermilled, 127.

— among British and Indian troops in Mesopotamia during war, 246.

— — wheat-eating populations, 245.

— columbarum : pathological features distinguishing it from polyneuritis, 124.

—: Crowell's experiment on prisoners in Philippine Islands, 244.

—: dietary sources of antineuritic factor, 247.

—, diets in relation to, 248.

— due to diet of over-milled cereal, 243.

—, Eijkman's work on, 13.

—: historical, 123.

—, human, and avian polyneuritis, 123.

—-like condition in swine, 126.

Printed under the authority of HIS MAJESTY'S STATIONERY OFFICE
by JOHN JOHNSON, at the University Press, Oxford

𝔓𝔯𝔦𝔟𝔶 𝔊𝔬𝔲𝔫𝔠𝔦𝔩
MEDICAL RESEARCH COUNCIL
(*Formerly Medical Research Committee, National Health Insurance.*)

LIST OF PUBLICATIONS

(The prices given are net: those in brackets include postage.)

June, 1932.

The following publications relating to the work of the Medical Research Council can be purchased directly from **H.M. Stationery Office,** at the following addresses: Adastral House, Kingsway, London, W.C. 2 ; 120 George Street, Edinburgh ; York Street, Manchester ; 1 St. Andrew's Crescent, Cardiff ; 15 Donegall Square West, Belfast ; **or through any bookseller.***

In addition, numerous memoirs upon work aided by the Medical Research Council have appeared in Scientific Journals : particulars of these may be seen in the Annual Reports.

ANNUAL REPORTS

Medical Research Committee, Nos. 1–5, 1914–15 to 1918–19.

Medical Research Council, 1919–20 to 1929–30.

(Price of each report from 1920–1 to 1925–6, 3s. 6d. (3s. 8d.) ; from 1926–7 to 1928–9, 3s. (3s. 2d.) ; 1929–30 and 1930–31, 2s. 6d. (2s. 8d.).)

SPECIAL REPORTS, &c.

Alcohol :

No. 31. Alcohol : its Absorption into and Disappearance from the Blood under different conditions. By E. Mellanby. [1919.] *Out of print.*

No. 34. The Influence of Alcohol on Manual Work and Neuro-muscular Co-ordination. By H. M. Vernon. [1919.] 2s. (2s. 1d.).

No. 56. The Effects of Alcohol and some other Drugs during Normal and Fatigued Conditions. By W. McDougall and May Smith. [1920.] 1s. (1s. 1d.).

(Book). Alcohol : its Action on the Human Organism. Second Edition. [1924.] 1s. paper covers, 1s. 6d. cloth bound.

Anaerobic Bacteria : *see* WOUND INFECTIONS.

Animals, Diseases of :

No. 121. Borna Disease and Enzootic Encephalo-Myelitis of Sheep and Cattle. By S. Nicolau and I. A. Galloway. [1928.] 5s. (5s. 2½d.).

Bacteriology (MISCELLANEOUS) :

No. 35. The Reaction of Culture Media, by S. R. Douglas, J. W. H. Eyre, P. P. Laidlaw, and C. G. L. Wolf. Second Edition, revised by P. P. Laidlaw. [1927.] 6d. (7d.).

No. 49. On the Destruction of Bacteria in Milk by Electricity. By J. M. Beattie and F. C. Lewis. [1920.] *Out of print.*

No. 51. The Laboratory Diagnosis of Acute Intestinal Infections, including the Principles and Practice of the Agglutination Tests. By the Committee upon Pathological Methods. [1920.] 4s. 6d. (4s. 8d.).

No. 64. Catalogue of the National Collection of Type Cultures. Third Edition. [1931.] 2s. (2s. 1d.).

See also SURGERY (No. 138).

Blood Physiology :

No. 72. The Acid-base Equilibrium of the Blood. By the Haemoglobin Committee. [1923.] 2s. (2s. 1d.).

See also SHOCK, SURGICAL.

Borna Disease : *see* ANIMALS, DISEASES OF.

Brain Surgery : *see* SURGERY.

Bright's Disease : *see* NEPHRITIS.

* For overseas agencies see p. ix.

Burns:

No. 141. The Tannic Acid Treatment of Burns. By W. C. Wilson. [1929.] 1s. (1s. 1d. .

Cancer :

No. 99. An Investigation into the Statistics of Cancer in Different Trades and Professions. By Matthew Young and W. T. Russell. [1926.] 1s. 6d. (1s. 7d.).

See also RADIUM.

Catgut : *see* SURGERY (No. 138).

Cerebro-spinal Fever :

No. 2. Report of the Special Advisory Committee upon Bacteriological Studies of Cerebro-spinal Fever during the Epidemic of 1915. [1916.] *Out of print.*

No. 3. Bacteriological Studies in the Pathology and Preventive Control of Cerebro-spinal Fever among the Forces during 1915 and 1916. By M. H. Gordon, Martin Flack, P. W. Bassett-Smith, T. G. M. Hine, and W. J. Tulloch. [1917.] *Out of print.*

No. 17. (I.) A Report upon the Seasonal Outbreak of Cerebro-spinal Fever in the Navy at Portsmouth, 1916–17. By Paul Fildes and S. L. Baker. (II.) The Treatment of Cerebro-spinal Meningitis by Antimeningococcus Serum at the Royal Naval Hospital, Haslar, 1915–16–17. By G. P. Adshead. [1918.] 2s. 6d. (2s. 8½d.).

No. 50. Cerebro-spinal Fever. Studies in the Bacteriology, Preventive Control, and Specific Treatment of Cerebro-spinal Fever among the Military Forces, 1915–19. By M. H. Gordon and others. [1920.] 4s. (4s. 3d.).

No. 124. The Meningococcus. By E. G. D. Murray. [1929.] 3s. 6d. (3s. 8½d.).

Chemotherapy : *see* STREPTOCOCCAL INFECTIONS.

Child Life (ANTENATAL and POSTNATAL INVESTIGATIONS) :

No. 10. The Mortalities of Birth, Infancy, and Childhood. By A. K. Chalmers, W. A. Brend, L. Findlay, and J. Brownlee. [1918.] 1s. 6d. (1s. 7½d.).

No. 74. The Relation between Home Conditions and the Intelligence of School Children. By L. Isserlis. [1923.] 1s. (1s. 1d.).

No. 81. The Effect of Maternal Social Conditions and Nutrition upon Birth-weight and Birth-length. By M. Bruce Murray. [1924.] 1s. (1s. 1d.).

No. 82. Maternal Syphilis as a cause of Death of the Foetus and of the New-born Child. By J. N. Cruickshank. [1924.] 1s. 6d. (1s. 7½d.).

No. 86. The Estimation of Foetal Age, the Weight and Length of Normal Foetuses, and the Weights of Foetal Organs. By J. N. Cruickshank, M. J. Miller, and F. J. Browne. [1924.] 2s. 6d. (2s. 7½d.).

No. 101. Poverty, Nutrition, and Growth : Studies of Child Life in Cities and Rural Districts of Scotland. By D. Noël Paton, Leonard Findlay, and others. [1926.] 10s. (10s. 4½d.).

No. 109. A Clinical and Pathological Study of 1,673 Cases of Dead-Births and Neo-natal Deaths. Compiled by E. L. Holland and J. E. Lane-Claypon. [1926.] 3s. 6d.(3s.7½d.).

No. 114. Social Conditions and Acute Rheumatism. [1927.] 2s. 6d. (2s. 8d.).

No. 117. The Toxaemias of Pregnancy : A Clinical and Biochemical Study. By J. N. Cruickshank, J. Hewitt, and K. L. Couper. [1927.] 4s. (4s. 2d.).

No. 118. The Cause of Foetal Death in 144 Cases. By A. C. Palmer. [1928.] 3s. (3s. 2d.).

No. 145. The Causes of Neo-natal Death. By J. N. Cruickshank. [1930.] 1s. 6d. (1s. 7½d.).

No. 157. Nutritional Anaemia in Infancy: The Influence of Iron Deficiency on Infant Health. By H. M. M. Mackay, L. Goodfellow, and A. Bradford Hill. [1931.] 2s. (2s.2d.).

No. 162. Intelligence and Disease. By Shepherd Dawson assisted by J. C. M. Conn. [1931.] 1s. (1s. 1½d.).

See also NUTRITION ; RICKETS.

Dental Disease :

No. 70. The Structure of Teeth in relation to Dental Disease. By J. Howard Mummery. [1922.] 2s. (2s. 1d.).

No. 97. The Incidence of Dental Disease in Children. By the Committee for the Investigation of Dental Disease. [1925.] 1*s.* 6*d.* (1*s.* 7½*d.*).

No. 140. Diet and the Teeth: An Experimental Study. Part I. Dental Structure in Dogs. By May Mellanby. [1929.] 17*s.* 6*d.* (18*s.*).

No. 153. Diet and the Teeth: An Experimental Study. Part II. A. Diet and Dental Disease. B. Diet and Dental Structure in Mammals other than the Dog. By May Mellanby. [1930.] 2*s.* 6*d.* (2*s.* 8½*d.*).

No. 159. The Influence of Diet on Caries in Children's Teeth (Interim Report). By the Dental Committee. [1931.] 6*d.* (7*d.*).

Diphtheria :

No. 115. The Prevention of Diphtheria. By J. Graham Forbes. [1927.] 2*s.* (2*s.* 1½*d.*).

(Book). Diphtheria: its Bacteriology, Pathology, and Immunology. By the Bacteriological Committee. [1923.] 12*s.* 6*d.* (13*s.* 3*d.*).

See also EPIDEMIOLOGY (No. 75), STATISTICS (No. 137).

Dysentery :

Reports upon Investigations in the United Kingdom of Dysentery Cases received from the Eastern Mediterranean:—

No. 4. I. Amoebic Dysentery and the Protozoological Investigation of Cases and Carriers. By Clifford Dobell. [1917.] *Out of print.*

No. 5. II. Report upon 878 Cases of Bacillary Enteritis. By L. Rajchman and G. T. Western. [1917.] *Out of print.*

No. 6. III. Report upon recovered Cases of Intestinal Disease in the Royal Naval Hospital, Haslar, 1915–16. By Paul Fildes and others. IV. Report upon combined Clinical and Bacteriological Studies of Dysentery Cases from the Mediterranean. By S. R. Douglas and L. Colebrook. [1917.] 4*s.* 6*d.* (4*s.* 7½*d.*).

No. 7. V. Report upon 2,360 Enteritis ' Convalescents received at Liverpool from various Expeditionary Forces'. By E. Glynn and others. [1918.] 2*s.* (2*s.* 2*d.*).

No. 15. A Study of 1,300 Convalescent Cases of Dysentery from Home Hospitals : with special reference to the Incidence and Treatment of Amoebic Dysentery Carriers. By Clifford Dobell, H. S. Gettings, Margaret W. Jepps, and J. B. Stephens. [1918.] 1*s.* 3*d.* (1*s.* 4*d.*).

No. 29. A Contribution to the Study of Chronicity in Dysentery Carriers. By W. Fletcher and Doris L. Mackinnon. [1919.] 9*d.* (10*d.*).

No. 30. An Investigation of the Flexner-Y Group of Dysentery Bacilli. By H. S. Gettings. [1919.] 1*s.* (1*s.* 1*d.*).

No. 40. Studies of Bacillary Dysentery occurring in the British Forces in Macedonia. By L. S. Dudgeon and others. [1919.] 3*s.* (3*s.* 1½*d.*).

No. 42. A Study of the Serological Races of the Flexner Group of Dysentery Bacilli. By F. W. Andrewes and A. C. Inman. [1919.] 2*s.* (2*s.* 1½*d.*).

See also FOOD POISONING.

Encephalitis :

No. 108. The Sheffield Outbreak of Epidemic Encephalitis in 1924. [1926.] 1*s.* 9*d.* (1*s.* 10½*d.*).

Enteric Infections :

No. 9. A Report upon the Use of Atropine as a Diagnostic Agent in Typhoid Infections. By H. F. Marris. [1917.] 1*s.* (1*s.* 1*d.*).

No. 48. A Report on the probable Proportion of Enteric Infections among Undiagnosed Febrile Cases invalided from the Western Front since October 1916. By W. W. C. Topley, S. G. Platts, and C. G. Imrie. [1920.] 3*s.* (3*s.* 1½*d.*).

See also BACTERIOLOGY ; FOOD POISONING.

Epidemiology :

No. 75. The Schick Test, Diphtheria and Scarlet Fever. By S. F. Dudley. [1923.] 1*s.* (1*s.* 1½*d.*).

No. 111. The Spread of Droplet Infection in Semi-isolated Communities. By S. F. Dudley. [1926.] 1s. 6d. (1s. 7½d.).

No. 120. An Inquiry into the Relationship between Housing Conditions and the Incidence and Fatality of Measles. By J. L. Halliday. [1928.] 1s. (1s. 1d.).

See also SMALL-POX ; STATISTICS ; TUBERCULOSIS ; etc.

Flying, Medical Problems of :
Reports of the Air Medical Investigation Committee:—

No. 28. The Sense of Balance and Stability in the Air. By Henry Head. [1919]. 9d. (10d.). (Included in No. 53.)

No. 37. The Effects of Diminished Tension of Oxygen, with especial reference to the Activity of the Adrenal Glands. By C. H. Kellaway. The Ear in relation to certain Disabilities in Flying. By S. Scott. [1919.] 1s. (1s. 1d.).

No. 53. The Medical Problems of Flying (including reports on oxygen want, selection of candidates for flying, sense of balance, and flying strain). [1920.] 6s. (6s. 4d.).

No. 84. The Application of the Air Force Physical Efficiency Tests to Men and Women. By L. D. Cripps. [1924.] 1s. 6d. (1s. 7½d.).

Food Poisoning :
No. 24. A Report on the Investigation of an Epidemic caused by Bacillus aertrycke. By H. Marrian Perry and H. L. Tidy. [1919.] 9d. (10d.).

No. 91. An Investigation of the Salmonella Group, with Special Reference to Food Poisoning. By W. G. Savage and P. Bruce White. [1925.] 3s. 6d. (3s. 8d.).

No. 92. Food Poisoning : a Study of 100 Recent Outbreaks. By W. G. Savage and P. Bruce White. [1925.] 2s. 6d. (2s. 8d.).

No. 103. Further Studies of the Salmonella Group. By P. Bruce White. [1926.] 5s. (5s. 2½d.).

Goitre :
No. 154. Iodine Supply and the Incidence of Endemic Goitre. By J. B. Orr. [1931. 4d. (5d.) *See also* NUTRITION (No. 123).

Haemoglobin : *see* BLOOD.

Hearing :
No. 166. Reports of the Committee upon the Physiology of Hearing. I. The Localization of Sounds in the Median Plane. By J. H. Shaxby, and F. H. Gage. II. Some Factors in Auditory Localization. By H. E. O. James, and Marion E. Massey. [1932.] 1s.

Heart :
No. 8. Report upon Soldiers returned as Cases of ' Disordered Action of the Heart ' (D.A.H.), or Valvular Disease of the Heart. By Sir Thomas Lewis. [1917.] 1s. (1s. 1d.).

No. 147. The Electrocardiogram. By W. H. Craib. [1930.] 1s. 3d. (1s. 4½d.).

Industrial Health :
The Annual Reports of the Industrial Health (formerly Fatigue) Research Board, and special reports on particular subjects, are published for the Council in separate series. The subjects dealt with include accident causation, rest pauses, spells of work, movement study, vocational selection, and problems of particular industries. A list can be supplied on application to the Secretary of the Board, 38 Old Queen Street, Westminster, S.W. 1.

Influenza :
No. 36. Studies of Influenza in Hospitals of the British Armies in France, 1918. [1919.] 3s. 6d. (3s. 8d.).

No. 63. Studies in the Aetiology of Epidemic Influenza. By J. McIntosh. [1922.] 2s. 6d. (2s. 7d.).

Jaundice :
No. 113. Spirochaetal Jaundice. By G. Buchanan. [1927.] 4s. (4s. 2d.).

Light Treatment :
No. 131. Irradiation and Health : Two Experimental Studies. By Dora Colebrook. [1929.] 1s. 6d. (1s. 7d.).

Malaria : *see* QUININE.

Maternal Mortality : *see* CHILD LIFE and STREPTOCOCCAL INFECTIONS.

Measles : *see* EPIDEMIOLOGY (No. 120).

Miners' Dietaries : *see* NUTRITION.

Miners' Diseases, etc. :

No. 89. Report on Miners' 'Beat Knee', 'Beat Hand', and 'Beat Elbow'. By E. L. Collis and T. L. Llewellyn. [1924.] 1s. 6d. (1s. 7d.).

See also JAUNDICE (No. 113).

Miners' Nystagmus : *see* VISION.

Nephritis :

No. 43. Albuminuria and War Nephritis among British Troops in France. By H. MacLean. [1919.] 2s. 6d. (2s. 8d.).

No. 142. A Classification of Bright's Disease. By Dorothy S. Russell. [1929.] 8s. 6d. (8s. 10d.).

Nerve Injuries :

Reports of the Committee upon Injuries to the Nervous System :—

No. 54. The Diagnosis and Treatment of Peripheral Nerve Injuries. [1920.] 2s. (2s. 1½d.).

No. 88. Injuries of the Spinal Cord and Cauda Equina. [1924.] 1s. 6d. (1s. 7½d.).

Nutrition :

No. 13. An Enquiry into the Composition of Dietaries, with special reference to the Dietaries of Munition Workers. By Viscount Dunluce and Major Greenwood.

Out of print.

No. 87. Report on the Nutrition of Miners and their Families. By the Committee upon Quantitative Problems in Human Nutrition. [1924.] 1s. 3d. (1s. 4d.).

No. 105. Diets for Boys during the School Age. By H. C. Corry Mann. [1926.] 2s. 6d. (2s. 7½d.).

No. 123. Iodine in Nutrition : a Review of Existing Information. By J. B. Orr and I. Leitch. [1929.] 2s. 6d. (2s. 8d.). *See also* GOITRE (No. 154).

No. 135. The Carbohydrate Content of Foods. By R. A. McCance and R. D. Lawrence. [1929.] 2s. (2s. 1½d.).

No. 146. The Antiscurvy Vitamin in Apples. By Mary F. Bracewell, E. Hoyle, and S. S. Zilva. [1930.] 9d. (10d.).

No. 151. A Study in Nutrition. An Inquiry into the Diet of 154 Families of St. Andrews. By E. P. Cathcart and A. M. T. Murray, assisted by M. Shanks. [1931.] 1s. (1s. 1½d.).

No. 155. Studies of Nutrition : The Physique and Health of Two African Tribes. By J. B. Orr and J. L. Gilks. [1931.] 2s. (2s. 2d.).

No. 158. The Quantitative Estimation of Vitamin D by Radiography. By R. B. Bourdillon, H. M. Bruce, C. Fischmann, and T. A. Webster. [1931.] 1s. (1s. 1½d.).

No. 165. Studies in Nutrition. An Inquiry into the Diet of Families in Cardiff and Reading. By E. P. Cathcart and A. M. T. Murray, assisted by M. Shanks. [1932.] 6d. (7d.).

No. 167. Vitamins : A Survey of Present Knowledge. By a Committee appointed jointly by the Lister Institute and Medical Research Council. [1932.] 6s. 6d.

See also CHILD LIFE ; RICKETS ; DENTAL DISEASE.

Pituitary Extract : *see* STANDARDS.

Pneumonia :

No. 79. Bacteriological and Clinical Observations on Pneumonia and Empyemata, with special reference to the Pneumococcus and to Serum Treatment. By E. E. Glynn and Lettice Digby. [1923.] 5s. (5s. 3d.).

Pneumothorax, Artificial : *see* TUBERCULOSIS.

Print, Legibility of : *see* VISION.

Protozoan Infections :

No. 59. A Report on the Occurrence of Intestinal Protozoa in the inhabitants of Britain. By Clifford Dobell. [1921.] 2s. (2s. 1½d.).

Quinine :

No. 96. Clinical Comparisons of Quinine and Quinidine. By the Committee upon Cinchona Derivatives and Malaria. [1925.] 1s. (1s. 1d.).

Radium :

No. 62. Medical Uses of Radium : Studies of the Effects of Gamma Rays from a large Quantity of Radium. By various authors. [1922.] 5s. (5s. 3d.).

No. 90. Medical Uses of Radium : Summary of Reports from Research Centres for 1923. [1924.] 1s. (1s. 1d.).

No. 102. Ditto for 1924. [1926.] 1s. 6d. (1s. 7d.).

No. 112. Ditto for 1925. [1926.] 1s. 3d. (1s. 4d.).

No. 116. Ditto for 1926. [1927.] 1s. (1s. 1½d.).

No. 126. Ditto for 1927. [1928.] 1s. (1s. 1½d.).

No. 144. Ditto for 1928. [1929.] 1s. (1s. 1d.).

No. 150. Ditto for 1929. [1930.] 9d. (10d.).

No. 160. Ditto for 1930. [1931.] 1s. (1s. 1d.)

Rheumatism : *see* CHILD LIFE (No. 114).

Rickets :

No. 20. A Study of Social and Economic Factors in the Causation of Rickets, with an Introductory Historical Survey. By L. Findlay and Margaret Ferguson. [1918.] *Out of print.*

No. 61. Experimental Rickets. By E. Mellanby. [1921.] 4s. (4s. 2d.).

No. 68. Rickets : the Relative Importance of Environment and Diet as Factors in Causation. By H. Corry Mann. [1922.] 2s. 6d. (2s. 7½d.).

No. 71. The Aetiology and Pathology of Rickets from an experimental point of view. By V. Korenchevsky. [1922.] 4s. (4s. 3d.).

No. 77. Studies of Rickets in Vienna, 1919–22. [1923.] 7s. 6d. (7s. 10½d.).

No. 93. Experimental Rickets : The Effect of Cereals and their Interaction with other factors of Diet and Environment in producing Rickets. By E. Mellanby. [1925]. 3s. 6d. (3s. 8d.).

Salvarsan : *see* VENEREAL DISEASES ; STREPTOCOCCAL INFECTIONS ; STANDARDS, BIOLOGICAL (No. 128).

Scarlet Fever : *see* STATISTICS (No. 137).

Scurvy : *see* NUTRITION (No. 146).

Shock, Surgical :

Reports of the Committee on Surgical Shock and Allied Conditions :—

No. 25. Wound-Shock and Haemorrhage. [1919.] 4s. (4s. 5½d.).

No. 26. Traumatic Toxaemia as a Factor in Shock. [1919.] 1s. (1s. 1d.).

No. 27. Blood Volume Changes in Wound-Shock and Primary Haemorrhage. By N. M. Keith. [1919.] 9d. (10d.).

Small-pox :

No. 98. Studies of the Viruses of Vaccinia and Variola. By M. H. Gordon. [1925.] 3s. 6d. (3s. 8½d.).

No. 106. Small-pox and Climate in India : Forecasting of Epidemics. By Sir Leonard Rogers. [1926.] 2s. (2s. 1½d.).

No. 143. Diagnostic Value of the 'Vaccinia Variola' Flocculation Test. By W. L. Burgess, James Craigie, and W. J. Tulloch. [1929.] 1s. 3d. (1s. 4d.).

No. 156. Further Investigations on the Variola-Vaccinia Flocculation Reaction. By James Craigie and W. J. Tulloch. [1931.] 3s. (3s. 2½d.).

Spinal Deformities : *see* SURGERY (No. 161).

Standards, Biological :

No. 69. I. Pituitary Extracts. By J. H. Burn and H. H. Dale. [1922.] 1s. 6d. (1s. 7d.).

No. 128. II. Toxicity Tests for Novarsenobenzene (Neosalvarsan). By F. M. Durham, J. H. Gaddum, and J. E. Marchal. [1929.] 1s. 9d. (1s. 10d.).

See also VENEREAL DISEASES (No. 44) and NUTRITION (No. 158).

Statistics (Miscellaneous).

No. 16. A Report on the Causes of Wastage of Labour in Munition Factories. By Major Greenwood. [1918.] 1s. 6d. (1s. 7d.).

No. 60. The Use of Death-rates as a Measure of Hygienic Conditions. By John Brownlee. [1922.] 3s. (3s. 1½d.).

No. 95. Internal Migration and its Effects upon the Death-rates : with Special Reference to the County of Essex. By A. B. Hill. [1925.] 3s. 6d. (3s. 8d.).

No. 137. Scarlet Fever, Diphtheria, and Enteric Fever, 1895–1914 : A Clinical-Statistical Study. By E. W. Goodall, M. Greenwood, and W. T. Russell. [1929.] 2s. (2s. 1½d.).

Streptococcal Infections :

No. 119. A Study of some Organic Arsenical Compounds with a view to their Use in certain Streptococcal Infections. By L. Colebrook. [1928.] Price 1s. 3d. (1s. 4d.).

Surgery.

No. 125. A Study of Intracranial Surgery. By H. Cairns. [1929.] 3s. (3s. 2½d.).

No. 138. The Preparation of Catgut for Surgical Use. By W. Bulloch, L. H. Lampitt, and J. H. Bushill. [1929.] 4s. (4s. 3d.).

No. 161. The Intervertebral Discs. Observations on their Normal and Morbid Anatomy in relation to certain Spinal Deformities. By O. A. Beadle. [1931.] 2s. (2s. 2d.).

See also Burns ; Shock, Surgical.

T.N.T. Poisoning :

No. 11. The Causation and Prevention of Tri-nitro-toluene (T.N.T.) Poisoning. By Benjamin Moore. [1917.] 1s. (1s. 1½d.).

No. 58. T.N.T. Poisoning and the Fate of T.N.T. in the Animal Body. By W. J. O'Donovan and others. [1921.] 3s. (3s. 1½d.).

Tuberculosis :

No. 1. First Report of the Special Investigation Committee upon the Incidence of Phthisis in relation to Occupations.—The Boot and Shoe Trade. [1915.] 3d. (3½d.).

No. 18. An Investigation into the Epidemiology of Phthisis Pulmonalis in Great Britain and Ireland. Parts I and II. By John Brownlee. [1918.] Price 1s. 3d. (1s. 4½d.).

No. 22. An Inquiry into the Prevalence and Aetiology of Tuberculosis among Industrial Workers, with special reference to Female Munition Workers. By Major Greenwood and A. E. Tebb. [1919.] 1s. 6d. (1s. 7d.).

No. 33. Pulmonary Tuberculosis : Mortality after Sanatorium Treatment. By Noel D. Bardswell and J. H. R. Thompson. [1919.] 2s. (2s. 2d.).

No. 46. An Investigation into the Epidemiology of Phthisis in Great Britain and Ireland : Part III. By John Brownlee. [1920.] 2s. 6d. (2s. 7½d.).

No. 67. Report on Artificial Pneumothorax. By L. S. T. Burrell and A. S. MacNalty. [1922.] 2s. 6d. (2s. 8d.).

No. 76. Tuberculosis in Insured Persons accepted for Treatment by the City of Bradford Health Committee. By H. Vallow. [1923.] 6d. (7d.).

No. 83. Tuberculosis of the Larynx. By Sir St. Clair Thomson. [1924.] 2s. 6d. (2s. 8d.).

No. 85. An Inquiry into the After-Histories of Patients treated at the Brompton Hospital Sanatorium at Frimley, during the years 1905–14. By Sir P. H.-S. Hartley, R. C. Wingfield, and J. H. R. Thompson. [1924.] 1s. 6d. (1s. 7d.).

No. 94. Tuberculin Tests in Cattle, with special reference to the Intradermal Test. By the Tuberculin Committee. [1925.] 3s. (3s. 3d.).

No. 122. The Intradermal Tuberculin Test in Cattle : Collected Results of Experience. By J. B. Buxton and A. S. MacNalty. [1928.] 1s. 6d. (1s. 7½d.).

No. 149. Tuberculosis in Man and Lower Animals. By H. H. Scott. [1930.] 4s. (4s. 4d.).

No. 152. Studies of Protection against Tuberculosis : Results with B. C. G. Vaccine in Monkeys. By A. Stanley Griffith. [1931.] 9d. (10½d.).

No. 164. The Value of Tuberculin Tests in Man with special reference to the Intracutaneous Test. By P. D'Arcy Hart. [1932.] 2s. (2s. 2d.).

Venereal Diseases :

No. 14. The Wassermann Test. By the Committee upon Pathological Methods. *New Edition.* [1921.] 1s. (1s. 1d.).

No. 19. The Laboratory Diagnosis of Gonococcal Infections. Methods for the Detection of *Spironema pallidum*. By the Bacteriological Committee. *New Edition.* [1923.] 1*s.* 6*d.* (1*s.* 7½*d.*).

No. 21. The Diagnostic Value of the Wassermann Test. By the Committee upon Pathological Methods. [1918.] *Out of print.*

No. 23. An Analysis of the Results of Wassermann Reactions in 1,435 Cases of Syphilis or Suspected Syphilis. By Paul Fildes and R. J. G. Parnell. [1919.] 2*s.* (2*s.* 1*d.*).

No. 41. (I.) An Investigation into the Ultimate Results of the Treatment of Syphilis with Arsenical Compounds. By Paul Fildes and R. J. G. Parnell. (II.) A Clinical Study of the Toxic Reactions which follow the Intravenous Administration of ' 914 '. By R. J. G. Parnell and Paul Fildes. [1919.] 2*s.* (2*s.* 1*d.*).

No. 44. Reports of the Special Committee upon the Manufacture, Biological Testing, and Clinical Administration of Salvarsan and of its Substitutes. I. [1919.] 1*s.* (1*s.* 1*d.*).

No. 45. Unsuspected Involvement of the Central Nervous System in Syphilis. By Paul Fildes, R. J. G. Parnell, and H. B. Maitland. [1920.] 1*s.* (1*s.* 1*d.*).

No. 47. The Accuracy of Wassermann Tests, applied before and after death, estimated by Necropsies. I. The Wassermann Test applied before death. By H. M. Turnbull. [1920.] 2*s.* 6*d.* (2*s.* 7½*d.*).

No. 55. (I.) Results of the Examination of Tissues from Eight Cases of Death following Injections of Salvarsan. By H. M. Turnbull. (II.) The Influence of Salvarsan Treatment on the Development and Persistence of Immunity, as indicated by Measurements of Agglutinins. By E. W. Ainley Walker. [1920.] 3*s.* (3*s.* 1½*d.*).

No. 66. Toxic Effects following the Employment of Arsenobenzol Preparations. By the Salvarsan Committee. [1922.] 2*s.* (2*s.* 1½*d.*).

No. 78. The Serum Diagnosis of Syphilis : The Wassermann and Sigma Reactions compared. [1923.] 5*s.* 6*d.* (5*s.* 9*d.*).

No. 107. The Effect of Treatment on the Wassermann Reactions of Syphilitic Patients. By E. E. Glynn, R. E. Roberts, and P. M. Bigland. [1926.] 3*s.* 6*d.* (3*s.* 8*d.*).

No. 129. The Wassermann Test. Technical Details of No. 1 Method M.R.C. (Modified). By E. J. Wyler. [1929.] 9*d.* (10*d.*).

No. 132. The Treatment of Syphilis : A Survey of Records from St. Thomas's Hospital. By L. W. Harrison. [1929.] 2*s.* (2*s.* 1½*d.*).

Ventilation, etc.:

No. 32. The Science of Ventilation and Open-air Treatment. Part I. By Leonard Hill. [1919.] 10*s.* (10*s.* 5½*d.*).

No. 52. The Science of Ventilation and Open-air Treatment. Part II. By Leonard Hill. [1920.] 6*s.* (6*s.* 4½*d.*).

No. 73. The Kata-thermometer in Studies of Body Heat and Efficiency. By Leonard Hill and others. [1923.] 5*s.* (5*s.* 2½*d.*).

No. 100. Methods of Investigating Ventilation and its Effects. By H. M. Vernon and others. [1926.] 2*s.* (2*s.* 1½*d.*).

Vision :

No. 65. First Report of the Miners' Nystagmus Committee. [1922.] *Out of print.*

No. 80. Second Report of the Miners' Nystagmus Committee. [1923.] 9*d.* (10*d.*).

No. 110. The Legibility of Print. By R. L. Pyke. [1926.] 4*s.* (4*s.* 2*d.*).

Reports of the Committee on the Physiology of Vision :

No. 104. I. Illumination and Visual Capacities. By R. J. Lythgoe. [1926.] 2*s.* 6*d.* (2*s.* 7½*d.*).

No. 127. II. Dark Adaptation (a Review of the Literature). By Dorothy Adams. [1929.] 5*s.* (5*s.* 2½*d.*).

No. 130. III. Two Studies in the Psychology of Reading. By M. D. Vernon and R. W. Pickford. [1929.] 2*s.* (2*s.* 1½*d.*).

No. 133. IV. Experiments on Binocular Vision. By N. M. S. Langlands. [1929.] 2*s.* 6*d.* (2*s.* 8*d.*).

No. 134. V. The Adaptation of the Eye : its Relation to the Critical Frequency of Flicker. By R. J. Lythgoe and K. Tansley. [1929.] 2*s.* 6*d.* (2*s.* 7½*d.*).

No. 136. VI. Some Experiments on Peripheral Vision. By Myer Salaman. [1929.] 2s. 6d. (2s. 7d.).

No. 139. VII. A Re-determination of the Trichromatic Mixture Data. By W. D. Wright. [1929.] 1s. 3d. (1s. 4d.).

No. 148. VIII. The Movements of the Eyes in Reading. By M. D. Vernon. [1930.] 9d. (10d.).

No. 163. IX. Psychological Factors in Peripheral Vision. By G. C. Grindley. [1931.] 1s. (1s. 1d.)

Vitamins : *see* NUTRITION.

Wassermann Test : *see* VENEREAL DISEASES.

Wound Infections :

No. 12. The Classification and Study of the Anaerobic Bacteria of War Wounds. By J. McIntosh. [1917.] *Out of print.*

No. 39. Report on the Anaerobic Infections of Wounds and the Bacteriological and Serological Problems arising therefrom. By the Committee upon Anaerobic Bacteria and Infections. [1919.] 6s. (6s. 3½d.).

No. 57. Studies in Wound Infections. By S. R. Douglas, A. Fleming, and L. Colebrook. [1920.] 4s. 6d. (4s. 8½d.).

The following books were published under the direction of the Medical Research Committee and are obtainable from the publishers named :

Milk and its Hygienic Relations. By Janet E. Lane-Claypon. 9s. net. [Longmans, Green & Co.]

The Amoebae living in Man. By Clifford Dobell. 7s. 6d. net. [Bale, Sons & Danielsson, Ltd.]

The Intestinal Protozoa of Man. By Clifford Dobell and F. W. O'Connor. 15s. net. [Bale, Sons & Danielsson, Ltd.]

OVERSEAS AGENCIES OF H.M. STATIONERY OFFICE

IRISH FREE STATE : Messrs. Eason & Son, Ltd., 40/41 Lr. O'Connell Street, Dublin.

CANADA : The Imperial News Company, Ltd., 235 Fort Street, Winnipeg ; 975 St. Antoine Street, Montreal; 517 Burrard Street, Vancouver; Wm. Dawson Subscription Service, Ltd., 70 King Street East, Toronto.

AUSTRALIA : Messrs. Angus & Robertson, Ltd., 89 Castlereagh Street, Sydney, New South Wales. Messrs. Albert & Son, Ltd., 180 Murray Street, Perth, Western Australia. Messrs. Fuller Oldham & Morris Pty., Ltd., 36 Elizabeth Street, Hobart, Tasmania.

NEW ZEALAND : Messrs. Whitcombe & Tombs, Ltd., Auckland, Christchurch, Dunedin, and Wellington.

SOUTH AFRICA : The Central News Agency, Ltd., Cape Town, P.O. Box 9 ; Johannesburg, P.O. Box 1033 ; Durban, P.O. Box 938 ; Port Elizabeth, P.O. Box 356 ; Pretoria.

INDIA : Messrs. Thacker, Spink & Co., Calcutta and Simla. Messrs. Thacker & Co., Ltd., Bombay. Messrs. Higginbothams, Ltd., Madras and Bangalore.

GOLD COAST : The Wesleyan Methodist Book Depot, P.O. Box 100, Cape Coast. Branches at Accra, Kumasi, and Sekondi.

U.S.A.: The British Library of Information, 270 Madison Avenue, New York.

DENMARK : Mr. A. Busck, Kjobmagergade 49, Copenhagen.

FINLAND : Akateminen Kirjakauppa Helsinki, Akademeska Bokhandeln, Helsingfors,

HOLLAND : N.V. Martinus Nijhoff' Boekhandel, Lange Voorhout 9, s–Gravenhage.

GERMANY : Messrs. A. Asher & Co., Behrenstrasse 17, Berlin, W. 8.

NORWAY : Cammermeyers Boghandel, Karl Johans Gate 41–43, Oslo.

SWEDEN : A–B, C. E. Fritzes Kungl. Hofbokhandel, Fredsgatan 2, Stockholm.

JAPAN : Maruzen Co., Ltd., 11–16 Nihonbashi Tori-Nichome, Tokyo.

LONDON :
PUBLISHED BY HIS MAJESTY'S STATIONERY OFFICE.

To be purchased directly from H.M. STATIONERY OFFICE
at the following addresses:
ADASTRAL HOUSE, KINGSWAY, LONDON, W.C. 2;
120 GEORGE STREET, EDINBURGH;
YORK STREET, MANCHESTER;
1 ST. ANDREW'S CRESCENT, CARDIFF;
15 DONEGALL SQUARE WEST, BELFAST;
or through any Bookseller.

1932.

Price 6s. 6d. net